COLLINS MAGAZINE ANNUAL

New Year Resolutions—cover design by John Verney

COLLINS MAGAZINE ANNUAL

FOR BOYS AND GIRLS

VOLUME FOUR containing

two complete serial stories,
good short stories by favourite
authors, interesting articles on
many different subjects,
verses, drawings, photographs,
things to make and do,
puzzles and many other
features as they originally
appeared each month in
COLLINS MAGAZINE

COLLINS

14 ST. JAMES'S PLACE, LONDON, S.W.1

1951

PRINTED FOR THE PUBLISHERS IN GREAT BRITAIN BY
MARDON SON & HALL LTD. BRISTOL

INDEX

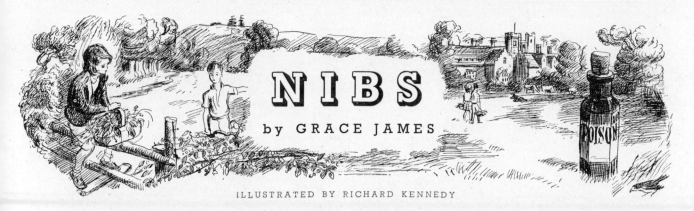

NIBS

by GRACE JAMES

ILLUSTRATED BY RICHARD KENNEDY

Nibs (who tells the story), Cressida and Musgrave Blake have been staying for the holidays with Shirley and Oliver Blackett. They have together been trying to retrieve the fallen fortunes of the Blake family, by starting money-making schemes. The last of these was a tea garden, to which came Mr. and Mrs. Roland and their children, on their way to stay with the vicar. In this instalment, Nibs tells how Mr. Roland inspired her last, and most exciting idea.

BATTLE, MURDER AND SUDDEN DEATH and their father and mother, who were called Mr. and Mrs. Roland, stayed on with Mr. Vavaseur for a bit and we saw a good deal of them.

Mr. Roland was an author. He wrote books. Often, Battle, Murder and Sudden Death had to be kept away from him because they stopped his thoughts coming properly. I could quite understand this. They were the most interrupting people I had ever met.

One day, when Mrs. Blackett had asked me to pick some flowers, I found Mr. Roland in the rose garden. He was sitting on a marble seat clutching his head in his hands. I felt quite alarmed and was going away quietly when he looked up.

'Hullo Nibs,' he said, with a wan smile.

He looked so miserable that I said, 'Is anything the matter?' It passed through my mind that Battle, Murder and Sudden Death had done something really awful and the police were going to take them to prison in a Black Maria.

'The lamp of genius refuses to burn.'

'Oh . . .' I said, rather disappointed.

'Nibs, I have come to an *impasse*. I am well and truly stuck, or rather my heroine is. A nice girl, Drusilla by name. Drussie for short. I have got her into a pub and for the life of me I can't get her out of it. She's been there some hours.'

'That will be all right. Pubs shut in the end and people *have* to go. Mr. Stubbles at the Horse and Jockey says "Time Gentlemen, please" and they all stream out. Charles told me about it, I haven't been into a pub myself.'

'H . . . m . . . That might do, she'd only have to wait another three hours or so.'

'I've sometimes thought of being an author.'

'Don't, far better sweep a crossing.'

'That might be rather fun. Do you get money for being an author?'

'Not nearly enough. It hardly keeps Battle in breeches.'

'You do for sweeping crossings, lean on your broom, you know and hold out a ragged cap and suddenly a kind lady puts half-a-crown in it.'

'And turns out to be your long-lost Aunt from Australia. Goodbye, Nibs, you've done me good.'

At the time, I only thought how queer authors were, but later on, I was to remember what he had said.

The next day, Mr. Roland had a holiday from being an author and took Mrs. Roland and Battle and Murder and Sudden Death into the town to have their photographs taken. So we had a bit of a holiday too, only it was raining, which was a pity.

We stayed in the hall where there was a nice crackling wood fire. Oliver looked at the *Motorist* and Cress looked at *Vogue*. Mus did nothing and Shirley blew the fire with the bellows which it didn't need. I took up *Home and Country* which is the Women's Institute magazine and has about 'How to make the best of the Sunday Joint' and things like that.

'Bit of a rag,' said Mus, 'don't know what you see in it, Nibs, all knit one purl two and why Baby is sick. Ugh!'

'It says Hedgerow Harvest . . .'

'Now what on earth . . . ?'

'Hips and haws . . .'

'What ever use . . . ?'

'You make them into vitamins for babies . . .'

'What did I tell you?'

'At least the Government does and they pay you.'

'Oh, *do* they?' put in Oliver, looking up from the *Motorist* with a faint show of interest. 'How much?'

'It doesn't say. There's something about dandelion roots.'

'Awfully hard to gouge up,' said Shirley.

'And herbs and things. You can make awfully decent

'Lean on your broom and hold out a ragged cap.'

medicine at home and save money at the chemist or else you can sell it to your friends.'

'That might be best,' said Cress thoughtfully.

'Not a bad idea,' Mus went on. 'Isn't there some poetry about it?'

Excellent herbs had our fathers of old,
Excellent herbs to ease their pain.
Alexanders and Marigold,
Eyebright, Orris and Elecampane,
Basil, Rocket, Valerian, Rue
(Almost singing themselves as they run)
Vervain, Dittany, Call-me-to-you,
Cowslip, Melilot, Rose of the Sun.
Anything green that grew out of the mould
Was an excellent herb to our fathers of old.'

'We strained it through a table-cloth.'

'Gosh!' said Oliver, 'I can't think how you mug up all that stuff!'

'Why shouldn't we make medicine,' I suggested, 'and sell it.'

'Where would we get the things? Alexanders . . . now I ask you? We don't even know what they are.'

'You are just making difficulties. It's as easy as pat. It says so in *Home and Country*. You just distil . . .'

'How do you do that, and what's Dittany?'

'The last bit of the poetry sounds rather hopeful,' said Mus.

"Anything green that grew out of the mould
Was an excellent herb to our fathers of old."

'Anything!' I cried triumphantly. 'Listen to that!'

Oliver stretched himself and threw the *Motorist* on the floor.

'We'll have to get going if Nibs says so and might as well be soon as late. I wonder if we could make any explosives. That would be fun.'

'Listen,' I said. 'A very lucky thing has happened. Only yesterday, Mrs. Blackett and Georgette tidied-up the medicine cupboard.'

'Not the little one outside the boys' bathroom . . . Gosh!' cried Oliver, 'I put my . . .'

'No, the big one in Mr. Blackett's dressing room.'

'Gosh! Poor Father . . .'

'They turned out ever so many bottles and jars and jolly little pill boxes. They will just do for our herb medicines. The dustman doesn't call till Thursday which is the finger of Providence.'

'Come on,' cried Oliver, now entering quite heartily into the scheme. 'We'll make some jolly good stuff with elecampane and Call-me-to-you and a bit of hip juice or elderberry to make it pink. Let's get the bottles and cart them up to our secret place. We don't want to be disturbed.'

'We ought to wash them,' I said. 'Let's take them up to West Summer House where there's a sink and water.'

We had a very good morning, though five people round *one* sink is rather a lot and there was a bit of splashing and we broke some bottles.

In the middle of it all, Shirley said she was starving, so we made tea and had ginger biscuits out of a tin. We poured the dregs into one of the bottles. Shirley said it would do for one of our medicines and why go further.

'No,' I said, 'I don't think it would be quite honest to sell people tea slops.'

'Oh, are we going to sell it?'

'Of course we are.'

'Who is going to buy it?'

'Lots of people. Everybody has to have medicine some time and this will be better and cheaper than what you get at the chemist.'

We washed sixteen bottles and eight jars, outside and in, except one blue bottle with a red label which said poison. We left that because we thought it might be handy if we wanted to make some poison ourselves.

We sat down to lunch with the happy feeling of a well-spent morning. Something accomplished, something done, like the Village Blacksmith.

I nearly told Mrs. Blackett about our plan when I saw her take *Home and Country* to read during her lay down after lunch, but I didn't quite because she is inclined to worry and the doctor said she shouldn't.

We found some baskets and sticks with crooks to reach down things from the hedges and off we set.

'Let's go to Hunter's Piece,' said Oliver, 'that's the most likely place for mushrooms.'

'But we don't want mushrooms,' Shirley objected.

'Don't we! I always want mushrooms.'

'Why not go to Deader's Meadow,' suggested Mus.

'Let's go to that overgrown bit behind the gardeners' cottages,' put in Cress.

'It doesn't really matter where we go,' I cried desperately, 'so long as we get a move on. We must get these medicines done today. It's our only free afternoon for ages and you know we simply can't concentrate when Battle, Murder and Sudden Death are about. What about Threepenny Marsh? Mr. Vavaseur says it's the best botany place in the county, and there's bound to be some melilot and elecampane about and we can come back by Twinklebury Meadow and get things out of the hedges.'

So it was settled at last and we went to the Marsh which was fortunately fairly near.

'There isn't any valerian,' said Cress critically. 'I know that, I've seen it in Cornwall.'

'Here's eyebright,' said Mus, 'that's quite for certain.'

'It's very small,' objected Shirley, 'quite a tiny flower and not exciting.'

'Who said it had to be exciting? Our fathers of old didn't care two hoots about that.'

'I say, Nibs,' said Oliver, 'could you spot a bit of elecampane? I feel that's important.'

I couldn't because I had no idea what it looked like, and I didn't know what Alexanders looked like either.

'Look here,' I said in desperation, 'let's just pick whatever we think would be suitable. I don't suppose it matters much. It says so in the poetry, doesn't it Mus?'

Fortunately Mus backed me up. 'Rather! Of course it does.

"Anything green that grew out of the mould
    Was an excellent herb to our fathers of old."

There you are. What could be plainer?'

After this, we filled our baskets pretty quickly.

'Now,' said Oliver, 'I vote we leg it straight back and begin to cook.'

'Let's do Twinklebury Meadow,' urged Cress, 'it isn't much further and we might find something exciting in the hedges. We haven't used our sticks yet.'

In Twinklebury Meadow we collected some unripe blackberries, elder and sloe and Deadly Nightshade.

Soon we were all in West Summer House where new problems quickly arose.

'What do we do now?' asked Cress.

'Make the medicine of course.'

'How?'

That was just the question. I hadn't thought of this bit.

'Chop up the things, I suppose, and mix them with water.'

'That wouldn't look a bit like medicine.'

'Perhaps if we boiled it . . .'

'That's the ticket,' cried Oliver. 'Switch on the electric ring. There's an old saucepan in one of the potting sheds which they use for making glue. I'll fetch it. You get the stuff ready meanwhile.'

It wasn't so easy as you might think, but at last we got it done. We strained it through a tablecloth and the tablecloth was green but the medicine was a dirty brownish yellow.

'We might touch it up with a little Drummer dye,' suggested Mus.

'H'm . . . I suppose that would be all right.' I hesitated.

'Of course it would be all right, vegetable dye you know . . .'

Oliver said, 'I'll just hare along to Popples on my bike and get some.'

While Oliver was gone we boiled the Deadly Nightshade. I was relieved when it was safely corked up in the blue bottle labelled *Poison*.

Oliver came back quite quickly with several packets of Drummer Dye and I must say it improved the look of the medicine very much. We cleared up all the mess of which there was a good deal, as may be imagined. We washed out the sink and swept the floor. You would hardly have known we had been there except for the shining row of medicine bottles on the shelf. I felt we had done a good day's work.

'Let's call it a day,' I suggested. 'We've worked frightfully hard, so let's just get tidy and slack about and listen to the wireless till teatime. We'll think up something for the labels tomorrow.'

So we left it at that. There was a big log fire in the hall and it was all very jolly and comfortable. There is something so satisfactory in having done a good job of work. Mr. and Mrs. Roland came in with Battle, Murder and Sudden Death who had bought whistles in the town and blew them except when they were eating. When they

simply couldn't eat any more, they were sent away into the garden to have their madness out before bedtime. Mr. Blackett threw a fresh log on the fire and all was peace and serenity, but it was the calm before a storm.

At last, Charles came and took away the tea things. He switched on the lights and drew the curtains. Mus told me quietly that he was going to have a last look at the medicine bottles, before dark as he wanted to get the size in his mind for labels. So he went out and so did Mr. Roland because Mrs. Roland said it was time to collect the children.

Mrs. Blackett asked me to fetch her knitting and I had hardly done this and picked up some dropped stitches for her when Mus came bursting in with Mr. Roland at his heels. They both looked white and worried.

'The . . . the poison . . .' stammered Mus, 'it's . . . gone!'

'Gone . . . where . . .?'

'Poison, what poison? What are you talking about, my boy?'

'*Poison!*' screamed Mrs. Roland. 'Have the children taken poison?'

'They . . . they seem all right, my dear . . . er . . . just as usual.'

'Then what's all the fuss about?'

'We . . . we made some medicine . . .' I began, 'it's really all my fault . . .'

'Never mind about that now. What's all this about poison? Out with it!'

So I told him as well as I could and he said 'Hum!' and, taking a torch, went out into the night. We all followed. We didn't find the poison. It had just vanished. At last we had to give up and come in again. Battle, Murder and Sudden Death were taken away to bed.

'What of the B.B.C., sir?' suggested Charles suddenly. 'Dangerous drugs . . .'

'Well, what of it? What do you mean, my lad?'

I saw what he meant. 'Oh Charles, how clever you are,' I cried. 'Couldn't we ring up the B.B.C. and ask them to give out a warning. "Lost between Tooting and Putney," you know.'

'Tooting and Putney . . .' said Mr. Blackett, bewildered.

'It generally is, but this time it would be here.'

'Jolly good idea!' agreed Oliver. 'That will make it all right if anything will.'

Cress took Mr. Blackett's arm. 'Don't you think we might do that?' she suggested gently. 'Could you ring

'I bent over the counter to look at the address.'

them up now and say a dangerous drug had been lost?'

'That's an idea Cress,' said Mr. Blackett, just as if Cress had thought of it which, of course, she hadn't. 'I'll put the call through at once' and he went straight to his study while the rest of us cowered miserably round the fire.

'Don't take on too much Nibs,' said Mrs. Blackett, very kindly. 'What must be must.'

'Oh, do you think it need?'

'There, there, perhaps it won't. We'll hope for the best.'

3

At last Mr. Blackett came back and said it was all right and the message would be given out before the nine o'clock news. He was quite brisk and almost cheerful.

'Off you go now,' he said, 'and get yourselves ready for dinner.'

After dinner we went into the hall for coffee. Mrs. Blackett did her knitting because she said it steadied her. Mr. Blackett walked about and smoked a cigar. I felt exactly as I do in the dentist's waiting room, my hands were damp and I yawned. Then Mr. Blackett switched on and we heard first the pips and then Big Ben. Then silence, it seemed for ages.

'Oh!' cried Shirley. 'The wireless has gone wrong.'

'Hush!' Then it came:

'We have been asked to broadcast the following warning: Lost between four and six o'clock, this afternoon, in the grounds of Merivale Great House, Berkshire, a bottle labelled *poison* and containing—'

There was a sound of running and bustle outside and a door banged. In another moment Charles and Georgette and Higgins and Mr. Roland burst into the room. Mr. Roland was waving the poison bottle above his head.

'Found!' exclaimed Higgins, clasping his hands. 'Glory be!'

'Hurrah!' yelled Charles. 'Hallelujah!'

'*Vive la Suisse!*' screamed Georgette.

Mr. Roland sank into a chair and began to laugh helplessly.

'What . . . ?'

'Where . . . ?'

'Is it full?'

'Is it empty?'

'It's . . . it's all right . . .' panted Mr. Roland. 'That little devil of a Murder, we found it under his pillow when we went to tuck them up. The bottle was quite full. He couldn't have had any.'

'Glory be!' murmured Higgins.

'All's well that ends well,' said Mrs. Blackett, 'though I should think a dose all round, just in case . . .'

'We did,' said Mr. Roland, grimly. 'Castor Oil.'

Though all ended well, I think we were a little shaken by recent events. Mr. Blackett implored us to go steady so we did and for a time led quite ordinary lives. We even tried to be useful.

One morning, I had to go to the village because Georgette was out of marking ink and there had to be some for Mus's new pyjamas.

Mus wanted green ink, Cress wanted picture postcards, Shirley wanted toffee apples, Mrs. Blackett wanted a ball of string.

'Here's a ten shilling note, Nibs love, you'd better get jam pot covers as well. A dozen of the large size. Ask Mrs. Popples if the snap fasteners have come in.'

Cress wanted a hair slide. Thank goodness, Mr. Blackett didn't want anything.

Mr. Roland was sitting in the hall with a biggish parcel on his knee.

'Oh Nibs, be an angel,' he said.

'Do you want me to post the parcel?'

'Right as usual. Your woman's intuition is infallible.'

'Hand over then.'

'You'll have to register it. It mustn't be lost because of Sudden's winter woollies. It's wherewithal my child, the first part of my novel bound for the publishers.'

'Of course,' I assured him, feeling rather important. 'I'll go to the post office first of all and bring you back the little bit of paper to say it's all right.'

'Invaluable child!'

'Mr. Roland,' I said. 'Have you made a fortune with . . . with writing you know?'

'Good Lord, no!'

'I thought it seemed too easy . . .'

'It isn't at all easy,' said Mr. Roland, ruffling up his hair, 'and of course I make *some* money or you may be sure I wouldn't do it.'

'Could a person . . . ?'

'What?'

'Oh nothing really . . . I was only thinking . . . I'll go now, or I'll miss the post.'

'Yes do . . . there's a good girl.'

I put the parcel in my bicycle basket and went along to Miss Trimble who is the Merivale post mistress, lost in thought.

'And what was it for you this morning?' she said, 'Registered parcel? Why, you've never sealed it. That won't do! Never mind, I'll do it for you though we aren't supposed to, not really. Where's the sealing wax? And where did I put my glasses? Now the address, let me see —the writing's not too clear . . .'

I bent over the counter to look at the address.

'Messrs. Blunt and Derbyshire—Publishers. Yes, that's it. 15, Little James Street, London. Little James Street . . . rather nice . . .'

'You'd be surprised what a difference there is in addresses. We get a lot of it in our business.'

'Blunt and Derbyshire,' I repeated to myself. 'Little James Street.' I had a very special reason for wanting to remember the address.

'It will be one and four Miss Nibs, and here's the receipt, thanking you.'

I went to Popples and it's a wonder I didn't forget anything because my mind wasn't really fixed on shopping, for I was full of a new idea. I rode home very slowly, lost in thought, again.

And now, I think it is time to confess I had a secret. Nobody knew, not even Cress, not even Mother. I had written a novel, at least part of one. It was about the Crusades and rather like Sir Walter Scott, only a bit different—a good deal different as a matter of fact. I wrote it in an old exercise book which I kept in a drawer under my vests. It had taken a long time, indeed the beginning part was when I was a mere child. I don't know why I had kept it such a secret except that it seemed more fun. Somehow I didn't want Cress to read it, anyway not till it was finished. Mus would not have mattered so much. The novel was called *Lady Dulcibella*.

Now, my plan was to send the novel and write a letter at the same time to Messrs. Blunt and Derbyshire, Little James Street. I thought Messrs. Blunt and Derbyshire might be pretty sure to publish it because hundreds of books are published and they must want them. Then they would pay me, not so much as Mr. Roland because I am a beginner—but still some, perhaps even five pounds which would make a jolly good start with the fallen fortunes.

The more I thought about this idea, the more I liked it. I went straight upstairs and found *Lady Dulcibella* under my vests where I had put her. It was a bore to have to write a letter for I was in a fever to get the parcel off, but I was resolved to do things properly. So I borrowed Cress's fountain pen as there was no ink in mine and thought and thought what I had better say.

At last I put:

'Dear Messrs. Blunt and Derbyshire,

I beg to send you a history novel written by myself. I beg to tell you my name and address, as you are bound to write to me, I hope. It is Miss Nibs Blake and I am staying with Mrs. Blackett at Merivale Great

House, Merivale, Berks. It isn't my real home but you can put care of can't you? I thought you could print the novel and if you do, I should like a blue cover, please. I hope you won't mind paying me some money for it. I hope you don't mind me asking, but it's for our fortunes which are unfortunately rather fallen. It needn't be much, about five pounds would do and I should think myself a queen. An early answer will oblige.

    With kind regards and oblige,
        Yours sincerely,
            Nibs Blake.'

I packed up the parcel, addressed it and rushed back to Miss Trimble. It only cost fourpence. I went home again feeling light as air. Nothing to do now except enjoy myself and wait for an answer from Messrs. Blunt and Derbyshire.

One morning when I came down to breakfast there was the letter for me. I gazed at the typewritten address. 'Miss Nibs Blake!'

'Golly!' I thought. 'My publishers!'

I had been the first to come down, but now I heard steps on the stairs so I put the letter in my pocket. I felt I must read it alone.

Then, during breakfast, a fatality happened to me. I broke my plate. I don't mean the plate I was eating off, perhaps that would not have mattered so much. No, it was the gold band I have to wear over my front teeth to train them not to stick out. I am afraid they have that tendency. I don't know exactly how it happened, but I was crunching up a bit of toast and marmalade.

'Oh dear!' I said. 'What shall I do? A dentist in London made it and put it on. I . . . I'm afraid it's rather special.'

'Don't put yourself about, Nibs love,' said kind Mrs. Blackett. 'We'll think of something. It doesn't hurt you any, does it?'

'Oh no, it's only that if I don't wear it, my teeth will begin to stick out again and Mother doesn't like it. It's a bother with school beginning so soon . . .'

'I'm going to town tomorrow,' said Mr. Blackett, 'got some business in the City. I'll drive you up Nibs. Give me the dentist's address and I'll ring him up and make an appointment. You don't have to worry any more about it.'

Mr. Blackett made the appointment for eleven o'clock. 'I am afraid you'll have some time to fill in. I shan't be through my board meeting till about three . . . Now I wonder . . .'

'I'll . . . I'll walk about,' I suggested, 'and look at shop windows.'

'That would never do,' said Mrs. Blackett, firmly.

'There's Cousin Monica,' said Cress. 'You could have lunch with her.'

So they arranged it all. I did not look forward to my day. Mooning rather disconsolately in the garden, I suddenly remembered my letter from Blunt and Derbyshire. I tore open the envelope. Inside was a grand typewritten letter. This is what it said:

"Dear Madam,

    We have read your novel, *Lady Dulcibella*, with much interest. We find the work original and entertaining and should much appreciate meeting you in order to talk it over. Would it be convenient for you to call at our offices some time in the near future . . .'

Golly! Original and entertaining! Call at their offices. Could I? I was actually going to London. But Cousin Monica . . . I didn't see my way very clearly. In the end,

'*Do I ring or just go in?*'

I did nothing about it, only shifted the letter into my coat pocket next morning before starting for London.

Well, the dentist part was all right. Afterwards I waited a long time. Nothing happened and nobody came. Twelve o'clock—half past twelve—still nobody and I was getting very hungry. Suddenly, I remembered something. Cousin Monica was in Brighton! She always went to Brighton in September. So she probably never got the telegram and certainly she wouldn't come. What should I do? Mr. Blackett wouldn't be ready for me till three when it had been decided I should go to his office. All at once I knew what I would do. I put up my hand and stopped a passing taxi. 'Blunt and Derbyshire,' I said to the driver, 'Little James Street.' And I got in.

At last we stopped and I saw a door with Blunt and Derbyshire on a brass plate. I paid the taxi man.

I was wondering whether I ought to ring a bell or walk straight in as if it was a shop, when a man came out, quite young-looking and cheerful. He was whistling.

'Hullo!' he said, smiling . . . 'I mean, Good afternoon. Can I do anything for you?'

'I . . . I was wondering . . . Do I ring or just go in . . . ?'

'It depends,' said the young man, looking at me rather hard.'

'I've come to see Messrs. Blunt and Derbyshire.'

'Could I help?'

'I'm afraid it would have to be them.'

'But I *am* them.'

'You can't be, you're too young.'

'At least I'm Blunt. Richard Blunt.'

'I'm Nibs Blake.'

'Oh! Miss Blake! Of course, I remember, you sent us that delightful story . . .' Yes, he said delightful.

'Well, what about it?' he went on. 'Would you like to come along inside?'

But as he spoke, he gazed down the sunny street, rather longingly, I thought.

'I'm frightfully hungry,' I said.

'So am I! Let's go and get some lunch.'

Off we went, chatting easily as if we had known each other all our lives. People are silly to talk about publishers so solemnly. Really, they are very jolly people. The lunch place was jolly, too, each table in a little tiny room of its own rather like the old-fashioned pews you see sometimes in village churches. It was warm and cosy and private in our pew. We each had a whole little beefsteak pudding to ourselves simply oozing with the most heavenly dark brown gravy. There was a mountain of mashed potato with no lumps and small, pale green Brussels Sprouts. I think Richard was surprised at the amount I ate.

Because Richard was so nice and ordinary and not a bit what I had expected a publisher to be I found myself talking away to him and telling him all about ourselves. I told him about Father and Mother and the fallen fortunes, about Mus and Cress and the Blacketts and if I stopped for one minute, he said:

'Go on, it's most interesting.'

After a long time, I said: 'Ought we to go away now? Won't the waiter want to wash up or something?'

'Well, he can do as he likes. We aren't going away yet. About your novel, Nibs, er . . . *Lady Dulcibella*, you know.'

'Oh yes, I'd nearly forgotten. I am glad you thought it was interesting, or was it Mr. Derbyshire who read it?'

'We both read it. Lord, how we laughed!'

'Laughed!' I was surprised because *Lady Dulcibella* is a serious work. Richard was silent for a moment. He took up a fork and began to draw lines on the tablecloth.

'Look here Nibs . . . have another cup of coffee?'

'I couldn't.' Somehow I felt a tiny bit anxious.

'Look here then—you are a sensible girl.'

'Yes I know. When people say that it's generally the beginning of something nasty.'

'Well, I don't think it need be nasty this time. It's how you take it. If we were to publish your book, I think it might be successful and sell well, but—and it's rather a big but, it would be as a sort of joke. People would laugh, not only at the funny parts. Do you take me?'

'But . . .'

'Let me finish. As the work of a little girl, *Lady Dulcibella* is rather remarkable. Very few little girls could have written it. But she can't stand on her own legs as it were. Why, my child, you don't know what you are writing about, how could you?'

'Is it the lovering bits?' I enquired in rather a small voice.

'Well, yes, and other bits too, in fact most of it.' Richard ruffled up his curly hair and looked worried. 'Cheer up, Nibs,' he said. 'We'll publish it if you like.'

I thought. It's no good saying I wasn't disappointed, of course I was.

'You decide,' I said. 'I feel a bit muddled up.'

'No . . . no . . . it's for you to say.'

'Then you'd better give me back *Lady Dulcibella*. I like her and I won't have her laughed at. So there!'

Richard sighed, but he looked pleased too.

'Good for you Nibs. You're a brave girl. Will you shake the hand that dealt the blow?' He held his hand out across the table and I took it.

'Always the best of friends, I hope. Now I've got some more to say.'

'I . . . I don't think I want to hear any more.'

'You'll like this bit better. We want you to go on writing Nibs.'

'Why?'

'Because we think you have got it in you and one day you will probably write something really good. Besides, it will help you to get a lot more out of life and it may make you yourself a more worthwhile sort of person— Hang it all . . . it's difficult to put it over to you.'

'I don't understand very well.'

'I daresay not. Take my word for it.'

'What shall I write about?'

'I was coming to that. Write what you really know.'

'But that would be dull.'

'Oh no, it wouldn't. Write about the Blacketts and Charles and Georgette and all the people round you. Write about your fallen fortunes and other children will like to read it and laugh in the right places and not in the wrong ones. Come Nibs, is it a bargain?'

'If I do, will you print it and shall I get five pounds?'

Richard laughed. 'I can't make any rash promise, but I think it's quite likely.'

'All right then.'

'By jove, Nibs, do you know what time it is? Ten minutes to three. I must be getting back to the office. What *will* Derbyshire say! Anyway I can tell him I've done a successful stroke of business. What about you?'

'I must go to Mr. Blackett—his office you know. It's written on this bit of paper.'

'Good! Come along. I'll drop you on my way.'

Mr. Blackett's office turned out to be quite near. It said *Blackett's Ltd.*, on a very large, very bright brass plate.

I ran up the stairs thinking I should have to do quite a lot of explaining. Mr. Blackett was ready with a box of chocolates in his hand which he gave me.

'That's right Nibs—felt sure you wouldn't be late. May as well start at once. Get a cup of tea on the way down if we want it.'

In the car Mr. Blackett was very silent. This was unusual and at first I wondered if he could be cross but I decided he was turning something over in his mind. After all I suppose Grown-Ups must have things to think about. He did not ask a word about Cousin Monica or the dentist or about how I got on. Perhaps it was just as well. I had plenty to think about too.

At last Mr. Blackett roused himself and turned to me with his usual kind smile.

'Well, Nibs, will you give me a penny for my thoughts?'

'Grown-up thoughts are not always very interesting . . .'

Mr. Blackett chuckled. 'Bet you mine are worth a penny,' he said. 'I've got some good news for you. I shouldn't wonder if your Dad and Mum wouldn't be coming home pretty soon.'

'Father and Mother . . .'

'That's right. They've discovered a seam on the property somewhere near the house. There's likely to be big money in it too . . . Pendlebury's been pretty decent . . .'

'A *seam*, but that's what you sew . . .'

Mr. Blackett laughed aloud. 'What a woman it is! Nothing to do with sewing. It's *coal* Nibs . . . it's coal . . .'

'But Mr. Blackett, do you mean . . . ?'

'It's going to be all right for you all . . . properly managed that is. I think I see my way . . . nothing settled yet . . . nothing settled. But you may take my word . . . between you and I Nibs. Shouldn't say anything to the others, not yet awhile—just our little secret . . . Understand?'

'Oh yes, Mr. Blackett,' I breathed.

So our fortunes were going to be retrieved after all!

THE CHILDREN'S PARTY

Written and illustrated by John Verney

The inside story of an amazing drama is printed exclusively in 'Collins' by a reporter who was an eye witness. Why did the Bostocks receive an invitation at breakfast time? What prevented the balloons inflating? Who mended the broken chair? For the first time details of this thrilling mystery are available to our readers.

THE COLOURED PHOTOGRAPH on the cover was taken by me at the Symes's evening party. I'm a reporter on the *Rottenborough Weekly Advertiser,* our local rag, and as Mrs. Symes invited the Press my Editor sent me along.

I took the snap just as the Bostock children were fighting off the finals of the musical chairs. And what a fight it was! Of course I left that bit out from my half-column describing the party in the *Advertiser.* In fact I had to be pretty polite all round. But I don't see why I shouldn't say what I think in *Collins.* None of the people concerned are likely to read it.

I showed the photo to Mrs. Symes afterwards, (she's on the right by the gramophone) and she thought it was, if anything, flattering of the Bostock children and of the various parents present, but so dreadful of her she begged me not to publish it in the *Advertiser.* It seemed a pity to waste the photo, so I'm letting *Collins* use it instead.

That's me, by the way, standing beside Mrs. Symes. I used a remote control for the photo, you can just see the bulb in my hand. Mr. Symes is the ugly fat bloke in the absurd green suit towards the back. Osbert and Edith Symes are floating about somewhere too. You can spot them for yourselves.

The party was a pretty good flop I thought. I expect you have all been to plenty and know the form. Nothing to drink except ginger beer and fizzy lemonade, the food made apparently of sawdust coated in pink candlegrease and the ice cream largely custard powder. Luckily the butler, hired for the occasion, raked me up a glass of beer and two ham sandwiches in a quiet moment, on condition I gave him a write up. A low commercial type I thought. Still he can't say I haven't kept the bargain.

Why do people give parties I always wonder? What good do they ever do anyone? With a view to providing an answer to those questions and with a little use of my imagination, the conscientious reporter's best friend, I have been able to piece together a few of the facts behind the Symes's party. Such as they are you might like to hear them. It may fill in the odd twenty minutes for you in a dentist's waiting room or somewhere.

The Symes's live in a cold draughty Georgian house just outside Rottenborough. The staircase and hall are rather imposing, as you can tell from the photo, but the rest of the house is on a smaller scale. Old Symes writes background music for the films and earns more in a week than I do in a year. Mrs. Symes is very active locally on education committees and what-not. Rather intense, but a good sort at heart. They have two kids Osbert and Edith. Most people find them dull but I like them myself. A bit highbrow perhaps, but nice and quiet and not too good at everything—the opposite of the Bostock children. But I'll be coming to them later.

A few mornings after Christmas Mrs. Symes came tripping in to breakfast. 'I've just had a good idea, that's why I'm late,' she said, rather as a hen might have done, who had been delayed laying an egg.

Osbert and Edith looked up from their shredded wheat with alarm. Their Mother's good ideas usually meant their doing something they didn't in the least want to do.

'You'll never guess! This is really exciting,' said Mrs. Symes. 'I'm going to give an evening party for you two before you go back to School.'

Osbert and Edith groaned loudly. And Mr. Symes hidden behind the morning paper groaned louder still.

'Oh Mummy, not a party. They are such hell,' said Edith.

'And I really thought it was going to be a good idea this time,' said Osbert. 'The new T. S. Eliot play or something of that sort.'

'Wherever will you give it,' said Mr. Symes, 'not here I hope?'

'Of course here. This house is made for giving parties. Can't you just imagine the hall with the furniture moved out and balloons on the chandelier and a Christmas tree in that corner under the staircase and decorations everywhere and all the boys and girls playing oranges and lemons and dancing Sir Roger de Coverley—or whatever you do dance nowadays. Can't you imagine it?'

The family sat for a few seconds imagining it. But they still didn't seem very enthusiastic.

'Who's going to move the furniture,' asked Mr. Symes.

'Why you dear, of course. And my brother Bill. I'm asking him for the weekend. The dance will be on the Saturday night, so you and he will have all day to clear the hall.'

'Dancing!' muttered Osbert. 'Suppose I'll have to wear those patent leather pumps which pinch my toes.'

'Will it mean asking a lot of people?' asked Edith nervously. She was going through a poetry-writing period and liked to be by herself as much as possible. In fact her favourite expression was 'I want to be alone'. She had heard someone say it in a film once.

'Of course it will mean asking a lot of people,' said Mrs. Symes cheerfully, who didn't seem in the least perturbed by her family's attitude. 'That is what parties are for. A lot of people have asked you to their parties and now it's your turn to ask them. In fact,' she continued smiling, 'a party is much the best way of getting a lot of people off your conscience, when they are on it, without having to talk to any of them.'

'There is that to it I suppose,' said Edith.

'Will it mean asking the Bostocks?' asked Osbert.

The same thought had been in Edith's mind. Of all the boys and girls they knew Mark and Susan Bostock were their chief abomination. Mark was at Boreham College with Osbert, Susan at St. Hildas with Edith. And the Bostocks were near neighbours. As the two sets of parents quite liked each other and persisted in the delusion that their respective children liked each other too, Osbert and Edith, Mark and Susan, had to meet from time to time in the holidays. But not more often than any of them could help. For Mark and Susan despised Osbert and Edith, just as much as the latter disliked them.

Compared to the Bostocks' Osbert and Edith were indeed

rather dim. For Mark and Susan were the tough and successful type and they excelled at school work, at games, at everything. They were always coming out top in examinations, carrying off cups at gymkhanas, and winning tennis tournaments. And whereas the Symes children were delicate—Osbert always had a snuffle even in mid-summer and Edith suffered from hay-fever even in mid-winter—Mark and Susan Bostock were invariably in splendid mental and physical trim all the year round.

'Of course we must ask the Bostocks,' said Mrs. Symes. 'They'll help to make the party go with a swing. Besides they asked you over to play tennis last summer.'

'But we didn't go. Don't you remember Mummy we had flu,' protested Osbert and Edith hopefully.

'That doesn't make any difference. They asked you. Besides I thought you were so fond of Mark and Susan . . .'

At this point Mr. Symes intervened. 'If you had known your Mother as long as I have you would realise she'd made up her mind and it's quite useless to argue. Besides, when the time comes, I dare say you will enjoy the party more than you think.'

As it turned out Mr. Symes was prophetically right.

In due course an invitation was sent to the Bostocks. When it arrived, they were at breakfast and actually at that minute discussing the Symes children.

'She's a lazy little beast,' Susan was saying of Edith. 'Always shirking lacrosse practice. I pull her hair every time I pass her in the corridor. How she squeals!'

'I can't stand that sly grin on his face,' said Mark of Osbert. 'Makes me want to kick him. As a matter of fact I jolly well ducked him in the river last summer.'

'Now dears, you mustn't talk like that,' said Mrs. Bostock thinking what a fine manly boy Mark was. 'I know Osbert and Edith are rather tiresome, but it's not really their fault. With a father who writes music you can't expect them to be normal like you. I'm so sorry for their poor mother.'

'What do you know about this!' cried Susan who had just opened the Symes's invitation and waved the card above her head. 'Talk of the devil . . . The scruffy Symes's are actually throwing a party. I didn't know they had it in them.' And she read out. 'Osbert and Edith Symes request the pleasure of Mark and Susan Bostock's company at their party on the 15th January. 6-10 p.m. Parents welcome. R.S.V.P.' 'Shall we go? I bet it's a dud party.'

'May as well I suppose,' said Mark. 'We can always break the place up.'

Then, his breakfast finished, Mark jumped up from the table upsetting his chair and sending a couple of plates crashing to the floor.

'Come on, Susie,' he yelled rushing out of the room. 'Remember you promised to practise footer with me this morning.'

'O.K. but let's do a little wrestling upstairs first,' shouted back Susan knocking her chair over too and bounding out of the room after him. And soon the bumping and banging told Mrs. Bostock that her two children were warming themselves up before spending the morning chasing a football up and down the lawn.

'The dear children are always so full of energy at this time of day,' she murmured to her husband, as she tidied up the mess they had left behind.

For the next fortnight Osbert and Edith were kept so busy sending out invitations and making paper decorations to hang in the hall, they had no time to themselves at all. While Mrs. Symes looked round for a contractor to provide supper and chairs and bought lots of little

presents from Woolworths to hang on the Christmas tree, and made all those hundred and one preparations that are apparently necessary for even quite a small party. Mr. Symes, as he had no film music on hand, amused himself in the local gramophone shop trying out suitable dance records.

The day before the party Mrs. Symes's brother Bill Snelgrove and her mother Mrs. Snelgrove arrived to stay. The former was very tall and strong and useful for reaching the top of the Christmas tree and moving the heavier bits of furniture. Mrs. Snelgrove, was a wonderful cake maker and had undertaken to produce the party cake, a three-decker masterpiece. But Mrs. Symes was a little dubious as to how she would enjoy the party itself.

On the day of the party the flap began after breakfast. Everything went wrong. The Christmas tree fully decorated toppled over. The contractor forgot to bring chairs and had to send his lorry for them all the way to London and back. The balloons were so tough they wouldn't blow up. Even Bill Snelgrove's breath was hardly sufficient. Edith dropped her party frock in the bath. Osbert couldn't find a single clean collar. Mr. Symes broke the only record of Sir Roger de Coverley.

And worst of all Mrs. Snelgrove put her beautiful cake on a chair while the table was being laid and Bill Snelgrove, too exhausted by blowing balloons and moving furniture to notice any more what he was doing, sat down on it. Luckily Mrs. Snelgrove wasn't in the room at the time and Bill Snelgrove and Osbert were able to patch it up quite effectively with pink poster paint and red ceiling wax. So that Mrs. Snelgrove who was short-sighted never noticed.

However all was at last ready and in order by 6 p.m. when the Symes's, all clean and tidy, and trying to look as though giving a party was a common-place every-day affair and no trouble at all, stood waiting for their guests. Osbert had managed to cut a hole in his pumps where they pinched and wore black socks hoping no one would notice. At 6.5 p.m. when no one had arrived Edith suddenly wondered whether she had put the right date on the invitation cards. But at 6.10 the guests began to pour in. Foremost among them were the Bostocks. The parents greeted each other warmly and Osbert and Edith shook hands with Mark and Susan, all grinning sheepishly.

The party began with a conjuror. Personally I thought he was useless, but on the whole the children seemed to swallow the stuff though there was some barracking from a group at the back of the room, led by Mark and Susan. Then followed the Christmas tree. By this stage in the holidays all the children had seen so many Christmas trees, that they were getting blasé and found it difficult to express adequate surprise and delight when handed a toy thimble or a pair of brass ear-rings. Most of them however hid their lack of appreciation better than did the Bostocks.

Mark when called forward to receive a small trumpet hardly said 'thank-you' and as he walked away chucked it contemptuously into a corner. Susan was given a wee doll's house cradle. She wouldn't have been seen dead with a doll's house, so she handed the cradle immediately to a sissier younger girl.

However, the crackers were as always popular and with paper hats and a few funny noses and moustaches, the party already had the appearance of being a success when musical chairs started.

Bill Snelgrove, as his contribution to the evening, had bought a lovely new leather football, which he announced would be the prize for the winner of the musical chairs.

'That's more like it,' Mark whispered to Susan. 'Here's something worth coming for.'

There was never much doubt as to who the two finalists would be. All the children who danced round and round the ever dwindling number of chairs showed keenness. But none showed that almost ferocious determination to win, the secret to all success in life, which was evident in Mark and Susan. Osbert of course was knocked out more or less literally by Mark quite early on. And Susan managed to give Edith a black eye at the same time that she grabbed a chair away from her.

At last Mark and Susan confronted each other alone from opposite sides of the remaining chair. While the gramophone played a silly little jig, they stalked slowly round it eyeing each other like a couple of tom-cats and keeping hold of the chair with both hands.

'What happens when I stop the record?' Mrs. Symes whispered to me.

'Try it and see. This is going to be fun!' I whispered back.

The moment the music stopped the scrap started. Neither Mark nor Susan could turn round to sit on the chair as the other would have pulled it away. They wrestled with it backwards and forwards uttering snarling noises and kicking at each other's shins. Then the chair broke. They both fell backwards, but in a flash they were up and struggling for possession of the chair seat which lay on the floor. And we left them to it; after all no one likes to interfere in a family squabble.

By the way Mrs. Bostock is on the left of the photo, a trifle embarrassed. Major Bostock is towards the right. I fancy he is pretending they are not his children anyway.

But we shall never know who would have won because the fight was spoilt by the Vicar stepping forward and separating them.

'You shouldn't be so rough with your little sister, young man.' he said sternly to Mark. 'She's only a girl.'

I don't care to think what Mark and Susan were going to say to the Vicar, when Mrs. Symes hastily announced that they had both won and the prize would be shared between them. Bill Snelgrove handed the football to Mrs. Bostock, remarking, not very tactfully I thought, that its possession would doubtless be settled when they got home.

Supper followed immediately. Mark and Susan have quite a reputation locally as eaters. They soon showed that their reputation was in no danger of declining. In fact, over-excited by the musical chairs, they were rather showing off their appetites to some of the others.

It was now that Osbert and Edith displayed a latent cunning which makes me guess they will not after all be such a flop in life as their parents fear. At a moment when Mark and Susan, vying with each other, in front of an admiring audience, as to who could eat most, had exhausted the resources in front of them, Osbert offered them a plate with two enormous slices of the party cake. And on each slice was a particularly lurid lump of icing.

'Have some cake,' he said innocently. 'I'm afraid they are rather large slices. You can always leave some if it's too much for you.'

'Oh you'll *never* be able to eat all that!' piped up Edith beside him.

'Won't we just!' grinned Mark and Susan. And eat it they did, though Osbert and Edith were quick to perceive a faint expression of disgust cross their faces when they swallowed the icing.

Shortly afterwards Bill Snelgrove took Osbert on one side. 'What happened to that bit of cake we patched up. I went to cut it off just now, but it had already been taken.'

'Yes I threw it away,' said Osbert. 'I was afraid someone might eat it.'

After supper everyone danced to the gramophone. Mrs. Symes was the first to notice Mark and Susan's absence. She asked their mother where they had got to, but Mrs. Bostock hadn't seen them since supper. Nor had anyone else. A few of us went off to search for them over the house. We found them at last in an upstairs bathroom. They were being sick. Awfully, awfully, sick. We helped them, pale and speechless, to be taken home at once.

'I am so sorry. What rotten luck,' Osbert said politely to Mrs. Bostock as he escorted them all to the front door. 'I do hope Mark and Susan feel better in the morning.'

After the departure of Mark and Susan the party soon broke up. Parents, anxious lest their own children might fall a sudden prey to whatever food poisoning had smitten the Bostocks, seemed anxious to get them away as soon as possible. By 9.30 all the guests had left and the Symes family were left to survey the desolation of their home. The hall, which without either furniture or guests, seemed colder and draughtier than ever, was ankle-deep in a litter of paper hats, crackers, streamers, and all the debris of a party.

As usual on such occasions, the Symes's's, though worn out, sat up speculating on the success or failure of their hospitality and picking holes in their departed guests.

'It was rather sticky to begin with,' said Edith, 'but I thought it ended quite well.'

'Oh I thought it ended beautifully,' said Osbert.

'Bill,' said Mrs. Symes to her brother, 'I'm so glad we've got you here to help us get the place straight tomorrow. And Mother, your cake looked simply marvellous!'

'It certainly did,' everyone agreed.

'It certainly did for the Bostock children,' laughed Mr. Symes who had a weakness for puns. 'I saw them each eat an enormous slice of it. No wonder they were sick.'

'If you will excuse me I'll go to bed now,' said Osbert hastily. And Edith accompanied him.

Later, Mrs. Symes who had been to say goodnight to them rejoined the other grownups. 'Really Osbert is a queer boy,' she said. 'What do you think he asked me just now? "Mummy would a large mouthful of poster paint and ceiling wax kill you?" Now what on earth do you think could give him an idea like that?'

Only Bill Snelgrove could guess, but he wisely kept his guess to himself.

In fact Mark and Susan by the following morning were as fit as ever. It will take more than poster paint and sealing wax to kill those two I fancy.

There was a happy sequel to the party, which provides, at least in this case, a possible answer to the second question I posed at the beginning. The very morning that Osbert and Edith were to go back to school, in fact even while they sat despondently on their trunks waiting for the taxi, Mrs. Bostock rang up Mrs. Symes to tell her that Mark and Susan were in bed with the mumps.

After some hasty telephoning to the family doctor and to Boreham College and St. Hildas, Mrs. Symes announced to Osbert and Edith that they were in quarantine and wouldn't be able to go back to school for two more weeks.

And as the same applied to all the other children who had been at the party, perhaps Mrs. Symes's good idea was after all not such a bad one.

BLACK

ILLUSTRATED BY GEOFFREY WHITTAM

'Beyond the orchard. Punch Bowl Farmhouse peeped from behind leaning fruit trees.'

10

HUNTING WHIP

by Monica Edwards

MRS. THORNTON PUT DOWN her gloves on the hall chest, hung up her coat and went into the sitting room. Andrea, reading on the window-seat, glanced up with an abstracted smile and said tea was ready. Dion, roasting chestnuts, made room by the fire. 'Come and get warm,' he said. 'It's like midwinter already.'

Lindsey, drawing horses at the gate-legged table, said 'Did you go to the sale after all?' and Peter, the youngest, jumped up from the hearthrug, fell over Dion, got up again. 'And did you,' he said, half joking, 'come home with the farm in your pocket?'

Mrs. Thornton sat down. She was looking a little bewildered and she said, 'I'm afraid I did.'

'WHAT?'

Andrea was out of her book, Dion on his feet, Lindsey staring, Peter just blank.

'But you said you didn't really want it.'

'You said you mightn't even bother about the sale.'

'You aren't really serious?'

'Tell us quickly or I'll burst.'

Still looking slightly astonished, Mrs. Thornton said, 'Don't be absurd. Of course I'm serious. There's a sale catalogue in my coat pocket—'

Dion rushed out of the room and came back waving it. A pink map fell out on to the floor and was pounced on, opened and spread out by Andrea. All four pressed round it on the carpet.

'I hadn't thought,' said Mrs. Thornton, 'that it would go so cheaply, but the hammer just came down at my one and only bid. I felt pretty terrified at first. It seemed an awful thing to say two words and find you'd bought a farmhouse and seventy wild acres. It's practically a ruin, that's why we didn't really want it. But I just couldn't bear to see it going so cheaply, and it *was* going, for less than the amount Daddy and I had agreed about, so I said my little piece and the hammer came down, and I haven't felt so awful as I did then, since I was small and at school.'

'We don't mind about the ruin,' Dion said, still staring at the map. 'It looks wonderful, and now I shall really be able to do some proper farming.'

'I expect so,' said his mother absently.

'All those commons for riding!' Lindsey's finger circled the pink area. 'And stables for the ponies.'

'No more hard roads!' said Andrea.

Mrs. Thornton said, 'There's no bath. There isn't even any water. I mean no piped water. It's all down a very deep well. Every bucket has to be drawn up.'

'I know,' said Dion; he was reading the catalogue. 'It says here that the well is a hundred feet deep, and in a tiled and timbered well-house.'

'There isn't electricity,' Mrs. Thornton said, 'or gas.'

'What is there?' Lindsey asked, wondering.

Andrea said happily, 'Oh, oil lamps and candles and that kind of thing. You carry them about.'

'The thing that really matters,' said Lindsey, looking up 'is shall we be in time for Christmas?'

'Oh yes, easily, I should say,' her mother said.

Lindsey sighed deeply with vast satisfaction. 'Anyone would think you weren't glad we've got it,' she said, 'but I know you are.'

'Of course I am. But I'm still a bit dazed about everything and I don't want you to expect anything wonderful.'

Dion sat back on his heels. 'Is it good farming land?'

'Terrible, I should think,' his mother said. 'Light and sandy and overgrown with heather, bracken and ragwort.'

'We'll need a prairie-buster,' said Dion happily.

'And years of hard work,' Mrs. Thornton added.

Peter jumped up. 'As if it mattered!' he said, and the kettle boiled over with a sputter.

It might have been a symbol, a sort of omen, of the boiling over of the Thorntons. Their smoothly ordered lives were upheaved with a very great sputter, and no one could have enjoyed it all more. Here they were, in such a boiling-up of solicitors and agents and valuers and removers and even belated offers to re-purchase the farm from them, in case they might have decided they didn't really want it. The four children suffered agonies because there were torturous delays while obscure things in the deeds were being investigated. In the end an odd assortment of lorries was hastily hired and Mrs. Thornton lifted up a thankful heart because the day was fine and calm.

A double horse-box came for the two ponies. It fell to Dion and Lindsey to go with these, and Andrea and Peter and the golden retriever puppy, which Mr. Thornton had recently brought home as a prospective watchdog, with the driver.

There was terrible trouble getting small, grey Sula into the horse-box, though Mrs. Thornton's Moonstone, accustomed to much showing, walked up like a lady. Sula did edge up the ramp twice but each time rushed down again backwards, and twice got right away down the lane, to the great interest of the gathering crowd.

Moonstone, very white and very elegant, stood waiting aloofly in the box like the well-mannered animal she was. Lindsey rushed back with some oats in a saucepan and with much patience and plenty of bribery they got the smaller pony in. They shut the ramp up quickly after her.

There was a scuffling of people and puppy getting into the car and Dion jumped up beside Lindsey in the front of the horse-box.

They drove right into Highnoons village, past the village hall, the Three Horseshoes, the shingle-spired church and up, up, up, higher and higher. The village was left behind, the sides of the lane grew steeper and the trees closed in overhead like an interlaced tunnel. Leaves lay thickly and the wheels of the car and horse-box rustled through them.

'I thought the farm was in a valley,' Dion said. He stooped and cricked his neck to see better.

'It is, Daddy said so. Must be a high sort of valley. Wish we could get out of this deep lane and see what the country is like. We'll ride over it hundreds of times before we're old and staid.'

Then the car slid to a stately halt. Dion opened the little door at the horse-box front. Lindsey followed and they found the others on the high crest of a fork in the lane, studying a smallish sign-post. The lane went on higher still to the left but to the right it dropped very steeply. The sign-post said, 'Sandy track to Devil's Punch Bowl,' to the left, and 'Impassable to motors. Farms only,' to the right.

Andrea, looking very grown-up for fifteen, was saying, 'I'm sure it must be to the left because it says Devil's Punch Bowl and it *is* Punch Bowl Farm.'

The driver said, 'Your Dad said right at the sign-post, and it says "farms", see. And what's more, it says "impassable to motors", so what? Can't risk this turnout, and I've got to get back before lighting up.'

'We'll walk the ponies,' suggested Peter.

The driver walked round to the ramp and began undoing it, expressing the hope that the dapple-grey would unload a bit easier than she loaded. She did. She walked out with a most relieved expression and looked at the horse-box as one might look at a dungeon from which one has unexpectedly and safely escaped. Moonstone stepped down like an old hand, which she was, and Andrea took her head-collar rope.

'May I lead Sula?' Peter begged of Lindsey, who had her rope, and Dion dashed back into the horse-box to get the saucepan with the oats.

'No, but you can ride her and I'll lead her,' Lindsey said, ' I had her rope first and you are the youngest.'

Peter said he couldn't help being the youngest, but he submitted to being legged up. After saying good-bye to the horse-box driver they moved off down the steep rough lane with the ponies, the puppy and the saucepan.

Beyond the orchard, Punch Bowl Farmhouse peeped from behind leaning fruit trees. Grey stone, pearl-grey timbers, diamond-paned windows, and a steep, wide roof of most ancient tiles, so encrusted with moss and lichen that they seemed as green as red.

' It *is* in a valley,' Dion said, surprised.

They passed the long house beside the lane and came to their own orchard gate.

'Look at the grass for the ponies,' said Andrea, opening the gate which had to be lifted and then pulled, 'and in December, too. Must be good land, Dion.'

'Those hill fields may be different.' Dion glanced up to where the land rose steeply, higher than the farmhouse roof.

Lindsey was staring, saying nothing. Peter pressed Sula on. 'I want to explore *every*thing, this minute,' he said.

Dion shut the gate and they went on, up the track to the farm. The removal lorry, pulling out empty, passed them by the little garden gate. Mrs. Thornton called down to them from a bedroom window.

'Put the ponies in the Barn field, through the yard.'

'Right!' Dion and Andrea, oozing excitement and energy attended to the ponies. Peter had already disappeared, complete with the saucepan and the puppy, but Lindsey stood still in the middle of the yard. She smiled up at her mother, saw the broad high chimneys, looked down to the nettles in the garden, the crumbling stone walls that held the garden from falling down into the farmyard, the sagged tiled barn, the cowshed, stables, the tall holly tree by the pond.

'Like it?' her mother said, in the window.

'Mm!'

Dion and Andrea left the ponies grazing and rushed to the stable with its three old-fashioned stalls, the calf-box, the cowshed, the roomy, musty barn and the little tiled pigsties. Then round the outside of the house.

'That's the well-house. A hundred feet deep. Shall we wind some water up?' Andrea said.

'Not now. Too much to see. That must be an outdoor cellar. Looks like Lindsey in it.'

'Never mind; come on. Doesn't the roof come down

low at the back? We could slide down it in the winter and land just here.'

Round the next corner.

' This must be where the old wing was. Did you know there was another wing, ages ago? It says so in the sale catalogue. Look, those must be the footings of it, those grown-over stones. It stretched out here.'

' Why was it pulled down? ' Andrea said.

' Dunno. Burnt down, I expect. Look, do you see the bricked-up fireplaces of the old wing, still there in the outside wall? One upstairs and one down.'

Andrea led on past the blue front door with its flanking of Tudor feathered brick. 'We must ferret it all out,' she said, and suddenly saw Peter's face grinning up from a window by her ankles.

'Cellar down here!' he called. 'It's rummy. Come and look; it's through the kitchen.'

'When you've finished exploring,' Mrs. Thornton called from above them, 'there's a packed lunch indoors.'

'We'll never finish exploring,' Dion called back, 'but we may as well stop for re-fuelling.' They turned back and Mrs. Thornton called after them, 'Where's Lindsey?'

'Oh, somewhere! Down another cellar, I think, round by the well-house.'

At the kitchen door they called her and she came leaping down a steep path above a walled bank that faced the kitchen, her long plaits swinging on her shoulders. 'I've been climbing the yew-tree,' she said. ' You know that's Yew Tree field, of course? '

' Of course,' said Andrea, and Dion added, ' If there's a yew tree it will have to come down. They're deadly to cattle.'

' Not my yew tree!' said Lindsey stoutly. 'You must fence it off.'

Dion wouldn't argue but went inside the kitchen. Peter came in from the other side, up the indoor cellar steps, with the yellow puppy on its lead. He had cobwebs in his hair and whitewash on his jersey. 'Where's the food?' he said, sniffing round. 'Can I have one of these pies?'

Andrea, following Dion, looked round the kitchen with a glance of surprised disappointment. 'I say, it's rather dark and dismalish,' she said. 'The walls are nearly black, and the ceiling's frightful.'

'Imagine it,' said Mrs. Thornton from behind a pile of crates, 'with the walls all cream-washed and a new window just there, to let the sun come in. And with the ceiling freshly whitened between those heavy rafters. Then we'll dig out that bricked-in inglenook, paint the window-frames and have a new sink. . . .'

' Mm,' Andrea sounded a little cheered. ' It might be rather nice. It's awfully roomy.'

' And when the dresser has all the coloured plates and things on it—' began Mrs. Thornton, pouring drinks from a thermos flask.

'We *must* have Jersey cows!' Dion suddenly said, from the middle of a private dream.

' Yes, Jersey cows, of course,' Mrs. Thornton replied.

' Jugs of yellow cream and pounds of golden butter!' Andrea made round eyes and patted her middle.

Peter recited through currant bun, 'No more marge to make me large!'

' No more mince to make me wince,' chanted Dion, and they all began to improvise jingles, Mrs. Thornton contributing ' No more cider to make me wider,' and Lindsey bursting in with ' No more skeeter to make me fleeter.'

Dion, staring at the wide cellar door, broke in again and said, 'I wonder if there were cellars under the old wing, as there are under this one.'

The children's father opened the back door, stooped and

walked in. 'Why not?' he said. 'Very likely there are.' Then to Mrs. Thornton, 'I've settled with Holleybone to carry on here as before, but he says he doesn't like Jerseys, give him a nice dairy shorthorn.'

'You won't, of course,' said Mrs. Thornton, pulling out a crate for him to sit on and passing sandwiches.

'We shan't need him when I've left school,' Dion said, 'though I might do with an assistant. You won't want to bother, Dad. You'd be drawing the cows when they were gasping to be milked. Do you really think there might be cellars under the old wing?'

'Your guess is as good as mine,' Mr. Thornton said. Then to the children's mother, 'To-morrow we start on the kitchen. Can you have it cleared of all this clutter?'

Dion gulped his hot cocoa and went down the brick steps to the indoor cellar. He looked carefully round it. Brick floor, under all that rubbish. Stone walls, with inset shelves and alcoves. Windows level with the garden. The old wing lay out to the left so it would be along that wall he must look, if the cellars had communicating doors. It all looked very stout and solid. Not the merest suggestion of a door. He wondered how the Elizabethans had gone from one wing to the other on the ground floor, and rushed up the brick steps again.

No sign of a vanished doorway in the kitchen. He looked in the larder; a long, narrow place but white-washed throughout. It seemed quite innocent. He looked in the washing-room. Terribly shabby and dilapidated, but no hidden doorway. Just an old cracked copper and the usual whitewashed walls, now nearly grey.

Round the corner of the house, he stood among the nettles and stared again at the wall with the bricked-in fireplaces. On one side of the lower fireplace the wall was of Bargate stone, as was most of the farmhouse, but on the other side it was of two-inch Tudor bricks.

'That must be the place,' he thought at once. 'The door was there, the door to the other wing. Funny, to think of people walking through it, out here to this nettle-bed. Wasn't a nettle-bed then, though.'

He looked around him, imagining chairs and tables, walls and windows. 'Those little bricks are Tudor. Then the wing must have been destroyed quite soon after the house was built—unless people just used the old bricks from that wing, which they probably did. Funny, no one seems to know anything about it, and there aren't any records, father says.'

He looked again at the fireplace wall and tried to remember what was behind the bricked-up doorway. 'The larder, I think—' and rushed inside to make sure. It was the larder, but it looked as innocent as before. Yet people had walked through it every day, a great many years ago, going into a part of the house that had vanished.

Lindsey came into the larder. 'Have you found anything?'

'Yes. The old way into the vanished wing. They came through here, it was a passage; wouldn't it be queer if we could go back in time, and see it all how it was? Gosh, yes! What mightn't happen then?'

*   *   *

THERE WAS LAUGHING on the wind from up in Yew Tree field, and Dion paused a minute in his digging to listen. He was standing on the footing of the vanished wing, prodding, and sometimes digging with a strong garden fork, absorbed in his week-old search for lost cellars. His most recent discoveries lay in a tiny pile beside the stone path; an old rusty iron hinge, two red tiles, rather chipped, a saucepan lid which, being made of tin, could not be antique, and a broken dish of willow pattern ware.

The excavations had been very difficult. There was too much Bargate stone and he hit it with every thrust.

'What I need is a pick,' he thought, and then saw Andrea moving along the top of the hazel hedge, high above where he was standing. Then the white ears and mane of Moonstone, whom she was riding, and Lindsey on little grey Sula.

Lindsey was riding bareback because Sula had grown so fat during the summer that her saddle wouldn't fit her.

Seeing their brother, the sisters waved. 'Found anything?' called Lindsey. 'We've been right round the Punch Bowl to Gibbet Hill,' said Andrea, 'and seen the murdered sailor's stone. The one with the curse on it.'

'What curse?' said Dion, jabbing with his fork at a creeping bramble bush.

Andrea drew rein. 'You know they had to move the stone when they made the new road? Well, there was a curse on anyone who moved it, but they said they had to, and now it's up near to where the gibbet was. You know, where they hanged the murderers.'

'And did the curse work?'

Andrea smoothed Moonstone's mane. 'How would we know?'

Lindsey said, 'Do move on, Andrea. Sula's getting fidgety.'

The ponies disappeared from Dion's view, down behind the well-house roof, then into the yard. He wiped his fork on the nettles, picked up his afternoon's discoveries and walked towards the workshop.

'Any luck?' his mother called as he passed the back door and he stopped to show her, by the doorstep. 'Not much,' he said.

Ten minutes later they were all round the sitting room table, which was crowned with a yellow-shaded lamp. Soft golden light poured down on fruit cake, plain buns, brown bread on a board, and a cluster of variegated jam-pots. The large brown teapot was crowded round with yellow teacups, and the buttercup plates, which no longer had cups but were loved for themselves alone, ringed round the oval table with an egg in an egg-cup on each.

Peter reached for the salt. 'I like eggs for tea much better than I do for breakfast,' he said.

Mrs. Thornton passed teacups. 'The floor is very humpy,' she said, 'and the table, being a gateleg, it's quite impossible to get all the legs on the same level at once. I have wedged two, but it doesn't help much.'

'You won't be altogether pleased, I dare say,' their father said, 'but we have made arrangements for school—'

Groans and sighs round the table and everyone began eating again.

Lindsey said where was it?

'Across the Punch Bowl, past the gibbet and a few minutes over the common,' Mrs. Thornton said, handing bread on a fork. 'We can show you on a map. You'll have to cycle, I expect, and even with cycles you'll have to walk where the track is bad. But you might be able to go on pony-back in the summer—some of you.'

'And you don't have to go till after Christmas, so praise heaven for a shockingly long holiday,' their father added.

'Has anyone noticed,' Lindsey said, not wishing to talk about school, even about riding to it, in this glowing moment of comfortable family tea, 'Has anyone noticed how the wind is getting up?'

'It's going to be an absolute roarer,' Dion said as he reached for the honey. 'I heard it in the yew tree.'

Lindsey watched him spread the honey, waiting for the jar. 'I hope it roars till bedtime,' she said, 'and then drops. I like it now, when we're all together in here with lamplight and the logs crackling, but when I'm in bed in the dark it isn't a bit the same.'

(Continued on page 47)

Supplies dropped over a camouflaged camp deep in the Burma jungle.

THE TEMPERAMENTAL GLIDER

by Peter Fleming

Peter Fleming served as Colonel on Lord Mountbatten's Staff and was attached to General Wingate for this operation into Burma. In his books 'Brazilian Adventure', 'One's Company' and 'News From Tartary' he writes of his travels in different parts of the world. In this story the risk of enemy action is added to his dangers.

EVERY STORY ought to have a heroine, and Jean is the heroine of this one, although—or rather because—she disappears almost as soon as the curtain rises. Jean was a pony, an ugly, brindled, very sure-footed pony about thirteen hands high, and although she would not have done for the Household Cavalry she was probably the best charger in General Wingate's command. She had been ridden on training by Brigadier Mike Calvert and when in March, 1944, Wingate launched the main part of his guerilla force deep into Burma by air, Mike naturally did not want to leave Jean behind. He himself was going with what was known to us as the blitz party, consisting of four gliders whose occupants were to seize the large and theoretically deserted clearing in which the rest of the force was to land, a long way behind the Japanese lines. There was no room for Jean with the blitz party, so Mike asked me to bring her in.

Wingate's plan was for part of the Brigade to go in by glider on the first night, taking bulldozers with them to make an air-strip in the clearing so that the rest of the force could follow by Dakota on subsequent nights. If you take a pony in a glider you have to make a sort of stall for it in the tail. We did this for Jean, but at the last minute the glider was damaged. This meant hurriedly borrowing a fresh glider and, because the new glider was not equipped with a stall, it also meant leaving Jean behind. I took my Chinese orderly instead, and some extra rations.

It was the belief of the admirable American officers who had organised that part of the operation that one Dakota aircraft could pull two loaded gliders; events proved that this belief was a bit optimistic. We and our sister glider were Nos. 15 and 16 in the queue, and quite soon after we had taken off I was surprised to see that our sister glider was no longer with us. There was the long white nylon tow-rope streaming beside us in the evening air; but there was nothing on the end of it.

Before take-off the pilot, a nice American, had asked me to detail one man—there were fifteen of us altogether—to come forward from the stern of the glider in case she needed trimming slightly. This man was called forward almost as soon as we were off the ground, and after him another, and another, and another, until in the end everyone was crammed like sausages in a tin as near to the nose of the glider as they could get. The trouble was that the controls on our new glider were not working, at least the flaps were not. They were operated by three little handles above the pilot's head. He tried to turn them, I tried to turn them, various other people tried to turn them. They wouldn't budge a millimetre. For five or ten minutes she would fly on an even keel. Then she would embark on a series of suppressed aerobatics, swooping about exactly like a kite on the end of a string when a gust of wind catches it. The whole framework would shudder in a most alarming way, creaks and groans would make themselves heard, and we would suddenly find ourselves hopelessly out of station—far above or far below the aircraft pulling us, instead of straight behind it. We were 8,000 feet up on a dark night, and it was really a very frightening experience.

Night had fallen as we crossed the mountains behind Imphal, and before long, far away below us, we saw a thin silver ribbon and knew that it was the River Chindwin and that we were over Japanese occupied territory. We had been air-borne in this rather excruciating way for an hour and a half when the glider was seized by a paroxysm of extreme violence. She slipped steeply downwards and sideways, all the loose stores and equipment went clattering across the floor and the whole structure shuddered so fiercely that it was clear even to an optimist like me that the beastly thing was on the point of coming to pieces in mid-air. There was only one course open to the pilot. He cut. That is to say, he put up his right hand and punched a knob in the roof over his head and we parted company with the Dakota.

The first thing we noticed was the silence. It came on us suddenly. Instead of the urgent, overbearing roar of the aircraft's engines, we heard only a gentle, reflective swishing sound as we floated through the darkness. But though we felt this to be a change for the better, our situation was extremely unpromising. Far below us in the moonlight lay a solid black carpet of jungle, towards which we were slowly, inexorably and rather unsteadily descending in wide circles. I am bound to say that at this point it looked very much as if we had had it. There was only one minute break in the thick black canopy of tree tops—a tiny little speck of white like the lining showing through a small tear in a black coat. We made for it, swinging nearer and nearer to the unfriendly earth until all of a sudden tree tops were flicking past my window, we were through them, we were coming into a strip of sand dotted with boulders and—crash—we had landed. We had landed in the bed of a stream where it splayed out in the bottom of a gully. The nose of the glider was smashed and the pilot and I were now buried under a blasphemous mass of soldiery. The reason I said that Jean, the pony, was the heroine of this story was because, if we had had her with us in the tail then, she would have been bound to cause casualties at this stage and we really should have been in a bad way. As it was, no one was seriously hurt.

The first thing we had to do, after posting men to watch the edges of the clearing, was to get rid of our secret documents. We had the Brigade Intelligence Officer on board, and he had with him all the ciphers, maps and other secret papers that the army needs in the field. They travelled in a receptacle which was just too large to be called a chest and just too small to be called a trunk, and when we started burning them it was clear that we were in for a very long job. The last thing we wanted to do was to draw attention to our presence, but the bonfire got larger and larger and brighter and brighter.

There was a dirt road crossing the stream just below the spot where we had landed, and above the cheerful crackling of the flames we could hear, in the distance, a Japanese lorry rumbling towards us. Then, as if this was not enough, there was a sudden roar overhead and a night-fighter shot over the tree-tops at nought feet and gave the bonfire a burst of cannon fire. Nobody was hit, but it

' After a week we reached the Chindwin. It was about 500 yards wide. The problem was, how were we to get across it with the boots, arms and rations we should need the other side?'

was not a very friendly welcome to the jungle. We heard afterwards that it was an R.A.F. aircraft on a routine patrol with orders to shoot at all lights. Eventually the last fat cipher book was reduced to ashes and we withdrew discreetly into the jungle, found a track, marched hard for four or five hours and lay up in thick cover above a village in which we could hear the Japanese garrison turning out, rather irritably, to go and look for us.

We had no idea where we were, and we had no map of that part of Burma, which was actually rather an advantage as we had no possible means of checking our position on it and it would only have led to arguments. On the other hand we had enough rations to last us for eight days, we were well armed and I saw no particular reason why we should not do what I intended to do, which was to walk back to India, get into an aeroplane (preferably not a glider) and rejoin our Brigade in the field. Until we did this we were simply being a dead loss to the taxpayer.

It turned out to be comparatively easy. We moved through the silent and not unfriendly jungle by night, kept off tracks all the time and by great good luck always managed to find water. On two quite exciting occasions we bumped into the Japanese, but they were looking in the wrong direction and never saw us. After a week we reached the Chindwin. It was about five hundred yards wide, there were no boats to be seen and we were awkwardly placed in a little sort of shrubbery between the river and the (as it were) towpath which was a main Japanese line of communication. The problem was, how to get across that large river with the boots, arms and rations which we should need on the other side?

Someone had the brilliant idea of making a raft by filling our packs with empty water-bottles and other buoyant objects, including packets of American rations which we fondly supposed to be water-proof. The plan was that the men who could not swim would hang on to this, the boots and weapons would be stacked on it and the swimmers would propel it across after dark. We spent the whole day assembling this remarkable craft—we could not cut bamboos or make any noise because we were in the middle of a Burmese village—and when night fell we

carried it lovingly, in sections, down the steep high bank on to the muddy foreshore and put it gently in the river. It floated. We were delighted. We stripped, loaded everything on the raft, issued our four inflatable life-belts to the non-swimmers and prepared to set sail. Alas, in the course of these preparations our splendid raft had lost her buoyancy and was now completely waterlogged. Not only was it clear that she would never float, but the sodden packs were almost too heavy to carry away.

The situation at this point was so hopeless as to be almost comic. Here we were—eleven British, one American, one Canadian, one Indian and one Chinese—clad only in our shirts and bitterly cold, paddling about in the moonlit mud under a steep bank inhabited by Burmese and patrolled by the Japanese, with our last hope of crossing the river apparently gone. Once more, it looked as if we were done for.

However, things are seldom as bad as they seem. One of the officers in the party was a very strong swimmer, and I sent him off with the four non-swimmers in their rather amateurish Mae Wests. One man was drowned, the others all got across somehow. Meanwhile the rest of us wrapped up boots and weapons in the groundsheets and though some of these sank in mid-stream, we all reached the other side, and two volunteers—one of whom swam that 500-yard-wide river five times in the course of the night—went back to fetch essential things which had had to be left behind. Forty-eight hours later the Japanese Army crossed the Chindwin in force and began their advance on Imphal, so we only got home by a short head.

A few days later we were flying back into Burma over the jungles through which we had moved so stealthily by night, on our way to rejoin General Wingate's forces in the field. And Jean, the little pony? She had gone in by Dakota already and took part in many more exciting adventures than the one I have tried to describe before being flown out again to India at the end of the campaign. She only just missed establishing a record by being the first war-horse in history to set out for the battlefield in a glider. If she had established it, I don't suppose that this story would ever have been written.

JANUARY IN THE COUNTRY

by Michael Champion

MOST FOLK would name the lane that leads to the sea wall "The Road to nowhere." It winds down off the hill like a tunnel between high thorn hedges, dark, smelling of winter earth and rotting leaves. Then the hedges disappear, the fields become flat and open, reeds, plumed and rustling line the path. At the sea wall the lane stops. On one side of the great bank are the pastures, dotted with cattle, and on the other side is the tide of Severn, roaring over mud and rock.

The flats are dreary perhaps, ruled only by moon, wind and tide, but to anyone who loves wild places they are a delight. They are the wintering place of a great variety of duck and waders. Before dawn is the best time to study these birds. It is a never failing thrill to slop out over the ooze at low tide in the darkness, and to huddle down under a ledge of sandstone, with the tide at your feet and the sea wall a mile behind. Some of the wild fowl feed by day

PHOTO: E. HOSKING
Curlew are the wariest of all birds.

PHOTO: LAMER
When you see a track, make a sketch of it on the spot.

and, others feed at night, so at dawn there is a sort of two-way traffic in the air. In the darkness the bird watcher must become more of a bird listener. Sound travels clearly over the flats and the pompous quacking of mallard, having a last feed in some muddy runnel, and the far-off whistle of Widgeon seems very near, although in reality far away.

Before it starts to get light, high up in the sky comes the whisper of wings. These are the Mallard, who have been feeding in the fields all night, returning to the estuary to rest during the day. Here they all seem to fly on a definite route, using a clump of ash trees on the sea wall as a land mark, and changing course down river at a certain spit of sand. For twenty minutes they stream over, in twos and sixes and tens. As they go they chatter to each other in low voices. Perhaps one lot will circle and land in the tide close by with a tremendous splash. Landing on water in the dark is not so easy: ask a flying-boat pilot. Yet the duck have no flarepath lights or flying instruments.

While the last of the Mallard are going over, Snipe, who have been probing in the mud along the shore, with bills half as long as their bodies, decide that it is time to be off to the rushes and reeds inland. With daylight the Peregrine falcon will be raiding the flats, so such a shelterless place will not be safe for them. One after another they rise and fly off emitting a queer screech as they go.

Long before sunrise, individual stones and ripples on the tide close by, become discernible, but it is still much too dark to use the field glasses. Everywhere there seem to be wildfowl; Widgeon flying low and in small bunches up the tide line, or floating lazily on the water. The drakes whistle and the ducks chuckle back at them. Curlew flight out to the fields to feed, also whistling to each other but with a completely different note. They are, perhaps, the wariest of all birds, odd looking creatures with their long curved bills and equally long shanks. It is easy to decoy them overhead by a practised whistle through the fingers.

As the sky slowly flames into the blaze of sunrise the watcher must keep absolutely still. The sight of Mallard preening on the rocks, quite close, the yellow crest of the drake Widgeon, little dunlin dancing along in the shallows: how well worth a long cold wait they are.

* * *

Can you read tracks in the snow? It is exciting to be able to tell what animal has passed by on its midnight hunting. Of course, snow is not the only place where 'footings' can be read; soft mud around ponds and by streams is equally covered with signs.

Now the best way in which to learn how to read tracks is to make a book. Just a small note-book which will go easily into your pocket. Then, when you see a track, make a sketch of it on the spot, and write underneath the date and the place, and what sort of creature you think it is made by.

One way to make a lasting record of a footprint in mud is to fill the depression with freshly mixed plaster of Paris, and make a cast of it. In snow, the mark can sometimes be impressed on to a thin piece of silver paper.

There are two things to be studied when trying to find out what sort of animal has made a track. First there is the general pattern of the paw-marks, or trail. Look at this one:

I expect most people know what that one is. Yes, it's old long ears rabbit, hopping along lazily over the snow. A hare's trail is similar, only bigger. It is fun to see what enormous leaps these fellows sometimes make. Here is the trail of a fox at the lope, daintily placing its hind pads in the mark of its fore.

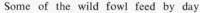

Then the second thing is the 'footing' itself. Here are three to start your collection.

fox   otter   badger

It must be remembered that hind and forefoot marks differ, and that tracks on soft and hard surfaces appear to differ a little. The fox's pad mark is small and neat. The otter's is large and hand-like, and the web between its toes can be seen, quite easily. The first otter prints that I ever saw were by a little tidal creek, with steep oozy banks. The tracks led out of the water up to the top of the bank, a distance of fully fifteen yards. Here the animal must have stopped, with its blunt muzzle and intelligent eyes scouting over the countryside. The trail then turned and disappeared down into the water again.

Brock the badger has wide and strong paws, well made for digging out his set, or grubbing up wasps nests. Like the otter, he also has five toes, although the inner and smaller one shows only faintly in the foot-print.

Well! There is a start for the tracking book. After a week or two you will have found out the mouse, and probably the stoat too. For wherever he goes there is blood along his trail. He is the killer of the countryside. Many different kinds of birds will be in the book. The more that is searched for and found the more fascinating you will find that the hobby becomes. So here's to the first fall of snow!

ALL THAT GLITTERS

by Kathleen Mackenzie

ILLUSTRATED BY ANTHONY GRIFFIN

It is as well to be careful when you are wishing, in case you too, may find yourself in the same predicament as Robert, Katherine and Janet. They meet with a strange adventure and only just escape disaster, leaving an unexplained mystery behind them

'YOU MUST ADMIT,' said Katherine, ' it's a super doll's house.'

' Not bad,' replied Robert grudgingly; not because he didn't agree with her, but because he was so indescribably bored with the whole afternoon that he couldn't be enthusiastic about anything.

If you were interested in dolls' houses it was a particularly fine one, large, beautifully furnished and with electric light. It stood high off the ground surrounded by a paved terrace with a carved balustrade round the edge on which were tubs with artificial geraniums, and a steep flight of steps to the floor.

Robert, Katherine and Janet were alone in the nursery. Sounds that the party was going its ballooned and crackered way, enlivened by music, came from below. They had escaped during ' sardines ', after the huge tea. Robert felt more strongly than ever that they ought never to have come. It was all Aunt Cora's fault, of course. They had come to spend a week with her, and she had announced on the first evening, in her usual wafty way, that she had accepted an invitation for them to a party. Aunt Cora had brushed away as unimportant the fact that they had no party clothes with them, and in spite of Robert's Cassandra-like prophecies, and Katherine's misgivings, they had found themselves at the party, where, knowing no-one and shamefully conscious of the inadequacy of their tidiest Sunday clothes, they had spent a wretched two hours. Even the tea, good as it had been, had not made up for the subsequent misery.

' What,' said Robert, ' is the earliest that we can go? ' He was standing moodily kicking the high fireguard and fiddling with the things on the mantelpiece.

' Don't know. It's only half-past five. Oh, do be careful, Jan, for goodness' sake don't break anything.'

Janet was beside the doll's house, putting her hand through the windows and taking things out to look at them.

' Look at this coal scuttle,' she said. ' It's got a little shovel at the back. And there's a darling little knife on the table.'

Katherine joined her, and they both gazed through the windows of the drawing room. It was carpeted in a thick, self-coloured velvet, and the window curtains and chair covers were of rose silk. There was an oval gate-legged table in the middle of the room, with a pot of huge pink flowers on it, a high-backed sofa with gilt legs and two armchairs to match. A revolving bookcase was standing beside one of the chairs. There was an open bureau against the side wall with a little blotter on it, and a quill pen in an inkstand made of a glass bead. There was a gilt waste-paper basket, a copper coal scuttle and copper fire-irons in the fender. On the mantelpiece was a clock and two rather ugly, glass vases. There was a bowl of fruit on the bookcase under the window and two standard lamps with real electric light bulbs, both of which were on, as were all the lights in the house. The beauty of the room was slightly marred by the presence of two repellent dolls—obviously the master and mistress of the house. The master, in a shapeless brown suit and red bow tie, was half-sitting, half-leaning against one of the chairs. His wife, whose blonde hair was piled untidily on her head, was sitting stiffly on the sofa, her china legs ending in painted high-heeled boots stuck out in front of her.

' Isn't it funny,' said Katherine, ' that no one has ever made a decent doll's house yet.'

' There's a nurse in the nursery,' said Janet, ' and a baby. The nurse is awful, but the baby is the best of the bunch. Look at the high chair, and the cot, and the tiny little Noah's ark. It's a lovely nursery. I'd love to live in it. I've always wanted to live in a doll's house.'

' That's just the sort of idiotic thing you would say,' said Robert unkindly. ' What would be the point of living in a doll's house? If you were small enough to live in it, it would be just the same as living in an ordinary house.'

' It wouldn't. It would be miles nicer. This is a much grander house than ours to begin with, at least it's much more grandly furnished.'

There was a clatter as Robert dropped the ornament he had been fiddling with—a small green beetle. It hit the side of the fireguard and rolled across the floor.

' Do be careful, Robert,' said Katherine anxiously. ' It would be the last straw to break something. Where is it? '

' It's there beside Jan's foot.'

Janet stooped to pick it up. ' Do come and look at the doll's house, Robert,' she urged. ' It's absolutely marvellous. It's got everything you could possibly want. You could keep house in it beautifully.'

*   *   *

' What's happened? '

' What can it have been? ' cried Janet seizing hold of Katherine.

' We have been blown somewhere,' said Robert slowly, ' only I didn't hear any explosion. But we must have been blown somewhere. This is quite a different place.'

The three gazed about. Straight ahead of them was a flight of stone steps, leading up to a balustraded terrace on which, at intervals, were stone pots planted with what looked like enormous scarlet hydrangeas.

' Katherine,' said Robert's voice, and it sounded queer.

' What's happened? ' she asked, a strong feeling of foreboding coming over her.

' Look there! ' He waved his hand over the balustrade. ' Do you see what that is? It's that beastly doll's house, only either it's grown enormous, or we've grown tiny.'

It became only too clear that for some reason, for which

they could offer no explanation, they had become tiny. That seemed the more probable solution than that the house and furniture had become larger.

At first Katherine was all for attracting the attention of the people at the party downstairs, in hope that they would be aware that metamorphoses of such a startling nature had occurred in the nursery and could do something about it, but Robert dissuaded her.

'Too dangerous,' he said, 'it's more than likely that we'd be yanked off to some circus or fair. We must easily be the smallest people in the world, and a wonderful curiosity that people would pay pounds to come and see. It must be something in this nursery that has magicked us like this, and if we stay up here we have a chance of finding what it is, and getting magicked back again.'

'But how are we going to live?' Katherine asked.

'In the doll's house, surely,' said Janet. She had been as badly frightened as anybody, but had quite got over her fright and was secretly rather glad that they would now be able to do what she had wished, actually to live in the doll's house.

The two elders agreed that it was the best plan, at any rate, for the moment, and accordingly they set off to explore the house.

The drawing-room they ignored, for the present. There was, as well, a dining-room, a kitchen and a hall on the ground floor. As far as furniture went, the dining-room was excellently equipped, although there were several things in it not usually found in dining-rooms. These included a piano, which of course wouldn't work, a spindly-legged settee, and a piece of furniture that was quite obviously a dressing table, but which was being used as an odd sideboard, with an outsize plant on it, the leaves of which resembled an aspidistra but with large green cabbage-like flowers as well. 'Simply too hideous for words,' Janet said.

'It doesn't matter about the decorations,' said Katherine. 'It's plates and knives and forks I'm looking for.' She knelt down in front of the sideboard and pulled at one of its cupboard doors. Only one of the hinges worked and the door fell drunkenly forward, nearly braining Katherine. Inside, however, was a plate basket and inside the plate basket was the cutlery. The spoons and forks were enormous, about the size of salad servers, and the knives

looked terribly blunt, but they were implements with which it was possible to eat.

Then they went into the kitchen. The stove, though it looked most realistic, was useless, of course, but Katherine said they would be able to use the copper pots and pans and the little copper kettle.

'If we had anything to cook with, or on,' said Robert.

'Here are some biscuits,' said Janet, who had found several tins filled with the kind of biscuits sold in dolls' shops, very fat, more like buns, and very, very stale.

Robert took a bite out of one, and then went straight to the window and spat it out. 'Biscuits!' he said. 'Baked by Mrs. Noah, I should say.'

But Janet was not listening. 'There are plenty of cups and plates and dishes,' she said, pointing to the dresser.

'What's the good of all the crockery in the world, if there's nothing to eat off it but beastly stale biscuits?' asked Robert.

'Let's go upstairs,' said Janet.

There were two bedrooms and a bathroom. The bathroom was useless, of course, all the fittings being made of wood, painted white, but the other rooms were more satisfactory. There were two beds in one, and one in the other beside a cot. (This was the nursery.) Janet skipped up to the bed and climbed on to it. It had sheets, pillows, blankets and an eiderdown, and looked most comfortable, but Janet found the mattress and pillows very hard, and the sheets and blankets very short. There were no springs and it creaked dreadfully as she got in.

Standing beside the table was the nurse, with a simpering expression on her painted face. Sitting in a high-chair was an idiotic-looking child.

Robert said: 'I'm going to move that ghastly creature. I can't sleep in here with it grinning at me.' He strode over and seized the nurse round the waist, (she was quite as high as he was) and tried to lift her up. She was unexpectedly heavy. He started to shunt her over to the wardrobe and tripped over the rug, tried wildly to save himself and then fell, nurse undermost, knocking the high-chair over as he did so. The chair fell on to the washstand. There was a sharp crack, and when Katherine and Janet flew to the rescue they were appalled to see the baby's china head had broken off and was lying,

'He started to shunt her over to the wardrobe, tripped over the rug and then fell.'

with the imbecile look on its face, under the dressing table.

'Gosh!' said Janet. 'How awful! We've broken it.'

'Serve it jolly well right,' said Robert, getting stiffly to his feet and rubbing the shin which the nurse, with almost life-like malevolence, had kicked with her china foot. 'Bundle the beastly little thing into that cupboard, and help me shove this horror in too.'

'What if Audrey wonders where they are?' said Katherine dubiously.

'Can't help that,' was the short answer. 'She'll think someone's pinched them.' Robert marched over to the cupboard and pulled the door. It looked like a solid mahogany wardrobe, but its appearance was deceptive. It was very much lighter than it looked, and immediately fell forward, completely extinguishing Robert, who, for one moment, bore its weight and then collapsed at the knees and subsided with the cupboard over him. Katherine and Janet rushed forward to his rescue. Muffled shouts and kicks from inside the cupboard allayed their fears that he had been killed. Between them they raised it up and liberated the scarlet-faced Robert. They pushed the cupboard back, and then while Robert held it, in silence the girls dragged the nurse towards it and propped her inside. She had a maddening tendency to slip forward, but they slammed the door on her and fortunately it had a catch which worked. Then Katherine tactfully put the baby on its head in the ottoman.

'Well,' said Robert, obviously controlling his temper with an effort, 'that's that. Have we been over the whole house now?'

'There are two more bedrooms in the roof,' said Janet.

'Let's go and collect the bedding from them,' suggested Katherine. 'We could do with a bit more.'

The party silently wended its way up the last flight. While the girls were collecting the blankets, Robert strolled to the window and saw something from it which instantly cured his bad temper. Just level with the attic window sill, a little way away, was what looked like a broad road, suspended in space, but which he remembered was a shelf which ran the whole length of the wall behind the doll's house. And in a flash he remembered that on the shelf he had seen a box of chocolates. He called Katherine excitedly, and explained to her that if they could only get on to the shelf they could get some food.

'But how will you get on to it?' asked Katherine anxiously. 'It's awfully wide to jump, and it's a terrible long way to fall.'

For an answer, Robert seized a chair, and pushing it out of the window, balanced it with the back legs on the sill and the back itself, which just reached, on the shelf.

'Are you going to climb on to it? Do you think it's safe? It looks solid, but one doesn't know with doll's house furniture,' said Katherine.

'I'm going to try, anyway.'

It was a breathless moment while Robert gingerly tested it, but as no ominous creaks were heard, he trusted his weight to it and got across.

'Do you want me to come too?' asked Katherine, not at all relishing the idea.

'Half a sec. I've found something better to get across on,' was the reply, and in another minute Robert began to push a huge plank across from the shelf to the window. It was very unwieldy but he managed it. The plank was yellow in colour, flat on one side and slightly raised in the middle on the other, and with a number of straight black lines and figures marked on each side, and Katherine suddenly realised that it was a ruler. It wasn't much pleasanter to go across than the chair, but at least it looked strong and with Robert's hand to help her she got across. Janet

refused to be left behind, and they dragged her across, too.

'Keep to the wall,' said Robert, hurrying along with the girls behind him. They had to step over or round several things—an enormous pair of scissors, a huge cotton reel, and a thing that looked like a gigantic round footstool, but was a pincushion, until the way was blocked by a white wall which was the side of the chocolate box. They looked up at it. It towered above their heads because the lid had not been put on properly, and one corner of it reared into the air, leaving a hole quite large enough for Robert to get in by.

'Give me a leg up,' he said.

'Stand on this,' suggested Janet, pushing a bone thimble, the size of a gigantic flower pot, towards him. It made an excellent stool, and in a minute Robert was inside.

It was very dark in the box, and the smell of chocolate was nearly overpowering. When his eyes got accustomed to the darkness he could see the chocolates all looking like large chocolate cakes in frilled paper cups—rows of them.

'Be careful not to get the hard ones,' said Katherine's voice outside. 'Hard ones are usually square.'

'I'd better try them, if I can find something to stick into them.'

'Perhaps there's something out here,' said Katherine, looking around. 'What are you sitting on, Janet? Would that come out?'

Janet had sat herself down on a silver bar with a knob at the end, sticking out of the overgrown footstool. When they pulled, it came quite easily.

'Gosh,' said Katherine. 'I suppose it's a pin! It looks more like a sword or a spear.' She carried it over to Robert, but he did not need it as he had already used his pocket knife.

'Here you are,' he said, his head and shoulders appearing over the side of the box. 'Can you catch?'

He handed out several chocolates. They had a disaster with one. Robert dropped it to Janet who missed it: it fell on its side (it was a round, flat peppermint cream), rolled like a hoop, and bowled away over the edge of the shelf. It was no time to bother about things like that, and telling Janet to be more careful, Robert handed out another.

When they had eight, Katherine said she thought they had enough. 'Each one is as big as a Christmas cake,' she said. 'It'll take ages to eat them all.'

'We want a store,' said Robert. 'Someone may remove the box.'

They took the eight in relays back to the house, and hid them in a cupboard in the kitchen.

'What about water, or something to drink?' asked Katherine.

'There was a saucer of milk beside the fire, for the cat.' Janet remembered.

Taking the largest pitcher he could find, and a smaller jug for ladling purposes, Robert volunteered to go for the milk if the girls got supper ready. No one said anything about meeting the cat, but as Robert descended the terrace steps, he thought: 'It will be larger than an elephant. If it takes me for a mouse it will be jolly!'

He met nothing, however. It seemed quite a long way, particularly as he had to go all round a black, and quite impenetrable thicket, which he recognised as the hearth rug. When he got near the fire, he saw the saucer looking about the size of a gold-fish pond. The edge of the saucer came to just above his knees, so that it was not difficult to ladle out the milk, but he was surprised to find how thick it was. 'I suppose it *is* milk,' he thought. 'It looks more like custard.' He was also surprised to find that the pitcher was very heavy, when full, and he had to stop a great many times on the return journey.

Meanwhile his sisters had been setting the table.

'We'll eat in the dining-room,' Katherine had decided, 'then we can see if anyone is coming and hide if necessary.'

The smallest plates they had been able to find in the doll's house were the size of pudding plates and terribly thick. The cups, too, were enormous.

Janet brought a vase containing a paper bloom like a blue sunflower, for the centre of the table. 'I think it looks awfully nice,' she said, standing back to admire it.

Robert snorted. 'Can we begin?'

No one was very hungry, but there was nothing to wait for, and they drew up their chairs and sat down.

'I like your "darling little knives", Janet,' said Katherine, after she had made useless attempts to cut the chocolate. 'It's lucky we've got Robert's pocket knife.'

The cake was filled with a coffee mixture and was very good, though extremely rich, and the chocolate icing (very hard) was nearly an inch thick.

'How I wish the fruit was real!' said Katherine afterwards, thinking longingly of the bowl of oranges and bananas on the bookcase in the drawing room.

They were just getting up from the table when they heard a loud noise outside, and then an enormous voice booming: 'Someone has left the doll's house lights on.'

All three looked at each other for one moment in consternation, and then there was a general stampede. Janet and Robert made for the kitchen, Janet upsetting her chair as she did so, while Katherine bolted under the table. Then they were aware of an enormous something outside the window, and the lights went out. In the darkness Robert and Janet missed the door and collided with each other, in which encounter Janet nearly had her nose broken and Robert stubbed his toe. Katherine remained unhurt, but quaking, under the table.

Then the huge creature outside the window moved away, and the light from the nursery made it possible to distinguish things again. Then, suddenly, that light too was extinguished, and they were left in pitch darkness. There was a loud crash as the nursery door was slammed, and then silence.

Janet's voice was raised in panic: 'Robert, Katherine, where are you?'

'Here I am, stupid,' said Robert. 'Don't go blundering about. You've hurt me enough already.' But he put out a kind hand and felt for Janet's. When he grasped it she said, more calmly, 'What are we going to do?'

'Find the switch and light up again.'

'Won't they think it funny if they come in again?'

'Can't help that. We can't spend all night in the dark. Do you remember where the switch is?'

'On the left of the house, as you faced it,' said Katherine, crawling cautiously out from under the table. 'Where are you? Gosh, it's dark!' There was a muffled bang, and she added quietly, 'That was my head.' Then she stood up.

'Don't move,' said Robert. 'I'm going to find my way out.' He began to step gropingly forward. Bangs of varying loudness and one large crash marked his progress, but at last he said, 'I'm at the window. It won't be long now.'

Outside on the terrace it was not so dark. A glow from the fire made it possible to distinguish the walls of the house, and he was able to feel his way along to the corner, and just round it he walked straight into the switch. He recoiled in pain, rubbing his forehead. It was too stiff to move with one hand, but when he hung on it with both hands, and lifted his feet off the floor, there was a sharp click, and light streamed out from a window just beside him.

Looking through it he could see into the dining room, with its upset chairs, untidy supper table, broken vase, and Katherine and Janet holding hands, relief that the light was on again breaking over their faces. Robert leaned through the window and grinned. Then he climbed through and joined them.

'Thank goodness for that!' said Katherine.

'What are we going to do now?' asked Janet.

'We can clear the table,' replied her sister. 'We can't wash up, there's no water. I don't know how we're going to manage without it, Robert. What *are* we going to do? We can't live like this for very long.'

'That's what I want to talk about. As soon as we've cleaned up this mess, let's go somewhere and have a council.'

'Where shall we go? I wish we could light a fire, it's beastly cold.'

'We could go down and sit in the fender. It's warm enough there,' said Robert.

for ANGEL-FISH

This is an Angel-fish, and he
is not what he pretends to be.
Although he has a saintly name,
he is not good or kind or tame,
but quite the opposite, in fact
his soul is permanently blacked.
He is, the 'dikker' says, audacious,
lovely to look at, but voracious,
and all the little fish that swim
dive for their lives away from him.

And yet, no doubt, his children find
him full of fun and wondrous kind,
and when they look him in the face,
this angel-fish who fell from grace
(which isn't easy, for you see
he has the smallest vis-a-vis)
they do not know his glassy eye
is swivelling round for lesser fry,
nor do they know his chiffon fins
drive him towards a thousand sins.

So though this angel of the dark,
this tiny selachoid, this shark
finds that his beauteous presence chills
his smaller brethren round the gills,
somebody loves him. (All the same
he has a most deluding name.)   V.G.

'Supposing someone comes and finds us? We don't want to be seen.'

'We shall have plenty of warning and if anyone comes we can hide behind the coal-scuttle.'

They bundled the supper debris into the kitchen, piling it on to the table. Katherine looked at the white sink, with its shining taps and said, 'It seems too stupid for words to have a sink, and not be able to use it.'

'Come on!' said Robert.

They set forth taking a cushion from the drawing room to sit on.

It was rather dark on the floor, but the fire, and the light streaming from the doll's house windows enabled them to see their way. They went round behind the coal-scuttle and found there was a gap between the wall and the fire-guard, quite wide enough for them to pass through. The fire was dying down but still gave out a pleasant flow of warmth, and they sat down, facing it, with their backs against the fender.

As soon as they were settled, Robert opened council.

'We must think back,' he said, 'what we were all doing when we were changed. There must be some cause for it. People aren't just transformed like this for no reason.'

'*A large tiger-like face stared at them.*'

'I don't think I was doing anything.' said Katherine.

'I know I wasn't doing anything,' said Robert.

'I was just looking at the doll's house,' said Janet, 'and wishing that we were small enough to live in it.'

The other two regarded her with horrified astonishment.

'You actually wished it?' cried Robert in a terrible voice. 'Well, you jolly well got your wish. And so did we!'

Poor Janet was squashed speechless.

Katherine looked thoughtful. 'We hadn't eaten anything,' she said a moment later. 'In books there's always either a fairy who grants your wishes, or you eat some magic bean or something.'

'Well, there wasn't a fairy, silly,' said Robert. 'There aren't any. Nor a magic bean.'

'I wonder,' said Katherine suddenly, 'if it was one of the things on the mantelpiece that you were fiddling with, Robert.'

'There was only the usual junk,' was the reply. 'Wait a bit, though, there was that little beetle thing that I dropped.'

'And Janet picked it up,' said Katherine excitedly, 'and was just wishing we were small enough to live in the doll's house at the time. I wonder if that was it'

'But why should it be? It was only ordinary green stone, carved like a beetle. Something like that scarab ring of mother's.'

'That's it then, probably. It may be steeped in magic.

It's worth trying anyway, to find it, I mean, and to try and wish ourselves back to a normal size.'

'Anything is worth trying,' said Robert. 'We shall probably starve if we go on this size much longer. Pity it's so dark. We must look first thing in the morning.'

At that moment Janet felt something breathing behind her and looking round was stricken almost dead with terror to see, on the other side of the fender, a large tiger-like face, many times larger than the largest tiger, glaring at her. She gave a loud shriek and started back. Katherine and Robert looked round just in time to see the huge mouth open, while a loud wailing noise, louder than a ship's siren, issued from it.

For a moment stark panic reigned. Katherine went white with fright, Janet bellowed, and Robert felt a queer prickling feeling at the back of his head. He was the first to recover.

'It's all right,' he said. 'It can't get at us.'

Even if it couldn't, it was unnerving enough. The cat was staring unwinkingly at them. Then it mewed again, and put out a paw, which it tried to squeeze through the lattice of the fender. Fortunately its paw was too large. The children huddled together watching it. Then Robert stooped, and picking up a piece of coal at his feet, hurled it at the cat. It bounced against the fender and fell with a clatter. The cat blinked.

'Come on,' shouted Robert, 'throw everything you can find at it.'

There were several pieces of coal and cinders lying about and the three of them flung all they could find at the creature. One or two went through the mesh of the fender and hit the cat, and when a particularly well-aimed shot of Robert's caught it on the nose, it suddenly turned, and silently bounded away. They saw it leap on to the window-sill and disappear through the window.

'Quick!' said Robert, as soon as it was gone. 'Back to the house!'

'Suppose it comes back before we get there?' gasped Katherine.

'We must risk that. Come on!'

Dragging Janet still whimpering with fear, they fled towards the steps up which they scrambled, panting, and flung themselves into the house. Once there Robert slammed the front door, shouting 'Shut all the windows.' And not till he and Katherine had done this did they feel safe.

'Gosh!' said Katherine. 'If we have any more of that sort of thing I shall quietly die. We simply must find the magic to turn us the right size again. Why anything, even a mouse, would frighten one to death.'

'Let's go to bed,' said Robert, 'and then as soon as it's daylight we'll start hunting for that beetle.'

'We shall have to sleep with the lights on' said Janet, 'unless Robert turns the switch off after we are in bed.'

'We'll sleep with them on, then,' said Katherine firmly. 'No-one is going outside the front door again to-night.'

Going to bed didn't take long. No washing was possible. The girls looked into all the chests of drawers and cupboards to see if there were any clothes they could wear as nightdresses, but they were all empty.

'We shall have to sleep in our underclothes,' said Katherine. 'I only hope it's for one night.'

'The mattresses are awfully hard and lumpy,' said Janet, wriggling down under the bed-clothes. 'And the sheets are made of canvas I think.'

'The eiderdowns are dreadfully stiff and heavy,' said Katherine. 'I wonder if they will ever stay on the beds. I hope we shan't be cold.'

She went into Robert's room to see how he was getting on, and found him in bed looking rather uncomfortable.

'They fled towards the steps.'

He had hung one of the bedroom mats over the light, so his room was quite dark.

'Whoever stuffed these mattresses,' he said, 'used dried peas.'

Janet was wakeful and excited for a bit, but long after she had fallen asleep Katherine lay, trying to find a comfortable spot on her bed and keep the eiderdown on, staring at the room and wondering if they would be able to terminate their unpleasant experience in the morning.

When she awoke it was still dark outside, but the nursery clock, booming like Big Ben, told her it was seven o'clock. She stretched herself, yawned and got up. There was no inducement to remain in her very uncomfortable bed, besides she wanted to tidy up before it got light, so that if they did find the beetle and it did transform them back to their proper size again they could go home at once.

The noise she made woke Janet and she too got up to help. They found an imitation carpet sweeper, useless of course, and two brooms, one long and one short, and a dustpan. The brooms had very stiff bristles and were not very suitable for uncarpeted floors. Robert, when he got up, said he thought they were wasting their time. Obviously the doll's house was never properly swept, and they hadn't made it any dirtier by staying in it one night.

'It wants a good spring clean,' said Katherine.

'Well, you're not going to give it one,' said her brother. 'If you make the beds it will be more than enough.'

It was getting light, and after a careful reconnaissance for the cat, Robert went along the terrace and turned off the light. Then he led the way down the steps. Once on the floor they spread out, bending anxiously forward, looking for the scarab. As might be expected, Janet, who had more idea than the others where she dropped it, found it. And like the silly ninny, as Robert said, instead of consulting with them as to the best wish to be made, which would have been, to transplant them back to Aunt Cora's their proper size, and no questions asked, cried out:

'I wish we were back our proper sizes!'

* * *

When things steadied again, they were standing gazing at each other, with the doll's house shrunk to its proper size, and a small cat regarding them through the window.

I haven't time to tell you how they got out of the house. The journey was fraught with many alarms and was achieved in a burglarish manner, as both Robert and Katherine felt that to explain their presence to incredulous grown-ups would be more than they could face. Janet would have liked another look at the doll's house comparing its appearance now with what it had looked like when lived in, but the others wouldn't wait. They said the whole thing had been Janet's fault from beginning to end. It was only she who had been silly enough to think for one moment that it would be fun to live in a doll's house, and now that she had had her wish she knew as well as they did that fun was the last word to be applied to it. As for 'having a last look at it,' Robert said, he never wanted to see it, or any other doll's house again as long as he lived.

They got out of the house without being seen, though it involved a long, smelly wait in the cupboard under the stairs, the abode of brooms and brushes and old boxes and tennis racquets and, Katherine felt sure, spiders.

They prepared a number of inadequate explanations for Aunt Cora, none of which were needed, as Aunt Cora, having packed them off to the party had received a sudden invitation and had dashed off to London to spend the night and go to a concert. She had left a note explaining this, and had not returned when they got back.

Audrey, to whom the doll's house belonged, cannot think to this day how the nurse got herself shut in to the cupboard, after disposing of her decapitated charge in the ottoman, nor how the store cupboard in the kitchen got filled with chocolates, nor who had left three of the drawing room cushions in the fender, nor who broke the vase in the dining room and left a pitcher of milk in the kitchen sink. She thinks it was fairies. Her mother, nearer the mark, thinks it was some tiresome child at the party.

When Aunt Cora returned, she was so full of her concert that it was some time before she asked them if they had enjoyed the party.

'Very much, thank you,' said Katherine, Robert and Janet politely.

for BUTTERFLY

The butterfly is a coquette,
    She flirts with every flower,
With painted wings she dances through
    Her brief insensate hour.

Her life is short, but what cares she,
    She knows she looks her best,
And nothing really matters much
    If one is properly dressed.

Fluttering, foolish, fancy free
    Inconsequent she goes,
To give a columbine a kiss
    To die upon a rose.   V.G.

[Fox

JOHN BARBIROLLI
conducting the BBC Symphony Orchestra.

[Picture Post

SIR THOMAS BEECHAM
rehearsing in the Albert Hall.

SIR HENRY WOOD
founder of the 'Prom' Concerts.

What Does The Conductor Do?

by DESMOND McCORMICK

Famous conductors demonstrate the vigorous physical energy and delicate, sensitive control of which they must be masters. A conductor throws himself body and soul into his work, at rehearsals as much as at the final performance. There can be no half measures for him.

WHEN BACH AND HANDEL directed the performance of one of their works they would sit at the harpsichord in full view of the players and while they were primarily concerned with the filling-in of the harmony at the keyboard they would, from time to time indicate with a wave of the hand the start of the piece, or a change of tempo, or a difficult entry for an instrument or voice. This of course was not conducting as we know it to-day, but it was the first stage in its development. By slow degrees during the Haydn-Mozart period the keyboard instrument as an essential part in the texture of the music faded, and was finally dropped altogether. Then there followed a stage when the leader of the orchestra (who always sits at the first desk of the first violins and is clapped as he comes on to the platform a minute or two before the conductor) started the music off with a flourish of his bow and steered his colleagues through the intricacies of the score. But orchestras and choruses grew rapidly in size and Beethoven, and composers who succeeded him, wrote more and more complicated music which required correspondingly more attentive direction and the leader's bow could rarely be upon the strings of his instrument. Then it was that composers took to standing up before the players or singers with a scroll of paper in their hands and giving at first hand so to speak, their directions. Beethoven

'conducted' many of his works but so impetuous and excitable was his temperament that often chaos ensued. Composers do not always make good conductors though one would imagine that they ought to know better than anyone else what their music should sound like.

The art of conducting (and it is a very great art) is probably not more than a hundred years old; and it is less than that since the stick or baton which is to be seen in every conductor's hand to-day was used. The prominence and publicity given to conductors of our time is even younger than that. Whether or not this prominence is a good thing remains to be seen. It certainly has its dangers, not the least of which is that the uninformed often go to concerts 'to hear Toscanini or Beecham' and not to hear Beethoven or Mozart. For the conductor now ranks (and quite rightly too) with the great virtuoso performers of instrumental or vocal music. He is like the man who pulls the strings to make the puppet work; who can make it dance or make it walk, who can make it live or die. If he is a conscientious conductor—and all the great ones are—he will so direct the performance that the very minutest details of the composer's wishes are respected. It is only the second-rate conductor who takes unwarranted liberties with the music he is directing.

Quite apart from the actual notes

which a composer puts down on paper there are a whole host of words and marks (called dynamic marks) with which he is able to make his meaning clear. Try and get hold of the score of Elgar's Enigma Variations for instance, and study it. Elgar was a master of orchestration, which is to say that he knew exactly how to set out his music to the best advantage for the instruments of the orchestra. He also took infinite pains with his dynamic marks, so much so that in comparison with a Mozart or early Beethoven score you might say that he was unduly fussy. There is hardly a bar of his music without a ' stage direction'; changes of tempo can be realised exactly by reference to a mechanical instrument called a Metronome; 'hairpins' opening and closing indicate an increase and diminution of sound; notes with dots over them are to be played staccato or detached, while others have a line over them which means that they require emphasis like the italicised words in this article. These are only a very few of the dynamic marks, and if you want to know what they all mean you will need a musical dictionary beside you, for their number is legion.

Now before a conductor comes to the first rehearsal of a work he will have devoted many hours to its preparation. He has not only read the score but he has also memorised it and knows what every bar, chord, and note sounds like. He has been over every part (sixty or seventy of them in the average orchestra) and made certain marks which will be of assistance to the players and save time during rehearsal. This rehearsal time is very precious and costs money, so every care must be taken to ensure that it is not wasted. In short, he comes to the rehearsal with a crystal clear knowledge of what the composer means and wants. He now has to communicate this to the players, and this is where the art of his profession comes in. And as well as art (which means of course—skill) he must have personality which implies the ability to put his ideas across to the

[Fox

PIERINO GAMBA (11 years old)
rehearses the Philharmonia Orchestra.

[London Philharmonic

WILHELM FURTWÄNGLER
with the Berlin Philharmonic Orchestra.

[BBC

SIR MALCOLM SARGENT
who has conducted many Children's Concerts.

players in rehearsal and, at the performance itself, to inspire them with that subtle 'something else' which flows like an electric current between the performers and the audience.

In the conversation which Alice had with the Hatter at the tea-party, the Hatter, you will remember, indignantly denied that you could beat time. His conclusion was a correct one in the sense in which he meant it. But the fact remains that beating time *is* the first requisite of the conductor. For it is only with a clear and accurate beat that a large body of players or singers can be kept together and the music be given that precision which is its most vital, though by no means only, quality. The conductor holds 'the stick' between the thumb and first finger of his right hand and with it he describes a geometrical pattern according to the number of beats required in every bar of the piece. Here are two which you can learn to do yourself:—

Pattern A

Pattern B

Pattern A is for Waltz-time, which has one strong beat (the first in every three) and this is made *downwards* from your forehead to your waist; the second beat *outwards,* and the third up to the point from which you started the first beat. Pattern B is for March-time which needs two strong beats, the first and third, so you will notice that number three goes right across your body from left to right. It is a good plan at first to keep your elbow fairly close to your side and describe the pattern straight in front of you and not to one side. If you can master these you will be well on the way to becoming a conductor. By the way, stand firmly, don't bend your knees and jitter about like the so-called conductor of a dance band.

It is the very tip of the stick which marks the beats, and orchestral players never lose sight of it, for by means of it they can respond instantaneously to the most subtle variations of speed. But what about the left hand? What part does it play? To a very large extent the conductor uses it to point the expression marks. The clenched fist will produce force and emphasis to a chord or passage; the upturned palm will indicate an increase of tone; and the downturned palm the reverse. These are only a few of the things it can do, and of course every conductor has his idiosyncrasies which his players quickly learn. But one thing you will rarely see a conductor do with his left hand is to allow it feebly to imitate his right. At one moment it is extracting a crescendo at the next pointing an intricate entry to one of the wind players, or exhorting the whole orchestra to a tremendous climax of sound. Then, with just a turn of the wrist, the storm can be quelled and give place to the most delicate pianissimo. Should there be a choir and soloists performing with the orchestra then the

conductor's work is even more exciting, for not only has he to control a very large and intricate 'instrument', but he has also to keep the balance between the three units of his forces. Indeed, like a general, he needs to be a clever tactician and his head must be ice-cool.

Enough has been said to show that conducting is not just a matter of 'beating time', nor yet of standing up before an orchestra and weaving with the arms beautiful and fascinating arabesques 'in time to the music.' The conductor must know what he wants and see that he gets it. He must subordinate himself to the composer whose music he is interpreting; he will never introduce innovations for their own sake in the music of the great Masters. If he is conducting Beethoven then he will give you Beethoven, and not Beethoven à la Bogusitsky (or whatever his name may be). Finally, he must be an acutely sensitive musician, unerring in his judgment, and with the ability to inspire confidence and loyalty in the players under his command. It is a tremendous task which demands above all a commanding personality.

These photographs, taken by a special process by 'Camera Talks', follow the lighted point of *a conductor's baton in action. The first is a slow movement, the second a quick beat.*

A School for Adventure

by Richard Graves

NEAR SYDNEY, in Australia, is a School for Adventure. Fifty or sixty boys and girls from different parts of the city come to a corner of the 38,000 acre National Park, and spend one week-end each month in camp there.

I am going to follow two of the people at this unusual school. One is Sally, who is at her second camp, and the other is Terry, an old hand who has the 'signs' for all the subjects. Sally is twelve, Terry sixteen.

'What's on this week-end?' Sally asks, coming over to Terry who is busy putting up his one man hike tent.

'Ropes and cords,' Terry answers without turning his head for he is concerned with the pitch of his tent, and an ugly sag in one corner.

'What do we do?' Sally asks eagerly, but Terry takes no notice until he has finished the job in hand, and then he looks up.

'Better get your tent fixed, and your gear all straight. One of the 'Masters' will have a look round before we start, and next thing you know you'll be missing some of the work,' he advises.

A group of boys and girls move across the sunlit glade and one calls out, 'We're going for specimens Sally.' The little girl is off.

'Hi!' Terry calls after her, 'You'll want to take a knife with you, you can have a loan of mine, only don't dig it in the ground, it's as sharp as a razor.' Terry has learnt that a really sharp knife is a mark of personal efficiency.

Sally joins the group, now crossing the shady creek under the care of one of the 'Masters'. These 'Masters' are other boys and girls who have learnt the work, proved their reliability, and for this won their 'Master' signs.

In a short time a big heap of grass has been stacked in the centre of the glade, and a girl who has her Ropemaster sign gathers the youngsters around her. She shows how the grass can be spun into strands, and the strands twisted into cords and the cords into rope, and the rope into cables. Within half an hour all the boys and girls are doing what the Ropemaster has taught them, and less than an hour later, a cable of grass rope 50 yards long, and capable of taking a strain of three tons has been made, and singed, on a fire, to make it smooth. One end is taken and tied to a high branch of a nearby gum tree.

The Ropemaster girl shows how to climb using a footlock and soon every boy and girl in the camp is climbing the rope saying 'Look, no hands,' as they climb to the top of the rope, taking a secure footgrip, and then clasping the rope tightly to their body with their arms, letting go with their hands.

'Gee, that was fun, I never thought you could make grass into rope,' Sally says to Terry. She is flushed with excitement, because she was the first girl to be able to climb the rope and touch the branch forty feet above the ground. All afternoon the boys and girls learn how to plait and spin, and make different sorts of cords and ropes from fibrous bark and other natural materials, so that the finished work is either a smooth round lariat plaited cord, or a broad pliable strap, for a belt or a pack.

Sally is really excited now. She has made for herself several yards of soft pink cord from the inner bark of a tree and it is the prettiest rope she has ever seen. She is wearing a belt plaited from the cord green leaves of a native sedge, and finished off so that it is almost perfect.

After lunch the rope is taken to a cliff top, and small groups under other leaders learn how to climb rock. There are no accidents. There never have been, in any of these camps.

And then comes tea time, and the gathering of wood by the boys for the evening campfire. Terry sits beside Sally in the circle round the campfire that evening, and Sally asks him, 'What other things can I learn to do?'

'Oh everything,' Terry answers easily, 'You can learn to make your little japara tent into a coracle, and travel down a river in it. You can learn to make and use a firebow and drill to get fire when you have no matches . . . You can learn to make a hut and thatch it, and how to make traps to catch wild pigeons and rabbits, or how to find and cook natural foods to eat, or how to get water in desert areas, and even how to boil water if you have no billycan or pot in which to hold it.'

Sally looked unbelievingly at Terry, 'I suppose you'll tell me you can teach me how to get the time from the sun, and direction from the stars, if I haven't got a watch or a compass.'

'That's right,' Terry answered seriously, 'and we can teach you how to get good drinking water from the roots of trees, and how to find a bees' nest, or make a bridge across a river, or a pack to carry your gear, or a comfortable bed . . .'

'And when I've learnt all this,' says Sally, 'How can I use the knowledge?'

'When you've learnt it all,' says Terry, 'You'll have the six signs, and maybe a few Master signs, and when you've done a 'Survival Week-end', you can take a group as a leader on one of our Adventures.'

'What are the Adventures like?' Sally asks, and Terry tells her about the last adventure he was on. 'We went over Barrington Tops to Gloucester Tops. Gee, it was terrific, no tracks of course, and the maps were only approximate. Most of the time we were in dense forests of Antarctic Beech, all draped with

A grass rope is used to climb a cliff face. It goes between the climber's legs, over his shoulder and is held in his right hand.

moss, and dripping with the cloud mists. And then we came into forests of tree ferns that were like something left over from the coal ages. The mist was so thick for three days that we couldn't see more than a few yards, and our compasses were almost useless. Murray Grundy, that big fair fellow over there, climbed one of the tallest trees and sat right at the top for three hours to get a sight and a bearing, and then we were on our way again. We marked a trail between the two Tops, and now others use the trail we blazed.'

'Tell me about some of the other Adventures,' Sally asked settling down on her groundsheet, and Terry told her about the time they went over Gingers, 'Six thousand two hundred feet, and the snow shut us in for two days.'

'Isn't it dangerous?' Sally asked, and Terry shrugged his shoulders, 'It would be if we weren't properly taught,' he explains; 'For instance, there was the week-end when we had the trip across the Hawkesbury at Cowan Creek. It is alive with sharks, and we had nearly a mile of deep water to cross. We made coracles from our tents, and everybody got across safely, but even if we'd made the coracles correctly it could have been dangerous if even one person did not know how to sit in them properly.'

Bush made table and seats are comfortable for camp meals. To become a group leader a week-end must be spent living off the land with no camping or feeding equipment at all, only a bush knife. Proper training is essential to correct bushcraft. (By kind permission of the 'Sydney Morning Herald')

'When you've finished the eight training week-ends and won all your signs, then you can go out for a three day Survival Week-end with a few other girls. You do the week-end living off the land. You're not allowed matches or food, except six ounces of flour, some salt, some sugar and tea. You take no camping gear. All you can have is your machete, or Bush knife. You've got to get your fire without matches, set up a sun clock, make traps and get your food from the bush, and cook it without utensils, make a lean-to and thatch it, and make a camp bed, and then you get your Survival sign, and only after that are you allowed to go on Adventures.'

'Are there any books about this work?' Sally asked.

'No,' Terry replied, 'We decided we wouldn't put any of it in writing. You can't learn this sort of thing from books. You've got to do it with your ten fingers.'

The singing at the campfire swelled into a chorus, and Sally and Terry stopped yarning and joined in.

Next day, all the members of the Bushcraft School spent putting the things they had learnt to practical use. One pocket of Sally's rucksack was full of samples and specimens to show the girls at school on Monday.

The 'bus from Waterfall Station called for them at four o'clock, and when the campsite was empty there was no sign that anyone had ever camped there, it was so clean.

This is really a School for Adventure, and already many of the boys and girls have adventured to find out new things to their profit and advantage. One boy perfected a small acetylene lamp for campers and fishermen that is only five inches high by an inch and a quarter wide, and is now having these made for general sale; another has learnt so much about plaiting that he makes a good income from plaiting kangaroo hide into belts and watch straps, having more orders than he can fulfil; another boy, so impressed the manager of a very big engineering company with his initiative and intelligence, that he is being specially trained for an important job; another, a fourth year medical student has already made some valuable discoveries concerning the healing properties of many native plants; another discovered a native type of fibre from which rope has been made which is twenty five per cent stronger than the strongest manilla rope.

It is a School for Adventure, started by a group of boys and girls who were tired of 'doing nothing', and wanted to 'get out in the bush and do things'.

Already they have shown that Bushcraft sharpens the five senses, and gives a keener zest for living; that it builds self reliance, and self dependence. They all agree that even living in a city, Adventure is possible, but that you must be properly trained if it is not to end in disaster.

The Mouse in the Wainscot

Hush, Suzanne!
don't lift your cup.
That breath you heard
is a mouse getting up.

As the mist that steams
from your milk as you sup,
so soft is the sound
of a mouse getting up.

There! did you hear
his feet pitter-patter?
lighter than tipping
of beads on a platter,

and then like a shower
on the window pane
the little feet scampering
back again?

O falling of feather!
O drift of a leaf!
The mouse in the wainscot
is dropping asleep.

IAN SERRAILLIER

BIGGLES in Arabia

by Captain W. E. Johns

There have been repeated requests from readers for a story about Sgt. Bigglesworth, Air Ace and hero of many adventures. Here at last is the first instalment of a new exciting one in which Biggles, Ginger and Bertie become involved in some dangerous trafficking on the shores of the Dead Sea.

' Bring the other machine down. We may be here some time.'

'COME IN BIGGLESWORTH. Sit down.'

The speaker was Air Commodore Raymond, administrative head of the Special Air Section, New Scotland Yard; and the man to whom he spoke was Sergeant Bigglesworth (known to his friends as Biggles) his chief pilot, who had just entered the room.

' I've some news for you,' informed the Air Commodore, a curious smile hovering about the corners of his mouth.

' Go ahead, Sir,' invited Biggles sombrely. ' I can take it.'

' For your pains you've been promoted.'

Biggles started. ' I've been what! '

' Promoted.'

' To what? '

' Detective Air-Inspector, which, incidentally, is a new rank at the Yard.'

Biggles stared. ' Suffering Icarus! ' he breathed. ' That's terrific. When Bertie learns this, he'll swallow his monocle.'

The Air Commodore laughed. He picked up a single loose cigarette that lay on his desk and offered it.

Biggles looked at it, frowned, and then lifted his eyes to the Air Commodore's face. ' What's wrong with it? ' he queried suspiciously.

' What makes you think there's anything wrong with it? '

' Because when one has a box at one's elbow it isn't usual to offer a visitor a second-hand sample,' answered Biggles.

The Air Commodore laughed again. ' True enough,' he agreed.

Biggles took the cigarette, examined it closely, smelt it and handed it back. ' Did you really want me to smoke it? '

' No. You might enjoy it but it wouldn't be good for you.'

' What would it do to me? '

The Air Commodore put his fingers together and gazed at the ceiling.

' After a few draws you would sink back in a peace that passes the understanding. Wonderful music, melodious beyond imagination, would caress your ears as you wandered in an exquisite dream-world. You would then become a giant, floating on clouds to a world where pain is unknown and life an eternal harmony of joy.'

Biggles sighed. ' That's just what I've been looking for all my life. May I have a thousand? '

' Unfortunately I've only got one.'

' Who handed you that paradise story? '

' A man who has smoked one of the cigarettes.'

' Dope, eh? '

The Air Commodore nodded slowly. ' I sent for you because we're up against a menace that might, if it is allowed to run wild, turn the world upside down. It may be in your line, or it may not. I'll tell you about it, then you tell me.'

' Do you mind if I get my boys down? ' requested Biggles. ' If this case is to be handed to us I'd like them to get the facts from the start. As a matter of fact, Algy Lacey is away. I've given him a week's leave, and he's gone sailing somewhere.'

The Air Commodore reached for his inter-com telephone, and a minute later Air Constables Lissie and Hebblethwaite came into the room. ' I was just saying, we've a rather nasty job on hand. Some time ago, Doctor Guthram Darnley, the celebrated Asiatic traveller and explorer, undertook to cross the least known territory left on earth, the Rub al Khali, which is that part of the great Arabian Peninsula lying between the Red Sea and the Persian Gulf. This is the real desert, a wilderness of calcined earth and sand. Water-holes are few and far between; they are guarded jealously by fanatical tribesmen who fight among themselves, so you can imagine what sort of reception an infidel would get. For this reason only one or two white men have seen the country—or at any rate, the southern area, which Darnley proposed to cross. Naturally, he did not go alone. He had a fairly considerable force of Arab camel-men with him, enough to carry his water and stores, and present a bold front to raiding tribesmen. Most of these men were changed several times during the journey. I mention this because, in view of what is coming, it is important.' The Air Commodore pushed the cigarette box to Biggles and at the same time helped himself.

'At the moment we are interested only in one of his several discoveries,' he continued. 'He found great areas of sand, but there are also wide stretches of flat, hard earth, and gravel, locally called *sabka,* which are sterile simply because there is practically no water. These regions are sometimes split by *wadis,* which are valleys in which a little brackish water may be found—enough for the needs of small groups of tribesmen who never in their entire lives know what it is to drink to repletion. As one hole dies up they move to another.

'In one such *wadi* Doctor Darnley found what might be truly called a lost tribe of Arabs. At the time of his arrival there were about thirty survivors, all men, and they were in a pitiable condition. His first impression was that they were all suffering from sleepy sickness; but then, realising that such a disease in such a place was out of the question, he found that the comatose condition was brought about by the smoke of their fires. As you know, dry camel dung is the normal fuel in the desert, although sticks are used if they can be found. It happened that in this *wadi* there grew a shrub that burnt freely. The smoke, they discovered, induced very pleasant sensations, and they stayed on to enjoy it. They must have been in ignorance of what they were doing because all drugs, and alcohol for that matter, are forbidden by their religion—although that doesn't prevent them from selling it to other people.

The trouble was they stayed too long, for when the time came to go, they lacked the strength to travel. What was worse, their camels had been eating the shrub and were in an even worse condition than the men. In such a country a man, even an Arab, without his camel, is finished. So these wretched Murras found themselves marooned, so to speak, when Doctor Darnley arrived. They were living by eating their useless camels. The Doctor could do nothing for them, for the position of his own party was precarious.

'On examining the shrub that had caused the mischief, a woody plant about three feet high with a greyish leaf, the Doctor found that it was new to him. As you may know, nearly every plant that grows in a waterless district must by some means protect itself from excessive evaporation, otherwise it will be shrivelled up by the blazing sun. Some coat themselves with gum, which, acting as a varnish, prevents their moisture from escaping. The shrub with which we are concerned comes into this category, and to make a long story short, the Doctor ascertained that this gum was a potent narcotic.

'Doctor Darnley collected some seeds of this plant, brought them home and gave them to the Royal Horticultural Society for scientific investigation. A few plants were raised at Kew in artificial conditions approaching as nearly as possible those of the *wadi;* but the plants died, so that to-day not one exists in cultivation. The shrub was identified as a new form of Artemesia. The natives call it *gurra,* which is perhaps easier to remember.' The Air Commodore stubbed his cigarette.

'Realising the dangerous nature of this drug we saw to it that it was given no publicity.'

'The first indication that we had that this new dope was no longer a secret was when a lady in the West End of London rang up her doctor in a panic to say that her husband appeared to be dying,' continued the Air Commodore. 'Actually, he was not. He was under the influence of a drug. An unfinished cigarette lying beside him turned out to contain *gurra.* Very soon other cases were coming to our notice, a regular traffic was going on in the underworld. Worse was to come. In the early hours one morning a police officer picked up a man unconscious in the street. Thinking he was drunk the officer got him to a police station. He wasn't drunk. He'd been doped—with *gurra.* He had also been robbed. You'll now see our difficulty. We can't issue notices warning people against accepting cigarettes from strangers without revealing the whole story, which might do more harm than good. We've got to get, literally, to the root of the thing. We've not only got to find the man or the syndicate that is smuggling the stuff into the country; we've got to find out where he's getting it from. Only a minute quantity would be required to treat thousands of cigarettes. The only way to kill the racket is to destroy the stuff at its source. Of course, it would be something if we could lay our hands on the big man behind the graft. That he is a big man we may be sure, for his profits must have been enormous. You see, what is going on here is also going on in America and on the Continent.'

'Hm.' Biggles thought for a moment. 'If it is a fact that *gurra* occurs only in one place, in Arabia, it shouldn't be a difficult matter to cut off the supply at its source.'

The Air Commodore nodded. 'Just so. That's where I thought you might come in.'

'You mean—we might fly out and destroy the whole growth?'

'Yes. It burns readily.'

'How much is there?'

'According to the Doctor perhaps three acres, sometimes sparse and sometimes thick.' The Air Commodore looked at Biggles seriously. 'Don't get the idea that the destruction of the stuff in its original habitat is going to be a simple matter. There are several factors to consider, each one not pretty to look at. First, there's the country itself. If anything went wrong, you'd have no hope of getting out alive, not even if you took as much water as you could carry. A white man couldn't live in that furnace without special preparations. Then again, fresh Arabs may have arrived there, and if you fell into their hands they would certainly kill you.'

Bertie stepped into the conversation. 'How about dropping a few incendiaries into the beastly stuff—if you see what I mean? No need to land at all that I can see.'

'There's a snag about that,' the Air Commodore pointed out. 'What about the Arabs already there? They may still be alive, and you'd burn them up too. The effects of such an act, if it became known, would send the whole Arab world up in arms.'

'I didn't think of that,' murmured Bertie.

Biggles resumed. 'What I can't understand is how the stuff came to be commercialised in the first place. Was Doctor Darnley the only white man in his expedition?'

'He was.'

'Somebody must have talked.'

'The Doctor assures me that he told his men nothing about the stuff. He had with him only three men who had ever made contact with outside civilisation.'

'Did these three coastal Arabs stay with the Doctor throughout the trip?'

'Yes. He picked them up at Aden. They had been with him on a previous expedition.'

'One of these men must have spotted more than the Doctor imagined,' declared Biggles. 'I take it that Doctor Darnley can supply the exact position of the *wadi* in which the plant grows?'

'Oh yes, but he pointed out we've no proof positive that the plant doesn't grow somewhere else. If it does, no doubt it would demand exactly the same conditions. But there, one feels that if the plant did grow somewhere else, the natives would have discovered the dope long ago.

'So you think that if the stuff could be destroyed in its natural home the supply of *gurra* would dry up?'

'It's a reasonable assumption,' averred the Air Commodore. 'But that presupposes that someone has agents there collecting it. If so, they wouldn't be likely to let you destroy it without putting up a stiff opposition.'

'Naturally,' said Biggles slowly. 'But we could at least try it. We should certainly learn something. Did you by any chance ask the Doctor if an aircraft could get down anywhere near this place?'

'I did, and he assured me that a landing could be made practically anywhere. There happens to be a conspicuous landmark. Between fifteen and twenty miles to the north there is a mountain system in the form of a horseshoe, with its ends pointing to the south-west. If you follow the westerly end and continue for about ten miles, you will come to the *Wadi al Arwat*, which is the Arab name for the *wadi* in which we are interested.'

Biggles smiled. 'I see you have all the gen handy.'

'I was hoping you'd go,' confessed the Air Commodore, 'although in view of the nature of the thing, I had no intention of sending you if you thought it too risky.'

'I could minimise the risk by taking two machines, each capable of seating two or three passengers,' suggested Biggles. 'Only one machine would land. The other would stay in the air as a relief in case of accidents.'

'That's an idea,' agreed the Air Commodore. 'But I want you to realise that thirst and hostile Arabs are factors not to be treated lightly.'

'So I have discovered,' murmured Biggles drily. 'Did you by any chance get the names of these three coastal Arabs who went all the way with Doctor Darnley?'

'Yes, I have them here.' The Air Commodore picked up a slip of paper. 'The most intelligent, his general organiser and interpreter on several expeditions, was Abu bin Hamud. The other two were known as Kuatim and Zahar. All three speak English, more or less. Are you thinking of calling on them? If you are, I can get you photographs of them, and the *wadi*. Darnley brought back a big collection of pictures.'

'I'd like to see them,' said Biggles. 'It struck me that as I shall be in Aden, I might have a word with them.'

'I can help you there,' offered the Air Commodore. 'A retired Middle East Political Officer, named Captain Jerry Norman, has made his home in Aden. He speaks all the dialects. He's a good type. Everyone knows him. If you want advice about anything or anybody you couldn't do better than go to Jerry.'

'Thanks,' acknowledged Biggles. 'All you want me to do is to burn these poison plants?'

'Unless, of course, you can lay your hands on the man who is making a fortune out of this stuff.'

Biggles got up. 'That's a taller order but I'll see what can be done about it,' he promised.

Five days later, two four-seat Proctor aircraft, single-engined, low-wing cabin monoplanes, on loan from Air Ministry Communication Headquarters, but without service insignia, stood ticking over on the sun-scorched aerodrome at Aden, where Biggles and his party had arrived overnight after an uneventful trip out along the

'Biggles correcting the bumps put the machine in to land.'

regular air route. Near the machines stood Ginger and Bertie, clad in tropical kit.

'Here he comes now,' observed Ginger, as Biggles appeared, walking briskly from the direction of the administrative buildings.

'Sorry to keep you waiting, but I've been busy,' apologised Biggles, as he joined the others. 'I thought it would be easy to find these three Arabs of Doctor Darnley's, but there's nothing doing. Apparently no one has seen them for a long time. Abu bin Hamud put in a brief appearance some months ago but the other two seem to have completely disappeared. I dashed along to see Jerry Norman, the chap the Air Commodore told us about, thinking he might be able to help. I found him at the Club. Nice, amiable chap.' Biggles smiled. 'That's why I'm late. He knows the three men because it was he who engaged them when he was helping Darnley to organise his show; but he has no idea of where they are now. However, he's promised to make enquiries while we're away. Of course, we may not need these men; on the other hand, they might be able to tell us something. All right. Let's get off this blistering dirt-track. You know the plan. I land with Ginger and set fire to the stuff. You, Bertie, circle and keep an eye on us unless I signal you to come down. We get the job done as fast as we can. Let's get off.'

In a few minutes both machines were in the air, climbing to altitude on a course that was roughly north-east.

At first, the territory below was more or less under cultivation, but this soon gave way to wide areas of wilderness, with herbage round water-holes and groups of palms standing like islands in the surrounding desolation. These became fewer, until at last the scene became a colourless expanse of naked earth, sterile except for an occasional straggling growth of camel-thorn or acacia. Overhead, a sky of steely blue was reflected in every depression on the ground, so that a hollow sometimes appeared as a lake of pale blue shadows. One looked in vain for a touch of green.

As time passed, the terrain became ever more hopeless in its awful loneliness and barren desolation, and Ginger found himself admiring the courage of Doctor Darnley and those few white men who had faced its blazing challenge. All was as lifeless as the moon. Still, Ginger was in no way disappointed or surprised. What he could see was what he had expected to see. He had seen deserts before, and most deserts are alike in their weary monotony. He was only thankful they were covering this one the easy way.

The machine roared on, thrusting the thin, sun-drenched air behind it, often bumping unpleasantly as it encountered up-currents and 'sinkers' caused by the convulsions of sun-lashed air and sand.

'I thought it would be easy to find these three Arabs, but there's nothing doing.'

Fifty yards to the left, Bertie in the reserve machine drove a similar uneasy course.

It seemed a long time, although actually it was less than two hours, before Biggles touched Ginger on the knee and pointed ahead, slightly to the north. Thrust up for perhaps a thousand feet from the sand was a curving system of hills that could, with a little imagination be likened to the shape of a horse-shoe.

Biggles took the machine straight to the far end of this conspicuous landmark, and then, turning, followed it southward until it broke down in a more or less flat plain that stretched east and west almost as far as the eye could see. Roughly in the middle, running southward towards the distant Arabian Sea, was a dried-up water-course, a little gash in the earth, which Ginger knew—as there were no others in sight—could only be the *Wadi al Arwat*, their objective.

Although still some way off he surveyed the place with interest and curiosity. The foliage of the narcotic shrub had been described as grey; but he could see nothing that answered to this description. Indeed, from the air at any rate, any herbage the *wadi* supported—and there seemed to be very little—could only be described as dirty brown, if not actually black. At all events, nothing moved, although there was a certain amount of debris scattered about that might have been anything.

He looked at Biggles, who was also staring down, having dropped his port wing for a better view. Biggles returned the glance and remarked: 'Queer.' Looking down again he went on: 'I don't get it. I don't see much in the way of scrub growing there. Nor can I see anything that looks like a water-hole. I can't imagine what that dark-coloured stuff could be. No matter. We'll soon know.' So saying

he cut his engine and put the nose of the aircraft down in a glide towards the object of their scrutiny.

He flew round the place twice, the first time at about two hundred feet and the second time even lower. Ginger watched closely for a movement; but he saw none.

'There are no Arabs there now or they would have shown themselves,' observed Biggles, as, correcting bumps all the time, he put the machine in to land.

Ginger relaxed with relief as the Proctor ran safely to a standstill. Then he started as, for the first time, some of the objects on the ground showed signs of life. Half a dozen vultures flapped along the ground before taking wing in a slow, spiral course towards the merciless sun.

'I don't like the look of that,' muttered Biggles. 'Those stinking birds are gorged with food. Did you notice how they took off? They were definitely overloaded.'

As Ginger jumped down the rays of the sun struck him like a blow. Heaven and earth alike seemed to glow. All around the hot air danced and trembled on the shining surface of barren, hard-baked *sabkha*. The silence was complete. Nothing interrupted a dreadful stillness. Even the drone of the reserve machine circling overhead, seemed to be smothered by an overwhelming hush.

'Phew! What a dustbin!' he murmured, and then followed Biggles who began walking slowly towards the *wadi*, which he now saw was a gully torn in the sands by storm-water during a deluge in the past. It was quite shallow. About a hundred yards wide at the rim, and thirty or forty feet deep, narrowing at the bottom, it meandered away following the fall of the ground.

Reaching the object of their flight Biggles stopped and looked about him. Then he took a cigarette from his case, tapped it on the back of his hand, and lighted it. 'Looks as if we've wasted our time,' he remarked evenly.

This expressed precisely what Ginger was thinking; for with the exception of one or two straggling bushes the whole area had been burnt. Where the main growth of scrub had been, was now a charred area of earth from which projected a few woody stems.

But this was not all. There were other things, and they were not pretty. Scattered about were bones, mostly complete skeletons of men and camels, to which scraps of sun-dried flesh still adhered. But from the bleached condition of some of the bones it was evident that the owners of these miserable relics had been dead for some time. There were two exceptions. Lying at the foot of a big rock in the *wadi*, as if they had sought the meagre shade it would provide, were two Arabs, their bodies emaciated to mere skin and bones.

Biggles went down to them, and a glance was sufficient to reveal that one of them at least had been dead for some days. The body had not decomposed, but had merely been shrivelled up like a mummy by the relentless sun. The other looked as if death had only recently overtaken him, and the cause was in plain view. Under the foot of a rock a hole had been scooped. The bottom, rather darker than the surrounding sand, still showed finger-marks, as if the last act of the wretched Arab had been to strive to reached the liquid that lay below. Clearly, the place was the water-hole. For all practical purposes it was dry.

Dropping on his knees, Biggles turned the body over and looked at the face. A sharp intake of breath suggested surprise, but he did not speak. The eyes of the Arab were closed. Biggles raised an eyelid. Then, moving swiftly, he bent low and laid an ear on the man's chest. Suddenly he sprang up. 'Water!' he snapped. 'Fetch water!'

Gasping in the heat Ginger ran back to the machine and returned with a water-bottle. Without a word he handed it to Biggles who, not without difficulty, after splashing a little on the immobile face, got a small quantity between the black and shrivelled lips. He went on dabbing the lips with a wetted corner of his handkerchief.

Ginger sat down on the skull of a dead camel and watched Biggles working on what at first they had supposed to be a corpse. He marvelled at Biggles's patience, for he felt sure that it would all be to no purpose. The heat was appalling, and he moved constantly so that the fierce rays did not strike his exposed skin always in one place. Then, looking again at the unconscious face, a strange feeling came over him that he had seen it before.

'You know, Biggles,' said Ginger in a curious voice, 'I've got a feeling I've seen that chap somewhere.'

'You've seen his photo,' said Biggles quietly, still working on the patient. 'He's one of Darnley's men—the one named Zahar, if my memory serves me.' He splashed more water on the thin face.

'I think you might as well bring the other machine down,' he went on presently. 'We may be here for some time and there's no point in leaving Bertie up there.

Ginger complied without enthusiasm. If the truth must be told he was by no means happy about the turn events had taken. Death stood too close. His last victim still lay on the burning sand. If anything should go wrong they would soon be lying on the sand beside him. However, he made the necessary signal and watched the reserve machine land and taxi up to their own, where the engine was switched off.

'And what goes on, old boy?' asked Bertie as he jumped down.

'I don't know, except that the place is a charnel-house,' answered Ginger moodily. 'There's an Arab. Biggles thinks he's still alive and is trying to bring him round. The *gurra* is all burnt out. There's nothing here except bones. The place gives me the willies.'

They walked to the *wadi* to find, to Ginger's astonishment, that Biggles's efforts had been successful, the Arab's eyes were opened, although they still held a vacant stare.

But in ten minutes the man was able to sip. A little while later he was grabbing at the cup, muttering incoherently. Slowly his eyes cleared as consciousness returned.

'Talk about snatching a bloke from the beastly jaws of death, and all that sort of thing,' murmured Bertie, polishing his eye-glass.

'It was worth trying,' remarked Biggles, satisfaction in his voice. 'Apart from any other consideration, it would have been a pity had there been no survivor to tell us what happened here.'

'Does it matter?' enquired Ginger. 'I mean, the stuff is burnt. Somebody else has done the job. That suits me fine. It's warm enough here without lighting bonfires.'

'I'm not so sure about that,' replied Biggles thoughtfully. 'I've an idea that there's more in this affair than meets the eye. While you were away I found that and had a look in it.' He pointed to a small lizard-skin bag, tied at the throat with a strip of the same material.

Ginger picked it up, untied the knot and inserted his hand. When he withdrew it, and opened it, it was to reveal a number of tiny brown pellets sticking to it. There was also a yellow object about the size of a marble. This, too, was sticky, and he had difficulty in removing it from his fingers and getting it back in the bag. It left a queer, sickly, but aromatic smell.

'You realise what that is?' asked Biggles.

'*Gurra*, I imagine.'

'I don't think there can be any doubt about it,' declared Biggles. 'I'd say the little brown things are seeds of the plant that produces the stuff.'

'Then it looks as if this chap came here to collect both gum and seeds.'

'One or the other, certainly. He didn't come alone either. There were at least two of them. I've been looking at his pal, the one who died, and unless I'm mistaken it's Kuatim, another of Darnley's camel-men from Aden. Now we know why they couldn't be found.'

'Absolutely,' murmured Bertie. 'It looks as if they ran into a considerable spot of bother—if you see what I mean. I wonder what went wrong.'

'That's what I'm hoping this chap will be able to tell us,' replied Biggles. 'Maybe they reckoned on finding water in the water-hole, instead of which they found it dry. Maybe their camels strayed. Maybe they lit a fire, and the whole place caught fire and doped them. Anyhow, the fact remains that they got stuck here. One died, and the other was at his last gasp when we arrived. Judging from the way that the rest of the bones have been picked by vultures, I imagine the original Arabs that Darnley saw here all died long ago. Another fact that emerges is, Darnley is obviously wrong in supposing that the *gurra* was a secret of his own. These fellows knew about it or they wouldn't have come back. The important question is, did they come to get some for their personal use or had they other ideas about it? That's what I'm hoping Zahar will tell us. According to Darnley he speaks English.'

At this juncture the Arab muttered something, but what he said no one knew, for the language, presumably an Arabic dialect, was unknown to any of them.

'Try him in English,' suggested Ginger, as Biggles allowed the man to take a little more water.

Apparently the Arab overheard this, for he suddenly burst out with: 'There is no God but God.'

'That's better,' said Biggles smiling.

'May the sword of God strike the traitor and all his brood,' croaked Zahar.

'Who was the traitor, O Zahar?' asked Biggles quietly.

'Abu bin Hamud—may his face be blackened.'

Biggles threw a quick glance at the others, eyebrows raised. 'So *that* was it,' he said softly. Then, to Zahar. 'You came here with him, eh?'

'I did, may God forgive me.'

'Where is he now?'

'*Allaha alim.* God is the knower. Hamud took our camels and left us here.' The sick man's strength was returning, and he raised himself on an elbow. 'Wallah! What Arabs are you?' he demanded hoarsely.

Biggles did not smile, knowing that to an Arab all men are Arabs of one tribe or another. 'We are friends of Darnley Sahib,' he explained.

'Tell us what happened here. Presently we will take you back to Aden.'

'Where are your camels?' demanded Zahar, looking round.

'We came in an aeroplane,' Biggles told him.

'God is great,' breathed Zahar. 'It was his will. I, and Kuatim, came here with Abu bin Hamud—may his children perish! He said there was a place he knew where there was a sort of hashish that we would sell to the *farengi* (foreigner) for much money, and grow rich.'

'You have been here before?' prompted Biggles.

'That is the truth,' agreed Zahar. 'At that time there were many Arabs here dying. When we came again, all were dead, and the bones of their camels had begun to whiten in the sand. That doubtless, was the will of Allah. Then, said Abu bin Hamud—may God punish him!—we will collect this gum, and seeds of the plant, and afterwards destroy everything, so that we alone shall hold the secret.

(Continued on page 49)

33

OIL ABOARD

PHOTOGRAPHS BY CAMERA TALKS

All through the years, winter and summer, war or peace, the fleets of oil tankers ply steadily across the seas with their precious cargoes of oil and petrol, the life blood of modern mechanised civilisation.

A tanker's crew numbers between 40 to 45 men, according to the size of the vessel. Under the Captain, the First Officer has the main responsibility for the safe carriage of the cargo, which is stowed away in about 27 oil compartments. Crude oil is carried mainly, and also refined petrol. The vessel shown in these pictures is one of the 'Esso' fleet, the largest in the world. Ships cross regularly to the British West Indies, the round voyage taking about a month. The average cargo is 14,000 tons, but the latest vessel 'Esso Zurich' can carry well over 22,000 tons. Loading, through pipelines, takes between 18 and 20 hours. On arrival in

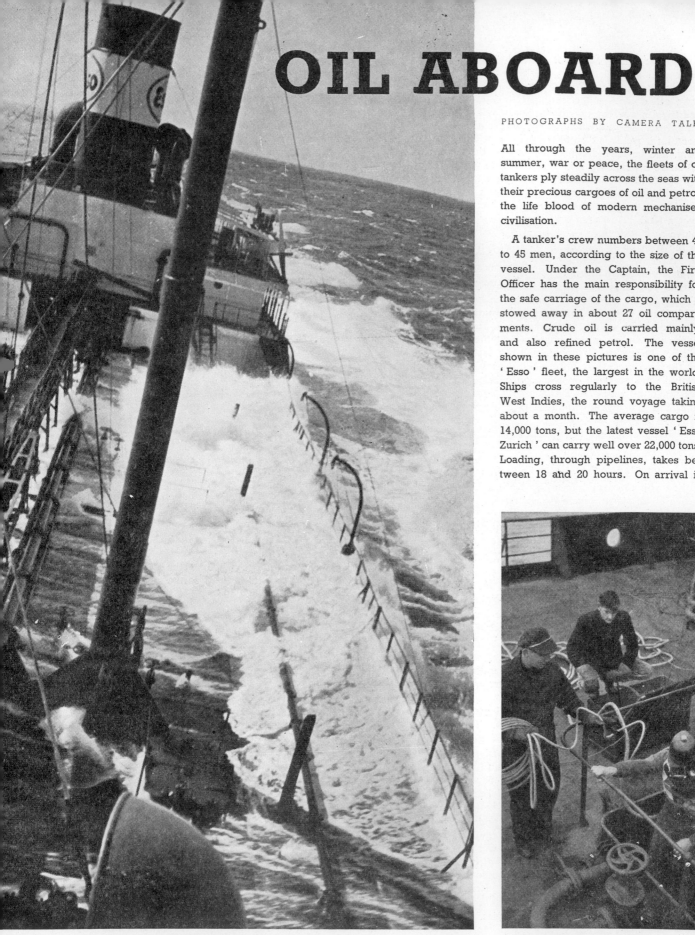

The decks of the oil tankers are awash constantly because of the heavy load carried. Come wind come weather the tankers battle through the seas, with their valuable cargo.

An officer climbs down for a routine inspection of the tanks wearing safety gear for protection against gases.

Swinging the lead to determine the depth of water under the vessel's stern.

Canvas windsail used for ventilating the tanks where gases form and must be extracted.

The Chief officer takes a bearing. This is done every four hours.

On arrival 8-inch hoses are connected to the tanks on board. The oil is pumped ashore at the rate of 350 tons an hour, through each hose. This tanker, the 'Esso Cayenne', is being unloaded at Hull.

Samples of oil taken from each tank are sent to a laboratory for testing.

Heaving in one of the heavy mooring ropes, 8 to 10 inches in circumference.

The pumpman watches the oil pressure and steam gauges during the discharge of cargo.

port, a red flag is hoisted, to denote that dangerous cargo is on board and careful precautions are taken to ensure that no accident happens, which could result in fearful explosion and fire.

Deck boys are taken on at the age of 16, and by dint of hard work and the passing of very exacting examinations, can, within 10 years, secure a Master's Certificate.

You can travel to Trinidad as a passenger on a tanker, if you get one of the limited number of berths available. This is no luxury cruise, but you can share the life of the crew, and feel your voyage across the ocean is not only cheaper, but more exciting.

The after-deck is washed down immediately after leaving port, and during the voyage, though often the sea rushes in to relieve the crew of this job.

Some of the crew of 40, being paid off at the end of the voyage.

You Need Rope for Adventures

by ·RICHARD GRAVES

Sydney Morning Herald

Testing a length of rope made out of grass.

ALMOST EVERY ADVENTURE calls for rope, and it is much more thrilling to make the rope for yourself than to go into a shop and buy it . . . besides there may not be a shop where you need your rope.

The materials that you choose for making your rope must answer the following three tests: first of all, the fibres must be long enough to spin together; secondly, they have to be strong—take a few fibres and pull them gently; thirdly, they must be pliable—tie a thumb knot and gently pull it tight. If the material does not cut at the knot it will do.

It is best, first, to learn how to make a cord with your fingers. You need two people to help you. Take the fibre, and divide the loose end into two equal wisps. Take one wisp yourself, and get your friend to take the other, and both of you twist the material clockwise between your finger and thumb. The third person who is holding the two ends will feel them wanting to twist together. They will twist ANTICLOCKWISE and

should be twisted, keeping an even strain on both strands, which will then lie round each other. There is no need to hold the ends where the two strands started to twist, as these will stay together. This is called 'laying up' and the work of twisting is called 'spinning'. The two strands must be of equal thickness, and lie evenly, without the one being tight and the other twisted round it. When the material in the strands starts to thin out, the spinner simply adds more, and continues spinning. If you are using fine fibres from, say, the inner bark of willow, your strands need be no thicker than one eighth of an inch, but if you are using green meadow grass your strands may need to be half an inch thick.

Willow or other bark fibre will give you a rope one inch in diameter with a breaking strain of more than 2,000 lb., but green grass rope of the same thickness will only take a strain of 80 to 100 lb. The twisted strands, after being laid together should be again twisted and laid together so that three of these triple cords make your rope.

Twisting with fingers is slow and tiring, and you can make your rope much more easily and in shorter time by making a spinner or crank from a piece of wire or bent stick, or by setting up a rope-walk. By this means three or four people can make a fifty yard length of strong rope in about half an hour. To spin with cranks, the spinner holds an armful of material under the left arm, and feeds the loose ends into the spinning strands with the right hand, allowing the material to pass and twist loosely through the left hand so that it 'bites' together. When the strands are of sufficient length they are joined at the spinner's end to a single crank and laid together back towards the crank turners. While this laying-up is taking place it is necessary to keep the cranks turning to maintain the twist on the strands.

The finished rope should be passed

over a quick flame to singe off the furry ends.

Before trusting yourself to your handmade rope, test it in a tug-of-war with at least three people at either end. If they cannot break it you can safely trust it with your life.

You may be entirely on your own and so have no help with spinning, and in this case your best plan is to plait the grass or material, using the lariat plait. Take four wisps and tie them together to a convenient tree. Take the right-hand wisp and bring it over two wisps, and around and under the centre so that it points to the right. Now take the left-hand wisp and pass it over two, around and under the centre so that it points to the left, and repeat alternately with top right and top left wisps, adding more material when the wisps start to thin out. You should be able to make sixty yards an hour by this method.

Half-inch rope would be only one quarter the strength of inch rope, so you need four such strands to give you strength, because the plaited cords will be only about half an inch in diameter. Remember that twice the thickness gives you four times the strength.

You might need a broad plaited band for a strap or belt. This is easily and quickly made as you see by following the diagram. Always work from the outside towards the centre.

There are hundreds of materials you can use for plaiting and by keeping your eyes open and applying the three tests, you will soon have a wide collection ranging from waste horsehair found on fences and hedges to fibrous inner bark of many dead woods, water reeds, and, of course, a whole range of weeds, sedges and grasses.

Sometimes these materials, if green, may be stiff, and inclined to be brittle. If this is so try passing them through flame for a few moments. Often this 'heat' treatment will make them soft and pliable.

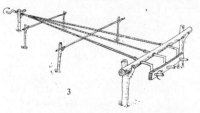

1

The strands must be of even thickness and be twisted clockwise into a cord. Three cords will make a rope.

3

A rope-walk adds speed and strength to rope making.

2

Spinners or cranks can be made from wire or bent sticks and used to spin strands.

4   5   6

If you are alone, plaiting is the easiest method, with either three, four or more strands.

IT IS SUMMER NOW ON THE PAMPA

by Anne Marow

As we blow on cold fingers and hurry home out of the biting wind, cattle riders in the Argentine are sizzling under a burning sun. But a menace worse than snow can come swooping out of their warm skies.

Peons, on horseback, drive the animals peaceably to their grazing-ground.

Paul Popper

ON THE ARGENTINE pampa it is scorching summer, now. (Can you imagine Christmas day at midsummer, with the candles on the Christmas tree wilting in the heat and bending double, till they look like wax croquet-hoops?) All day, brilliant sunlight pours down on the plains, making mirages of water from sheer dazzle of heat on the hard earth; it pours down steadily, from a cloudless sky, on miles of ripening maize, on thousands of cattle browsing, and here and there a peon riding slowly, from one rare islet of trees to the next, to see that the wells are working and the drinking-troughs full. He seems to be riding carelessly, slouching, half-asleep; but don't believe your eyes about that. Wait until the horse stumbles in the rough ground, or shies at an armadillo; then you will see how perfectly the descendant of gauchos understands his horse.

At this time of year, any essential cattle work is done in the cool of dawn. Steers that must be branded, or dipped, or injected against disease, are brought in overnight to a corral near the house; at sunrise estanciero and peons are busy on the job; and then, two or three peons, on horseback of course, drive the animals peaceably to their grazing-ground. (No Spanish-Indian would dream of doing any farm work on foot; teasing him, people say he will walk a mile to catch up his pony in order to ride 300 yards and fetch the milking-cows; he would feel unmanly, and all wrong, *walking* behind the cows!) The corral work is much less exciting than *rodeo al campo* in the old gaucho fashion. They still do that sometimes

in winter—rounding up the cattle in the open plain, to single out the one they want, catch and throw him with a lasso, and operate then and there. But it is bad for the animals—it over-excites them, and besides, they may break their legs in falling—so most estancieros discourage it. So there are fewer and fewer people now who can use a lasso—with that simple-looking movement that is so very skilled. Could you trip a galloping steer with a running noose? Cattle are generally de-horned nowadays, to prevent them from goring each other if they fight; so the trick is *pielando*—catching the animal by the foot. That means that one side of the thrown loop must lie along the ground, the other still be in the air, at just the instant when the animal will put his foot through it; and in the same second you must pull it tight so that he pitches forward on to the ground. Try it, standing still, with your sister walking slowly past you to be tripped; she won't be in much danger of a fall, I dare say—though she may get rather bored with the game.

Except round the estancias, the only patches of shade are at the tanks. These tanks are filled by Artesian wells, at the juncture of four huge fields; and beside them, to give shade near the troughs, trees have been planted—nearly always a kind of acacia, the paraiso, which has bitter leaves and bark, and is almost the only tree the locusts will not eat. So the plain, which is flat as the sea for hundreds of miles, is dotted with these dull little clumps of paraiso, each with its spidery metal windmill breaking the straight horizon.

No trees are native to the pampa, except that queer lonely tree, the *ombu*, which the gauchos thought unlucky—and few of those are left. There is seldom even a shrub; once in forty or fifty miles you may come to a single thorn bush, or a squat little prickly-pear, and that is almost a landmark. There are hardly any rivers or streams, in all that vast space. Almost the only surface water is the salt water of the lagoons—and in summer most of these dwindle to salty hard mud, and do not fill again until it rains. Only the big ones are lakes all the year round; and there, flamingoes stalk on the shore, or fly beautifully in long, low lines across the water on great wings the colour of a sunset sky. The lagoons are just about as old as the hills—older than the plains. They have remained since the prehistoric time when the whole low pampa lay under the waves of the South Atlantic.

The Spanish conquerors in the sixteenth century were more interested in silver and gold from the Andes than in the great plains covered with man-high, feather-tufted, pampas grass, so they seldom penetrated far beyond the banks of the Rio de la Plata, River of Silver, the overland route from Ecuador to Buenos Aires and the Atlantic. It was not till later that some of their descendants, those hardy cattle-men, the gauchos, began to dispute with savage Indians the mastery of the plains. Perhaps you have read W. H. Hudson's book about his boyhood there, *Far Away and Long Ago*; or *El Ombu*, which tells of the life that gauchos and Indians lived, raiding each other's settlements and stealing each other's finest horses and cattle, until about 150 years ago. He tells the true stories told to him in the 1840's and '50's by old gauchos who remembered the cruelty and tragedy of former days, the hardships and the endurance of men who were born to the saddle, and had never seen a town.

But now the Spaniards and Indians of the pampas have settled down together, and intermarried for several generations, and been joined by immigrants from every country in Europe. On a small estancia where I lived, there were people of thirteen different nationalities working. An employer did not mind whether a man came from Poland or Dalmatia or Denmark, but wanted to know whether he understood cattlework, or was a good ploughman, or a handy carpenter or blacksmith, or could bake good loaves. For each estancia, five or six miles from the next, and probably a good deal further from railway or shop, has to be almost a village in itself; an international village, with Spanish as its language. Perhaps the Italian gardener's Spanish is a bit irregular, and the Scottish bullman's would hardly be recognised in Madrid; but here nobody is fussy, and everybody manages to understand and make himself understood.

During the hottest hours, after an early lunch, everybody takes a siesta. All sensible creatures go to sleep. Human beings vanish into the darkened houses; horses, unsaddled, snooze where they are tethered, in the shade of the paraisos; dogs doze on the verandah, cats in the kitchen doorway. Out on the plain, the conscientious rhea and his gadabout wives keep still; armadilloes and skunks reckon that later on, when it is cooler, will be quite soon enough to see about the next meal.

Then, towards four o'clock, life begins to stir again. Animals and humans wake up, and find the climate pleasant. Somebody canters away north, to the 'town' on the railway line, to fetch the mail; somebody else goes to fetch in the milking cows; others go east, to move a hundred head of cattle from grass, which is drying up, to lucerne, which is still green. And before sunset the boundary rider goes right round the outside of the estancia, to drive the cattle inwards from the wire fences. They are inquisitive and sociable creatures, and like to watch the road, where once in a way a horseman or a lorry passes by; but at night a lorry may contain cattle-thieves, who will cut the wire and carry off any beast lying conveniently near. So every morning the boundary rider must inspect the fences, and count the cattle if the wire seems to have been tampered with; and every evening he must get them away from the road, before they lie down to sleep. Then he returns, in the fading light, to the cluster of low white houses among the trees, to eat his *puchero* and drink his *mate* with the other peons. Later, perhaps, when the stars are clear, and the cool little night breeze is blowing, and the crickets are rattling like castanets and the fire-

Hispanic Council

He seems to be riding carelessly, half-asleep, but don't believe your eyes about that.

flies are dancing, somebody will bring out a guitar; and one will play and several will sing, the slow, monotonous, rather melancholy songs which are peculiar to plainsmen all over the world.

In an ordinary summer, it is a pleasant enough life; easy-going, unhurrying; a life made comfortable by two good Spanish traditions, the siesta, and 'manana' (which means 'never do to-day what you can put off till tomorrow.') Only very rarely does anybody choose to leave this life for the towns.

* * *

But not all Argentine summers are ordinary. Now and then—perhaps after three years, or five, or seven—sooner or later, the locusts come.

From time to time, for some reason that nobody knows, several billions of locusts from the Brazilian jungle fly south to breed. They travel slowly—only fifteen or twenty miles a day—and in an unswerving line, due south. They are big brown grasshoppers with strong transparent wings, and they come flying in a steady column, perhaps two or three miles wide, and thirty or forty miles long. They keep this formation, so that if you knew exactly where they were, northward, and ruled lines on a large-scale map, you could tell for certain whether they would pass over your land or not. But it is like flying-bombs; the important thing is not whether they fly overhead but where on their straight line they drop. At sunset the whole swarm settles on the ground; and the females, heavy with eggs to lay, may come down earlier. Where they sleep, there they will have breakfast; so if they have

settled in your garden at night there may not be a leaf or a blade of grass left next morning, nor any tree (except paraiso) that is not as bare as in midwinter. And where the female settles, there, in hard ground, she will lay her eggs; she leaves them in a sort of bag, thrust down into the earth about an inch and a half, so that the heat of the sun, baking the soil, will hatch them. And when they hatch, there will emerge from every bag a hundred insects the size of mosquitoes, which will eat and eat, and grow and grow, on your land, for about six weeks, until they are nearly two inches long and as fat as a ripe pea pod; not till then will they grow wings and fly away; and by then, of course, the ground will be a barren desert for miles around. So the first and most important task is to try to prevent the swarm from settling.

The ordinary means of doing this are fire and noise (in scorching midsummer!) When you see a long brown cloud, the colour of a dust storm, lying close along the horizon to northward, you know what is coming. You cannot possibly defend the whole estancia, but you probably try to save the big maize-crop, and also the garden to have some fruit and vegetables left to eat. So you prepare a row of bonfires to windward, and light them as the leaders of the swarm arrive; if the wind is steady, the smoke blows across the garden or the crop, and the locusts, disliking it, fly a bit higher, and do not loiter there—or perhaps they do not see the tempting greenery. The swarm flies very low—only just above the trees; and once it arrives overhead it is no longer like a brown dust-cloud, but mottled black. Sometimes, I believe, the creatures are so many, and fly so thick, that they blot out the sun entirely; but when I saw them they were in looser formation, and came driving and rustling on endlessly, countless sinister flakes against the blue sky, like living black snow in a nightmare. It took two days for the column to pass.

The wind had dropped, so the bonfires were no good. That left only one hope —noise. Locusts are supposed to dislike noise. So there was no siesta for anybody in those two days. Out we all went, to walk up and down, round and about the big garden, all day, making every sort of banging and clanging we could find instruments for. Some had trays and kitchen-spoons, some used two frying-pans as cymbals, some banged petrol cans with hammers. By the second day we had simplified it—remember that the days were very hot! We had pierced holes in the sides of petrol cans and biscuit tins and slung them round our necks like drums; and Isabel, who was eleven, had the best idea of all—she tied a cowbell on a loose girdle, so that it hung in front of her and jangled at every step she took. Obviously not even a locust could *like* the din we made. It was not till the end of the second day that somebody from another estancia remarked knowledgeably that locusts had no ears. That was more than we could bear. ' Anyway,' we said, ' they can feel the vibration, and they hate that! '

All the same, thousands of them settled on the garden trees, and on the vegetables, and on all the plants in all the flower beds, at sunset. They fly horizontally, like birds, but they like to sleep vertically, with their heads upward, all ready to climb the tree-trunk or flower-stalk at dawn, eating it bare as they go. So when they had settled, the next job was to go round shaking all the young trees and bushes, so that the sleepy creatures fell off, and could be killed on the ground. These full-grown locusts are nearly three inches long, with oily bodies inside hard cases, and sticky barbed legs; you really needed a shiny cloak and a sou'wester for the tree shaking job, because it was so very unpleasant when they fell inside your

clothes; and the squelching as you trod on them, or pulled the garden roller over the ground which was carpeted with them, was equally nasty. Looking back it seems odd that we struggled so hard, being so hopelessly out-numbered; but we did save something; when the last of the swarm had gone on southward, there were still vegetables in the garden, just enough leaves on the peach trees to prevent the fruit from drying up, and a fair amount of shade round the house; and the maize crop was all right.

But that was only the beginning. On two successive nights the swarm had settled all over the estancia; so it was a sadly safe bet that the hardest ground was full of eggs. There would be six weeks before they hatched; six weeks in which to prepare for the worst phase, when myriads of young ones would come up out of the ground and devour everything. The first precaution was to plough up all the roads and paths—if the eggs were exposed the sun would kill them. The next, to order from Buenos Aires as many miles of ' barrera ' as could be got—sheets of smooth zinc sheeting, each about eight feet long. That year, nobody could get enough; it was the worst and most widespread plague there had been for thirty years and everybody wanted barrera at the same time. So then the question was where to use to best advantage the relatively small quantity of it that came; and again the maize crop and the garden had first claim. That meant that the lucerne and the grass might all be lost; so it was prudent to send big troops of cattle away to hired pasture in uninfested districts if you could, and failing that to sell several hundred, however low the current price, since there would not be enough food for them all, once the eggs hatched and the *saltonas*—the wingless hoppers—began to eat. Next, everybody had to get to work to set up the barrera—no ' manana ' about this! The strips were planted longwise in the ground, end to end, to make a low wall all round the maize and round the garden. It was only a foot high, but the great thing was its shiny surface, at right angles to the ground; the young locusts could not jump as high as that, and would not be able to get any hold

on it, to climb over. The last preparatory job was the digging of big pits.

Meanwhile, the eggs had hatched. In a few days the mosquitoes had grown into tiny grasshoppers, and their number was worse than anybody's worst fears. The fields were brown with them. In no time they had eaten every blade of grass, every dock, every thistle, near their hatching place, and began to march, *en masse,* in search of other food. They always march with the wind; so one day the whole surface of the ground seems to be shuffling eastward, next day southward. I am not exaggerating; the whole place is alive with them; you cannot put your foot down—outside the barrera—without treading on them; cars plough through them on the road, skidding on their oily bodies. And when they are on the march, nothing stops them except the barrera.

We had deep and long pits *inside* the maize-field, against the barrera. The point of this was that though the barrera kept new hoppers out, thousands had hatched in the hard ground between the rows of maize. So a long line of people would walk through the high maize, like a line of beaters, driving the locusts forward—always before the wind, of course—driving them along the ground, so that they did not climb up into the maize. You walked slowly, sweeping on either side with a switch of maize stalks, or a double-thonged cow-hide whip. At length, the whole army of insects emerged at the far end, came to the shiny barrera, tried to climb it and failed, and turned left or right. Then—always going straight on, because they would not turn back into the wind—they would come to the pits, slither down a bit of zinc sheeting, and fall into the horrible welter of others, all hopping desperately, below. They were trapped; the slant of barrera round the edge prevented them from climbing out. In about half-an-hour, a pit four feet deep and wide, and seven or eight feet long, would be full. Then earth was shovelled back on top of it, and the rest of the horde would march on, to fall into the next pit. It was in every way horrible; the method of destroying them was as wholesale and nasty as their own destructiveness. But by then it was a question of either killing locusts by the thousand or having to kill your cattle by the hundred.

Some people were ruined. Well-to-do farmers, who could afford to keep up the fight, and had enough money put by in better years to tide them over this loss, grew more and more worried as the weeks went on, but were just all right. If you *could* save your maize it would pay for some of the loss in cattle, because scarcity was raising its world price. But many small-holders were finished. Perhaps they had not been able to get barrera; perhaps they had not been able to plough up enough during the hatching time; perhaps, almost single-handed, they had been beaten by the endless hordes. Their maize, like their pasture, was all lost; a year's livelihood had been eaten up by

They came driving and rustling on endlessly, like living black snow in a nightmare.

Photographs by Paul Popper

the locusts. Unless they could borrow until the next summer—there was nothing for it but to sell up and go.

And for some, the bitterest thing of all was still ahead. When at last the hoppers grew their wings and flew away north to the warm jungle of Brazil, estancieros relaxed; whatever maize or pasture had been saved should now be all right. 'Should be'; but there was still one danger. The original huge swarm had gone south. Millions had laid their eggs further south. The survivors of all these had still to return

northward to the tropic before winter—probably by the same route. On their homeward journey, too, they would settle each night, and eat each morning; and now most of the land was already eaten bare. Now, a swarm would eat even paraiso; would eat any washing that had been left hanging on the line. And sometimes they would descend on a crop that had been saved by the farmer's incessant struggles, and devour it in one night, before they flew on.

No. Not every summer on the pampa is 'ordinary.'

Smiley and Bobble

by Moore Raymond

ILLUSTRATION BY
ARTUR HOROWICZ

When the old dingo trapper gives Smiley a parrot, it lands the Australian boy and his cobber Blue in another dinkum tangle.

'Now I'll show you somethin' you can teach 'im.'

FOR ONCE IN A WHILE, Smiley's face was not wearing the customary grin that earned him his nickname.

He was nearly asleep on the horse he rode bareback as it ambled slowly through the heat-stricken mulga scrub. Eyes closed, he swayed gently to and fro, letting the animal make its own way home to the Murrumbilla schoolhouse.

Mr. Stephens, the schoolmaster of this dry and dusty Western Queensland township, had sent the 12-year-old boy to look for his horse, and he had found it with the usual mob near the Morven road.

Clip-clop-clip-clop . . . . over the bare and sun-baked ground . . . . clip-clop-clip-clop . . . . it was like a lullaby.

The horse gave a gentle whinny. Smiley woke up with such a start that he nearly fell off.

There must be another horse about, he conjectured. Then he realised where he was.

'We're close to Clatcher's place!' he whispered hoarsely to his mount—and he felt a little scared.

Clatcher was the dingo trapper who lived in a house that was little more than a hut on the outskirts of Murrumbilla. He earned a living by catching the wild dogs—the sheep-killers that were such a menace in this wool-growing area of Australia.

'That cove Clatcher's a deadly enemy,' muttered Smiley to the horse as he reined it to a standstill.

The fact was that Clatcher, a bearded and rough-looking man, always discouraged the Murrumbilla boys from hanging around his place. If ever he saw them about he shouted and shook his fist—and the scared youngsters ran off into the bush.

''E don't scare me really,' Smiley muttered defiantly to himself as he slid off the horse and slipped the reins over a branch.

Curiosity impelled him towards the hut, despite the uneasy feeling in the pit of his stomach. As he crept on bare feet through the mulga trees, he whispered the rhyme he and his mates believed to be a protection from harm.

'One, two, three, four, five, six, seven,
   All good children go to heaven,
   Penny on the water, twopence on the sea,
   Threepence on the railway for you and me.'

Suddenly he came upon Clatcher the trapper. It was a strange sight. The man was on his horse—not seated on it, but standing balanced on the saddle. His right arm was thrust into the hollow dead limb of a gum tree, and he appeared to be feeling for something.

Creeping forward to get a closer look, the boy stepped on a twig. It snapped loudly.

'What—!' exclaimed Clatcher, swinging round abruptly and startling his nervous horse. The animal shied away.

'Hey!' yelled the man in alarm, clutching the dead limb with his free arm to save himself from falling.

There he dangled—one arm inside the dead limb and the other clinging to the outside.

'Hey, git my 'orse!' he yelled—for he had caught a glimpse of Smiley peering out from behind a tree.

The boy's first impulse was to run away. But his

instinctive sense of honesty made him realise that he was responsible for the man's predicament—and even injury.

All this went through Smiley's mind in a flash as he quickly sidled up to the trapper's horse and swiftly caught the bridle before it could move further away. He hauled it under the dangling man.

'Thanks, kid, thanks!' panted Clatcher, placing his feet firmly on the saddle. In another couple of seconds he had withdrawn his arm from the hollow and slid to the ground.

'You're a smart kid,' he grinned through his beard, patting the boy on the back. 'I mighter been 'ung up there for months if you 'adn't saved me.'

Smiley was astonished at this display of friendly gratitude, especially as he was the cause of the incident that might have been an accident.

'I was lookin' in there for young parrots,' went on the trapper. 'I thought I could 'ear 'em squawkin'.'

Smiley looked at Clatcher in surprise. This wasn't the rough-spoken man who shouted curses at boys.

'I savee,' grinned the youngster. 'Galahs, I reckon.'

'Galahs is right.' Clatcher smiled back, but his eyes looked shifty. 'Would you like one?'

'Eh?'

'You can 'ave a young galah if you like. I'm bringin' up a couple, but I don't want both.'

'Aw, gee, mister, that'd be bonzer!' cried the delighted boy, following the man round to the other side of the hut.

On the back verandah was a large wooden case with a wire-netting front. Inside were half-a-dozen birds—a pair of black cockatoos, a pair of budgerigars, and, huddled in a corner, two young galahs as yet only sparsely fledged.

Clatcher reached in and lifted out one of the young birds. It squawked lustily at being handled.

'Take it easy, cobber,' murmured Smiley, stroking the yelling youngster with a gentle hand.

'Better carry 'im in yore 'at,' suggested the man.

Smiley removed the battered remnant of felt and turned it upside-down. In went the galah, still protesting loudly.

'There y'are,' said Clatcher, urging Smiley towards the scrub. His tone was curt and less friendly as he added: 'Now you'd better do a git.'

Thanking the man again, the delighted boy made off—little realising what trouble that parrot was going to cause him.

The bird shrieked all the way to the schoolhouse, where Mr. Stephens the schoolmaster, having taken delivery of the horse, asked Smiley where he got the little parcel of noise.

He was surprised to hear that the dingo trapper was the donor. So was Smiley's mother when the boy arrived home with the galah—still squawking.

'He must be hungry,' said the tall, sun-browned woman as she smiled tenderly on the baby bird. 'Get some honey in a teaspoon.'

Smiley hurried into the kitchen and soon returned with a spoonful of the golden liquid. Mrs. Greevins showed him how to hold it just inside the wide-open beak.

At the taste of the first drop the galah stopped squawking. Soon its tiny tongue was licking up the rest of the honey.

'I gotter tell me cobber!' exclaimed Smiley. 'Look after me parrot, mum, till I git back.'

He dashed down the verandah steps, through the gate, and past the row of squat bottle trees that lined the main road through the township.

Smiley arrived at the blacksmith's to find his best friend pulling hairs out of the tail of the horse his father was shoeing.

'Hi, cobber.'

'Hi, Smiley,' replied Blue—so nicknamed in those parts because he had red hair.

'I got a young galah,' panted Smiley. 'And I'm goin' to teach 'im to talk. Come and 'ave a squiz.'

Pattering beside Smiley as they ran down the road, Blue puffed various questions. What would Smiley call the parrot? What would he teach him to say? Where would he keep him? To all of which Smiley had the same reply: 'Aw, I dunno.'

They found Mrs. Greevins in the wash-house at the back, hard at work over the tub.

'Where's me galah?' panted the boy.

His mother straightened up from the washboard and smiled. 'All babies like to go to sleep after they've had their tucker.' She nodded towards the washing basket.

They crossed to the big wickerwork basket and looked down to see the little bird lying in a corner with its eyes closed.

'I s'pose yore goin' to call 'im Joey?' suggested Blue.

'Dicken on!' sneered his mate. 'Everybody calls their parrots Joey.'

Smiley always believed in original names for his pets. His tame kangaroo had been called Firsty, his goat was Bootlace, and once he had a pet lizard that lived behind a picture on the wall and was called Runalong.

'If you teach him to talk,' smiled Mrs. Greevins, 'he might suggest a name for himself.'

The boys laughed at this joke. But, as it turned out, it was not far from the truth.

Fed on honey—then honey and oatmeal as it got bigger each day—the galah soon grew strong wing and back feathers of gleaming grey, with a beautiful rosy breast

Smiley did not keep the bird in a cage, but in a shed at the back of the house—where he made a perch for the parrot to roost on.

Despite his mother's advice to wait a while, and despite his mate's ridicule, Smiley tried to teach it to talk from the very first day.

' 'E's goin' to say " Hi, Smiley!" And then 'e's goin' to say " Hi, Blue!" And then I reckon I'll teach 'im—' He paused, wondering what would come next.

'I s'pose,' put in Blue sarcastically, 'you'll teach 'im to recite poitry.'

'I reckon 'e'd say it, too,' retorted Smiley. ' 'E's goin' to be the most marvellous talkin' parrot in the world'

So, over and over again, while the galah sat and watched him—or else shuffled up and down the length of his perch—Smiley loudly repeated the phrase: 'Hi, Smiley!'

But the parrot simply blinked its bright little eyes and chuckled.

However, there was one compensation. The bird would step daintily on to Smiley's outstretched forefinger and remain perched there while he carried it about. Soon it learned to sit contentedly on his shoulder.

'Hi, Smiley!' patiently repeated the boy again and again. But the galah would only chuckle and squawk and make clicking noises. And still Smiley could not find a name for his exasperating pet.

Then several things happened at once.

One day the parrot, having been transferred to the boy's shoulder after a meal of cracked corn, expressed its feeling of contentment by chuckling and bobbing up and down against Smiley's cheek.

'It bobbles!' exclaimed Smiley to Blue.

'It what?'

'My parrot's a bobbler!' laughed Smiley, enjoying both the invention of the word and the antics of the galah. 'That's what I'll call 'im . . . . Bobble!'

'Haw-w-w!' Blue's exclamation began as a sneer and ended in a tone of admiration. It was just the right name, he decided in a flash—and he said so.

'Bobble-bobble-bobble!' cried Smiley, jiggling the bird up and down.

'Bobble-bobble!' joined in the redhead.

The galah nipped the lobe of Smiley's ear, then danced up and down, rubbing its soft head against his cheek.

'Hi, Smiley!' cried a shrill voice.

Both boys froze with astonishment. Who called that greeting? There was only one possible source . . . . one obvious answer . . . . Bobble!

'Hi, Smiley!' yelled Smiley.

'Hi, Smiley!' squawked Bobble.

'Hi, Smiley!' cried the two boys in unison.

But Bobble had evidently decided he had said enough for the time being. Despite their frequent repetition of the phrase, the boys could not persuade him to repeat the salutation.

However, next day Bobble became talkative again, and he seemed to take a delight in squawking his owner's name.

On Monday afternoon began the strange adventures of Bobble.

Smiley and his bird sat in the wash-house, watching Mrs. Greevins at work over the scrubbing board. That was the way she earned a living for herself and Smiley—by doing the washing for some of the more prosperous inhabitants of Murrumbilla.

Mrs. Greevins had, as usual, taken off her wedding ring and stuck it firmly into a soft bar of soap. She always took her ring off to do the washing because it was rather tight, and it hurt her finger if she kept it on while she rubbed and scrubbed.

Discovering she had run out of starch, Mrs. Greevins sent Smiley off to the store to get some in a hurry.

'And don't take Bobble,' she said, 'or you'll start showing him off and you'll never get back.'

Returning from the store, Smiley saw his mother standing with some neighbours at the foot of a bottle tree just outside the gate. They were staring up at the galah, who sat on the topmost twig.

'He's gone and flown away with my ring!' exclaimed Mrs. Greevins to her son.

Though she did not know it, this was not strictly true. What had actually happened was this . . . . Bobble, thinking the soap might be something good to eat, had strutted across the bench and sunk his beak into it, just at the spot where the wedding ring was stuck in.

'Shoo, shoo, shoo! Leave my ring alone!' Mrs. Greevins had cried, waving her hands.

The bird had taken fright and had flown out to the bottle tree, carrying the ring with it. It could not help doing so, because the soap-smeared ring was firmly stuck over the curved beak.

But Mrs. Greevins did not know that. 'Come down here, you thief!' she exclaimed.

'Bobble, Bobble, Bobble!' called Smiley.

But the scared bird stayed there.

'If I was you,' said a woman neighbour, 'I'd throw stones at it and make it drop the ring.'

'No, no!' cried Smiley. 'Don't chuck gibbers at Bobble. I'll climb up and git 'im.'

'You'll never climb that tree,' commented one of several men who had joined the group. He was obviously right, because the trunk was large and limbless to a height of fifteen feet.

In the end someone got a long ladder, and Smiley scrambled up. Amid the cheers of the small crowd that had gathered, he cautiously reached out and enticed Bobble to step on to his forefinger.

With his other hand the boy pulled the ring off the curved beak and slipped it into his shirt pocket.

'It was stuck on ole Bobble's beak,' he explained when he reached the ground and handed it to his mother.

The amused spectators dispersed, and Mrs. Greevins went back to her washing. Blue called for Smiley to go cray-fishing. It seemed that the incident was closed.

But two days later Smiley and Bobble met Clatcher in the main road.

'Is that the galah I gave you, kid?' grinned the dingo trapper. 'I hear it pinches gold rings.'

Smiley began to protest, but the man broke in: 'What do you call 'im?'

'Bobble. And 'e can say 'Hi, Smiley!', and—'

'Hi, Smiley!' squawked Bobble.

'And 'e likes nibblin' me ears.'

Clatcher held out his finger for Bobble to step on—and the bird did so. 'Now I'll show you somethin' you can teach 'im.'

Clatcher gazed hard at the bird and ordered: 'Open yore wings.'

Bobble stretched wide his beautiful grey wings.

While Smiley stared in amazement, Clatcher chuckled: 'I'll give you the oil, kid. When you tell 'im to open 'is wings, jist turn yore finger back a bit. It put's 'im off 'is balance and 'e's gotter open 'is wings to git balance again. But don't overdo it, kid, or you'll give away the secret.'

'Gee, mister, yore a dinkum sport.'

Smiley spent the rest of the afternoon showing Bobble's new trick to a number of admiring people. Only to Blue did he reveal the simple secret.

The following Tuesday, Smiley came home from school to find the shed open and the parrot gone.

'Bobble! Bobble!' he called as he ran round the yard —then into the house. His mother told the anxious boy she had not seen the bird.

'He might have seen some wild galahs and flown away into the bush with them,' she commented sympathetically.

'Aw, no! Me cobber Bobble wouldn't leave me!' cried the boy plaintively. He searched everywhere, getting more and more despondent.

Suddenly an idea came to his mind. ''E's gawn to see 'is mate! That's where 'e's gawn!'

Smiley dashed down the road, cut off into the bush, and made for Clatcher's place.

Without waiting to ask permission, he dashed across the yard and up the verandah steps to the big cage.

Two black cockatoos . . . . two budgerigars . . . . and one galah. That was all. Miserably the boy turned to go back to the township.

He was halfway to the gate when Clatcher came cantering up.

'What—?' the dingo trapper began angrily on seeing the boy. Then he checked himself. By the time he had dismounted he was smiling a welcome.

Smiley poured out his tale of woe.

'Don't worry, kid. I bet you'll find yore parrot all right. If you don't, I'll give you the one I was savin' for meself.'

''E ain't the same as Bobble.' Smiley was inconsolable.

'Look,' went on Clatcher, taking up a small bottle of yellow liquid. ''Ere's some dawg decoy. You can 'ave a lot o' fun with this. A couple o' drops'll bring the dawgs for miles. I don't mean jist wild dawgs, but tame ones too.'

The boy thrust the bottle into his trouser pocket and walked miserably off, hardly caring about the new present.

He was nearly home when he was met by a breathless Blue.

'Gee, Cobber,' puffed the redhead, 'yore goin' to git roared up a treat!'

'Eh?'

'Bobble's gawn and pinched Mrs. Gaspen's brooch and they—'

'Bobble! Where is 'e?'

'At yore place. 'E stole the brooch and they can't find it and—'

Smiley did not wait to listen. He raced home to find his mother talking to Sergeant Flaxman, head policeman in Murrumbilla.

'I've heard of magpies stealing jewelry,' the sergeant was saying as he held Bobble perched on his forefinger. 'And jackdaws and bower birds. But this is the first time I've known a galah to take a fancy to—'

'Bobble never stole a thing!' burst out Smiley. At the sound of his voice the parrot fluttered on to his shoulder.

'Well, the evidence against the bird is very strong,' replied the sergeant grimly.

He went on to tell how Mrs. Gaspen, the doctor's wife, lost her ruby-and-emerald brooch.

Mrs. Gaspen was getting ready to go to the Women's Circle meeting, as she always did on Tuesdays. And she always wore her best brooch and a pearl scarf-pin. She left them on her dressing table when she went out to see about the cakes she was taking to the meeting—and when she came back they were gone. She found the pin on the verandah. After a frantic and vain search for the brooch, the sergeant was called in.

'I heard a parrot had been seen on the Gaspen's verandah,' the sergeant told the boy. 'Then I heard a voice calling out, "Hi, Smiley!" And there was your parrot sitting on a tree in the Gaspen's yard.'

'Did 'e 'ave the brooch in 'is mouth?' asked Smiley.

'Well . . . . no, he didn't,' the sergeant admitted. 'But it's strong evidence against him. I think you'll have to get rid of him, Smiley.'

'No, no! Bobble don't steal! 'E never stole me mother's ring and 'e never stole the brooch!'

'Hi, Smiley!' cried Bobble, rubbing his soft head against the boy's cheek.

'I'll never let 'im outer me sight again. Fair dinkum I won't, sergeant.'

Mrs. Greevins put in: 'You can't take him to school.'

'I'll keep ole Bobble locked up in the shed when 'e's not with me,' Smiley assured them.

The boy's distress, coupled with his promise, made the sergeant relent.

'All right, Smiley. But it will mean goodbye to Bobble if he does it again. And by the way, you'd better go and have a good look for that brooch in the Gaspens' yard.'

'Too right, sergeant. And I'll git me cobber Blue to 'elp me.'

But the brooch was not found that day—or the next—and eventually the search was abandoned.

Smiley kept his word about Bobble. The parrot was either in his company or locked up in the shed.

But before long he was again visited by Sergeant Flaxman. This time the policeman hauled him over the coals for sprinkling the dog decoy on various doorsteps, thus causing all the dogs in the town to congregate and start a great hullabaloo with their yapping and fighting.

'If you do it again, I'll shove you in the lockup for a night,' said the sergeant sternly before riding off.

'Don't 'e pick on me a terrible lot?' grumbled Smiley.

Then came the climax.

Again the theft took place while Smiley was at school. Before he could reach home he heard the news.

Bobble was now accused of stealing a gold wristwatch from Mr. Thorby, the owner of Yarramanda, a big sheep station in the vicinity.

He had driven in from the homestead and was on his way to Brisbane for business reasons. Deciding to stay the night at Hawkin's Hotel, he took a shower bath to wash away the dust of the journey to Murrumbilla.

Naturally he removed his wristwatch. He left it on his dressing table and went into the bathroom. During his brief absence it disappeared.

Outside in the hotel yard was a galah that fluttered about, crying 'Hi, Smiley!' at intervals.

Smiley arrived at Hawkin's Hotel to find a lot of people searching the yard, while Sergeant Flaxman was making unavailing attempts to catch the galah.

'Bobble!' cried the boy.

'Hi, Smiley!' squawked the bird—but it did not fly to him. Instead, it fluttered further off, despite more calls from the boy.

The keen-eyed sergeant threw a stone. It hit the parrot on the breast and knocked it to the ground.

'Bobble!' yelled Smiley, flinging himself at the injured bird. He tripped over a stone and sprawled full length.

The parrot fluttered away from his outstretched hands, took wing, and flew off . . . . over the hotel, over the trees, and somewhere over the river it disappeared.

'That bird's gone bush,' said the angry sergeant. 'And good riddance.'

'Bobble'll come back to 'is cobber,' said the boy.

'If he does, he'll be done for. Make no mistake about that.' The sergeant meant what he said.

'A reward of a fiver for anyone who finds my watch,' Mr. Thorby was repeating to all and sundry.

But Smiley hardly heard as he sadly left the hotel on dragging feet and went trudging down the road.

He was soon joined by Blue, who could not desert his mate in such a time of sorrow.

'I dunno 'ow ole Bobble got outer the shed,' sighed Smiley to the redhead. 'There's only two keys. I got one and Mum's got the other. And Mum wouldn't let 'im out, I know.'

The two boys went through the gate and round to the shed. The door was shut. Smiley turned the knob—but the door refused to open because it was locked.

'Hi, Smiley!' called a familiar voice.

'Stone the crows!' cried the boy, shoving his key into the lock. He thrust open the door.

'Bobble!' shouted Smiley.

'Bobble!' echoed Blue.

QUIZ

1. Who established the printing press in England, and in what century? 2. What famous London street is associated with the Press? 3. Who was the Secretary to the Admiralty, who kept a famous diary? 4. What book published yearly, is of especial interest to children (apart from other considerations) on account of some very popular personal points? 5. Give the name of the official report of proceedings in Parliament. 6. (a) What character in fiction originated the phrase: 'Elementary, my dear Watson', in matters of deduction? (b) What character started a fashion of lace-collared, velvet suits for boys? 7. What famous siege is dealt with in the Iliad? 8. The following names belong to animals in fiction. What kind of animal is each? Flicka. Babar. Hunca Munca. Orlando. Flag. Mrs. Tiggy Winkle. 9. What was the name of the white whale hunted by Ahab, captain of the ship 'Pequod'? 10. Where would you expect to find an otter and kite working together usefully? 11. Whom do we associate with each of these ships: (a) Argo (b) Endurance (c) Trinidad (d) Destiny? 12. How many errors are there in this passage? He decided, while at Queen's College, Cambridge, to rewrite Charles M. Dicken's *Barnaby Rudge* and *Quentin Durward* into a long, twelve-thousand-word novel, and to issue it anonymously under his brother's name. He also planned a novel about a bedridden widower whose cruel wife made him chop up mahogany logs all day in the Kent woodlands. 13. What happened on 10 June, 1829, between Hambledon Lock and Henley Bridge? 14. Which goes faster—a briskly trotting man or a boat striving to win the boat race? 15. If you found a fossilised diplodocus would its total length be in the region of (a) 12 ft. (b) 25 ft. (c) 75 ft? 16. The same word is missing from each of these quotations. What word? (a) And the noise of the — at play, and the dear, wild cry of the birds. (John Masefield). (b) Which from our pretty — we pull (Christopher Marlowe). (c) For he hears the — ' innocent call (William Blake).

Hidden Names of Birds compiled by Janet Blackwell (13)

1. The girl vaulted over the fence. 2. Edith rushed into the room. 3. The boys wanted to explore. 4. The lad raked the garden. 5. The hippopotamus wallowed in the mud. 6. Jack dawdled to school.

Answers on page 62.

SCRAFFIATO

by Joseph Natanson

To IMPROVISE, is to compose something quite perfect on the spur of the moment, without any previous preparation. One always hears about the magnificent improvisations of the great pianists of the 19th century, and, above all, of Chopin, the greatest pianist-composer of all times, who would sit at the piano in front of a crowd of admirers and play a beautifully polished composition by Chopin which nobody had ever heard before and, unfortunately for us, would never hear again. But all that has nothing to do with papier mâché.

Everybody knows how to make papier mâché. First you have to make the paste, by mixing flour with a little cold water and adding boiling water until the paste thickens. Second—tear tissue paper or toilet paper into small bits; if you wish to make larger things like trays, big vases or bowls, you can use newspaper, but this you need to soak for an hour or so and then squeeze gently before using it. Third—you must find a mould. One is always told to choose something which is larger at the top than at the bottom and without any indentation so that it is easy to remove your work from the mould. This means that once you have made a bowl and a saucer you are almost at your wit's end.

Now look at the photographs. In one you see all the things that I have used in order to make the dish, tumbler and flower vase which are shown in the other. It will not take you long to discover how everything was made and how I used my moulds, the string, rice, the rubber pipe cut into bits and the sequins. You will have to look at the jar upside-down to find the shape of the tumbler. To provide a solid bottom for the mould, I had to cut a circle of cardboard to cover the mouth of the jar. The dish was a straightforward job, but the vase was a little more complicated. The upper part was made inside the wine glass and the base from the saucer in a doll's tea service. When both parts were dry, I joined them with four wooden buttons, using glue, and then coating the whole thing with several layers of tissue paper to straighten the joints.

I do not grease china or metal moulds, but wood or cardboard ones should be greased if you want to avoid trouble when removing the papier mâché.

The first layer that you put on (or inside) the mould should be very damp so that it sticks well all over the surface. Be careful not to leave any part of the mould uncovered, yet do not make too much overlapping. For the second layer, use paste with dry bits of paper, pressing them gently until wet through. Be careful to keep the thickness even everywhere. Seven to ten layers will make quite a solid form, and then you must leave your work to dry.

A deep mould, like my wine glass, will take a long time to dry. As soon as I saw that the edges were dry as far as one inch down, I removed the whole thing gently and it dried in the air without losing its shape.

When the papier mâché is dry, you can make small corrections if, on holding it up to a bright light, you see that some parts are thinner than others. It is at this stage, too, that you should apply the decorations in relief. With a drop of glue, stick on rice, rubber curves, string or anything else you think suitable, to keep it steady on the spot where you want it. Paste over the decoration and cover in the usual way with two or three layers of tissue paper, being careful to press it well into place all round.

You are still wondering, because I have forgotten to tell you, how I removed the tumbler from the jar in spite of the under-cutting of the rim. Nothing simpler. When it was dry, I took a razor blade and cut it from top to bottom on one side and gently pulled it apart just enough to slip the jar away. I made the cut in a wavy line so that I could join it, with a little glue, precisely as it was before. I added a few layers of paper outside and inside to make an 'invisible mend' that was impossible to detect.

The last part of the job is to give the papier mâché a beautiful finish. Rub it with fine sandpaper to make it as smooth as possible. Then comes the problem of colour and shine. Painting with poster colours and afterwards varnishing, or simply painting in oils, is enough to make it waterproof but the effect is always rather cheap and dull. In the old days they used a lacquer for papier mâché work but that is too complicated and requires too much patience to appeal to you or me. I thought about another technique which potters used in Italy in the 15th century and which has since been neglected. It is called 'scraffiato', which is an Italian word meaning 'scratched', although the idea originally came to Italy from the Near East where scraffiato was invented centuries before—if it was invented there at all and not taken from somebody else who lived still further back in history.

Dilute some black Indian ink with a little water, and paint over the pot or vase, box or dish, or whatever you are making. It must be Indian ink to be waterproof when dry. And it must be quite dry when you apply white poster colour over it. But this time, before the white dries, scratch your decoration through with a sharpened match. This means that you do not paint the whole surface at one go, but do it in stages. When the white is absolutely dry, liberally varnish the whole thing inside and out with copal varnish or any oily and transparent varnish, and dab on at random some transparent artist's oil colours—crimson, viridian or transparent golden ochre, or all three alternately so that they will run beautifully in the varnish. Being careful that each layer of varnish dries thoroughly, varnish the papier mâché again and again, this time without adding colours; then you will be able to keep flowers in water in your vases. Sequins stick well to varnish, and coated once or twice will be quite solidly embedded.

As you see, you do not need any preparation for you should easily find at home all the materials for your work. And if from several different moulds and some odds and ends for decoration you can shape something pretty and even useful, you can call it 'Improvisation in papier mâché.'

Unexpected components are used in making these papier mâché objects. Rice, rubber piping and sequins are among the ingredients. By following the instructions you will find out the secret of an old Italian craft, and how you can make dishes, vases and bowls of taste and merit.

BLACK HUNTING WHIP *(Continued from page 13)*

'I like eggs for tea much better than I do for breakfast.'

After tea there was tack-cleaning in the kitchen for Andrea and Lindsey. They hung their bridles on great hooks in the broad central rafter. Had the hooks hung lamps or hams or neither? Lindsey thought, and tried not to notice that outside in the dark away from all the warmth and light and company, the wind was nearly a gale in the high bare trees.

Peter got out his Hornby engines and laid a track round the sitting room carpet, and Dion sat in the middle of the track and drew plans at the gate-legged table. They were plans of Punch Bowl Farm, as it was now and as it might have been, long ago.

So soon the quiet bliss of after-teatime sinks into the dreary round of bedtimes. Peter first, then Dion, grumbling because he hadn't finished his plans. Lindsey was washing in rain water, caught from the farmhouse roof, and it was soft and silky.

Supper at the scrubbed kitchen table was a last-minute comfort in a howling world, and then they went upstairs, Andrea with her candle blowing wildly in the draughts from under doorways.

There was thunder in the night. A worse thing in the winter, Lindsey thought, than ever it was in the summer. She burrowed down further under her blankets and pushed her fingers into her ears.

In the boys' room, Peter slept through the three sharp claps, but Dion liked thunder, and he was a light sleeper. He was at the window looking over the orchard field before the second crash and watched the lightning zig-zag down the stormy sky. All was black as blindness between the flashes. Not a star or a glimmer of moonlight. And the great wind screamed round the ancient house and roared in the high trees. Dion was staring into darkness,

imagining leaping lions, when the big crash came. And such a crash it was that he jumped and bit his cheek, and Lindsey called out, 'Oh, Mummy! Are we struck?'

Mrs. Thornton padded from her room to her daughters (though Andrea seemed disinterested in the storm) and Dion called, 'There wasn't any lightning that time. Queer.'

'You never see the one that hits you,' Lindsey quavered.

'Well, you can see we aren't hit,' Dion answered, opening his door to explain. The third flash lit the house with a cold blue light and he turned to look out of the window. 'Mother! Dad! The elm tree's down!' he called. 'I saw it right across the orchard. That was the big crash.'

'I told you we'd been struck,' Lindsey was nearly sobbing and her teeth were chattering.

Peter slept on. Dion came to his door again and said, 'We weren't, chump. It must have been blown down. There wasn't any lightning, and I ought to know because I was at the window when it crashed.'

Lindsey sighed very heavily. Dion could see her across the landing, with her bedclothes pulled round her head. Their mother was sitting on her bed, looking rather sleepy and trying not to seem anxious.

'Do you think it's passing over?' Lindsey asked in a hopeful voice.

Andrea turned over with a lot of creaking and said rather impatiently, 'If you had any thought for anyone but yourself you'd be more concerned for the ponies than for your own skin. They're both in the orchard field, out in the whole caboodle, while you're nice and dry in bed.'

* * *

WITH THE FIRST grey film of morning Lindsey was out of bed and running barefooted across the landing and into the boys' room. Peter and Dion slept on, but Lindsey

'*The fork disappeared. It vanished completely.*'

went to the orchard window, rubbed it with her pyjama jacket and stared out into shadowy greyness.

The valley brimmed over with the pale windy dawn like a dish overflowing with milk and water. Stretched across the orchard lay the mighty elm tree, its bare branches spread widely over the grass.

Where were the ponies? Lindsey's anxious eyes were screwed to peer through the dimness to the corners of the orchard field. She could not see the ponies. Both were grey and so was everything else. Her breath steamed on the window so she rubbed it off, but it filmed on again almost at once. She opened the window and leaned out.

Dion, hearing the creak of the hinges, woke up and looked sleepily at her. 'You'll catch it if Mother sees you,' he said and yawned, 'leaning out in the cold with no dressing-gown on.'

For a moment Lindsey said nothing. Then, with a horrified catch in her voice, 'Dion! Look! I—I think it must be Sula. Under the elm tree. Something grey and still.' She turned agonised eyes on her brother. 'Oh, do come quickly and say you think it isn't Sula! I couldn't bear it if it was Sula. I just couldn't.'

'Of course it isn't.' Dion got out of bed and reached for his dressing-gown.

'You haven't seen yet!' Lindsey was anguished.

'I'm coming. Here, put this on. Your teeth are chattering again.'

'It's only b-because I'm so w-worried.'

Dion tied the cord round her waist, looking out over her shoulder as he did so. 'Gosh, there *is* something under the tree,' he said in a high surprised voice.

'Not Sula?' It was an appeal rather than a question.

'Oh, I shouldn't think so, old thing,' but his face

betrayed his uncertainty and Lindsey stared at him, turned, and rushed from the room.

Dion pulled on his clothes and dashed after his sister. He was down at the elm tree a few minutes after her and found her on her knees, bending back the crowding branches with her hands. She looked up at him and he was astonished to see her face absolutely radiant with flooding relief. 'It isn't Sula,' she said.

Dion looked down into the branches and saw the quiet outstretched form of his mother's Moonstone. 'Lindsey! You little beast. Don't go rushing into the house with that joyful face, anyway. You ought to be ashamed. Poor beautiful Moonstone!'

Lindsey's eyes filled with sudden scalding tears.

'Oh, Dion! I wasn't glad it was Moonstone—of course I wasn't. How could I be? It was only that I was so relieved it wasn't Sula, and there didn't seem to be room for any other kind of feeling but the oceans of relief.'

Dion looked at her for a moment, 'Sula's standing by the cart shed. She's perfectly all right, Lin.'

'I know.' It was a small ashamed voice. Lindsey slipped gentle fingers under the wet forelock, stroking it back from the dark frightened eyes, and spoke soothing things under her breath to the helplessly waiting horse. Then hearing quick feet from the house, she stood up and walked slowly the other way.

All that morning Mr. Thornton, Holleybone and the vet worked to uncover and rescue Moonstone. And all that morning Lindsey stayed inside her room.

By early afternoon the almost impossible had been attempted and achieved. A deep straw bed was in the calf-box and Moonstone lay upon it, her pale coat pearly on the golden of the straw and her large eyes dark and full of pain, staring round the box at those who kept watch beside her. Moonstone might easily recover, the vet had said, though probably never again would she be ridden or driven. She had injuries to her shoulder and spine which would leave her unable to work, but she might still live her full span as a brood mare and family pet.

Moonstone was Andrea's favourite. She had loved her because she was elegant and proud and breedy, because of her rosettes in the tack room and because of her milky white coat. She and Lindsey would quarrel fiercely about the two ponies. Lindsey thought Sula was worth ten of Moonstone because she had so much character. But with Andrea the breeding counted most. She planned to breed horses when she was older; thoroughbreds of course.

Moonstone had been pretty good. She had stood only second to one of the best hacks in the country, and often she would be placed first.

Andrea was sore inside. She was sad and angry and wouldn't speak to anyone. She swung off on her own, up through the wet stubble of Yew Tree field, through Lower Naps, Upper Naps, Upper Six Acres, Punch Bowl field and out into Highcomb Bottom and the great heather-lined circle of the Devil's Punch Bowl. What she did there no one knew but she was away until nearly tea-time. And when she came back she said nothing, except 'Where's Dion? I saw deer in the Bowl and thought he'd like to know.'

Where's Dion? Where was he?

'Isn't he digging round the footings?' his mother asked. She was lighting the paraffin lamps.

'Not when I came in.'

'In our room?' suggested Peter, who had been torn between excitement and tears all day, and except for the solace of his four white mice had been without comfort.

Andrea went upstairs and came down again. 'No.'

Mr. Thornton was writing a letter. He looked up and said, 'He was helping us clear branches not long ago. I think he was still there when we had finished.'

'Oh, I'll go and look,' Andrea said, then turned at the door and said shortly, 'Is she all right?'

'Moonstone? Yes, Lindsey's still with her and the vet's just seen her again. He says it's early to notice any change, but he's coming again in the morning.'

Andrea went out but she did not find Dion. Only Lindsey, closing Moonstone's window for the night.

Dion had been there, as his father had said, stoically helping to cut away the branches and when their work was finished and he had done all he could, his father gone to the house and Holleybone to his hedging, Dion prowled round the old footings once more.

He jabbed and thrust his fork along the footings, pulled out clinging ivy tendrils, stung his hands on nettle clumps. Holleybone, fair and short and silent, came by on his preliminary inspection of the orchard hedges. 'Pretty overgrown aren't they, Holleybone?' said Dion conversationally, nodding towards the tall hedges.

'Oh, ah.'

'I expect you'll have your hands full when the first cows come.'

'Ah.' Holleybone looked at his boots.

'Jerseys, I hope,' Dion went on, laboriously trying to keep the ball rolling and almost succeeding.

'Don't 'old wi' 'em. Give I a nice dairy shorthorn, a good roan, ah. Not one er them fancy breeds what needs a 'ot water bottle an' a footstool, look.' He stumped on along the orchard hedge, not noticing Dion's parting shot, 'The Jerseys lead the lot for butterfat and it says in the *Farmers' Weekly* they aren't delicate at all.'

Holleybone's short, square back disappeared into Hanger field and Dion turned back to his probing round the footings. He was working nearer to the elm tree, and when he came to the great earthy cluster of the roots he found he had to burrow and bend and squeeze past their spreading arms in order to follow the footings.

He noticed with a sudden rush of renewed interest that the fall of the tree had thrown up much earth from near the wing and exposed a foot or more of buried wall.

Taking his fork with both hands he made a strong, deep thrust in the newly torn earth of the root-bed, close to the wall, and lost his balance as the incredible thing happened. The fork disappeared. It vanished completely, as if the earth had opened to receive it, which was what had, in fact, happened.

Dion pitched forward. He was certain he had heard a clatter down below him, and if so, the long-sought cellar seemed a more than probable thing. It held his fork, why not himself too? He fell on his knees and tore with his hands like a terrier on the tail of a rabbit.

The small hole grew bigger. Stones and earth began to fall and echo hollowly a moment after. Dion scrabbled with doubled energy and slowly revealed in the long-buried wall the jagged frame of a broken cellar window.

Gripping with his hands on the top of the footing, he kicked at the sharp points of earth-crusted glass and cleared a space big enough to squeeze through. His small torch was in his pocket, happy day! It might so easily have been anywhere else and often was.

Hanging downwards, Dion pushed his head and shoulders through the window and switched on his torch. Two minutes later he emerged, screwed round, and slowly slipped, feet foremost, into darkness.

(Continued on page 63)

BIGGLES IN ARABIA (Continued from page 33)

This we did. In the morning we would return to Aden. But when I awoke at the hour of the first prayer, Abu had gone, taking all the camels with him, as was written plainly in the tracks in the sand. So Kuatim and I cursed him and his mother and prepared for death, knowing there was no escape. No rain falls. The water in the hole dries up. With the vultures we ate the camels of the Arabs already dead until only bones remain. Then Kuatim died, and I lay down to die too. That is all, Sahib. From the sleep of death I awoke to find you here. It was as God willed.' The Arab was recovering his strength, but he now sank back exhausted by his effort.

'As you say, O Zahar, it was as God willed,' answered Biggles. He turned to Ginger. 'Slip back to the machine and get a bar of chocolate and some Horlicks from the emergency rations.'

As Ginger went off Biggles turned again to Zahar. 'And Abu bin Hamud took the gum you had collected?'

'There was but little, and we collected it with much labour,' answered Zahar. 'The Arabs who were here had used most of it. They had used it for their fires and their camels had for long browsed on it. But that which was in my bag, and the bag of Kuatim, this Abu took.'

'And what of the seeds?' asked Biggles.

'We plucked them where we found them, but there were not many, and these Abu took also, doubtless to sell to the *farengi*.'

'Why do you think he left you here?' enquired Biggles.

The Arab hesitated. 'God is the knower. Perhaps so that he could keep all the money from the sale of the *gurra*. Perhaps he would have our camels, for mine was a nice cow. Or it may be that he feared we should finish our water too soon in the desert, and perish. Abu bin Hamud would think of such things, may God forgive him.'

'Why did you put fire to the place?' asked Biggles. 'Why was it not left, so that you could make money by it year by year?'

Zahar pondered the question. 'I know not the answer. Abu said it was to prevent others from finding the secret. It may be the truth. I did as he said without giving the matter thought.'

'He did not say where he would sell the stuff?'

'No. Of this he said nothing.'

'He did not mention a *farengi* by name?'

'No.'

At this point Ginger returned with the condensed food, and for the next half hour they sat round while the Arab ate and drank eagerly, with obvious benefit.

At last Biggles got up. 'Enough has been said here,' he told Zahar. 'We will talk again in Aden.'

'Then let us depart from this place for it is accursed,' said Zahar, as with some difficulty he got to his feet.

Biggles turned to the others. 'All he needs now is food. Give him a hand to get into the machine.'

(Continued on page 92)

TO BE A BALLERINA

by Pamela Brown

ILLUSTRATED BY G. F. BYRNE

THE RAILWAY STATION of St. Petersburg was very cold and grey one evening at the end of the last century, when Tanya Stepanovna Merlinova alighted from the train, clasping her spaniel puppy, Grishka. Tanya was nine years old, and this was the first time she had ever come to the big city. Dressed in a thread-bare frock and a cloak that was too large for her, she clutched a wicker basket that contained her only belongings in the world. Grishka whined and pressed closer to her. Tanya put her lips against his silky head and whispered comfortingly, 'Cheer up, Grishka. Aunt Natalya will soon be here to meet us. And then we shall be all right—'

At this moment a tall woman dressed all in black loomed up out of the mist in front of them.

'Tanya Stepanovna Merlinova?' she demanded briskly.

'Yes, ma'am. You are my Aunt Natalya?'

'I am. And what in heaven's name is this?' She took Grishka by the scruff of the neck, which he hated.

'It is Grishka. Shake hands, Grishka.'

'He'll do nothing of the sort. I can't stand dogs. There was no mention of a dog. I offered to take *you* over, now that you are an orphan—but not a whole menagerie.'

By this time Tanya was being hurried along the platform so quickly that she had almost to trot to keep up, and Grishka was panting along behind, at the end of his lead.

'But, Aunt Natalya, he is such a small dog. He takes up no room. And I will see to feeding him, and he can sleep at the end of my bed.' Aunt Natalya snorted.

'So that's the kind of up-bringing you've had, is it? No dog will ever sleep on a bed in *my* house! Didn't your parents ever tell you of my boarding house, and how well it is thought of in Petersburg? The dog must live in the back yard. Your dear mother and father would have wished it.' And their speed increased along the slippery pavements.

'And how did you find the journey?'

'It was long, but not boring, for we passed through so many places I have learned about at school.'

'School? H'm! No more of that nonsense for you. A girl's place is in the home. You will learn to help me run the house. Your dear mother and father would have wished it. But you can go on with your studies in the evenings. It will keep you out of mischief.'

The house at which they finally stopped was very tall, very black and had a tight-laced appearance, for it was squashed in between two other houses as dreary as itself. Tanya looked at the lace curtains in the window, the notice on the door—'Madame Merlinova, Superior Apartments' and she longed with all her heart to go home. And the realisation that she had no home—that this was to be her home—made hot tears well up in her eyes.

'Wipe your feet,' commanded Aunt Natalya, 'And leave the dog outside. I will chain him up in the back yard before I go to bed. You will rise at six in the morning. This is your room. And don't burn the candle too long. No lying in bed in the morning, mind. Goodnight, child. Sleep well.' And Aunt Natalya was gone. Tanya was glad about that. But when she looked around the little room she was horrified to find that she was surrounded by pictures of Aunt Natalya. The ugly wallpaper was covered with photographs and portraits in massive frames.

Here was Aunt Natalya as a grim-looking baby in a sun-bonnet, in her twenties, wearing a crinoline, and an expression of extreme disapproval, outside her house with a proprietary hand laid imposingly on the gatepost. Tanya giggled to herself rather hysterically, and then by the wavering light of the candle, unstrapped her basket. Tenderly she lifted out her icon and hung it on the wall. The little likeness of the Virgin Mary looked down at her comfortingly. She was kneeling before it when she heard a familiar noise outside the door. She ran to open it. And there was Grishka sitting grinning on the door-mat. She hugged him joyfully. 'You wicked little angel! However did you get in? Oh, you are a bad dog! Are you hungry?' Grishka growled an affirmative, and, foraging in her basket she found some rather crumbly remains of oat-cake and they shared it, sitting on the hard little bed, wrapped in the counterpane to try to keep warm. When it was finished, Tanya said firmly, 'And now you must go outside again. Yes, you must. We are going to be very good and grateful—You see—our dear mother and father would have wished it—'

Stifling a sob, she put the puppy outside the door again, and crept into the narrow bed.

Life with Aunt Natalya was hard. Tanya was up in the cold grey dawns carrying breakfast trays to the rooms of the lodgers, cleaning the brass on the front door which was so cold that it seemed to burn her hands, and washing dishes at the sink that she grew to hate with all her heart. It was only in the evenings that Tanya enjoyed herself. Then she could curl up in a corner by the kitchen stove and continue her studies, while the oil lamp hissed at her side.

But one evening she was interrupted by Aunt Natalya shouting, 'Tanya! Wake up, child! I've been calling for the last five minutes. Always with your head stuck in some book—'

'I—I'm sorry, Aunt Natalya. Can I do anything.

'To-morrow we shall spring-clean the second floor front, the big room. We are to have a new guest—and an important one—he is a master at the Imperial School of Ballet. Mind you are polite to him. It is not every day that we have such a distinguished guest.'

Next day there was such a sweeping and dusting and scrubbing that Tanya's legs ached from running up and down stairs, fetching and carrying. Grishka ran behind her all the time with his little pink tongue hanging out, yelping with delight at all the excitement. At four o'clock Aunt Natalya was dressed in her best black bombazine that smelled of moth balls, all ready to greet the new lodger. At last came the sound of horses' hooves in the snow, and a sleigh drew up outside the house. Tanya and Grishka, watching from an upper window, saw removed dozens of suitcases, a canary in a cage, and a harmonium, and, finally, the great man himself. He seemed broader than he was tall, with a very red face, a little beard, and a fluff of hair over his head like a baby chicken's down.

Aunt Natalya was on the front doorstep to greet him, smiling in a most unusual fashion.

'Welcome to your new home!' she cried, with a somewhat stiff curtsey. 'My name is Natalya Alexandreievna Merlinova.' The new guest swept past her into the house and up the stairs, saying, 'And mine is Sergei Semenovitch Semenov. My canary is called Didi. I wish to rise at

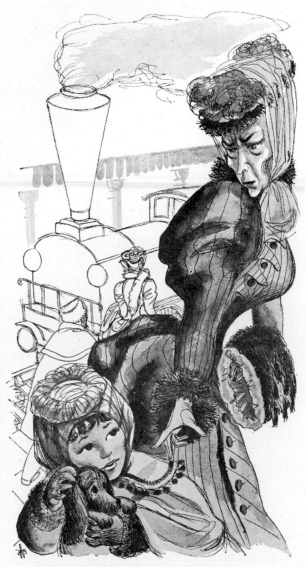

'And what in heaven's name is this?'

she could not help dancing all by herself in the cold corridor. When she heard Aunt Natalya climbing the stairs with supper for her musical lodger, she would fly back to bed and continue to dance in her dreams. It was Grishka who betrayed these solitary dancing sessions. He had developed a knack of managing to get in to say goodnight, however hard Aunt Natalya tried to confine him to the yard. One night as Tanya twirled and pirouetted on the landing, Grishka came bounding up the stairs as cheerful as ever. Tanya told him in a whisper to sit on the stairs and be an audience for her, but he seemed anxious to join in. On the harmonium Sergei Semenov started up a lilting waltz, and Tanya whispered, 'May I have the pleasure of this dance, Monsieur Grishka?'

She picked up the spaniel in her arms and held him with one front paw extended. Round and round they swung. Grishka's tongue lolled out, so that he looked as though he were laughing. But the excitement was too much for him, and he broke out into joyful barks. The harmonium stopped with a crash and Sergei Semenovitch Semenov stood in the doorway in a scarlet dressing-gown. With open mouth he watched the whirling, twirling figure in a white nightgown, clasping a brown and white spaniel puppy.

'And what, may I ask, is all this?' he demanded.

'—I'm sorry, sir. I was—we were—just dancing—it was the music, sir. We couldn't help it.'

'You like my music, eh?'

'Oh yes, sir.'

'And you like to dance?'

'I can't help it, sir, when I hear music like that.'

'Who are you, anyhow? What are you doing here?'

'My name is Tanya Stepanovna Merlinova. I live here with my Aunt Natalya. I bring you your breakfast every morning. Don't you remember?'

'Why, yes, yes! Of course! I always thought you were the servant. Well, you'll catch cold if you stand there.'

At this moment Aunt Natalya appeared at the top of the stairs looking like a thunder-cloud.

'Tanya!' she cried, 'what on earth do you think you're doing here at this hour? And with that hound.' She tried to chase Grishka down the stairs.

'I'm sorry, Aunt. I just—' Tanya began, but Sergei Semenov broke in firmly, 'I have been conversing with your niece. She came to stop the dog from barking outside my door. She is now returning to her room, and the dog will sleep by the stove in my room. Tomorrow morning we shall continue our conversation. Goodnight, Tanya. Goodnight, Madame Merlinova. Come, Grishka.' And he swept into his room. Aunt Natalya glared at the door as it closed, and ordered her back to her room.

Next morning she combed her hair more carefully than usual before she took his breakfast to him. He was up and seated at his desk as she knocked and entered.

'Good morning, sir. Here is your breakfast.'

'Ah, come in. Put down your tray and let me look at you. So you are the little one who loves to dance?'

'Oh, there's Grishka,' cried Tanya, 'it was so kind of you to let him sleep by your stove. He does hate that horrid cold yard. I do hope he was good.'

'I fancy he snored slightly, but probably I did too. But now to business. Who has taught you to dance?'

'*Taught* me? But—no one, sir—'

'You're sure?'

'Yes, sir.'

'H'm! So you just try to copy the dancing you have seen at the ballet, eh?'

'I have never been to the ballet, sir. My aunt does not approve of the theatre.'

Sergei Semenov spluttered with indignation.

six every morning and breakfast at seven. I shall be out all day, but you may leave me a cold meal in the evening, as I shall return late from the Marinsky Theatre. Driver, please take in my bags. Don't jolt Didi, or she will throw a fit. Which is my room? Thank you. I think that is all, Natalya Merlinova. Good day.'

From that day on, the roost was ruled by Sergei Semenovitch Semenov. At six o'clock every morning, Aunt Natalya would knock on his door and he would reply with grunts and growls as he awoke. Then he called for jugfuls of cold water, which he poured over himself, spluttering and gasping in his little tin bath. At seven o'clock Tanya would take in his breakfast and he would pat her head absent-mindedly and call her a good child. By half-past eight he was out of the house, and something seemed to have gone with him. Tanya was usually in bed by the time he returned in the evening.

It was only on Sundays that he varied his time table. On Sunday evenings he would stay in and play to himself on the battered harmonium. The sound of it poured through the house, sometimes soft and flowing, sometimes loud and jubilant, and Tanya would lie listening in the darkness of her attic. Sometimes it was too tempting, and she would patter down the stairs and crouch by the keyhole. And when the music became so full of invitation,

'Does not approve of the—well, really—I knew she was remarkably ugly—therefore I thought that she must have a lovely soul. And so you, Tanya Stepanovna, have never set foot in the Marinsky Theatre and yet you dance as you do. Incredible! Incredible! Dance for me now.'

'But I have the other lodgers' breakfasts to serve—'

'Let the other lodgers wait. When Sergei Semenovitch says "Dance—" he means "Dance—" Listen, child. This is the pas seul of the gazelle from Gorinsky's ballet, "The Huntsman". The little gazelle alone in the wood—you understand? Now—dance—'

It was the most beautiful music Tanya had ever heard. It made her think that she really *was* in a forest glade, dancing for sheer joy of living. Somehow it was better than ever before, for now she had an audience—a more critical one than Grishka. Suddenly the music stopped. Sergei wiped his brow with a red spotted handkerchief.

'Your dancing is—my child, you are—' he faltered, and then pulled himself together. 'You remind me somewhat of a giraffe. You are all legs and neck, and much too thin. You have no idea what to do with your arms, and your balance leaves much to be desired.'

'I'm sorry, sir,' said Tanya humbly.

'But—all that can be changed. And it shall be. Let me see your feet. Take off your shoes and stockings.'

'Please, sir, I—'

'Come along—come along—'

'I've got a hole in my stocking, I'm afraid.'

'Doesn't matter. Doesn't matter. Hm! Good feet—' He pondered, then said slowly, 'How would you like to become a pupil at the Imperial School of Ballet?'

'Oh—but how could I? There's Aunt Natalya—'

'Let's leave Aunt Natalya out of it, my child, there is a world beyond Aunt Natalya and her Superior Apartments. In that world you could learn to dance to delight the hearts of all who saw you. But only if you are willing to work harder than ever before. It will be harder than working in this particularly depressing house. You will practise and learn until you collapse, and even when you are a prima ballerina you must continue to practise and to learn and to practise again. Well, what have you to say, Tanya?'

'I will—I will try to please you, sir.'

At this moment Aunt Natalya was heard calling.

'Oh, here comes that woman to make a nuisance of herself,' cried Sergei angrily.

'Tanya Stepanovna,' said Aunt Natalya, as she entered, 'What are you thinking of? The other lodgers are calling for their breakfasts. And where are your shoes and stockings? Your behaviour is extraordinary.' She turned to Sergei and said silkily, 'I do hope she has not been annoying you, sir?' Sergei stepped in front of her.

'Madame, it is you who annoy me. You treat this child as though she were a kitchen maid, instead of your own niece. From now on I intend to take her into my care. She will attend the Imperial School of Ballet.'

'The Imperial School of Ballet? How dare you sir! How dare you—. The child is in my care.'

'I wish to adopt her.'

'The child is perfectly happy with me. She does not complain.' Sergei altered his method of attack.

'Then, Madame Merlinova, think of it from this point of view. When Tanya is a great dancer, for so she will be some day, think how the glory of it will reflect on you. "That is the aunt of the great Merlinova" they will say. Business will prosper—you will be a rich woman. And her training will have cost you nothing. All I ask is that she shall be left entirely in my care.'

'I shall be expected to provide nothing?' enquired Aunt Natalya suspiciously.

'Nothing. I shall take her before the governors of the school in a few days' time, and she will enter the school next month, if she can pass the examinations. All expenses incurred, I shall deal with.' Aunt Natalya sniffed.

'Well, I think you're taking a big risk. How do you know the child can dance? She's never had a lesson in her life. What's more, she's lazy and stupid. But there—it's in her blood—her mother and father were exactly the same—a hopeless lot.' Tanya's thin face flushed with anger.

'Madame, you may leave us,' said Sergei icily.

'Oh, very well. Take the child if you like. I can't say I shall be broken-hearted. In fact, the sooner she goes, the happier I shall be.'

And out she flounced, banging the door behind her. Tanya felt happiness swelling up inside her, so that it seemed as though she must burst with it.

The time until the examination day for the Imperial School of Ballet seemed to pass very slowly. The only excitement was when Sergei took her out to buy a new dress for the occasion. She was anxious for it to be of red velvet—the material looked so rich and warm—but Sergei insisted on white silk.

'It will make you look fairy-like,' he said, 'and that will appeal to them.'

On the morning of the great day they set off for Theatre Street. As soon as she saw the imposing façade of the building, and the Imperial eagles on the livery of the beadles in the doorway, she was stricken with fright.

'Do not tremble so, little one,' Sergei urged her, 'no one is going to eat you.'

There were many other little girls of about her own age waiting in a big room on the first floor, attended by six ladies in blue cashmere dresses, who, Sergei told her, were the governesses. The directress, a dignified black-clad lady, came over and exchanged a few words with Sergei, in an undertone, and Tanya knew by the way they were looking at her, that she was the subject of the conversation. Then all the girls were arranged in a crocodile, two by two, and led into the next room. Tanya shivered apprehensively in her thin dress as she waited for her name to be read out. At last it came.

'Tanya Stepanovna Merlinova—'

She stepped into the centre of the room and stood facing them, with her head held high.

'Walk, please, to the other end of the room.' It seemed to stretch endlessly before her, a sea of bare floor, fringed with misty faces. 'Run, please.' Tanya felt silly running in an aimless circle, but then she saw that Sergei had entered the room and was standing in the doorway, so she ran towards him, smiling.

'Sit down, please.' She did so, and after a while the teachers came and examined her legs and feet, as Sergei had done the night he had discovered her dancing.

'Thin—' she heard one of the instructors say, in a bored voice, and her heart sank. But when some of the children were told that they were unsuitable, and sent away, she was taken, with several others to the infirmary for a medical examination.

'Thin—' repeated the doctor, pinching her arms and legs, and shaking his head. But still she was included in those told to remain until after lunch. This was served to them in yet another room and consisted of tea and sandwiches. Sergei looked in and winked at her and went out again, and Tanya began to feel so tired that she wondered whether all this were worth it—just to be a ballerina. But her lunch soon revived her, and she quite enjoyed the musical test that followed. The intelligence test at the end was difficult, but Tanya's evening studies stood her in good stead, and she answered correctly.

At last they were lined up to hear the final choice, and, with a sigh of relief, she heard her name read out as one of the five chosen from the twenty contestants. She looked for Sergei Semenov and smiled a tired but happy smile. On the way home through the dusk she said to him, 'Oh, Sergei Semenovitch, what if I hadn't passed! How awful it would have been! But I'm sure you put in a good word for me, didn't you? Didn't you, now?'

'No, Tanya. It was a perfectly fair choice. I did not tell anyone that I had a particular interest in you.'

'Then what were you saying to that lady in black?'

'Oh—er—I merely said that you were the only one out of the twenty whose face was not like a currant bun.'

'There—I knew you had helped me,' laughed Tanya, 'Oh, I'm so excited! What fun it will be to go school again, and to learn to dance—and to be taught by you!'

'You won't be so thrilled when you see me in front of a class. My nickname, so I believe, is The Dragon.'

'I shall never call you that. You will always be my best friend.'

'But I shall show you no leniency, oh, no—you will have to be better than all the rest, as you are the little Ugly Duckling that I intend to turn into a swan.' Tanya skipped happily along beside him, until they came in sight of Aunt Natalya's house, then she sighed heavily.

'Here we are—back again—Aunt Natalya won't be a bit pleased that I've passed the entrance test.'

'Never mind, child,' Sergei comforted her, 'I am looking for some new lodgings, and soon you will be living at school with as many friends as you could wish for.'

'But what about Grishka, what will become of him?'

'He will live with me while you are at school.'

'But I shall miss you both,' she told him, 'if I only see you at class time.' Sergei held the front door open and whispered conspiratorially as they entered, 'Perhaps if you are good, you may visit me during your vacations.'

On the day that Tanya departed to become a boarder at the Imperial School of Ballet, Aunt Natalya kissed her stiffly on both cheeks, scowled at Sergei Semenov, and called Tanya an ungrateful chit. Then she banged the door in their faces, and that was the last that Tanya ever saw of Aunt Natalya. She felt this in her bones, and it made her happier than ever, as they made their way through the streets that were filled with autumn sunlight. As they walked down Theatre Street, Tanya looked up at the tall buildings that seemed less imposing and much more friendly than at her first sight of them on the examination day. It gave her a lovely sense of importance to be making for the entrance of the ballet school, and she felt that everyone must be staring at her and saying, 'There goes Tanya Stepanovna Merlinova—she's a student at the Imperial School of Ballet—'

In the foyer Sergei gravely shook hands with her, saying, 'From now on I shall be your teacher, as well as your friend.' And then she was alone in the doorway of a large room filled with other little girls of all ages, with her heart beating loud with excitement.

*   *   *

For the first few days of the term Tanya lived in a continuous daze of bewilderment. The maze of rooms and corridors baffled her, and she was never in the right place at the right time. Although the dancing lessons were elementary, they were too difficult for her, as she had never had any proper teaching in technique, while many of the other beginners had studied it previously. But soon she began to fall into the ways of the school, and to feel safe and happy in its strict but dignified routine.

Every morning they rose early, to wash in cold water, and then their hair was braided tightly back behind their ears by a maid. Tanya had to dress herself in the plain brown cashmere dress of the beginners, and make her bed, before the bell was rung for breakfast. Two-by-two they trouped into the dining-room to curtsey to the governess who inspected them to see that they were clean and tidy. Then came chapel, with the girls seated on one side, and boys on another. After this was breakfast, which everyone gobbled hungrily. Dancing lessons took up all the morning, and Tanya exercised at the barre until her limbs were stiff and aching and perspiration poured down her face.

After lunch they were taken out for a walk, but still within the bounds of the school grounds. In the uniform provided—a black silk bonnet and velvet-topped boots, Tanya hurried to keep up with the others, and remembered how bad she had been in the morning dancing class, and hoped that the afternoon classes in arithmetic, fencing, languages and music—would go better with her.

At four o'clock came dinner, and after that there was a little spare time in which they might read or sew, then dancing practice, when the seniors coached the juniors. At bedtime in the long dormitory each senior would come to see that her favourite junior was safely tucked into bed, lights were put out, and they all sank into the peaceful slumber that follows hard and absorbing work.

There was little to upset the pattern of the days. Some of the students were chosen to dance in the ballets performed at the Marinsky Theatre, but Tanya was not good enough yet to be included in these. She watched with envy the other excited little girls who were hurried off to rehearsals, thereby missing the afternoon lessons.

The other new girls who had arrived at the same time as Tanya had settled down quickly, all except one of them, called Sylvya Andreievna Sulaskaya. She was a wisp of a child, the duffer of every class, who fell over her own feet with nervousness when she tried to dance. One day, Tanya, who had had to return to the dormitory to fetch a handkerchief, found Sylvya on her bed crying.

'Why, Sylvya,' she said, 'Whatever is the matter? Don't cry like that. Stop—do stop—'

'I've lost my handkerchief,' sobbed Sylvya.

'Here's mine. There you are now. I should blow your nose, if I were you. Now, tell me all about it.'

'They've been teasing me again,' she sniffed.

'Oh, Sylvya, you mustn't be a baby! They don't mean to be unkind.'

'They do! They do! They say I speak all wrong and I haven't got any manners and I can't dance and I'm no good at anything—'

'But you are, Sylvya! Don't you remember in the Pantomime lesson when we had to imitate a monkey? You were the best and we all laughed like anything. I still laugh when I think of it.'

Sylvya seemed to cheer up slightly, but said, 'But you can't go through life imitating monkeys—'

'No, but that shows you can act. So when we get through all this awful bar practice and exercises, and we're doing bits out of real ballets, you'll be better than anyone else, because you can act. It's only the first steps you're finding difficult. And what about me? I'm always in the wrong place. I think we're a fine pair, if you ask me.'

'Tanya,' said Sylvya breathlessly, 'Will you be my friend and tell me all your secrets?'

'But—I haven't any secrets—'

'That doesn't matter. It's what all the girls say when they're vowing eternal friendship. I've heard them.'

'All right then. I'll say it too. Sylvya, will you be my friend and tell me all your secrets?'

'Oh, yes, Tanya! But—I *have* got a secret, only you must swear not to tell anyone—ever.'

'I swear. What is it?'

'My father—is only a cab driver.'

'But that's nothing to be ashamed of. I should think it's very interesting—driving people around all the time—'

'But if the other girls knew, they would tease me more than ever. Already they guess that my family is nothing like most of theirs.'

'Then what about me? I haven't even *got* a father—or a mother.'

'Then who looks after you?'

'Well, I suppose that is my secret. I oughtn't really to tell you, but seeing that I've promised—my guardian is Sergei Semenovitch Semenov.'

'The Dragon?' exclaimed Sylvya, astounded.

'Yes. But he's not a dragon really. He took me away from my aunt, and he made me go in for the entrance test and he bought my clothes and he's paying for anything I need. And now I'm afraid I'm disappointing him.'

'He must think you have promise—'

'He did at first—but by the things he says in class I'm afraid he's changed his mind. Especially after the day I fell down just as Petrovskaya had come into look at us.'

'Petrovskaya?'

'Yes, the ballerina—you know—that dark woman with green eyes who came in last week and talked to the dear Dragon for ages.'

'Oh, that woman. I didn't realise she was Petrovskaya. I thought she looked horrid. Like a slippery sort of snake. And she laughed at my arabesque.'

'I don't like the look of her. But she's a wonderful dancer. Before the term started I went every night to the Marinsky Theatre with Sergei, and saw her in lots of ballets, and she's terribly clever. But they say she's ever so old.'

'Didn't she have a lot of paint on her face when she came? My mother would have called her a hussy.'

'But she's a wonderful dancer,' sighed Tanya. 'I'd give anything to be as good as she is. I know what, Sylvya, let's try and stop being the duffers of the class, shall we? Let's practise together in all our spare time. We could help each other such a lot, you know, and then perhaps we'll be as good as the others—perhaps better—'

'Oh, yes, Tanya, let's! If I felt I had someone to work with, who would explain things to me, I wouldn't mind being teased any more.'

'We'll work and work—and work—' vowed Tanya, 'But now we must simply fly down to breakfast.'

From then on Sylvya and Tanya worked like slaves, always together. At first their efforts seemed useless. But gradually their eternal practice and perseverance began to take effect. Their limbs began to obey them better, they remembered the sequence of steps, their balance improved. Work became an obsession, and they had no thought for anything but their dancing. Silently and steadily Sylvya and Tanya worked their way up to a passable standard.

The week's lesson with Sergei was the testing spot. Girls were pale and trembling with nerves before them. Tanya was never frightened, for she knew that behind the domineering manner he put on during teaching hours was the golden heart that had come to her rescue. He would stand in front of the class beating time with a wooden baton, red in the face with exasperation.

'And now, ladies,' he would say, 'We will have grandes battements if it is not troubling you too much. I know you are all very weak old ladies, but I want a little exertion from you—one, two, three—one, two, three—straighten those backs—you wilt like lilies—I should advise a backboard for all of you. Sylvya Andreievna Sulaskaya, look at your toe. Point it. Point it, I say—you look like an Englishman playing football. Come along—higher, higher

'*With open mouth he watched the whirling, twisting figure.*'

everyone—have you the rheumatics, Tanya Stepanovna? Higher—*one,* two, three—yes, I know it is a cold day, but you will get warm by dancing. The lady in the back row is evidently taking a rest—come along—lift that leg—one, two, three. One, two, three.'

Or again—'Assemblez, glisser, pas de chat, assemblez, glisser, pas de chat,' he would chant, 'More elevation, please. Yes, I know that it is a hot day, but dancing will make you cool. Sylvya Andreievna, your pas de chat is more like the prance of an elephant. Lift those knees— Oh, that I should have to teach such imbeciles! Tanya Stepanovna, you are a beat behind. Listen to the music, can't you? You're *still* a beat behind—'

And Tanya would pant for breath and wonder if she would ever learn to dance well enough to satisfy him.

When she entered her second year, and was able to wear a blue cashmere dress, to show her rank, she realised she was leaving Sylvya behind. For the rest of her time, Slyvya remained in a state of happy mediocrity, while Tanya, dragged herself up into a position of respect. It happened so gradually that other people did not notice, except for Sergei, who marked it with a glow of satisfaction.

The proudest day of Tanya's life was the first time she was included to appear in the ballet at the Marinsky Theatre. Dressed in a gipsy costume, she had only to run across the stage, banging a tambourine, but she was as nervous as though she were playing the principal rôle.

for CAT

This is Catinka.　Soft as silk
　　　her fur,
smooth as milk
　　　her purr,
velvet night
　　　her paws,
steely bright
　　　her claws.

This is Catinka.　Of the wild
　　　fierce leap,
and the mild
　　　round sleep,
the absurd
　　　pink yawn,
and the bird
　　　at dawn.

Unpredictable, independent, too proud
　　　to eat sprats,
　　This is Catinka, Queen of Cats.

　　　　　　　　　　V.G.

The days, weeks and months sped by.　Soon she was in her turn a senior, and was given the honour of wearing a white dress, which pleased her, remembering Sergei's remark that white would make her look fairy-like.　And now each girl's thoughts were fixed upon when she would be allowed to make her début at the Marinsky, and in what rôle.　Tanya began to have extra private lessons with Sergei, which proved that the directors of the school were recognising merit in her work.　And then one day when she went for her lesson, Sergei said gravely:

'My child, the date for your début has been fixed.　And I have decided that you will dance the gazelle in "The Huntsman."　It suits your personality.'

'"The Huntsman—"　Oh—do you think I can do it?'

'Yes, I do.　You have plenty of time in which to work. It is not until a week after term has ended—your last term, remember.　It will be just before Xmas.'

'My last term—' Tanya repeated it softly.　It seemed impossible.　She could hardly remember any other life than the years at the school.　She could not imagine another life.　But the prospect of becoming a fully-fledged member of the ballet was alluring, though terrifying.　From then on she began to work with Sergei every evening, until she was limp and exhausted, and would retire to bed almost in tears of fatigue.　One evening when she went for her lesson, she found someone else in the room, talking to Sergei.　She looked at the dark coils of hair, the slanting green eyes, and recognised her.　It was Petrovskaya, now a 'ballerina assoluta,' of the Imperial Ballet, the highest position that a dancer could reach.　Tanya smiled and curtsied, happy to think that a great dancer should be present at her lesson.　If she had heard the previous conversation she would not have been so content.

'Who *is* this Tanya Stepanovna Merlinova that I have been hearing so much about?' Petrovskaya had demanded.

'But don't you remember her, Petrovskaya?　She's the little girl who understudied for a while last season—'

'That lanky child, all hair and eyes and legs?'

'She is not so lanky nowadays.　She is turning into a dancer of surprising quality.　And her elevation is amazing.'

'Oh, she is one of your protegées.　But she'll never be capable of playing a long rôle—'

'My friend,' said Sergei dryly, 'She is making her début before Christmas.'

'In what, may I ask?'

'She will dance the gazelle in "The Huntsman".'

Petrovskaya burst into peals of malicious laughter.

'Sergei Semenovitch!　Have you lost your senses?　Those fouettés in the pas seul—no child of her age dare attempt them!　Why, even *I* have never quite mastered them as I could wish.　Of course, the critics rave about mine, but then, what is that?　They will tear that child to pieces if she attempts anything so intricate.'

'My dear lady,' said Sergei quietly, 'The little Merlinova executes the pas seul without a fault.　It is amazing.'

'You mean—she is better than I?'

'She has not your experience and maturity,' said Sergei carefully, 'but as the gazelle she is unsurpassable.　You, my friend, are a beautiful woman cleverly impersonating a gazelle, but Tanya Stepanovna—she *is* a gazelle'

After a pause, Petrovskaya had said, 'I should like to see this prodigy dancing, Sergei.'

'I am expecting her at any moment for a lesson.　You may stay and watch if you wish.　She will be honoured.'

And Tanya, unable to see into the older dancer's heart, looked at her with admiring eyes, and said, 'I trust you are well, Madame Petrovskaya.'

'What an odd-looking child,' drawled the ballerina. 'She looks half starved.　Don't they give you enough to eat?　Your face is all eyes—'

Sergei said, 'Madame Petrovskaya wishes to see you dance.　Show her the beginning of the pas seul.'　He played the opening bars of the Huntsman music, and Tanya began to dance the steps that had become so familiar to her.　Gravely and unselfconsciously she danced, striving to do her very best, as a tribute to the importance of the visitor.　As she watched Petrovskaya's eyes narrowed. Suddenly she rose, crossed to Sergei and hissed in his ear, 'You are right, Sergei Semenovitch. And I shall never dance the gazelle again. Good day.' And she flounced out of the room. Tanya halted, amazed.

'Sergei—what's the matter with her? Wasn't I good enough? I tried.'

'You were *too* good, my child,' said Sergei quietly.

'I don't understand—oh, Sergei, I'm so tired! Must I dance any more today? I've had so much to do lately—I don't seem able to concentrate—'

'I will not *make* you dance if you are tired,' said Sergei casually. 'Rest by all means, if you *can* rest, knowing that your footwork in the pas de deux is a disgrace, that in the death scene you show no more emotion than that chair you are sitting on, that your arms look like—'

'Oh, stop, stop—' Tanya broke in laughing, 'yes, I'm being silly. But Petrovskaya put me off. Of course I must practise.' And back she went to the beginning.

The end of the term crept nearer. The exams in other subjects she passed quite well, without paying much attention to them, for her mind was occupied with the little gazelle who was accidently shot by the huntsman, in the dark forest glade.

Sergei was busy looking for an apartment for her, near his own and near to the theatre, and on her half-days off he took her shopping to set her up with a wardrobe suitable for a dancer of the Imperial Ballet. After the long years of wearing the plain neat uniform, the arrays of silks and satins in the shops bewildered her with delight.

Then came the last day. Everything that she did, she was conscious of doing 'for the last time.' The last time to put on her uniform, to dress her hair in school-girl fashion, to pray in the school chapel, to talk to her friends at breakfast. At the afternoon prize-giving, she received a beautifully bound copy of the Russian poets. Then she made a last tour of the school, saying goodbye to her bed, the dancing rooms, the bath-house, and all her friends and companions of the last eight years.

At last, a little tearful and timorous, she stood in the doorway, looking out into Theatre Street and the world. Then Sergei was at her side, carrying in his arms a familiar bundle. It was Grishka, more sedate and a trifle plump, but barking a welcome to his mistress.

The day before her début, Tanya received a visit from her old friend Sylvya. She opened the door of her apartment and found her standing there wrapped up in furs so that only her nose appeared. 'Why, Sylvya,' she cried, 'how lovely to see you. Come in, and take off your cloak. I've missed you so much since school broke up.'

'Oh, Tanya,' cried Sylvya, 'what a lovely apartment! Red plush curtains—oh, you are lucky!'

'Sergei said that I must find an apartment near Theatre Street so that I should be near the school and the theatre, but I found this little place near the park and I fell in love with it, so I had to take it. And I have the dearest old housekeeper to look after me, and she adores Grishka—'

'Grishka? Oh, yes, your little dog—where is he?'

'Asleep in his basket over there.'

'Oh, the little pet! Tanya, I think you're the luckiest girl I know. After to-morrow night you'll be a real live ballerina! I'm coming, and I'll clap until my hands ache.'

'Only if I'm good, please,' said Tanya seriously. 'If I'm bad, I give you full permission to throw things.'

At this moment there was a knock at the door.

'Oh, there's Sergei,' said Tanya. 'Come in Sergei. How cold you look! You've got snow on your beard like St. Nicholas. Come to the stove and warm yourself. And then we'll have tea.'

'How are you today, little one?' said Sergei, taking off his thick coat. 'Ah, and here is my star pupil, Sylvya Andreievna—'

Sylvya laughed, 'Star pupil, indeed! How cruel you are. But you will be pleased to learn, sir, that I have decided to give up dancing.'

'Well, well,' cried Sergei, 'congratulations. What are your plans?'

for DOG

This is a miniature poodle,
Composed, for the most part, of fluff.
He's trying, not very successfully
To look rather grown-up and gruff.

He thought, when he sat for his portrait
(With hair nicely dampened and curled)
He ought to disguise he was really
The jolliest pup in the world.

By nature he's happy as Larry
And bounces about like a ball,
And gallops and jiggles and wuffles,
And comes (now and then) when you call.

So, though he looks fearfully solemn,
He's wondering when, as he sits,
He can suitably find an occasion
To chew someone's slippers to bits.

V.G.

'I have been offered a part in a new play at the Alexandrinsky,' said Sylvya proudly.

'Well done, Sylvya Andreievna.'

'Sylvya! You didn't tell me—what a dark horse you are,' said Tanya.

'Ah,' sighed Sergei contentedly, 'all my little ugly ducklings are turning into swans.'

'Cygnets, perhaps,' said Tanya.

'I cannot stay long,' Sergei told her. 'There are so many things to be done. I wanted to tell you that I have arranged for you to be called for tomorrow night an hour and a half before the curtain rises.'

'It doesn't give me much time,' said Tanya anxiously.

'Quite enough,' said Sergei firmly, 'we don't want you hanging around getting nervous. You still have time for a quarter of an hour's exercise before you go on.'

'Yes, dear,' said Sylvya, 'your entrance isn't until half-way through the first act, is it?'

'Oh, dear, how near it is coming,' sighed Tanya, 'I daren't think about it—Oh, let's have a glass of tea and talk of something else.'

* * *

When Tanya awoke next morning, she wished that she could go back to sleep again and not wake up again until the début was over. But her housekeeper brought her breakfast, and helped her to dress her hair, and then she wandered around the apartment, toyed with her lunch, and lay down in the afternoon. She wished that Sergei would drop in to take tea with her as usual, but she knew that he would be busy at the theatre. As she wrapped herself in furs ready to set off to the theatre, her teeth were chattering with nerves. Then came a knock at the door and the housekeeper announced that the droshky had arrived. Outside the sleigh waited in the snow, the horses' breath steaming white in the cold air.

'Madame Merlinova of the Imperial Ballet?' demanded the driver, a small, skinny man with icicles on his beard.

'Yes,' replied Tanya with a thrill of pride, 'I am quite ready. It's a cold night, isn't it?'.

'It is, indeed, miss, and looks like more snow.' Tanya got in and wrapped the rugs round her, snuggling down amongst them for warmth. The driver whipped up his horses, and they sped through the snowy streets with a soft swishing noise. Tanya hummed a tune from the ballet to herself, visualising the steps. Then she looked around her. It seemed an unusual route to take to the theatre.

'Driver,' she cried, 'why are you going this way?'

'Short cut, miss. Snow ain't so thick.'

'Oh, I see. But it seems rather a long way round.' The driver whistled nonchalantly, and kept whipping up the horses. After a while Tanya said again, 'Excuse me, you've taken the wrong turning. We're going away from the Marinsky Theatre.' He made no reply.

'Driver! I want the Marinsky Theatre. Listen,' she shouted angrily, 'Listen to me. Turn back at once. Do you hear? Driver, listen to me. It's getting late. I've got to get there. Turn round at once or—I'll—I'll jump out. Oh, driver, please stop—' she implored, and then, 'well, at least tell me—are you kidnapping me?'

'I'm obeying orders,' said the driver implacably.

'Orders? Whose orders?' demanded Tanya, but he was silent.

The sleigh sped on through the black and white country-side. It began to snow again in thick flaky feathers. The horses' hooves were muffled by the snow. It fell on Tanya's hood and face as she sobbed helplessly among the fur rugs. Useless plans raced through her head. To throw herself out—to shout for help—but still, she would be miles outside St. Petersburg and she wouldn't be able to reach the theatre in time for her entrance—

'They'll all be waiting for me—my little brown and green costume laid out in my dressing-room. Sergei will be furious—no one has *ever* disappeared on the night of her début—my first chance—gone—' She spoke aloud through her sobs.

'Did—did you say your first appearance—missy?' asked the driver in an embarrassed tone.

'Yes—my début—'

'I'm real sorry for you.'

'Then take me back,' she cried passionately, 'oh, driver, please turn back! I don't know why you're doing this, but if you want money, I haven't got any, and I haven't any jewellery either. Why, *why* are you doing this?'

'Orders from a lady.'

'A lady—a dark lady? A lady in the ballet?'

'I'm giving no hints.'

'It was Petrovskaya! I *know* it was Petrovskaya!'

'But believe me, miss, I didn't know it was your début. I thought it was on account of some silly theatrical quarrel and it wouldn't matter—and she gave me a lot of money just when I need it bad—and promised me more if you missed the performance. But if I'd known what a *young* lady you was, and that this was important to you—'

'To agree to a mean trick like this—for money—oh, it's horrible,' said Tanya in disgust.

'Now, listen, miss,' retorted the driver hotly, 'the money wasn't for me. Oh, no! It was for my daughter. An actress she's going to be. I've never been able to buy her fine clothes and all the things she wanted, but I thought to myself when Madame Petrovskaya—there, I've said it now—when she offered me the money I thought, 'Now I can buy my Sylvya some new clothes when she goes to act at the Alexandrinsky.'

'Your Sylvya?' said Tanya, amazed, 'is your daughter Sylvya Andreievna Sulaskaya?'

'That's right—'

'Do you know what my name is?'

'Merlinova, I was told to ask for.'

'My name is Tanya Stepanovna Merlinova.'

'Tanya Stepanovna—not—not—my Sylvya's Tanya—her little friend—who helped her with her dancing?'

'Yes.'

'And told her she could act?'

'Yes.'

'Well—the saints forgive me for the deed I might have done! But what shall I do now? I've taken the money from Madame Petrovskaya—it's here—in my pocket—'

'Would Sylvya wear clothes bought by ruining me?' asked Tanya slowly. He groaned.

'Oh, heaven forgive me. I'm sorry, miss, but you don't know what it's like to be poor—'

'Don't I? I've never had a penny of my own all my life. Why, driver! You're turning the horses—where are we going?'

'Back to Petersburg. Giddap there—' He cracked his whip. 'I'll get you back to the theatre in time if I have to pull the sleigh myself. My little Sylvya would kill me if she knew what I'd nearly done. Oh, miss, you won't tell a soul if I get you back in time, will you?' he pleaded, 'My little Sylvya would—'

'No, I won't breathe a word—if only you will get me

'Sergei seized her by the arm shouting furiously, " Where have you been?"'

back in time. The curtain will be going up soon, and I only have twenty minutes before I go on—oh, hurry.'

As the sleigh glided forward, leaving a flurry of snow in its wake, Tanya and Sylvya's father looked anxiously at the clocks on the church towers as they passed. The hands seemed to move visibly, and Tanya's heart thumped with the horses' hooves. At last they were crossing the square in front of the theatre. The curtain had evidently gone up, for the entrance was deserted. The sleigh came to a stand-still outside the stage door.

'Goodbye. You have been kind to me,' said Tanya, jumping out, 'I won't forget you, I promise. But send the money back to Petrovskaya and tell her just what happened. She cannot hurt you.'

'Goodbye, miss. And—and you won't mention it to my Sylvya—will you?'

'Of course not! Goodnight!'

'Goodnight, miss,' he shouted, 'and good luck—'

Tanya ran through the stage door and found that pandemonium reigned. Sergei, in an uncontrollable state, seized her by the arm shouting furiously, 'Where have you been? Do you know the time?' Tanya shook free and ran down the corridor to her dressing room.

'I can't explain now. Leave me to dress. I'll be in time.' Hastily she put on her tights, and the abbreviated little green and brown tunic, dabbed some rouge on her face, for that was all there was time for, and tied on her ballet shoes with care. There was not time even to be

nervous. As she ran out of the door, Sergei, who had been pacing the corridor, seized her by the hand and hurried her towards the stage, saying, 'The whole place has been in an uproar. What have you been up to? We sent for Petrovaskaya, as she was the only other person we could think of who could dance the gazelle—and she kindly said she would dance. And now I've had to go and tell her that she will not be needed after all—' Tanya roared with laughter.

'I'd love to have seen her face—'

'Why do you laugh? It was nearly a tragedy. I can't think where you've been—and there's no time for exercises—oh, dear, oh dear—'

'Sergei Semenovitch, stop fussing,' said Tanya calmly, 'I'm ashamed of you. I am here, and I'm going to dance the gazelle. Everything is all right. I am very happy.'

Sergei whispered tensely, 'Here comes your cue. Good luck, my child. Remember you are a ballerina of the Imperial Ballet—and the Tsar sits in his box—'

'No, Sergei Semenovitch,' whispered Tanya, 'I am dancing in my nightdress on the landing. You are playing the harmonium, and only Grishka is watching—'

'Are you ready, little one?'

'Yes, I am ready—'

Then came the familiar phrase of music that was her cue. Sergei gave her a tiny push that propelled her floatingly on to the stage. The music swelled up, and the little gazelle was alone in the forest, dancing for joy.

Hen Blackbird.

Great Tit.

Blue Tit.

February In The Country

by Michael Champion

PHOTOGRAPHS BY L. HUGH NEWMAN

IT IS JUST FINE when there are frost ferns on the window panes in the morning, and the air outside makes the eyes water. It seems as crisp and as cold as the rime on the grass. 'Hurray!' everybody shouts. Soon they are rubbing the rust off their skates, and wondering how sore they are going to be after their first afternoon's skating.

Yes! It is grand to be alive in this sort of weather. Yet for the smaller birds, a cold spell means that they are facing death; a slow flagging of life through thirst, hunger, exhaustion. In the struggle, many fail. In the winter of 1947 whole species of birds were wiped out in some areas. Where I was living at that time the following summer did not hear the piping of the robin, or the laughter of the green woodpecker. They were all—dead.

Now, whether living in a big city or a tiny village, this is one way in which everyone can help. The first need of a bird in hard weather is water. Every source, in puddles and ditches, soon becomes hard ice. It is a simple thing to provide a shallow drinking bowl, with a few stones in the centre for the birds to perch on. In my experience the birds take some time to discover the water, but it is not long before it is in full use if it is not moved about.

Providing food is no harder than is providing water. A loaf of bread tied to a tree or railing will be a great attraction to many birds. Some people make special bird tables. All that is needed is a post about five feet long, and six inches in diameter. The round larch posts that people grow roses up are splendid. One end must have a level surface for screwing a board on to, and the other end should be pointed for

sticking into the ground. The board can be made out of the sides of packing cases. The best size to build it is about 2 ft. 6ins. square. Some folk who have no garden fix the board to their window sill. 'Why,' you ask, 'cannot you just throw the food on to the ground?' The whiskers which twitch from the most comfortable chair, beside the warmest fire, give the answer.

Here are some ideas on what to use for feeding. Porridge, bread, old cake, potatoes, bones. There is sure to be some waste of this sort left over from meals. The bones can be hung up for the Tits to pick at, and the rest can be made into a mash with warm water, and then turned out on to the table.

It is great fun to give the birds a grand feast every day, and a good feeling to know that, through a very small amount of trouble, many bird lives have been saved. Perhaps the greatest reward is being able to watch Robins and Chaffinches, Tits and Starlings, maybe Nuthatches or Green Woodpeckers, at close quarters out of your own window. They are strengthening themselves for the fight against cruel Jack Frost.

HEDGING

There are men working along the hedgerows. Farmers avail themselves of the slacker times in winter to see to the work of laying their hedges. They must be laid every seven years or so, or they become open and patchy so that any beast may barge through the gaps.

It seems queer that these rows of thorn bushes, Blackthorn and Whitethorn, have been planted at some time or other, years ago. They seem to be as natural as the grass, but they are not, for planted they have been.

When a hedge is laid, what in effect is done is this. The old stems are half cut through close to the ground and bent over. These then form the new hedge. As they are only half severed they continue to grow. Also, off the stub below the cut, half-a-dozen young saplings start to grow. These provide new stems for the time when the hedge is next laid, as well as giving strength to the hedge.

PIGEON FLIGHTING

The middle of a wood at sunset, on a winter afternoon, can be a bleak place. Yet the smell of turf, and the weird twists of branches and trunks are capable of exerting a strange fascination over the wanderer.

Perhaps this spell is cast over the very bones of a man, and comes from the time when wolves howled from the forest. In those days, men hunted boar and elk amongst the pines, with weapons chipped from flint. The superstitions and fears of those skin-clad ancestors of ours still lurk at the bottom of our subconscious memories. If it is not so, how is it that a slight movement in the deep of a shadow, the shriek of an owl, the bark of a fox, can send a thrill of terror, ice-cold, chasing down our modern spines?

It is at this ghostly time, sunset, that pigeons flight in from the kale fields and stubbles to roost in the woods. If you happen to know a certain spot in a certain wood, and lie up there on the right evening with a gun, there should be a good smell of cooking at home a day or two later; and the smell should be pigeon pie!

In spite of their gentle cooing, wood pigeons cause more havoc to farm crops than any other bird. That is why farmers wage such war upon them. In autumn, the number of birds nesting with us in the summer is three times multiplied by immigrants from Scandinavia. They are smaller and more wiry birds than our home-bred ones.

Waiting in the woods for the great

(Continued on page 85)

Another dog is brought to the Kennels for training. Many breeds are accepted but they must all be at least nineteen inches high and possess the right temperament for the exacting work.

SHARP EYES
WITH COLD NOSES

It is now a common sight to see a blind man being led along a busy street by a dog. Picking a safe way between the crowds, waiting at the curb for the best moment to cross, avoiding obstacles like ladders and lamp posts, the dogs use their own eyes for the sake of their masters.

For fifteen years the Guide Dogs for the Blind Association have been training dogs at their kennels near Leamington. All large breeds are eligible, but only a quarter of those who come for the initial tests are found suitable for the four months' training. The blind owners are trained too, for they must become sensitive to the feel of the harness handle, and both dog and man must learn to trust each other completely. Photographs by Camera Talks.

The Kennels employ four trainers who study the characters of the dogs and teach the blind how to treat and trust them. 75 per cent. of the dogs prove unsuitable.

Kennelmaids look after the dogs undergoing training, grooming and brushing each day —

—and preparing meals of one pound of meat and plenty of biscuits for them twice a day.

The trainer must gain the affection of his pupil, and accustom it to a harness specially designed for this responsible work.

It is through this rigid handle that every movement is transmitted from the dog to his master's hand giving him instant warning.

Learning to retrieve anything that may be dropped is an important part of the training carried out with a dumb bell.

The main training is done in the streets, where the dogs are taught to go round obstacles under which their masters could not pass, and if necessary to disobey orders to cross a street at the wrong moment.

'I've stopped. There is a step coming. Be careful.' A dog passes its final test over rough ground.

Even Umbrellas Are Interesting

Written and illustrated by G. E. Mottram

This story of royal and splendid umbrellas will make you treat your 'gamp' with deep respect.

'ANY UMBRELLAS to mend to-day?' chimes the popular song, but nowadays the old umbrella mender who travelled the town and country in search of 'broken ribs' and torn covers is very rarely seen.

The humble umbrella as we know it to-day actually has a pedigree quite as long and noble as a royal family, for it was first associated in the far East with Royal events and religious pomp and pageantry.

The word 'umbrella' is derived from the Latin 'Umbra' meaning 'shade', and the Italian translation becomes 'Ombrello'.

In ancient Greece and Rome, centres of high culture, a large circular fan was used by ladies of high degree to protect them from the sun; this was called an 'Umbraculum', and from this we gradually see the development of the parasol, perfected by the Japanese who made parasols of gossamer weight and brilliantly coloured to act as sun-shades.

The Burmese state umbrella is a thing of great magnificence, cloth of gold richly embroidered in three tiers, this is used for ceremonial occasions as a sign of great honour, and is really very closely associated with Buddhism.

When Queen Victoria was decorated with the 'Collar of the Royal Order of the White Elephant of Siam' the central ornament depicted a triple white elephant and on each side was shown two pyramids of nine umbrellas.

Siam uses this motif in many ways; on state funeral boats the central mast usually showed a pagoda of ten umbrellas of varying sizes.

The pagoda itself, so popular in the far East particularly in China is based on this 'Umbrella' principle and of course again has its foundations in religion.

The ancient relic-shrines of Hindustan show a bell-like cupola surmounted by a 'chatta', Indian word for sunshade, at the caves of Ellora and in far off Cambodia this symbol of the open umbrella is plainly recognised, while in Rangoon, capital of Pegu, there are innumerable pagodas and cupolas crowned with these brass 'chattas'.

The long title for a Burmese king ran as follows, 'Lord of the twenty-four umbrellas', while the real meaning of this was 'Governor of the twenty-four kingdoms'.

In China a red silk umbrella was always carried by a nobleman when paying official visits; this denoted his superior rank. The four highest positions of mandarin were entitled to carry three red silk umbrellas, while the Mandarins of lesser rank must only carry two, even the poorer classes imitated this fetish by placing red paper umbrellas at the tombs of deceased relations as a mark of great respect. The large circular coolie hat seen bobbing about the rice fields is very similar to an open parasol and obviously shows that the first duty of the umbrella was to protect from the sun.

European peoples adopted the umbrella and put it to the use of keeping off the rain, as the weather of Northern countries called for some protection against the ravages of snow, sleet and rain.

These first umbrellas were very cumbersome objects consisting of a long handle and ribs of whalebone with a covering of oiled silk or cotton to be replaced later with gingham. It was not until 1848 that William Sangster patented alpaca as an ideal covering for umbrellas while four years later Samuel Fox invented the 'Paragon' rib, light and elastic. This was formed by a strip of steel folded 'V' fashion which gave great strength to the structure, while the new French silk covers were mostly manufactured at Lyons and Crefeld. Actually a mixture of alpaca and silk was the ideal combination.

The great Swift gives us a cameo picture of Early Victorian life in 'A City Shower':—

'The tucked up seamstress
    walks with hasty strides
While streams run down her
    oiled umbrella's sides.'

Manchester having its unenviable reputation as Britain's 'wettest town' launched forth factories for producing the necessary umbrella whose products could be seen 'Gleaming like black giant mushrooms by the banks of the Irwell', nevertheless they provided excellent protection from wind and rain unless of course one blew inside-out and then the results were disastrous!

Charles Dickens was responsible for giving a permanent nickname to the umbrella which has clung to it right up to the present day, for in his novel 'Martin Chuzzlewit' he introduced the character of an old nurse Sairey Gamp, never to be seen without her substantial rolled up 'brolly'. This term caught the popular fancy and 'gamp' became slang for umbrella, a far cry from its Far Eastern splendours. But remember next time the raindrops fall, as you turn to your gamp, treat it with respect for it has a Royal Lineage.

*'The tucked up seamstress
walks with hasty strides
While streams run down her
oiled umbrella's sides.'*

The Burmese state umbrella is a thing of great magnificence used for ceremonial occasions.

BLACK HUNTING WHIP

by Monica Edwards

ILLUSTRATED BY GEOFFREY WHITTAM

PART TWO

THE CELLAR SMELT horrible. It was cold and slimy and Dion's pocket torch lit up a small wet circle out of which a toad jumped suddenly. He flashed the torch around him. Old Bargate stone walls, running moisture, a stone table in the middle of the slippery brick floor and a narrow flight of brick stairs going up to nothingness.

Dion walked carefully across the cellar and peered up the stairs. Over the top of the stairway, lying flat, a wooden door was placed. Staring at it, Dion tried to think where it would come out. Somewhere in the floor of the old wing, he thought, about half-way along. He might dig and try to find the door. It would be easier to come in by the stairs than through the high window again.

But wait a minute, he said to himself, why not keep the thing a secret for a while? Don't want young Peter down here, making everything a lark; or Lindsey, slipping in the slime and asking questions, dropping things and saying she's awfully sorry; or Andrea, bossing everyone about and taking the mystery out of the place; or parents, fussing about the damp and keeping our clothes clean.

He stepped gingerly across the floor to where he had entered the cellar. Perhaps, he thought, if I pulled some branches down over the window, it mightn't be noticed for ages. The tree won't be sawn up in a hurry; green elm is rotten wood for burning.

One more look round, then I'd better see about it or they'll all be out and finding the window. Must be pretty well tea-time and they'll be shouting for me. He flashed the dim light round the room again and up and down the walls. No doorway in those walls; then there was no direct way between the two cellars. Only up the stairs, through the house and down the other stairs. Funny. But old houses are queer, the way they're built. No plans, I dare say, and they forgot things as they were building.

Pity it's so dark. My torch needs a new battery. Now, how to get out.

He looked up at the high window. The sill was about level with the top of his head. Nothing in the cellar that looked moveable; no boxes or barrels or anything. That central stone table must weigh a ton, he pondered. Not even a piece of wood to rear against the wall. What a darn silly fool he had been to drop down into a place without first making sure he could get out.

So, with his flickering torch, he prowled round looking for anything loose or moveable. He almost didn't see the cupboard in the table because it was limewashed like the rest of the table. When he did see it his first thought was that he might be able to break the doorway off its hinges and use it as a step up to the window. But by now his fingers were stiff with cold and his fumbling with the rusty iron catch of the little door proved futile.

He heard a clear voice floating down through the high broken window. It was Lindsey's, without a doubt. Calling him, was she, or what? He listened.

'Sula! Sula! Come, pony, Sula! You mustn't think I'll be deserting you in future, Sula, but I've got to spend a lot of time with Moonstone now. I'm sure you'll understand, because you like her, too.'

He could hear her pushing past the fallen branches.

It suddenly occurred to Dion that this was his one chance of getting out of the cellar without a wholesale family discovery. It would have been fun to keep the cellar a secret entirely to himself, but if he had to share it with anyone Lindsey was easily the best person to share it with. She was odd and quick tempered, but she wasn't so childish as Peter and she was far from being the organising sort of person that Andrea was.

He cupped his hands round his mouth, straining his head near to the window. 'Lindsey! Come through the roots, it's Dion,' he called clearly and quietly.

He heard her pushing past the earthy tangle. 'Where are you?'

She was answering in his own quiet pitch, aware in her quick way that he didn't want everyone to hear them.

'Down here, in a cellar under the old wing. There's a broken window—a bit further along.'

'I see it.'

Her face looked suddenly down at him, her long plaits swinging towards him.

'I can't get out,' he said briefly, 'but I don't want the whole tribe rushing round.'

'The cellar, after all!' she marvelled, still struck with amazed wonder at it.

'I found it by accident. Can you help me out? I'll tell you about it afterwards, when we've covered up the window again, if you'll promise to keep it deadly secret.'

'Cross my heart! I'll go and find a packing case.' And she was gone. Sensible person, Lindsey, when she wasn't being dreamy.

In the cellar the darkness was thick. It seemed to Dion almost as if he could hear it, certainly as if he could feel it. He was glad when Lindsey's running feet were heard above the cellar roof and more than glad when he saw her face framed in the grey of the broken window.

'Look out!' she said, and dropped the packing case.

Dion caught the case and stood it on end. It was a strong one and would bear him easily. His toe-caps rapped against the wooden side of the case as he heaved himself up on the top of it. His head and shoulders came up through the window frame and he looked out on the cold quiet of a winter's nightfall. Another heave and he was out beside Lindsey and they were threading sawn branches among the roots to hide their deep secret.

In the house the tea was nearly ready. Dion and Lindsey blinked in the gold light of the oil lamps. It was a soft light, never really bright, but it was brilliant after the cellar and the garden. The kettle was boiling on the black range and the larder door stood open. The children's mother came through it with gingerbread in a meat tin. 'You can both wash your hands in the same water,' she suggested, cutting the ginger bread into squares and piling them like sticky brown bricks upon a large yellow plate. 'Then tea will be ready.'

Lindsey ladled moss-smelling rain water from one of a row of buckets by the sink, and Dion added hot water from a large black kettle. They soaped in silence and Mrs. Thornton made the tea. Everyone was thinking about Moonstone, she knew, but what she couldn't know was that two were also thinking of a long-forgotten, still hidden cellar.

The quietness was heavy round the tea table until Mr. Thornton said with careful casualness, 'I thought of going to look at a Jersey.'

Mrs. Thornton nearly said wasn't his brown one warm enough, then checked herself just in time as her husband went on, 'She calves about Christmas, first calf. Robbins of Starfleet mentioned her yesterday morning. Said he's selling up and going in for Friesians.'

The four Thorntons looked up expectantly and their mother put down the teapot. 'But George,' she said, 'what about the water?'

'Down the well,' said her husband. 'Buckets of it; only needs winding up.'

'Only!' said Mrs. Thornton expressively.

'One cow won't make a lot of difference. We've got to start sometime and this seems a nice sort of heifer. I think I'll look at her anyway.'

'Oh good!' Dion radiated approval, 'and a Jersey, too. May I come with you?'

'And I,' said Andrea, but half heartedly.

'When are you going?' Lindsey asked.

Peter banged his plate with his knife. 'No one's going without me,' he stated.

Mr. Thornton got up to pile logs in the modern fireplace which still concealed the ancient chimney. He built them pyramid fashion and said, provocatively because everyone wanted to know about the heifer, 'One can't, two won't, three might, four will, but it takes five to make a fire.'

'Five what?' said Peter, and Dion answered, 'Logs, silly. It's an old saying.'

'True, too,' his father added, resuming his place and slicing the madeira cake.

'Depends on what wood you're burning,' Mrs. Thornton put in.

'But what about the Jersey?' Peter's voice went up.

Mr. Thornton said he'd thought of tomorrow morning. Then, just dropping the remark into the conversation like a pebble into a pond he added, 'Robbins has a pony he's selling. A black.'

Feeling that this remark was verging on unfaithfulness towards Moonstone, none of the children said anything but all stopped eating. Mrs. Thornton said, 'A good one? What height?'

Mr. Thornton said he didn't know but they could look at it if they liked when they went to see the heifer. During which remark there was a crash in the kitchen and Mrs. Thornton rushed out of the room. She came back carrying a broken plate and half a wedge of cheese.

'It's that unspeakable dog,' she said. 'Took it off the table.'

Dion and his father had become absorbed in deep conversation about Jersey cows, their milk yields and butterfat averages and whether hay or silage would be better for them in the winter.

Peter was drawing up a long Christmas list and his mother was helping him, no doubt to keep his mind from brooding over Moonstone, Lindsey thought, and she went out to see if Andrea had finished doing the dishes and if so, whether she would play a game of Rummy.

She had, but didn't want to play Rummy. She was taking down Moonstone's pelham bridle and hunting saddle from their pegs on the kitchen wall and carefully rubbing them with neatsfoot oil.

'Why are you doing that?' Lindsey stood on one leg and rubbed it with the other one.

'I'm going to pack them away.' Andrea's voice sounded dejected.

'But what about the black we're going to see at Mr. Robbins'? He'll need tackle if we have him.'

'Will he?' Andrea sounded indifferent and went on rubbing. 'Then he won't have Moonstone's. It would be like wearing a dead man's shoes.'

All the next day it had been impossible for Dion and Lindsey to get down into the secret cellar. Lindsey would not leave Moonstone until the vet had arrived.

She listened with a worried face while he was saying that there was no marked change but that the mare was certainly no worse, and then they were all being called in to get ready for the drive to Starfleet. Mr. Thornton wanted to start immediately so there was a rush round the house for warm clothing.

'Has anyone seen my fur gloves? I left them in the lobby.'

'If you can't put your gloves in the glove drawer, Lindsey, you must expect to lose them.'

'May I borrow your Shetland scarf, Mummy, please?'

'All right, Andrea, but don't drop it in the mud like you did last time.'

'Are you coming, Mummy?'

'Can't possibly, Peter old man. Someone must do the dishes and make a lunch for you all, to say nothing of cleaning the house.'

'May I get a new battery for my torch please, Mummy? I haven't any money I'm afraid.'

'Very well, Dion, but I think that kind of thing should really come out of your pocket money. Here is half a crown; get three will you? We can do with spares for the other torches. Oh, and will you get half a dozen large cup-hooks, too? The round kind.'

And so they departed under a grey December sky, and Lindsey, who loved running, tore ahead to open the gate.

It would soon be Christmas, she thought, as she watched the car glide through. Would they be allowed to stop in Godalming to do some Christmas shopping? Getting back into the car she asked about this and was told they might possibly; it would depend on how much time they had left when coming home from Starfleet Farm.

But they had no time at all owing to the amount of the animals Mr. Robbins actually had for sale. There were two ponies to begin with, and six Jersey cows and heifers. Also a litter of spaniel puppies and a flock of superbly dignified Christmas geese.

The purchasing party at once split up, Dion and his father to look at the cows and the other three to look at ponies and puppies, though, as Mr. Thornton had flatly stated, 'No more dogs at present; Glen's too many sometimes and your mother wants cats,' they were sensible enough not to consider the litter of spaniels very earnestly.

There was much division over the ponies. The black, which was fourteen hands and a good riding type, was plainly the right size for the growing family, but he was plain, to put it gently.

'His head's too big and he shows the whites of his eyes,' Lindsey said. 'I think the little bay is much nicer. She's absolutely adorable. Look at her small Arab-like head and her colour is an awfully good bay!'

'I know,' said Andrea, leaning over the field gate and screwing up her eyes to see the grazing ponies better. 'It is a nice rich bay, but she's too small. Smaller than Sula,

' By the time Dion and his father appeared in the field, they were still riding the ponies.'

even. We must have a bigger one. And the black doesn't show the whites of his eyes as you say, but only the white of one eye. That may be due to an accident, such as hurting his eye on a post or something, and not to bad temper at all.'

' Shall I fetch them both up for you? ' suggested the elder son of Mr. Robbins.

' Oh, yes!' said Peter, but Andrea said it would only be putting him to trouble for nothing. So he said, ' No trouble at all,' and went to get another halter. Lindsey made a face at Andrea but Andrea was on her dignity and took no notice. So Lindsey said provocatively, ' I'm sure the little bay is Arab-bred, when you look at the high set of her tail and her little dish face. And she has enormous dark eyes, like all the Arabs have.'

Andrea said, ' She's too small.'

' Not for me, she isn't,' put in Peter.

Lindsey said the only thing that was right about the black was his height, and he was as thin as a toast rack. Mr. Robbins' son came back with the halter and caught both ponies without much trouble, though he said he didn't know much about horses, they were selling these for some- one else. Peter, helping with the girths, said what were their names and young Mr. Robbins said for all he knew they hadn't any. He said the black was only thin because he's been hunted hard and would put on weight wonderful with rest and good food.

Andrea tried the black pony first and Peter the bay, but Lindsey wanted to ride the bay when it was her turn, though Andrea said she was tons too heavy.

' Not her,' said young Mr. Robbins. ' That little 'un's up to weight. Carry you, she would.' Andrea almost asked him how he knew, since he had said he didn't know

about horses, but changed her mind, ' Well, I'll go round the field on the black again, as Lindsey doesn't want to. He's a very comfortable ride and has a lovely mouth.'

Lindsey stared at her in astonishment, for it almost looked as if Andrea had at last met the pony that she was prepared to love for itself and not for its good looks and breeding.

By the time Dion and his father appeared in the field they were still riding the two ponies, having long since been left to themselves by young Mr. Robbins, and were still in absolute disagreement among themselves. Dion said he didn't see what there was to argue about, the bay was a gorgeous little thing but too small.

Lindsey, watching Peter jump her over a bundle of faggots, said why did people think only of themselves, she wasn't a bit too small for Peter, who had never had a pony his own size, and she wasn't even too small for her, either.

' But you've got Sula!' Dion was indignant. ' Andrea and I haven't anything now.'

Andrea said it would be too silly to have *two* small ponies and nothing big, and appealed to her father.

' You wouldn't care to take the two, would you, sir? ' the farmer suggested as Peter cantered up to the gate. ' The little 'un does suit your young boy fine, and I can offer a lower price that way. They were brought up together and might pine a bit, being separated.'

As soon as the four young people saw that their father was considering, his chances of getting away with only one pony were so small as to be insignificant. But when everyone had finished talking, which all were doing together and very loudly, he said, ' What I want you all to remem- ber, and I'm sure Mr. Robbins won't mind my saying this,

'Holleybone had been drawn in to admire the first cow.'

these are not the only ponies in Surrey, and neither of them, individually, is the pony I had in mind for you.'

'Now think very carefully,' Mr. Thornton continued. 'Would you rather put all the money into one really good pony, such as Moonstone, or would you rather have these two together, which, at the reduced price for the two, come to around the same figure?'

'Oh, these two!' everyone said. 'Three ponies will be far more fun than two, though we really need four, of course,' Dion added.

'And that little 'un goes grand in harness, too,' said Mr. Robbins. 'Fair spanks along in a governess cart.'

He took the ponies' tackle from Peter and Andrea and everyone exclaimed over the small pony's rolling and showing her pale underside to the thin winter sunshine.

'A week's trial,' agreed Mr. Thornton, 'and we'll expect the heifer as well tomorrow morning.'

'The heifer?' said Andrea and Lindsey and Peter all together, having forgotten entirely about the cows.

'The heifer,' said their father, smiling. 'She's a pedigree attested Jersey and she is called Starfleet Countess's Duchess. She calves just after Christmas.'

'But we can't call her all that!' said Peter, and Lindsey said, 'What's attested?'

'Call her Starfleet, Countess, or Duchess,' suggested Andrea. 'There's plenty of choice.'

Dion said attested meant that she hadn't got tuberculosis.

'Come and have a look at her before we go?' invited their father and they all trooped round to the cowsheds. Starfleet Countess's Duchess was petted and praised and

exclaimed over, and Lindsey remarked how similar in shape were the Jersey cows to Arab horses. Both had short concave faces, width between the eyes (which were full and dark and large), and both had high-set tails and slender bone.

Coming out at last from the cowsheds the party was further delayed by the fine flock of Christmas geese which swept across their bows, so to speak, with the dignity and pride of a deputy of City aldermen. Before five more minutes had passed, Mr. Thornton had bought one for the Christmas dinner, but stipulating that it stayed at Starfleet till Christmas week in case his family got too fond of it.

And so home, with only two stops as they went through Godalming, for Dion's batteries and cup-hooks and for Peter to buy some balloons and coloured bells.

* * *

In the store shed Dion and Lindsey were mixing chicken food. Lindsey measured the dry meal into the bucket of boiled potatoes and Dion mashed all together with a chopper. 'Should you think the ponies and Duchess will be on the way, yet?' he said reflectively.

'Oh, no!' said Lindsey, scraping her tin in the bottom of the meal barrel. 'Much later in the morning, I expect. There'd be time to go down into the cellar first.'

There was a flutter at the door and nine brown and two black hens flapped in and crowded round the bucket. Lindsey pushed them back with her foot. 'They always wriggle in somehow,' she said, and Dion said the door didn't fit. 'Silly things, aren't they,' he said. 'They ought to be properly shut up in folding arks, you know, but Holleybone believes in free range.'

Lindsey said, 'Mummy'll hate them when she starts gardening.'

Dion picked up his bucket and began stepping over frantic chickens to the door. 'Andrea was washing up frightfully fast,' he said, 'because she said she wanted to get the stables and cowshed ready, and she was shouting encouragements—and other things—at Peter to make him carry his logs faster too, and help her.'

'Good. Then *we* needn't,' Lindsey opened the Barn field gate, 'and we can explore the cellar while they're nicely out of sight. You know I haven't even seen it yet.'

'But I ought to see to Duchess's stall.' They were in the Barn field and Dion was tipping mash into two round troughs. 'Andrea'll probably hang frilly curtains and arrange a vase of flowers on the sill but what a heifer wants is a dry bed, clean water and hay.'

'Oh, Dion, don't be silly. Andrea's perfectly capable, and Holleybone'll see to things being properly done.'

'He doesn't like Jerseys.'

They stood watching the gulping fowls for a moment and then turned back to the gate. Lindsey began to look slightly mulish. She said, 'I might possibly go down by myself if you won't come too.'

'Gosh,' said Dion in quick annoyance, 'I might have known you'd throw a spanner in the works once I let you into the secret.' He shut the gate with a bang and took the empty bucket into the store shed. Lindsey was watching Andrea and Peter going into the stable with a pitchfork and broom when he came out.

'Right,' said Lindsey. 'Come on. Got your torch?'

'Yes, but I want a screw-driver. Make sure Holleybone isn't around or anyone else. I won't be a minute.' He disappeared into the workshop and Lindsey walked on.

No sign of Holleybone or of her mother. They would be with Moonstone at this time of day, changing her dressings. She hugged her arms round her chest to keep out the sharp wind and waited for Dion by the high stark roots of the elm tree. He came quickly and together they pulled away the branches from the window. 'I'll go first, then I can help you,' he said, and slowly disappeared, feet foremost, into the damp-smelling hole of the window.

Peering down after him, Lindsey saw him jump carefully from the top of the packing case and reach up his hands to help her follow him. She screwed herself round, dangled one leg, then the other, felt her ankles grasped and guided, slithered another six inches and touched the box with her toe-caps. Then she was standing on the slimy brick floor, staring blankly at the bright fan of torchlight while Dion lit a candle-end and stuck it on the top of the stone table. 'There,' he said, blowing out the match and putting the box back into his pocket, 'what do you think of it?'

Lindsey shivered a little and looked slowly around her. The candle-light was pale on grey hanging cobwebs, it flickered among the deep quiet shadows and gleamed strangely on dark emerald slimes along the floor. 'Very cold, very dark, very wet and very dirty,' she said, 'but exciting. Pity it's so bare,' she added. 'I thought there might be all sorts of interesting old things down here.'

'Salvaged, I expect,' Dion said, 'when the old wing went, however that happened.' He climbed up on the packing case again and pulled the branches into the window frame. 'Anyone might be about,' he said.

Lindsey walked carefully across the floor and examined the stone staircase. 'Burnt down, I dare say,' she said. 'What did you want a screw-driver for?'

Dion said, 'This,' and Lindsey turned to see him squatting on his heels behind the table. She found him working on a small cupboard door built under the heavy slab of the table-top. The screws that held the lock were very rusty and his hand slipped round on the varnished handle of the screw-driver. He spat in one palm and rubbed both together. This time, with a better grip, he began to turn the screws. There were five. They lay in a rusty row on the table-top as he prised away the lock and then that also lay beside them complete in its two sections, and the door creaked open in Dion's eager hands.

Lindsey flashed the torch inside the cupboard, screamed and dropped it on the floor where it flickered and went out. 'Sorry,' she said, contritely, 'but it was quite four inches across.'

'What was?' Dion groped for the torch.

'The spider.'

'Spider!' The word was withering.

'I can't help it. It isn't that I'm frightened of them but they make me shrivel, and that one was hairy. I'd rather face a bull. It wouldn't run up my sleeve, at least.'

Dion found the torch and pushed the switch with his thumb. It was dead. 'Now you've done it,' he said. 'Bust the bally thing. I ought to have known you'd do something.'

'I'm sorry.' Lindsey fidgeted her feet because the spider might be near them in the shadows on the floor. Dion was holding the candle-end by the cupboard opening, peering inside and groping with his hand.

'Found anything?'

'No. Yes. A little book, I think.' He drew it out, all smothered in mould and cobwebs. Lindsey shivered, looking at it. 'It's filthy,' she said.

'So would you be if you'd been in that cupboard for a hundred years or more,' said Dion, blowing on it. 'The point is, it may be important.'

Lindsey looked at the damp brown object. 'It might tell us about the old wing,' she said hopefully.

Having blown off most of the cobwebs, Dion wiped the mould on the seat of his trousers and opened the book on the table in the primrose light of the candle.

'"Of new laide egs take eight and of freash flower one quartern,"' he read. 'Oh, what a blow! Recipes.'

Forgetting the spider, Lindsey leaned her arms on the table and said, 'Turn over, that's only the first page.'

Dion turned over. '"To cuer the hooping cough,"' he read, then turned over several more pages quickly. Here and there the leaves were stuck together with mould and damp and age, and in places the ink was faded past the point of legibility. But all the contents, so far as could be judged, were recipes. Then came several blank pages which Dion turned over carefully.

'Perhaps that's all,' said Lindsey, disappointed, but it wasn't. Suddenly, a new writing began, more than half way through the book. A much younger, less spidery hand. Dion's head went down quickly, nearer to the pages. Lindsey leaned closer on her elbows. They read together and the writing began:

'"Since uncle would not let me have a book for my journal but only for my studies, I am indeed fortunate to have found this book of old receipts. He will not miss it, it has not been opened since my mother died."'

The writing was very difficult to read in places and the wavering candle-light was not the best thing to help them. They read aloud together, one deciphering a word which the other could not, and the journal unfolded.

'"March 12th. My uncle persists in trying to break my splendid Blackmail to harness for drawing his carts. The pony has too much spirit and fire for such low drudgery, but it is indeed painful to see the treatment his resistance provokes from my uncle. Could dear father but see his Blackmail so! He would indeed lie restless underground."'

Dion turned over a page and found:

'"March 17th. Blackmail and I went far beyond the Punch Bowl and over Gibbet Hill, carrying the black hunting whip which was my father's and which he gave to me with Blackmail. A fine ride in a high wind, and the world was mine own and Blackmail's for a short hour or two, till our return. Then, mercy on us, what trouble with my uncle for having left uncleaned the cowstalls. His rage being as much directed against my pony, who has all innocence, but was called a Parasite, not earning that which he devoured. To bed early and without supper.

'"April 1st. It was my uncle's pleasure to make of me an April Fool in most painful fashion this morning. His humour was to tell me that Blackmail lay dead beneath the yew tree, whose fence had gone down. I, in anguish, ran to the yew tree, there to find the fence in order and my pony across in Hanger field, peacefully grazing. My uncle's laughter was an evil gale in the orchard."'

'Beast!' said Lindsey. Her voice rang with disgust for far away injustice. 'I know just how he felt—after Moonstone.'

'How old was he?' Dion was considering. 'Older than I am, I think. But what a pony!'

'It sounds a rather special one,' Lindsey agreed, 'and with a wonderful name. A black, I expect. Shall we call our black after him?'

Dion was carefully unsticking two pages. 'No, he isn't the type. I'd like to call him Tarquin but Andrea will want something else I suppose.'

The pages came unstuck but were here spoilt with damp and were unreadable. Dion turned over again and they read on without knowing what came before.

'"May 1st. When my father gave me my black hunting whip he told me how, when a boy, he had wanted above all else to carry it to victory in an agricultural show. But such were not many in those days, and never near enough for him to try.

'"Now he is dead it seems to me that I should try to do

'"Turn over quickly," Lindsey said, helping with a finger.'

this for him. How pleased he would be! And Blackmail is the one to make this possible for he is indeed splendid and with fire in his veins. All that is needed is the show, and it was thus with great excitement that I learned this day of a show to be held near Guildford in June. There are to be trials of leaping and of skill in the art of horsemanship. Blackmail is equal to all, and if I practise much it is possible I may not disgrace myself.

'"May 6th. In trouble with my uncle for neglecting my work about the farm and my studies also, to school my pony for the show. I must try to please him more, for my life with him is indeed becoming daily more difficult."'

Lindsey, looking up quickly, said, 'Sh-sh! Listen.'

'The cattle lorry!' Dion said.

'We can't have been down here all that time!' Lindsey stared at him. 'And it's going *away*. How didn't we hear it come?'

Dion shut up the journal. 'Too far underground and too interested in the diary,' he said. 'We'll have to rush, but we can come back and finish it later.' He pushed the book back into the cupboard, went over to the packing case and climbed up to make sure all was clear.

'Not a soul,' he said, and pushed the branches from the window. 'I'll go up first. Blow out the candle and then I'll haul you out too.'

'I can manage, thanks,' Lindsey said, and did so.

Together they re-threaded the branches across the deep window, turned, and ran down to the yard.

* * *

Andrea raised no objection about the naming of the new black pony and even said she thought Tarquin suited him quite well. She was relieved that no one had put forward any of the more obvious names for blacks.

Peter pleaded for the privilege of naming the little bay, but his father said all this was rather a waste of mental energy as the ponies were only held on trial.

'But we must call them *something*,' Peter argued. 'We can't say just the black and the bay.'

Mr. Thornton said he didn't see why not, but everyone else seemed quite agreeable to Peter's choosing, so he joyfully called her Red Clover.

'And it suits her, for she's round and red if a pony ever was,' his mother remarked.

'Fatter than Sula,' said Andrea. She was grooming the black in the largest stall of the stable, but everyone else except Lindsey was making a pet of Red Clover.

Lindsey was in the calf-box, having thought that Moonstone might be feeling left out of things. Moonstone was definitely better to-day, and after Lindsey had stayed with her for a bit she thought Sula must be feeling terribly neglected, so rushed round to the orchard and talked to her.

When she got back she found most of the family were now in the cowshed where Starfleet Countess's Duchess was taking in her new surroundings with large startled eyes. There seemed to be a little trouble going on and Lindsey saw that it revolved around Holleybone, who had been drawn in from his hedging to admire the first cow.

He stood in the broad gutter, his short figure nearly hidden among Thorntons, who were inclined the other way. 'Not 'er, I don't,' he was saying. 'Reckon I said not Jerseys at the start, an' I still says the same, without no disrespect if you get my meaning, sir.'

Mr. Thornton said he couldn't be serious, they had to keep the animal now she had arrived and what would they do when she calved?

The matter reached a deadlock when Dion said suddenly, 'I'll milk her. I'd love to, getting up early and all.'

Everyone turned and looked at him.

'You don't know how,' Peter said.

'You wouldn't stick it,' said Andrea, coming in from grooming Tarquin.

'Twice a day, seven days a week, and mucking out,' Lindsey added.

'If you'll let me get a word in edgeways,' Dion said. 'Even the best hand-milker in the world once had to learn how, and as to sticking it, perhaps I'll remind you all about that one day.'

Mrs. Thornton said reasonably, 'But where are you going to learn? You can't learn on Duchess, she won't have any milk till she calves and then it would ruin her to be milked by an absolute learner.'

'Of course I do, Mother. But I won't be a learner when she calves. As a matter of fact I'm not an absolute learner now. I've been milking off and on practically ever since we came here, and I'm getting along.'

Everyone registered astonishment and Mr. Thornton said might he ask where this had all been going on?

Dion said it was at Rockfield Farm, practically next door, and the Faithfuls had been most sporting about it, letting him start on Primrose because she let her milk down well, but now he was promoted to Snowdrop who was slightly more difficult, and all he had done in return was to wash the cows' udders and clean their quarters. He said he still took nearly twice as long as anyone else to milk a cow because it made his fingers ache so much, but the Faithfuls said he'd get over all that.

'So that's where you've been so many tea-times,' Mrs. Thornton said, with the voice of one making a discovery.

'Well, I may as well get back to me hedgin,' observed Holleybone, snatching at this loophole. His squat back filled the doorway and was gone.

Mrs. Thornton said she didn't see it would work when school began, but meanwhile there was lunch to think of. They followed Holleybone into the yard.

Andrea jumped up. 'Now riding,' she said. 'Unless Dion wants to ride Tarquin I shall. If you do, Dion, we'll have to draw lots.'

'I don't mind,' Dion said. 'I want to fence off a stall in the stable for Duchess's calf as Moonstone has the calf-box.'

Peter's voice squeaked up from behind three bales of hay, 'I want to ride Clover, please!'

'I'm having Sula,' Lindsey said, 'So you'll have to—or nothing.'

Twenty minutes later the three of them filed through the gate to Yew Tree field and the Punch Bowl, the yellow puppy at their heels, and Dion paused in his work to lean over the cowshed door and watch them go. For a minute they were outlined against the windy sky then they were away out of sight. Dion gazed at the ancient yew tree. Perhaps it was older than the Elizabethan house itself. It knew all that passed there, it looked as wise as death and as old as life.

Dion thought of another boy, long years ago now, racing up the steep bank to the yew tree looking for a dead black pony. His mood darkened at the thought of old injustice and he turned back sharply into the cowshed.

All that afternoon it rained and was cold and windy and dark. Peter had found a mallet and was being allowed to join in the glorious demolition in the kitchen, where the mess and dust and rubble had to be seen to be believed. Mrs. Thornton was so depressed by the chaos that she had retreated to the sitting room, though no one had been so thrilled as she at the first sight of the wide Tudor brick arch that was slowly returning to daylight after years behind plaster and new brick.

Andrea was fired by this discovery to efforts of her own, and had gone up to the Priest Hole room which she shared with Lindsey and was making appalling squeaky noises with a painter's scraper, removing layers of old whitewash and distemper from thick oak beams. These beams were full of dowel holes and square slots and wedge-shaped cavities. They had obviously been part of something else before they had been built into the farmhouse. A ship, most likely, Andrea thought, and was thrilled to think of it. The bones of her bedroom they were, and they had sailed strange seas, carried stranger cargoes, fought bloody battles, anchored in tropic harbours. Perhaps the floor had been a deck, the planks were old and wide. She fancied herself an able seaman, standing square before the mast, and scraped away with a whistle and a swagger.

Dion and Lindsey watched the excavation of the Tudor kitchen fireplace for a while then, thinking the same thought at the same moment, exchanged glances, fetched garden coats and said they would see if all the animals were all right. They did this, partly to keep within the truth and partly out of genuine concern, and then they moved quietly through the cold rain towards the fallen wing of the farmhouse.

The cellar was so cold with the rain that it felt like a tomb. The candle wavered weirdly on rivulets of water running down the dark walls and on three warty toads which blundered from the sudden light.

Lindsey shivered and wrapped her arms across her chest for warmth. Dion pulled out the diary and turned the pages to find where they had finished reading.

' "May 15th. My journal neglected these many days for I have spent much time with Blackmail. It is perhaps hardly necessary for me to say what trouble this is causing between my uncle and myself, though I do believe I have not neglected my duties because of my work with the pony.

' " Blackmail this morning jumped with supreme ease the long gate leading into Hanger field. I think I should judge he had four inches to spare." '

Dion glanced up sideways. ' I know that gate,' he said, ' and if it's the same one it's a corker.'

They read on eagerly, the cold and damp forgotten in the warmth of their interest.

' "May 21st. A fine morning, so beautiful very early that it was like spring water. The orchard full of birdsong and I heard a willow wren. The morning ran in my pony's veins for when I dared to hang a bar above the Hanger field gate, then, half frightened, put him to it, he flew it like a swallow. So happy we were, he and I, that we circled the field at a canter, I singing a hunting song and knowing at last that none could prevent my Blackmail and me from carrying my father's whip for him to victory in June." '

' Oh, I do hope he does! ' said Lindsey fervently as Dion turned the page. ' It will be awful if he's beaten now.'

They went on slowly, aloud, eyes screwed up in the weak light, fixed on the scarcely visible words.

' " He is indeed a great horse. To call him a pony seems now an insult, though he is but so in height.

' " June 2nd. After days without entry, I write again to record the gravest trouble with my uncle, whom I swear I have endeavoured to please with all my power but only succeeding in annoying him the more.

' " To-day, the show being but two weeks away, I made plea that Blackmail should be allowed this time in freedom from my uncle's breaking him to harness, as this frets and aggravates the pony, making him less perfect at the jumps. My uncle is not a patient trainer, indeed he is not patient in any undertaking. And Blackmail is too splendid, too proud for heavy labour.

' " The outcome of our most strained conversation was . . . " '

' Turn over quickly,' Lindsey said, helping with a finger of her own.

' " . . . that it was time I should be sent away to school, I being without discipline and lazy and of no use on the farm. Now I can only wonder what will become of me, but little caring if first I can carry my black hunting whip victoriously in June, and have done this small thing in my father's memory and honour.

' " June 10th. My life at Punch Bowl Farm is all but already ended, the show is nothing to me any more and my ambition for my father's hunting whip extinguished, for in two days I shall be far from this place, never, perhaps, to return here.

' " It began in so trivial a fashion, and it seems to me now that many grave matters spring first from small events. I had forgotten to feed the two roan calves in my eagerness to try Blackmail once more over the Hanger field gate with two bars above it, since his superb leap over this obstacle yesterday evening. The calves were not long without food, I should say not above two or three hours before my uncle discovered my omission, but in this one fault (or wickedness, as he himself termed it) he seemed to see again each separate thing I had done, but unintentionally, to annoy him since I came here two years ago. His rage mounted up in scorn as he spoke and I heard the chill thing, that I was to leave for school in two days instead of in the autumn as arranged.

' " No show, no victory for my father's whip, but worse, my pony will be sold with all his belongings. My own pony, my splendid Blackmail, my father's gift to me with the whip he had prized since his boyhood. Small wonder that I am filled with a cold black numbness of no feeling.

' " My pony I cannot hide, I can only hope that he will find a happy home as he so well deserves. But my black hunting whip they shall not have. Indeed I have already hidden it beyond all likely discovery, down deep beneath the third step of the great barn. And there, with it, my ambition.

' " Farewell, Punch Bowl Farm. Never will I come back." '

Lindsey's face was tragic.

' It can't be all,' Dion said. The old pages rustled sadly under his fingers and all were blank.

(Continued on page 114)

BERLIN AIRLIFT

by Ralph Hammond

How two million people living in the British Zone of Berlin were supplied with food, coal, raw materials and all their needs for sixteen months—entirely by air.

THE BERLIN AIRLIFT is closed now. But whilst it was operating far and away the busiest airport in the world was British-controlled Gatow Airport on the outskirts of Berlin. There were three aerodromes handling the airlift traffic at the Berlin end—Tegel (French), Tempelhof (American) and Gatow (British)—and though the Americans carried considerably more freight than we did, it was Gatow that handled the bulk of the traffic.

Through the big double windows of Gatow control tower, traffic control officers, linked to the pilots by radio-telephone, controlled all landings and take-offs. How did they handle this colossal traffic? Well, let's go back to the height of the airlift and listen in for a minute:

'*Okay, Two-five-two. Clear to land. Keep rolling after touch-down. There's a York close behind you . . . Four-three-five, you can line up after the next York has landed . . . Okay, One-nine-eight—, report at two miles. You're Number Three in the pattern . . .*'

You probably won't make much sense out of that. I'll try to sort it out for you in a minute. But that went on at Gatow every day, twenty-four hours a day all through the year that Berlin was blockaded—just two R.A.F. officers talking into a radio-telephone, controlling the world's busiest air traffic centre. A landing and a take-off every three minutes. Up to 950 plane movements handled in twenty-four hours. Aircraft off-loaded and taxi-ing out again within eighteen minutes of touchdown.

The airlift began because we and the Americans and the French control the western half of Berlin right inside the Russian Zone of Germany. The Russians wanted to control the whole city and so, ultimately, the whole of Germany. For this reason they closed their Zone to all traffic in June, 1948, refusing to allow the movement of trains, barges and lorries between Berlin and our Western Zones. They thought that by starving the German population of Berlin they could drive the Western Powers out of the city.

That left us only the air corridors and our answer was the airlift—Operation Plainfare. It started as a food lift. But soon we were having to lift in petrol, oil and raw materials for the factories, and then, as the winter of 1948/49 drew near, coal as well. We even had to fly in a steam roller to work on enlarging the runways at Gatow! At the peak of the lift American and British planes were flying in the equivalent of more than eight trainloads of supplies a day. Most of the four-engined planes, even over-loaded, couldn't carry more than ten tons at a time.

I started on one of those planes from Wunstorf, which was the first of the airlift fields to begin operations. Originally a German light bomber station, mostly grass, it grew to be a colossal airport with its own railway sidings. I was staggered when I first saw it. The loading apron seemed to be miles long, and it was massed with four-engined planes, mostly Yorks. The planes were crawling with maintenance crews, engines were being tested, tanks refuelled, and everywhere lorries were loading supplies into the thick-bellied fuselages. I watched one plane after another start

up and swing into line on the taxi-ing perimeter. The next wave for Berlin was queueing up for take-off.

As soon as I'd got my pass they rushed me down to the parachute store and then out on to the tarmac where my guide signalled to a plane that was just moving out into the queue, pivoting on its wheels with the blindness of a huge bumble-bee. It stopped and we fought our way through the back-wash of the engines to the door of the fuselage. I was hauled in. The door slammed to behind me and the plane began to move again. I was on my way, together with nine tons of flour chained down in bags along the centre of the fuselage. It was queer to think that when I got out again I should have run the blockade and reached our sector of Berlin.

The flight engineer gave me his seat up for-ard beside the pilot. He had been one of the great pilots of the war days in Coastal Command and he handled the huge plane with the ease of a driver handling a bus. Over the inter-com the pilot's voice asked, 'Been to Berlin before?'

'No,' I said.

'Have a look at this then.' With one hand he passed me a map. The other was on the four throttle levers, trimming the engines. 'The course is marked in. We fly north-east for the first three-quarters of an hour. Then we turn south-east into the northern approach corridor. It's all very dull really.'

It might be dull to him, but I was feeling pretty excited as we roared down the runway and swept up into the leaden sky. 'It's all a matter of timing,' he said when he'd finished his routine

Traffic Control officers looked eastward towards Berlin and controlled all landings and take-offs.

check-up. 'Like a train service. We've a margin of ninety seconds either side of our landing schedule. If we're outside that limit then we have to overshoot and return to base. They don't give you a second chance. Too risky.'

I thought of the continuous stream of planes landing at Gatow. 'What about the planes flying to the other Berlin airfields?' I asked.

'Air Safety Centre works that out,' he answered. 'Like a game. Certain types of aircraft are based at different airfields. At Wunstorf it's all Yorks and Tudor tankers. Daks at Lubeck. We move in in waves, each wave flying at the best speed for the type of aircraft. Waves for Gatow, Tegel and Tempelhof fly in at different heights. We're flying Angels three-five—that's height 3,500 feet. Provided we maintain height and speed there's no chance of a collision.'

I saw how this was worked as we swung into the approach corridor. The navigator reported, 'Minus thirty seconds.'

'That means we're thirty seconds behind schedule,' the pilot explained. 'He's got a time sheet and his radar tells him the exact moment we passed over the Eureka beacon at Restorf.'

When next the navigator reported we were over Frohnau beacon and the pilot pointed through the windshield, 'There's Berlin now.'

For perhaps five minutes we were looking down at nothing but the empty shells of buildings—miles and miles of devastated homes. Then we swung westward. The buildings thinned out and we were winging low over fir trees and a lake, losing height all the time, the speed checked by our landing flaps. A new voice sounded in my earphones: 'Clear to land, Two-five-two'—the voice

Before we had stopped two trucks were nosing out to meet us. The door was opened and the flour bags loaded into the lorry.

Hundreds of German workers kept the runways clear of snow day and night.

Photographs by Keystone Press

of Gatow Tower giving us the okay to come in. Through the windshield I saw the pierced steel runway of Gatow Airport rushing up to meet us, and a York was taking off along it in a cloud of dust. Then our wheels touched down, light as a feather for all our cargo of flour, and we were taxi-ing over to the off-loading apron.

Gatow was a disappointment to me after Wunstorf. There were no railway sidings, only a few hangars, and the tarmac apron was small by comparison with only four other planes off-loading. The reason, I discovered, was Organisation. Just as the approach was timed to the minute, so was the off-loading. Before we had stopped two trucks were nosing out to meet us, and by the time I had collected my suitcase, the door of the fuselage was open and a German labour party was loading the first of the flour bags into the lorry which had backed its tailboard against the fuselage. The crew had time for just one cup of coffee at the canteen and then they were off again, back to Wunstorf to make another flight into Berlin before going off duty for the day. They worked, those air crews!

Organisation was the key to the apparent emptiness of that incredibly busy airport. And like all good organisation it was really quite simple. In-coming aircraft reported to Traffic Control as they turned over the centre of Berlin for the final approach. They would give their number, say Flight 252. '*Report at two miles, Two-five-two,*' ordered the Traffic Control officer.

Meanwhile a plane would be coming from the off-loading apron, and as it passed the control tower the pilot reported: '*Four-three-five calling Gatow Tower.*' Back from Traffic Control came: '*Permission to taxi, Four-three-five,*' and the plane moved slowly off up the perimeter track. At the same time, through the tall windows of the control room, the officer-in-charge could see the wings of a plane emerging from the sky over Berlin. It was 252 and in a moment

the pilot was reporting that he was over the two-mile beacon.

'*Clear to land, Two-five-two,*' answered Traffic Control. And then to the plane waiting now at the end of the perimeter track: '*Four-three-five, you can line up after the next York has landed and take off immediately.*' So 252 landed and as his wheels touched the deck 435 was swinging into position at the end of the runway. He had little more than a minute in which to take off, for already another plane was dropping out of the sky towards the runway.

And so it went on, day and night for a whole year. But supposing something went wrong? Well, I was up there in the control tower when one of the worst storms they'd experienced hit the airport. Traffic was at its busiest. Planes were dropping steadily down out of the sky, others were taking off, all along the same runway, and all the time the Met (weather) people were plotting the course of the storm which we could see moving in on us, very black beyond the gathering dusk of the airfield. What happened?

There was no panic. Voices became a little tense, that was all. It seemed to close in very suddenly and then the control tower shivered under a sudden onslaught of wind and driving rain. It was impossible to see a thing. The airport landing lights were switched on and the Traffic Controller ordered Ground Control Approach (G.C.A.) to stand-by— G.C.A. is a radar approach control. Met notified gusts of 56 knots sweeping across the landing ground at right-angles to the runway. No plane should be asked to land in those conditions. At any other airport they would have been told to circle until the squall had passed. But this was the airlift with planes coming in at the rate of one every three minutes. It was the tail end of a wave—four more Yorks to land and then Daks following. The Supervisor took over and ordered all pilots to overshoot and return to base.

But the pilots had had a bad dusting. 'We're not flying back through that

stuff,' the first York answered. 'I'm going to try a landing. Okay?'

The Supervisor hesitated. He had to make a quick decision. It would be his responsibility if there was a crash. 'Okay,' he said, and we waited, breathless, for the next York to come in. Its red and green navigation lights emerged out of the rain-lashed darkness. They grew larger, and then, just before touchdown, the pilot switched on twin spotlights. They shone on an impenetrable sheet of rain. The pilot couldn't possibly see. The wheels slammed hard down on the deck. The great York with its 9-ton cargo bounced a clear hundred yards—and as the wheels hit the runway again, the wings tilted. For a second it looked as though it would be blown over. Then it righted itself, running smoothly up the runway; as the squall slackened, the next and the next came in, bumping badly, but safe.

Then the airport lights fused. Control ordered emergency lighting and Gatow switched over to Ground Control Approach. This radar apparatus is far too complicated to explain in a short article. But very briefly there are two screens; one shows whether the plane is to the left or right of its correct line of approach, the other shows the angle at which it is coming in. The pilot flies completely blind, operating on verbal instructions from the G.C.A. Controller. Literally, the plane is talked down.

So you see, Gatow functioned as smoothly in emergencies as it did in normal fine weather conditions. I could go on and on about this amazing airport that supplied more than half the requirements of more than two million people throughout the blockade. I shall always remember the reply of the Supervisor of Gatow Traffic Control when I asked him if he wasn't getting tired of such a nerve-racking job. 'I wouldn't be anywhere else in the world,' he said. 'I'm doing something here that no other traffic controller will do in my lifetime.' What he meant was, war or peace, this was the biggest air operation ever.

Summer is a-coming in,
Sing a loud cuckoo !

The seed grows, the mead blows,
The wood springs anew.

Sing, cuckoo !

girls & boys come out to play

By IAN SERRAILLIER

Girls and boys, come out to play!
The moon doth shine as bright as day,
So leave your supper and leave your slate,
Susan, Peter and Paul and Kate—
Are you coming?
Head over heels they leapt from bed,
And Tarry Awhile and Sleepyhead
Crept from the bench in the chimney nook.
The children came from the picture books,
Little Jack Horner, Miss Bo-peep—
'Somebody please look after my sheep!'—
Red Riding Hood hot from the wolf in the
    wood,
And baby Helen would come if she could.
(Who's Helen, you ask? Helen's my
    daughter.
Blue eyes, white hair, she's only a quarter.)
Jack and Jill and Marjorie Daw,
Miss Muffet, the spider, and Punch and more
Came with a shout, came with a bound
And danced in the moonlight round and
    round.

What shall we play till break of day,
Mulberry Bush or Nuts and May?
Said the owl in the willow, 'Tuwhit, towhoo!
I'm game to hunt the slipper or shoe,'
But as nobody offered a shoe or slipper
They had to do with a breakfast kipper,
Which answered well till it made a mess
Of Miss Muffet's beautiful blue print dress.
O come with a whistle, come with a call,
Come with a will or come not at all!
Who's clattering there? It's Old Mother
    Hubbard
Playing Grandmother's Footsteps in her
    cupboard—
'Any pies?' said Horner. Old Mother said,
    'None!'
But he put in his finger and pulled out a
    plum.
Up the ladder and down the wall,
A half-penny roll will serve us all:
But Jack rolled right from the top of the hill
And cracked his crown, and so did Jill.

Now for another game—what do you think
Of Hide and Seek or Tiddlywinks,
Oranges and Lemons (O for a taste!)
Or Follow My Leader?—hold on to my
    waist,
Through silvery meadows O follow me,
    follow
Over the hills and home tomorrow;
Through moon-white woods we'll twist and
    twine—
Now, Marjorie Daw, don't break the line.
But Marjorie stopped to play Pig in the
    Middle
With the dish and the spoon while the cat
    played the fiddle.
And the tail swept onward, on with a bound
To the windmill, over the river and round,
Till Wee Willie Winkie overhead
As he flew in the sky, in the witch-way,
    said:
'You children ought to be in bed!'

Girls and boys, go home to rest—
Jenny Wren's asleep in her nest,
The owl has floated back to his willow,
Punch is using his hump as a pillow.
The sleepy children droop and drop,
Unwound as weary spinning top,
And crawl to bed. Miss Bo-peep
(No sheep) is sobbing herself to sleep,
While downstairs huddle into a corner
Miss Muffet, spider, Little Jack Horner.
Open the door, you'll see Mother Hubbard
Curled up like a cat, top shelf in her
    cupboard.

Lastly, dragging leg on leg,
Tarry Awhile and Sleepyhead,
Dozing, climb the window through,
Stretch and yawn .... I'm sleepy too
And wonder, in the moonlight gleaming
What is baby Helen dreaming? ....
Sssh!

      Don't wake her.

          Goodnight.

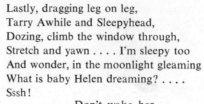

F

A Tiger Indeed

By PHILIP WOODRUFF

THE FOUR TIGER CUBS tumbled happily over each other on a stretch of sunny gravel by the side of a stream. It was a brook of clear water, hardly deep enough now to wet a cub's paws, but not many weeks ago, when the cubs were born, it had been a muddy torrent that would have drowned a deer or a grown tiger. Now the waters had fallen, leaving a clean shingly beach and a stream murmuring over golden stones.

If you had been flying high above the tigers' heads in an aeroplane, you would have seen, far away to the north, the snowy peaks and pinnacles of the Himalayas and beneath you a thick green carpet of tree-tops, stretching as far as you could see either way, making a belt between the dazzling snow of the mountains and the flat blue plains of India, where corn grows and men plough with bullocks.

If your pilot had flown lower, you would have seen that what looked like a carpet was not really flat at all. It was a tangle of steep little hillocks, broken cliffs, folds and ridges made by water running down from the hills. And you would have seen too that it was not all tree tops, but that here and there were glades among the trees where there was tall yellow grass. It was in these open places that the deer came to feed in the evening and it was here that the cubs' mother came to find the deer.

She was uneasy. It was the first time she had brought the cubs so far from the dark ravine where they had been born. There she felt safe; here she was closer to danger. But she knew she must teach them to move through the jungle and so to-day in the early morning sunshine, before she settled to rest after her night's hunting, she had led them through the tangled undergrowth, down the hill, across the glade, gliding through the tall grass as though they were stalking a deer, down to the sunny beach.

The cubs played happily, without fear, like every other young thing, kittens or puppies or small children. Then the biggest found a stick and pretended it was a bone; the others tried to take it away. But he was too strong for them; he was the only male tiger among them and oeing the biggest he got more than his share of food.

The mother tigress uttered a short sharp little grunt, for all the world like a pig. Four little faces, round, fluffy, trying to be fierce, looked up at her. She grunted again, and was on her feet, smooth and lithe in her movements in spite of her size. She was a big tigress, nine feet long from her nose to the tip of her tail, as heavy as three men together and much stronger. She was calling her cubs to tell them the outing was over; it was time to get into thick cover and sleep, for she must start her hunting early in the evening. The cubs were beginning to need meat and she needed a good deal herself. Her mate had been shot before the cubs were born; she had to kill for five.

She grunted again and began to move away, looking back to see if they were following. None of them risked a cuff from that heavy paw. They trotted obediently behind her, four striped figures, the biggest nearly the size of a Newfoundland dog.

They went back to the dark tangled ravine that was their headquarters, and there they slept. The cubs of course still spent most of their time asleep, just as puppies and kittens and babies do. When the sun began to sink their mother woke and fed them, for they still drank milk though it was no longer enough for them. Then she growled at them and walked away.

The cubs knew that they were meant to stay where they were, but the biggest, the tiger, wanted more adventure. He sat up, watching his mother go, and then ran after her.

She had only gone a few yards and then had turned to make sure they were not following. When she saw her son, two long bounds brought her to him. A savage snarl and a cuff with either paw, harder than anything he had ever known before, sent him back to his sisters. He did not try to follow again but sat watching his mother till she disappeared. Then the cubs curled up, making a close solid ball for warmth, and slept.

The tigress was back just before dawn, carrying on her back a spotted deer, very like our own English fallow deer. She had killed it on the edge of an open glade, three-quarters of a mile away, and dragged it through the undergrowth half-a-mile. But dragging left a track that anyone could follow, that no one could miss. When she drew closer to the ravine, she stopped dragging, took out the deer's stomach with her claws as neatly as a countryman guts a rabbit caught in a snare, and gripping the deer's neck in her mouth slipped her shoulder under its body and slung it on to her back. Then she carried it to the cubs, leaving no track but here and there the marks of her feet in the dust.

By the time the sun had risen, they had all fed and the fragments left of the deer could only serve as playthings for the cubs to gnaw at and squabble over. There was no more meat, and the tigress would have to kill again that night; she would have to hunt and kill and carry to the cubs.

Now a tiger that has only to look after himself will not usually kill more than twice a week. He will prowl through the clean night air beneath the starlit sky, along the sandy bed of a stream or through the dewy grass by one of the paths the deer make when they go to

drink; then the sound of teeth cropping grass will tell him there are deer about; then the stalk, the slow, slow, stalk, inch by inch. He must move so that no sound is made; sometimes among dry leaves he will take half an hour to put down one foot, shifting his massive weight to one velvet paw so gently that the leaf is crumbled to powder without a sound. Then the sudden rush, the leap, the warm struggling body beneath him, and the great beast stands on his prey.

But for the tigress who is alone and has growing cubs to feed, hunting must be strictly business. She must kill every night, or nearly every night; she cannot

afford mistakes. And if she is to carry the kill home she cannot afford to waste her strength on long journeys. If the deer are shy, she cannot follow them to another part of the forest. She must turn to cattle.

There are cattle in the forest all the winter, herds brought from far away to graze in the long grass of the glades. They wander among the trees at will by day; towards evening they turn slowly towards the rough enclosure of thorns and sticks their herdsmen have built. But some follow more slowly than the rest; some linger and stray and spend the night in the forest. They are an

easier prey than deer, slow, clumsy and noisy. For the tigress with cubs, they save time and strength.

So the mother of our cubs took to killing cattle. That meant, sooner or later, that men would kill her. Perhaps she knew, when she began, that there was danger, but if so, she soon grew used to the risk, for it was some time before the losses were heavy enough to bring men with guns. Meanwhile, the cubs' appetite grew daily, and she would sometimes hardly trouble to look for deer before she made for the grazing-grounds. The cubs were big enough to come with her now, not to hunt themselves, but to

'When he saw this strange beast bustling and chattering in the moonlight, he stopped.'

come to the kill. She need no longer carry the heavy corpse back to the ravine. Soon she would teach them to kill for themselves and then perhaps it would sometimes be two cows in a night.

The days grew hotter and the nights less chill. There was not so much dew now and the grass was drier in the morning. Instead of looking for beds that would be warm and dry at night, the tigress and her cubs looked for shade and water, cool spots where the breeze would pass beneath the boughs, but still, as always, cover where they could lie hidden from the eyes of men.

The cattle raised thick clouds of dust now as they wound slowly along the forest tracks towards their enclosure. A fog hung over the trail, dun-coloured, opaque, except where the evening sun slashed rays of glory through the trees. The tigers would be afoot already, the tigress waiting for her chance, the cubs eagerly crouching by her side, watching, knowing they must not move.

On one such an evening, they were all five on a high bank above a stream. Behind them was a thick patch of dry golden grass, as tall as a man. In front, there was a drop of fifteen feet to a small river; the water had eaten into the bank and left a sandy yellow cliff. Beyond the river ran a track, along which

the cattle slowly moved through hanging dust, small grey-white humped beasts, thin and poor by English standards. A man and a boy followed. The man walked slowly and in silence, suiting his pace to the cattle. The boy sang at the top of his voice a long long song, rising and falling, wavering and sinking and then rising again in a shout. He darted first to one side and then to the other, rounding up the stragglers.

Even if they had looked at the top of the bank, even if there had been no dust, the men would hardly have seen the fierce striped faces of the mother tigress and her son. The yellow grass was patterned with black shadow; you might look and look and never see the heavy band of black that crosses a tiger's brow. The mother was crouched on the edge of the bank, her head flattened to the ground, the tip of her tail twitching a very little. The cubs had been left a few yards further back; the tiger, the big one, always the most daring, had crept forward until he too could see what was passing. He licked his lips as he watched the cattle.

The sound of the boy's singing died away. The dust began to settle. The herd had passed, but the tigers did not move. The sun was down; it was growing darker moment by moment. At last,

it happened as the tigress had hoped. A belated cow came slowly along the track, following the herd but far behind them. The tigress showed no sign; not a muscle seemed to move. Already she was tense and crouched for her spring; there was no need to gather herself.

The cow came slowly along the track. By the water's edge, below the bank, it paused for a moment as though half in mind to drink. The tigress sprang. Her heavy weight crushed the little grey cow to the ground and her great jaws wrenched at the head. Its neck was dislocated at once; it could hardly have known what had happened.

The tigress stood on her prey looking round. She felt none of that exultation in the kill that would have been hers if this had been a deer, and she alone in the forest. She was out in the dangerous open, on bare sand, where she could be seen from a hundred yards away; that alone made her uneasy. And her cubs were close.

She was a big tigress but even she could not carry a cow up a perpendicular fifteen foot cliff of sand. She looked up stream. There a side stream came in, fifty yards away, and the sandy cliff tapered down to nothing. She dragged the body along the track by the side of the water, through the shallow river, into the grass. Deep into the cover she dragged it, and only when she was in the middle of the grass patch behind the cubs did she call them. They came eagerly, and the whole family spent the night tearing the flesh and growling over the bones.

Towards dawn, the tigress led the way to the river to drink; then back into the grass, passing the few remaining bones, the horns and skull, of the cow, to a hillock that would catch the breeze, crowned with two or three shady trees. Here, deep in six-foot grass, they settled down for the day.

But if they had written to the newspapers and published an advertisement, the tigers could hardly have said more clearly what they had been doing. There was a dark dry patch where some of the cow's blood had soaked into the sand. There was the track of her body in the soft dust, as though a sack had been dragged, with legs trailing behind it; there, in the wet ground where they had drunk, were the marks of their feet, clear for any man to read, a big tigress and cubs, three or four of them. The sand was dimpled everywhere with great footprints; pools of shadow lay in them when the first level rays of the sun reached the bank.

Anyone who knew even a little about tigers could see at once that the kill had been dragged into the patch of grass and could guess that, as there was shade and water nearby, the killers would be sleeping for the day near the scene of their meal. Anyone could guess that.

It was nearly noon when the biggest

cub woke. He sat up, stretched, yawned and listened. The forest was still; everything was resting in the dry burning heat; no movement of deer, no cry even of jungle fowl or monkey. He listened; nothing, all was still. His mother he could see a yard away, lying flat in sleep; his sisters were still. He was conscious that something had wakened him, but since his mother was asleep, all must be well. He was settling to sleep again when the bang of a shotgun ended the silence. Echoes rang; flocks of parakeet screamed; there was a squawk of outraged jungle-fowl.

Tigress and cubs were awake, the cubs trembling with fear, the mother sitting up, looking back towards the river and the sound of the shot. She growled a little growl to the cubs to be still; she looked towards the river and listened, her teeth bared in a silent snarl, her whiskers twitching. There were voices now, men's voices, a clapping of hands, the sound of large movements in the grass. Elephants had come up from the river on either side of the high bank from which the tigers had watched the cattle. They were moving to meet each other. They were going backwards and forwards, beating the grass with their trunks, like men cutting a field of corn. The men on their backs were calling to each other, clapping their hands. There were no more shots.

The tigress did not want to move. She knew that movement betrays. It is the unwary deer, moving idly, that reveals itself to the ear or eye of the hunter. She hated moving by day. But elephants and men were drawing nearer; she must go. She uttered that odd pig-like grunt that called the cubs and moved away. She looked once over her shoulder; they were following.

The tigress wanted to get away from the river, for that was where the track lay, where men came and went, where there was always danger. And she wanted to get away from those voices, to the tangled undergrowth of the deep ravines that led up into the mountains. She did not know that while she slept men had slipped silently through the trees on every side of the grass patch, that there were men hiding in the trees ahead of her. She moved swiftly but without effort, at a tiger's walk, which is faster than a man's fast walk, the head held low, the great limbs striding smoothly. The cubs had to trot to keep up.

They were coming to the edge of the long grass. Here the trees began, and beneath the trees there was scrub that would hide a tiger, but between the long grass and the scrub were a few yards lying open. The tigress feared the open; she paused here, her great head and half her shoulders thrust out of the grass, looking left and right, snarling a silent snarl of fear and anger. But she did not look up into the trees.

The ringing stinging crack of a rifle. The tigress uttered one short deep roar,

one tremendous cavernous cough; she bounded forward. She went in great leaps, clearing the shrubs and bushes, tearing through the forest, with no thought now of hiding.

The big cub ran at her heels, though he was soon far behind her, for he could not leap over bushes as she did. But there was no doubt where she had gone; he could hear the crashing of her flight. He ran, blind with terror, trying to get to his mother, his own mother who never before had left him forgotten.

The crashing ahead ceased. He ran on and found her. There she lay, sprawled on a bank as though she were asleep. But he knew she was not asleep. There was his mother, who meant food and safety and life, and she did not move. She was dead. He knew what death meant for he knew what had happened to the deer and the cattle. There was blood on her coat and on the ground, blood oozing from her mouth.

He did not stay by her long. Eager, excited voices were drawing closer and the crashing and flapping of the elephants. He ran on into thick undergrowth, a sick frightened little cub; he crouched trembling till nightfall. At night he came back to where he had seen her lying, but there was nothing left but a dark dry patch where her blood had soaked into the dust, and a piece of ground trampled and defiled by men and elephants.

The cub was alone now, for he did not know where his sisters were. He was alone now and he was hungry; if he was to survive he must learn to look after himself and to be a tiger indeed.

He was very lonely and very hungry. He went back to the bones of the cow and gnawed those but there was no meat on them. He went on, prowling along the forest paths as he had seen his mother do, till he heard deer feeding. But when he tried to stalk them his impatience gave him away. There was a sharp bell-like hoot from a doe and they scattered, crashing away through the trees far faster than he could run.

It was the same the second night. He could never get close enough to deer for the pounce with which the tiger kills. In the early morning, tired and weak, but desperate with hunger he began to hunt the jungle-fowl. He would see a hen, pecking and picking, coming closer

through the bushes; he would freeze to stillness, wait, wait, wait, and then she would turn away and he must pounce from too far, only to see her disappear into a tree with an indignant squawk. Or just as he drew close, the twitching tip of his tail would give him away.

At midday, he caught a lizard. It was not very satisfying, but it was something, and he soon found he could catch more lizards. He went on catching them until his need for sleep was stronger than his hunger. But when he woke, towards midnight, he was hungrier than ever.

The sounds of the forest were all round him. He heard the hoots of deer, disturbed by some other enemy far away, and some large bird, peacock or vulture, stirred on a branch above his head; there were wild pig rootling near the river. He snarled at the thought of the pig and his mouth watered, but he was afraid of pig. Even a grown tiger must be hungry to risk a fight with a wild boar. He found a dry water-course where his feet made no sound on the sand and he need not push his way noisily through thorns; he prowled along this, hoping, listening.

There was something moving ahead of him, too far for him to distinguish one sound from another. He moved a little faster. The sounds became clearer. It was something moving unconcernedly, making no attempt to keep quiet. Now, apart from men, no ground animal in the forest moves in this way but the elephant and the porcupine. This was a porcupine. The tiger-cub crept closer, but when he saw this strange beast, bustling and chattering in the moonlight, he stopped. Its carelessness frightened him. And when the porcupine saw him and advanced, chattering angrily, every spine erect so that it suddenly looked twice as big as before, he turned and ran with his tail between his legs. He would have run to his mother if she had been alive. He was still very little.

He did have one good stalk that night. He got quite close to a young *sambhar* stag, as big as a red deer on Exmoor. But he lost his nerve again, fortunately for himself; he crouched trembling in the grass, eager to sink his teeth in the haunch of the stag if it were dead but afraid of the living horns. Then the stag saw him, stamped its foot and shook its head. Again he ran away.

He killed nothing that night, nor for seven more nights. For ten days he lived on lizards that he caught by day. He grew thin and weak. But he went on hoping and hunting.

On the eleventh evening, as the light was fading and the last flights of parakeets flashed screaming to the trees, he crouched on a hillock overlooking a glade near the river. It was a small glade, covered with grass, not the six-foot elephant-grass in which he had spent the last night with his mother, but shorter, sweeter grass. And even in the dusk he could see something moving, something that slowly, fearfully, with long pauses,

(Continued on page 84)

BOY FILM STAR

by Nora Laing

Claude Jarman, aged eleven, feeding Flag, the fawn with whom he starred in his first film.

WHEN YOU SEE A FILM do you wonder about the boy and girl screen stars, and envy them the life they lead?

'Distant fields are always greenest' and although many motion picture children are perfectly happy with their lot, there are some who would willingly change places with you.

Probably many of you saw 'The Yearling', the picture in which Claude Jarman was such a success. From being an average, unknown schoolboy, he became a world figure, but with the glamour there came also plenty of hard work. Look, with me, more closely at his life and see for yourselves whether you would really like to change places with him.

Until he was ten years old Claude lived in Nashville, Tennessee. This American town, one of the most important in the South, has a population of 200,000 and is about the size of Birmingham. The Jarmans' house was a seven-roomed bungalow with a small front garden, called a 'yard' in the United States, with a patch of lawn, a magnolia tree and some shrubs. His family consists of his mother, father (a railroad accountant) and sister, Mildred Anne, one year older than her brother.

Each morning, Claude, like many British schoolboys, had to be hauled out of bed by his parents between seven-thirty and eight o'clock and sent to wash and dress in time for breakfast. This meal was usually set in the kitchen. Instead of porridge, Southerners, like a

great many South Africans, eat what they call grits, which is maize ground up fine.

In the winter time he set off for school, about half-an-hour's walk from his home, dressed in the usual clothes of an American schoolboy, corduroys and sweater. In the summer he wore blue jeans. Usually he teamed up with a few of his buddies who were also in the fifth grade. (The fifth grade corresponds to about the third form.) He studied arithmetic, American history, spelling and English.

When school was over at half past three, he raced home for a good tea of, perhaps, hot biscuits, strawberry shortcake and creamed chicken, before joining the gang to make for the drug store (known as 'the sweet shop' in the South) where they sipped sodas and ice-creams.

Southern people are particularly hospitable. Their homes are always open to their friends and especially the children of their friends. They believe in allowing boys and girls to entertain freely in their houses, usually on Fridays and Saturdays (weekdays are given up to homework) and the gang met to dance, play games, and as Claude himself puts it 'horse around generally'. It was in the autumn of 1944 when he was eleven, that the whole pattern of Claude's life changed.

During class the teacher called him up to the blackboard to demonstrate an arithmetic problem. He was standing, chalk in hand, his very bright blue eyes a little puzzled as he tried to work out the solution when the door opened and

in came a strange man. After one quick look of curiosity Claude paid no more attention to the visitor. He wondered vaguely why he was in the class-room but the man might have been anyone's father although something about him looked different from the usual run of Southern men that he knew. The stranger looked at Claude for a long while, then walked over to the teacher. To his surprise the teacher called him to her desk and introduced him to the visitor. 'This is Mr. Clarence Brown, Claude,' she told him. 'He comes from Hollywood and is a director of motion pictures.'

This information did not mean much to Claude so he just said 'howdy', felt rather self-conscious and started to slink back to his seat. But the strange man began talking to him again. He asked him whether he had ever done any acting. To which he replied, 'Only a couple of school plays,' and to whether he would like to act, Claude said he didn't know. Then, just before the visitor departed he said, as he shook Claude's hand, 'Tell your parents I'll be round to see them.'

This remark puzzled the boy. Why on earth should this Hollywood man want to see his parents. It all seemed, to use his own expression, 'a bit screwy' to him. But he delivered the message to his mother who smiled vaguely and did not appear to pay much attention to it.

The next day the director appeared and for a long time he remained closeted in the living-room with his parents. Later in the day when the visitor had left, Claude's father told him that Mr. Brown was going to produce a picture called 'The Yearling'. It was about a lad of Claude's age who owned a deer as a pet, and the studio was looking for a boy of a suitable type to play the part. Mr. Brown had been visiting schools and playgrounds throughout the eight southern states and by the time he reached Nashville he had looked over 12,000 boys between the ages of 10-12 years, but until he saw Claude, he had not found the ideal type to portray the character of 'Jody' in Marjorie Kinnan Rawlings' novel 'The Yearling'.

Claude was rather worried about the whole thing. He knew nothing about stage acting and less about the films. He enjoyed seeing westerns and thrillers on the screen but he had never had ambitions to act in them himself. He rather hoped that nothing would come of it and Mr. Brown would go back to Hollywood and forget about him. But Mr. Brown didn't. Claude was sent for.

When he and his father came to Hollywood for the test, it was his first trip away from home. Claude was given an appointment at the M.G.M. studios. He was dressed by the wardrobe department in the clothes he wears in 'The Yearling', and was told the lines he had to say. Cameras were focused on him. He felt in a daze but did exactly what he was told and then went home.

Although the director and producer

selected Claude mostly on his looks, natural brightness and Southern accent, his screen test proved him to be a natural actor, and so, as you all know, Claude got the part. Many of his contemporaries considered him the luckiest American youngster of 1945.

* * *

When Claude had been signed up for the part of Jody, he moved to Hollywood and, with his father, took a room in a hotel near the studio at Culver City, which is about 15 miles from Hollywood.

Before Claude could begin the actual work in the picture he had to meet and talk with many studio heads, and make the acquaintance of the rest of the cast and company. Then he had to be groomed for the part. Among other things this entailed the constant wearing of blue jeans when at the studio or the hotel, letting his hair grow long, and going barefoot.

Each day he had to be at the studio by nine. He was always accompanied by his father because there is a studio ruling that any boy or girl actress under seventeen must be accompanied by a guardian and attend school on the lot for a certain number of hours. It was a little humiliating for Claude to discover that the other five pupils were all girls. Besides attending classes, he had to spend considerable time being taught dramatics by the studio's dramatic coach. In the afternoons he was taken to the zoo where he had to make friends with the animals, especially the deer.

Those of you who saw the picture know that much of the tragedy, drama, comedy and pathos revolves around 'Flag' the pet deer of eleven-year-old Jody Baxter. But besides Flag, there were 469 animals, including 126 deer, 9 bears, 37 dogs, 50 assorted wild birds, 17 buzzards, 10 alligators, 1 owl, 83 chickens, 36 pigs, 8 rattlesnakes, 18 squirrels, 4 horses and 17 racoons employed in the film. Flag brought innumerable headaches to both the producer and director, because although wild deer of the forest were photographed for the picture, there had to be a nucleus of tame deer for two reasons, (a) it was necessary for deer of various ages to learn to know and trust the boy Jody and be his pet; (b) as a number of fawns were needed for the picture, the studio had to go into the fawn breeding business. For both purposes tame deer were gathered in several states and brought to California. Claude spent hundreds of hours feeding and caring for Flag because complete friendship and trust between the two had to show on the screen to make 'The Yearling' a success.

While Claude was taking his preliminary training at the studio, workmen were busy preparing a certain section of Florida for the shooting of the outdoor scenes. At the end of two months, Claude and his father, together with the rest of the cast and company were sent by train and cars to Florida on location, to start the shooting of the picture.

They came to the State in the midst of one of the worst dry spell in years. The sun glared down out of a cloudless sky. The real corn in the field wilted under the drought and the prop men had to run to the nurseries for corn and tobacco which had been specially grown in pots. The vans with the deer in them had to be surrounded by tubs of ice with sheets let down into them so that all air from outside was cooled. Later, when sunshine was needed the rains came! And —it poured for weeks.

On location, the director would not permit his players to use artificial make-up, because in the story, they are outdoor people. So the sun was supposed to make them up instead. When it rained the cast, including Claude, grew paler and paler. Then out came an order that every player must spend fifteen minutes under the sun lamp every morning.

Claude and his father stayed at a hotel in the nearest town. As this was seventy-five miles away from the location they had to get up each morning at six in order to be at work on time. Before breakfast, the fawns had to be fed too. This had to be done every two hours throughout the day, with specially prepared milk. For the first two months on location it happened to be summer holidays, so Claude had no schooling, but after that a teacher arrived and he had to go to school for several hours daily. Apart from these hours in the school tent, he worked on the picture in the grilling heat. There was little if any shade, and by six o'clock in the evening, when he was free to drive back to the hotel he was so hot and exhausted that all he had the energy for was supper and bed. Only very occasionally, usually on Sundays, did he have the time or energy to play croquet or shuffleboard.

There must have been many a time when he thought regretfully of his pals back in Nashville gathered together at the old swimming pool or playing baseball on a vacant lot.

All this time while Claude was gulping down his hurried meals, scrambling over rocks, chasing Flag, and being 'Jody', the Baxter cabin and farm, where most of the action in the story takes place, was being re-created on stage 15 in the studio at Culver City. The cabin and rail fences erected in Florida were taken down and shipped, log by log and rail by rail, for re-erection in the studio as soon as they were finished with on location. Many authentic props were also taken back from Florida such as old ploughs, and the knife used to cut shakes from Florida timber. Eighty one thousand and twenty-three pounds of Spanish moss, the distinctive feature of the Florida forests, was transported from Florida to California.

When he got back to Culver City Claude hoped the worst was over. Swimming, basket-ball and football for him. But he soon found he was mistaken. From now on, he was told, until completion of the picture, he must be

on the M.G.M. lot by nine o'clock each morning, with the sole exception of Sundays. Saturday would be a half holiday. All dreams of a carefree life speedily vanished. Accompanied by his parents he was at the studio punctually each day primed for work.

On arrival, his father went directly to the set, and chatted with the other parents or members of the cast, while Claude was hurried to his dressing room, to change into whatever costume he had to wear that day. The necessary make-up was put on, his hair combed in the desired style and he joined the rest of the cast on stage 15. If on arrival, he was told that he would not be needed for half-an-hour, two hours, or even ten minutes, he was rushed off to the school-room where he remained until sent for by the director.

He was pleased to find on his return to the studio school that there was now a sprinkling of boys as well as girls. Not only were there Margaret O'Brien and Elizabeth Taylor, but also Butch Jenkins and Dean Stockwell, both, however, very much younger than he. All these children were also working in a film, although not in the same one, so they were in and out all day like Claude, fitting in their compulsory three hours.

It was seldom that the Jarmans got home before six-thirty, and eight-thirty saw Claude in bed. These regular hours he was forced to keep proved to be a good thing because out of the fourteen months that he worked in ' The Yearling ' he was only absent one day. But there were times when he earnestly longed to throw away the role of ' Jody ' and get into a football scrimmage instead.

At last the film was finished. On the night of the premiere at the famous Carthay Theatre, Hollywood, Claude and his family were tremendously excited.

With his mother and sister in new evening dresses, he and his father arrived at the theatre feeling very self-conscious as he realised he would have to be stared at by hundreds of eyes.

Most of you know the rest. What a success ' The Yearling ' was and how popular Claude was in the part. Since then he has been in four films and is now working on his fifth, ' The Outrider ' with Joel McCrea and Arlene Dahl. Claude, now fifteen years old, admits that both good and bad attend the life of a child screen player. When he is a little older, he intends to retire from the motion picture business and go to a university, preferably one in his home town of Nashville. He has not yet decided whether he will study medicine or take an agricultural course and become a farmer, but he thinks it will probably be the latter. So, while many of you are probably wishing that you might some day have the luck to be in films, Claude Jarman is planning to get out of them, saving all he can from his salary in order to make *his* ambitions, far from the realm of picture making, come true.

2

3

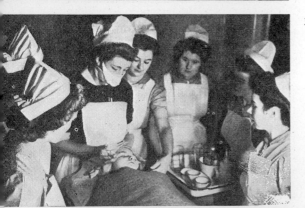

4

What are you going to be?

A HOSPITAL NURSE

STUDENT NURSE Training to be a nurse *used* to mean facing grim and tyrannical conditions, apparently designed to see just how much you could stand of hard work, uncomfortable living, and exceptionally unsympathetic treatment.

Now the story is very different. Nurses are given good conditions both for working and living. Their days are filled with a balance of lectures (1) physical training (2), and work in the wards and recreation. In their first year they watch their seniors do dressings (3), and while carrying trays (4) learn and absorb a good deal about diets, and the routine of life and work in a hospital. Nearly all hospitals provide each nurse with her own bedroom, common rooms and the chance to make friends and join in whatever is going on, or if she prefers, to read and study quietly.

After about six months she does her first Night Duty, and is shown by the Night Staff how the hours from 8.30 p.m. to 7.30 a.m. are spent; rounds of the ward, vigilance for any call from a patient (later writing up reports and records), the welcome hour off for a meal and the bustle to have all in readiness to hand over to the nurses coming on duty in the morning.

The cap is an important part of the uniform (provided free) for by its shape it shows the nurse's grade. With four weeks' holiday a year, a day off a week, and £200 a year from which she contributes to her board and keep, a Student has a good start to her new life.

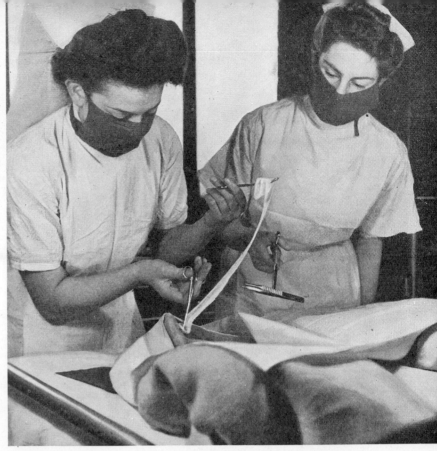

5   6

SECOND YEAR STUDENT

Having passed her first exam, the student now has more responsibility. She administers medicines and does simple dressings (5) and (6), all the time keeping on with her studies and lectures (7). She is given experience in different wards, surgical, orthopædic, children's, and, of course, the Operating Theatre. This fills in the picture of what happens all through the many departments in a hospital, for apart from actual nursing of patients there is a big administrative side which includes housekeeping, teaching, dieticians, and numerous other branches. The student will later decide if she wants to specialise in any of these. Her pay has increased to £210 a year, out of which she pays £100 for board and lodging. Non-resident students get laundry and meals on duty free.

7

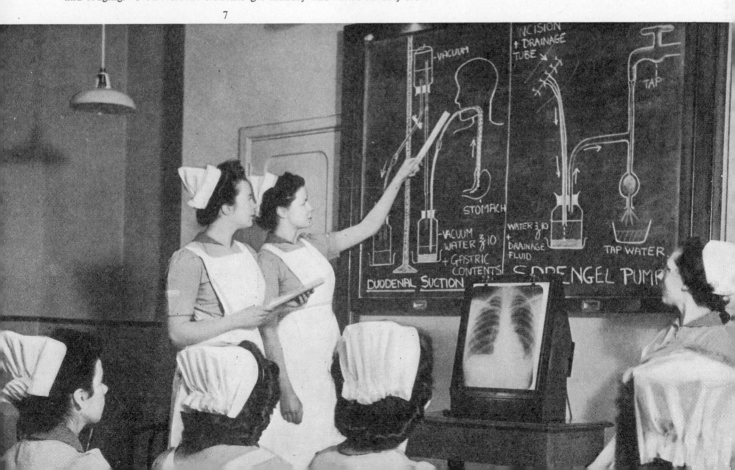

THIRD YEAR STUDENT

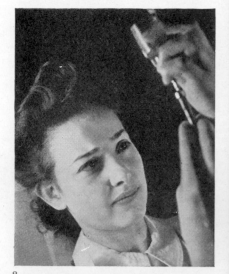

8

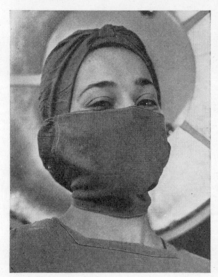

9

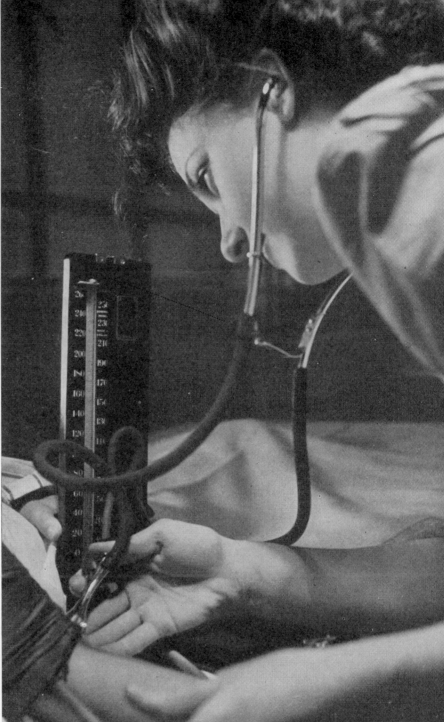

10

The student has her most important exam ahead of her at the end of the third year. She tackles such things as hypodermics (8) work in the theatre (9) and taking blood pressure (10). She knows something of the work in every ward (11) and on passing her exam qualifies as a State Registered Nurse, earning upwards of £315 a year. She may specialise, she may make her way up the ladder and become a Matron in her turn, or she may leave hospital and do private Nursing, or the many other branches open to her. She can become a Midwife, District Nurse, Health Visitor, or Industrial Nurse, working from her own home.

For certain branches of Nursing, such as District Nurse, extra training is essential. Children's Nursing (12) has a six year training, but the advantage that you can start at 17, and not wait until you are 18, which is otherwise the case.

11

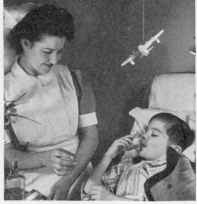

12

A Hundred Years Ago

BY MARGUERITE STEEN

'ARE YOU A GREAT SCHOLAR?'
Lucy Roberts asked little Grace Crawley, on the morning she visited Hogglestock.

'I don't know,' said Grace with a sheepish face. 'I am in Greek Delectus, and the irregular verbs.'

'And she knows an Ode of Horace by heart,' said Bob.

That chapter in Anthony Trollope's *Framley Parsonage* always gave me a shock. Was Grace (who, at nine years old, and, apart from having her hair bundled up in a net, looks in the illustration not unlike Alice in Wonderland) an infant prodigy, or just a show-off little prig?

Mr. Crawley, Grace's father and schoolmaster, was already behind the times, for it is more than a hundred years since it began to dawn on parents and teachers that children might learn their lessons more easily if they were made a little more entertaining; although 'A Lady', who compiled a textbook much used in schools of the day, 'had not thought it advisable to introduce any woodcuts or engravings which might take off the attention of children for whom this little book is professedly designed.'

This was not the opinion of Mrs. Markham, whose *History of England* was the most famous, if not the very first, of the attempts to make dates palatable to the little scholars of the early part of the nineteenth century.

One can't help thinking how Grace and Bob would have enjoyed Mrs. Markham, each of whose illustrated chapters starts off with a good, solid chunk of historical information, then branches out into delightful conversations between teacher and pupils. We haven't gone far before we know nearly as much about the rather priggish and superior Richard, aged ten, ('I shall be glad, mamma, when you come to a good king. It is very disagreeable to hear about bad people') as we know about the Norman Conquest. We are as ready to agree with George's—'Well, I like the fighting days of Edward III better than the dressing-up days of Richard II. If those fashions ever come in again, I'll wear flannel and fustian, and give up being a fine gentleman,' as we are to box Richard's ears for his smug comment on the customs of the Plantagenet nobility—'I am sure I had rather dine in our neat little dining-room with only our quiet servant to wait on us than in one of those great halls with all that noise and dirt.'

George becomes our favourite when he gives his silly little sister Mary away with a giggle: 'Mary wants to know if all kings sleep with their crowns by their bedsides!'—which makes one think there is something in it when Mary, after listening to her mother's description of a court jester, simpers, 'I could have done very well for some little princess's fool!' and gets smartly put in her place with, 'It requires some cleverness to be a good fool.'

It is the swashbuckling George who, in reference to the sports of the thirteenth century, gleefully chortles, 'The games of broken bones and bloody noses, Mary!—and mamma, I dare say, will tell us all about *them!*'—which Mrs. Markham, evidently knowing all about the tastes of small boys, promptly does.

Mrs. Markham was a grand story-teller, and it is hardly surprising when, in the middle of her account of the Great Fire of London, Mary breaks out:

'Oh, pray, mamma, do not go on with any more of that sad story!'—on which, you may be sure, George chips in—

'Do, mamma, do go on. I want to hear all about it.'

'How am I to please you both?' Mrs. Markham reasonably inquires, and one may fancy George pulling a face at Mary's answer:

'If there is anything good you may tell it, but nothing more that is horrible!'—which leaves one with the suspicion that Mary suffered from nightmares, and probably put her fingers in her ears during passages that made George bounce with delight.

Not all text books, however, were as lively as Mrs. Markham, and the little girls in mob caps, with frocks right off their shoulders, and little boys in long pantaloons with big straw hats who, according to Kate Greenaway's illustrations, studied their lessons from *The Children's Guide* cannot have had as much fun as Richard, George and Mary.

They must, however, have acquired an amazing vocabulary, for, from the sentence—

'Miss Jane Bond had a new doll and her good Aunt who bought it, gave her some cloth to make a shift for it—'—it is a mere forty pages to—

'Bi—tu'—min—ous. Sub—lu'—na—ry. As—tro'—lo—ger. Het'—er—o—dox.'

It is also something of a shock to come on the list of 'Moral and Practical Observations to be committed to memory at an early age,' of whose four closely printed pages the following is by no means an exaggerated sample:

'Complaisance renders a superior amiable, an equal agreeable and an inferior acceptable—' which, when you come to think of it, might easily have been rendered, Good manners make you popular in any company. One can only

hope that the pretty drawings, which are on almost every page, helped the young reader past his formidable spelling lists, his exhortations to 'look down upon the earth and see what wisdom and power ordained the whole,' and brought him happily to his 'Grace after Meals,' which ends the book.

We now come to the volume which

I mentioned at the beginning, by the lady who did not believe in pictures. *The Child's Guide to Knowledge* opens on a portentous note:

Q. 'What is the world?'
A. 'The earth we live in.'
Q. 'Who made it?'
A. 'The great and good God.'

Q. 'Are there not many things in it you would like to know about?'

What can 'A', as a polite child, answer but 'Yes, very much'? There is no cheerful Richard, or George, or Mary to share the brunt of the questioning; only poor little 'A', whose answers to the most unreasonable questions come with an amazing patness.

'How,' demands 'Q', for no imaginable reason, 'is butter made in Chile?'

Instead of being floored, as you or I might be, 'A' perks up to reply:

'The cream is put into large gourds or dry skins, which are then slung across a donkey's back, and the animal is kept trotting round a yard until the butter is made—'

—which suggests grounds for inquiry by the R.S.P.C.A.

'Q', who is obviously a real bully, after dodging from betel-nut to Hasselquist, Mark Antony to chamois leather, and japanned cabinets to putty—regardless of any line of connection—suddenly swoops on the subject of gold; which 'A', whose head by now, must be spinning, manages to remember is 'procured from the rivers Senegal, Gambia and Niger.'

This is not, however, enough for 'Q', who nags on:

'Has not Africa always been famous for gold?'

At which 'A', drawing a long breath, prepares for a last effort, and gasps out—

'Yes; the ancients had much from it, particularly King Solomon, for the famous Ophir is thought to have been where Sofala now stands; and Herodotus tells us that the king of Ethiopia brought Cambyses all his prisoners bound in chains of gold—'—before being taken away in an ambulance with brain fever; while 'Q', doubtless with a horrible grin of satisfaction, starts thinking up a fresh set of posers for the next victim.

According to the pencilled dates in the book beside me, about two pages were set at a time, to be learned by heart, and it takes little to imagine how 'A' must have dreaded the weekly General Knowledge lesson, and what a relief it must have been to turn to *Mary's Grammar,* by Mrs. Marcet, which at least begins on a human note:

'Miss Thompson says, that now I am seven years old, I ought to begin to learn grammar: but I do not want to learn grammar; it is all nonsense; only see what a number of hard words that I cannot understand!'

NOUNS, verbs and adjectives were, however, made distinct to Mary by a series of little stories—all, of course, of a highly moral and improving nature, but quite funny and 'real' enough to amuse children of to-day. 'The Secret,' about George, who invited William to his birthday party, but made him promise not to tell, and about the state of misery William was plunged into by his mother's acceptance of a dreary invitation to spend the day with his grandmother on the very date of the party, has the kind of quiet tension that makes one read on, without bothering about parts of speech or nominative and objective cases.

Little Jane Moore, from whose lesson books I have been quoting was, no doubt, proud and pleased to receive the volume which, now yellowed and shabby, must then have been smart in its stiff brown cover, in the back of which is pasted a label of crimson leather with lettering in bright gold leaf:

JANE MOORE
REWARD OF MERIT
MANESTY LANE SCHOOL
1837.

She must have worked hard, for the following year also she won a prize, and the two stood side by side on her bookshelf: *Moral and Religious Poetry* and *The Fairchild Family*: that astonishing children's book of the nineteenth century in which Mr. Fairchild, in order to teach Lucy, aged nine, Emily, aged seven, and five-year-old Henry not to quarrel, takes them to view a corpse hanging on a gibbet! Whether little Jane enjoyed this gruesome history there is no means of telling, but if Jane had lived long enough to hear her great-grand-children recite 'The pretty cow all red and white,' from the *Child's Garden of Verse,* she would certainly have remembered some lines from her *Moral and Religious Poetry*.

'The cows are lying in the shade,
The sun they find too hot.
They seek the shelter of yon glade
To find a cooler spot.
What useful animals they are,
Yielding us such sweet food;
They well deserve the greatest care
For giving milk so good.
And cream and butter too, and cheese,
From milk we can produce . . .'

'Ah, children,' says Great-Grand-mamma Jane, breaking off with a sigh, 'I'm afraid your Mr. Robert Louis Stevenson is only a copy-cat after all!'

A TIGER INDEED

(*Continued from page 77*)

was making for the path that led to the river.

If nothing frightened the thing in the grass, it would reach the trail just at the foot of the hillock where the cub lay. But that would be too far for a rush and a pounce. He must get down the hillock and be closer to the path before the thing showed itself.

What wind there was in his face and it was an easy stalk. He was close to the path when a head peered out from the grass. He froze to stillness. It was a barking deer, a small brown deer not much taller at the shoulder than a man's knee. When it is frightened it makes a noise like a dog barking. This one was a doe, and he knew how succulent her flesh would be. She waited, she sniffed, she listened. At last she came out, followed by her fawn. She herself was hardly as big as the cub, but he had

never killed anything bigger than a lizard. It was the fawn on which he set his eyes.

The moment came. The cub sprang and he was lucky. His teeth found the fawn's neck, his weight fell on its back. It was not much bigger than a terrier and its neck was broken; half by chance, he had killed it in true tiger style.

But before he had time to realise what he had done, a small hard head hit him in the ribs and a sharp forefoot slashed the skin of his side. In his hunger he had thought of nothing but the meal the fawn would make; now the doe was upon him.

He was hurt, surprised and angry. He lost his temper and with something that was trying to be a roar he charged the little doe. She tried to meet the charge with another. Her head missed his face and struck his left shoulder. At the same moment the claws of his right paw gripped her back, his teeth sank in her soft neck. Now she ran back to get

away, but the cub clung to her, tearing and biting. His blood was up, there was triumph in his heart as well as fierce hunger. She staggered and at last she fell. The cub clung on grimly. Her blood and her life ran away fast into the dusty ground. He clung on, biting deeper and deeper, till at last she lay still.

The cub stood on his prey. He was out in the open trail, out in the dangerous open, away from the covering grass. Jackals and hyenas by night, vultures by day would be eager to share his food. Enemies would find him. Without pausing to eat, he did as all tigers do. He dragged his meal into deep cover, first the doe, then the fawn. Then he lay down, his amber eyes afire, and with loving care began to lick the flesh of his kill.

He had killed. He was not going to starve. He would live and grow. He had killed and his heart was full of pride, for he felt that he was no longer a cub. Now at last he was a tiger indeed.

FIRE-MAKING

by Richard Graves

The method described here is taught at the 'School for Adventure' in Australia.

A REAL ADVENTURER is never at a loss for a fire. He uses the method which was used long before flint and steel, of friction between two sticks.

The equipment you need is a bow, a headpiece, a drill and a footpiece. Your bow has a thong, and this goes round a straight stick, or drill, so that when you draw the bow backwards and forwards the drill revolves rapidly, and so, spinning in a hole in a footpiece, it gets hotter and hotter, and grinds out a tiny spark which you must nurse into a flame. There are two separate steps to getting fire, first the spark, then flame from the spark.

Your bow should be cut from a green,

Sydney Morning Herald
You draw the bow backwards and forwards and must keep the drill revolving steadily.

or half green piece of wood, shaped like a pistol with the barrel part fifteen inches long, and the handle four inches. A hawthorn hedge is a good place to look for a suitable piece of wood. The barrel part should be about an half inch thick, and the handle about one inch. Trim them both clear of twigs or thorns, and flatten the far end of the barrel part till it is about a quarter of an inch thick. Half an inch from the end burn a small hole with hot wire. The hole should be about one eighth of an inch in diameter.

The thong is a piece of belt lacing (any saddler will sell you a six foot length). The belt lacing will be about a quarter inch wide, so split it in half lengthways with a sharp knife. This will give you two one-eighth strips. Pass the end of one of these through the hole at the end of the barrel, and tie a thumb knot on the top side (the side above the handle). The other end is wound round the handle and fastened with a clove hitch. The thong should be slack across the bow.

Now take a chip of knotty hardwood which will fit comfortably inside the palm of your hand. On the underside bore a hole about half an inch deep and half an inch across. This is the headpiece.

There are many woods which will serve for drill and footpiece, which are the two pieces which get the spark, but willow is one of the best. Both must be perfectly dry. The drill should be about three-quarters of an inch thick, straight, about a foot long, and pointed at both ends. The footpiece should be not less than an inch wide and about half-an-inch thick. On the flat side bore a shallow hole in which you will start the drill, and on the edge make an undercut 'V', with the sides perfectly smooth. The point of this 'V' should go to the edge of the hole you have bored on the top. Collect some tinder, and you are ready to start. Very dry fluffy bark fibre, or dry teased grass are among the best tinders.

Take a generous pile of tinder, and put it under the 'V' cut in the footpiece. Twist the drill through the thong so that the thong completely encircles the drill, which must be on the outer side and not between the bow and the thong. The thong coming from the bow handle must be on top. Put one end of the drill into the shallow hole in the footpiece, and the other end in the hole in the headpiece, so that when you draw the bow backwards and forwards the thong rotates the drill, and at the same time rides freely up and down on the drill. If you have the thong

on the drill in the wrong way it will cross itself and jam.

Kneel on your right knee and put the ball of your left foot on the end of the footpiece to keep it steady. The headpiece is held in the left hand, and the left wrist is pressed against the shin of the left leg. This leaves your right side free to operate the bow. Do not press too heavily on the headpiece to start with. When the drill begins to rotate you will see smoke at the lower end and must keep the drill revolving steadily, until a pile of 'punk,' or finely ground charcoally substance is in the 'V'. When the smoke is pouring freely from the drill and footpiece, press rather more heavily on the headpiece and work the drill rapidly for about a dozen strokes. This should start the spark. (You will know it is there because when you stop the drill there will be a thin thread of smoke rising from the 'V' cut in the footpiece.) Remove the drill and blow gently on the 'punk' until you can see the red glow of the coal. Pick up the tinder and remove the footpiece, leaving the coal lying in a nest of tinder. Fold the tinder over the coal, and either blow into the ball of tinder over the coal, or hold it loosely in your hand over your head to get a strong draught of air blowing on the coal. When smoke is coming thickly, drop the ball and give it a few strong puffs, and the whole will burst into flame. Once you have got the knack you will never lose it.

It is claimed by some that a little finely powdered charcoal put into the hole of the footpiece makes the spark easier to get. If the headpiece starts to smoke rub a little lead pencil in the hole, or lightly grease it.

The bow, footpiece, drill and headpiece for firelighting. Note how the thong is twisted round the drill.

FEBRUARY IN THE COUNTRY

(Continued from page 59)

flocks to come in to roost, can be the greatest sport, for a pigeon curling in a highwind is a difficult mark to hit. It is little use to lie in wait for them when there is no wind, because then they fly over the wood at a great height, and then whiffle down, almost vertically, without giving a chance of a shot. The best evening is one with a half gale blowing, which makes the ash poles crack together, and goes swish-swish through the dark old spruce trees. Best of all is the evening when the sky is lead-coloured, and gritty snow is flung like shot by a north-east wind. On nights such as these, the pigeons are anxious to get in; fly lower and within range.

The shooter must keep well out of sight in the undergrowth. If the birds see him even at the moment at which he fires, they swerve with unbelievable speed, so that the shots go harmlessly wide. So the man who would be a successful pigeon shooter must be a good woodcraftsman, and an accurate shot. Above all, he must keep out of sight.

It is, however, some of the other things which make pigeon shooting such fun. The rush to be in position under the firs an hour before sunset; muffling up in disreputable and favourite sweaters; fillin pockets with shiny red cartridges.

In the wood the hidden, silent man becomes as one with the surroundings. The hare that lollops past does not see him. Long-tailed tits hunting the larch stems in little packs, ignore him.

The inquisitive stoat comes almost to his feet before taking flight, and vanishing away. Soon comes nightfall, and the darkness silences the chinking blackbird. The woods are still and cold.

Trudging home down the ride, so much of wild life amongst the trees has been seen that it does not seem to matter whether the bag is heavy or light. And that is how it should be.

THE SHOP AROUND THE CORNER

A story with the Moral in the wrong place

by Barbara Bower

'Tom's eyes sparkled at the thought of nuggets, Dick's mouth grinned at the hope of a kangaroo, and Harry's hands trembled in expectation of a koala bear.'

ILLUSTRATED BY
SHEILA McGREGOR

ONCE UPON A TIME there were three little boys, and their names were Tom, Dick and Harry. They were so called because their father said he believed in plain names for plain people and most babies were plain, anyway, and you couldn't take a chance that they'd alter.

The boys and their parents lived in a dull house in a dull street in the dullest part of the town. No buses ran along it—only trams. There was no shop in it either. The nearest shop was round the corner on the right-hand side. It had a very small window, and the things behind it were nearly all black or brown or white. There were black letter-racks, and there were brown paper parcels that contained white typing paper. There were white boxes of paper clips. There was one ball of string. There was a rather rusty-looking knife on a card, and there was a pot of glue that had been there so long that three bluebottle flies had died on it.

The inside of the shop was as dull as the outside. Tom and Dick and Harry knew that because sometimes their mother sent them to buy a penholder or a new nib, a pot of ink or a packet of notepaper. Mrs. Stubbs (that was the mother's name) was not a great letter-writer, but three times a year she wrote to her brother Bert, who lived in Australia. She wrote before Christmas and before his birthday and before Midsummer because his birthday and Christmas came so close together. Somehow, between the days of these letter-writings the pen-nib got crossed or the ink dried up or the notepaper was dusty.

It was quite a long time since Tom or Dick or Harry had been sent to the shop round the corner, it was so long that a hopeful spider had spun a web round the three bluebottle flies on the glue pot, and the knife had got three more specks of rust and the tag end of the ball of string had been chewed by a mouse.

All this did not matter to Tom and Dick and Harry. What did matter was that their uncle Bert was on his way home from Australia.

'I expect he'll come back with his pockets full of gold nuggets,' said Tom, who had once borrowed an adventure book from the Free Library in the town.

'Or with a kangaroo,' said Dick, who had once been to the Zoo.

'Or with a Koala Bear,' said Harry, to show that he too knew about Natural History.

'You don't know your Uncle Bert!' sighed their mother gloomily.

The time came when they did know Uncle Bert. There was a bang on the door just as they were finishing supper. There was a stamping of boots in the passage outside, and Uncle Bert walked in.

Anyone could tell (even Tom and Dick and Harry could tell) that Uncle Bert kept sheep. He had a sheepskin coat and a sheepskin waistcoat and sheepskin gloves. His face was like a sheep's face, too, with a grey complexion and a long wobbly upper lip, as though he were undecided which tussock of grass to turn to next. Uncle Bert spoke bleatingly, too.

'Hullo, A-a-a-da!' he said. (Ada was Ada Stubbs, the mother of Tom and Dick and Harry.)

'Hullo, T-e-e-ed!' (Ted was the father's name.)

'Hullo, boy-o-o-s, I've brought you some presents. Right thing to do, eheh-eh!'

Then he flung a sheepskin bag on to the table so that the cocoa in the jug spilled over. And the sound of that bag, thudding and rattling and flumping made Tom's eyes sparkle at the thought of nuggets and Dick's mouth grin at the hope of a kangaroo and Harry's hands tremble in expectation of a koala bear.

The Uncle from Australia (all the way from Australia, mark you!) brought out three parcels from the sheepskin bag. They were not even proper parcels because they were not fastened with string. They were only three lumps screwed up in three pieces of brown paper.

'Take your choice,' said the Uncle from Australia, thrusting his thumbs into the armholes of his sheepskin waistcoat.

Tom chose the chunkiest parcel because it looked the likeliest to contain nuggets.

The paper tore with a crackling sound, and there, on the table was a pot of glue. On the top of the pot of glue were three dead bluebottle flies, and a wisp of spider's web.

'Thank you,' said Tom, 'Thank you very much, Uncle Bert,' and his voice was so solemn that it might have been the knell of the bluebottle flies.

Dick chose the next parcel, and the corners of his mouth turned down as he felt how very unlike the softness of a kangaroo was the hardness of the thing inside the brown paper.

And then a knife with six spots of rust on its blade lay beside the glue pot and the flies.

'Thank you very much, Uncle Bert,' gulped Dick. As he swallowed, the softest of dream kangaroos hopped, pouch and all, out of the kitchen.

There was only one parcel left. It belonged to Harry. Inside it was a ball of string with a loose tag-end. The end had been nibbled by a mouse. As Harry twisted it between finger and thumb, the soft enchanting ears of a little dream koala bear slid against his palm and ambled out of the kitchen.

'Thank you very much, Uncle Bert,' sobbed Harry. He sobbed because he was the youngest and because he was not able to bear so much disappointment so soon before bedtime.

'I ne-arly forgot the presents,' bleated Uncle Bert. 'I hadn't any time in Australia, but there's a handy little shop just round the corner here—a very handy little shop indeed.'

His long upper lip wobbled sheepishly as he looked down on his three sad nephews.

'Use your presents, my boy-os,' he bleated. 'Useful things are meant to be used.'

Then he gave Mrs. Stubbs a sheepskin rug which, as she said afterwards, would only hold all the cakes of mud from four pairs of hob-nailed boots. He gave Mr. Stubbs a sheepskin cap which, as he said at the time, would give him a cold every time he took it off.

Then Tom and Dick and Harry took their three dreary presents upstairs to their three hard beds in their drab little room under the gables.

Next morning they were awakened not by the chinking of nuggets, nor by the sound of a kangaroo fumbling in her pouch, nor yet by the licking noise of a koala bear, sucking honey, but by the rattling of trams on the road outside. The sight of their scruffiest clothes reminded them that it was Saturday and a holiday. Tom and Dick and Harry were glad about this for they had boasted to their school friends about the coming of their Uncle from Australia and of the presents he would be sure to bring.

No, they need not go to school. They could use their presents, use them up and forget about them.

Harry was the first out of bed. He was followed by Dick and then by Tom. Sadly, each one carrying his present as though it were a burden, the boys stumped down into the kitchen.

Uncle Bert was there, and he looked up from his porridge bowl.

'That's right, me boy-os!' he bleated, waving his spoon so that a fleck of porridge fell on to Tom's glue pot. 'Stick it!'

Tom set his glue pot on the hob. Nothing, he knew, would stick until the glue was melted.

'Carve out careers for yourselves!' continued Uncle Bert, and this time a splutter of porridge joined the rust spots on Dick's knife. The boy wiped the porridge away on his coat sleeve but the rust was immovable.

'Disentangle Life's tangles!' said Uncle Bert, and gobbled up his porridge except the little bit that had flopped on to Harry's ball of string.

After breakfast, Tom, who had melted down his glue, put on his cap, and wandered down the road, past the shop at the corner and into the Public Park. It was not a very exciting park ever, and to-day it seemed particularly full of dead leaves and starlings and seats that were in need of painting.

If only the pot of glue had been a pot of green or blue or red or yellow paint, Tom could have enjoyed himself. The pale golden sunlight, flickering hopefully down from a rain-washed sky, showed what even a little shining colour could do to a place like the Park. The sunlight gilded the pale leaves and shed a coating of silver on to the dark wet ones that lay round the boles of the trees. It showed up the spangles on the starlings' feathers.

Tom put down his glue pot on the nearest seat, dipped the brush into it, and set to work. Even glue was better than no paint. It shone like varnish in the sunlight.

There was not nearly enough glue to finish the whole seat because Tom was a lavish painter, and thought it would be better to put three good coats in one place than a smearing all over. When the pot was empty, he stood back and admired his work. Yes, it shone, but not so brightly as a nugget would have done. It only shone enough to remind Tom that there were nuggets in the world and that he had the wrong sort of Uncle from Australia.

The glue pot was quite empty so he carried it away to a corner of the Park where the bushes hid a rubbish dump. The bushes were so thick that even if he had bothered to peep between their twigs he would scarcely have seen the grand-looking lady, who had just come into the Park.

The lady's name was Julia Montmorency. She had golden hair and black eyelashes and a pink-and-white complexion. She was wearing a fur coat and silk stockings and high-heeled shoes. Underneath the coat was a sky-blue bathing suit, but not even the starlings saw this because the coat had such a big wrap over. She looked haughtily at three of the unpainted seats, but when she came to the fourth one, and saw that part of it had a clean and gleaming look, she sat down and began to sing a little song about blue eyes and blue skies and a moon in June and somebody who was true. Presently she shut her mouth and shut her eyes. She was tired because she had had such a very exhausting morning.

Meanwhile, Harry had been trying to make the best of his ball of string. He had tied one end to a lamp-post and

'He gave Mr. Stubbs a sheepskin cap which would give him a cold every time he took it off.'

then taken a loop round the next one, and so on until a Policeman had stopped him. Then he had gone round the corner (passing the shop on the way, and making a face at the new ball of string in the window) until he had come to a row of houses, whose doors all opened straight on to the pavement. He had tied a loop to one door handle and taken a turn round the next, and so on until the first householder had wanted to push a pram out of doors, and the second had wanted to go shopping, and the third had wanted to take her dog for a walk. Then another Policeman had stopped him.

After that he decided to go to the Public Park because he wanted to think. He wanted to think of all the things that could be done with a ball of string. It would be interesting to tie one end round the post of a bus-stop and wind the rest round the queue, and see what would happen when the bus came along. But to play that game it would be better to wait until twilight when the string would not be so conspicuous.

As he walked towards the Park he made many happy plans for his string, and he was still planning as he came near to the seat on which Miss Julia Montmorency was sitting. He might have passed by without seeing her, if she had not begun to drum with her high-heeled shoes on the gravel.

'Little boy!' said the lady, 'I can't get off this seat.'

'An' you won't be able to,' said Harry. 'You won't be able to—not unless you put your feet on the ground and straighten your knees.'

For the high-heeled shoes of Miss Montmorency were still drumming on the gravel.

'I've been asleep,' she said, as though that explained everything.

'Maybe you're still asleep,' answered Harry, who took an interest in everything. 'Maybe you're dreaming. Sometimes I dream I'm running, but I can't move a yard even when the wolves are coming after me.'

He glanced at the bushes beside Miss Julia Montmorency and because he was a considerate boy, added 'There aren't any wolves coming after you, though. I daresay you'll wake up soon.'

There didn't seem anything more to say, and, as he was much more interested in his ball of string than in a lady

'*Even glue was better than no paint. It shone like varnish in the sunlight.*'

who went to sleep and then dreamed she couldn't get up again, he began to stroll away.

'I'm not dreaming,' shrieked Miss Julia Montmorency, 'I'm stuck fast.'

'When my Dad got stuck fast with lumbago, my Mum used to put mustard plasters on him,' said Harry, 'but you'll have to go home before you can have that done.'

In the far distance a clock began to strike, but its voice was loud enough to set the starlings wheeling away, with such a swishing of wings and clapping of beaks, that Harry lost count of the strokes.

'It's eleven o'clock!' yelled the lady.

'If you're in a hurry—' Harry was tying the end of his string as he spoke.

'If I'm in a hurry? I'm due on the set in ten minutes!'

'Tea-set?' wondered Harry, 'Set of teeth? Badgers' set?'

But he didn't ask any of these questions aloud. He spoke helpfully.

'If you're really stuck—*sticky* stuck—why don't you take your coat off?'

'Because it's a very cold day and because I'm in a bathing suit,' answered the lady, 'and because my hands are stuck to the edge of the seat, and because I can't pull a park seat through the sleeves. Or CAN I?'

'I don't think so,' said Harry because he didn't think so.

Then he slipped the big loop of string over Miss Julia Montmorency's head and over her arms. When the string was fixed, he ran back a few yards, and tugged. It was good string: it didn't break. Miss Julia Montmorency was the first to give, and the park seat gave with her. It came scuffling across the gravel.

Harry went back another few yards, took one turn of the string round a tree, and tugged harder. There was a grating sound as the seat continued to rasp across the gravel. Then, quite suddenly, Miss Julia Montmorency came running on her high-heeled shoes slap bang into the tree. She left a nice comfortable patch of fur on the park seat, and the back of her coat looked as though it had moulted very thoroughly in one place only. Harry did not notice that, because he was too busy winding the rest of the ball of string round and round Miss Julia Montmorency and the tree. He hadn't got a knife, and his mother had often told him that if he bit off string and swallowed it, the loose ends would wind round his heart and kill him. Harry did not want to run a risk like that. Besides, he liked his string as it was—all in one piece.

So he went on running round and round until he became dizzy and fell down flat. His cap came off, and was picked up by a stray dog in search of occupation. Now a lady tied to a tree is not likely to come to harm, but a cap in the mouth of an excited dog may be damaged. Harry had been brought up to take care of his clothes, so off he ran across the Park and down a broad street and into a narrow one, and through the open doorway of a strange house, and upstairs, and under a bed. Then he snatched the cap from the mongrel dog, who immediately consoled himself with a bedroom slipper.

All this took quite a long time.

In the meantime, Dick had gone for a walk with his new knife. First of all, he tried to carve his initials on a lamp-post, but it was made of iron and painted black. There was green paint under the black, and Dick managed to uncover quite a lot of this before a Policeman came along and stopped him. Then he nicked a pretty edge along the window ledge of the shop round the corner, but another Policeman came and stopped him. So Dick, too, decided to go to the Public Park because he hoped to find peace and quiet and not to be interrupted while he carved his dull little initials on a dull Plane tree. He remembered that there was a tree with a good smooth trunk quite near to one of the Park seats.

When he came to the tree, he noticed that a lady was wrapped round it. This was a nuisance because even if he stood on tip-toe he would not be able to reach the empty piece of trunk above her head. Clearly, the only thing to do was to cut through the strands of string that were binding her to the tree. That should be as good a hint to her as any other that he considered it was his turn now to have a share in the tree-trunk.

The lady did not see him because her face was pressed to the rather grimy bark of the tree. She did not hear him either because just then the clock in the distance struck the half-hour, and the lady began to scream and to struggle. The last struggle timed nicely with the last slash of Dick's penknife, and the lady staggered backwards with lengths of string dripping off her like rain from a gutter. Dick picked the pieces up, and handed them to her.

'You got your ball of string in a tangle,' he told her.

Miss Julia Montmorency stared at him.

'Did you set me free?' she asked.

'Yes,' answered Dick, 'I've got a new knife and I wanted peace and quiet and so—'

'Peace and quiet?' repeated the lady. 'Peace and quiet—that's not a thing boys want as a rule. The trouble we have with the boys on the set, and the trouble we have with their mothers when we begin muddying them up.'

'Mothers don't like being muddied up,' agreed Dick, and he looked wistfully towards the tree-trunk.

'Do you mind mud?' asked the lady.

Dick shook his head, and remarked, 'Mud's sort of peaceful.'

'If only there were two more of you!' sighed Miss Julia Montmorency.

Just then Harry came back in search of his ball of string, and Tom returned to see if the glue was getting nice and tacky on the park seat.

Miss Julia Montmorency stared at them, and sighed very gloomily as she hugged her fur coat more closely round her sky-blue bathing suit.

'One's got a cold,' she said, 'the mother of the other doesn't want him to get mud in his curls, and the third's come out all over spots. What's the matter with you?'

'Nothing,' answered Tom and Dick and Harry.

'Would you mind sitting by a pool of water and making mud pies, and plastering each other with mud while you have your photographs taken?'

'No,' answered Tom and Dick and Harry.

'Then you come back with me, and we'll get the big scene shot to-day.'

For, as you may have guessed by now, Miss Julia Montmorency was a film actress, who had come out into the Park for a breather. She was wearing a bathing costume because it was her dress for her part in a film named 'Mudlarking.'

If you suppose that Tom and Dick and Harry made their fortunes, and became famous film stars, you will be quite wrong. They only acted for one afternoon, but they made enough money to go to the Zoo every Saturday afternoon until they got tired of it. They did not get tired of it until the Koala Bear that they grew so friendly with, had grown up, and until their favourite Kangaroo's

'He liked his string as it was, all in one piece, so he went on running round and round until he became dizzy and fell.'

babies had nearly worn her pocket through, and until the Uncle from Australia had gone back to his sheep farm. There he grew so much more like a sheep that his own men threw him into the sheep dip with a dozen or so from his own flock. He managed to struggle out, but after that he went to live in the bush because he thought life on a sheep farm too dangerous.

The moral of this story *should* be: DON'T PUT GUM ON PARK SEATS, or KEEP YOUR STRING FOR TYING PARCELS, but it *is* DON'T DESPISE THE SHOP AROUND THE CORNER.

MONICA EDWARDS

Author of *Black Hunting Whip*. The Punchbowl Farm of this story is a real place, the farmhouse, buildings, fields and countryside are almost exactly as described and many of the incidents really happened. Monica Edwards found the farm and bought it almost by mistake at the auction. She lives there now with all her family and the ponies, cows, calves, cats and dog, most of whom are characters in her story. Other books by Monica Edwards are, *No Mistaking Corker, The Summer of the Great Secret, The Midnight Horse,* and *The White Riders.*

THE DESERTED ISLANDS

Lying like a line of sea-forts beyond the barrier of the Outer Hebrides, are St. Kilda, Flannan, North Rona and Sula Sgeir, groups of islands with an eventful past, all once inhabited by self-sufficient crofting communities, but now, except for three lighthouse keepers on one of the Flannans, uninhabited. Magnificent cliffs remain, and swarming seabirds, and sheep.

PHOTOGRAPHED BY ROBERT ATKINSON

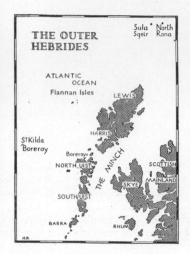

Puffins on the little railway by which sheep on Flannan are brought to the jetty when the flock is changed each year.

A map of the outer islands where the remotest flocks of British sheep graze without a shepherd.

Mrs. Gillies one of the last people to live on St. Kilda, used to spin the wool left about by the brown sheep.

The empty bay and village of St. Kilda. When the inhabitants ceased to be able to make a living on the island they were evacuated in 1930.

Loading from the rocks. In July the shepherd sets out on a forty miles voyage to visit his scattered flock. The sheep are passed from hand to hand and ferried out to the ship in a dinghy.

The tremendous cliffs of Boreray are shared by black-faced sheep and nesting gannets. For one hectic day the seabirds and seals are disturbed by the influx of men and dogs.

The deserted village where flocks of Soay sheep, first established on the island by Norsemen a thousand years ago, wander in and out of the houses.

BIGGLES in Arabia

by Captain W. E. Johns

PART TWO

AT SIX O'CLOCK the same evening, Biggles, Ginger and Bertie sat in a quiet corner of the Club lounge talking to Jerry Norman. Zahar had been taken home, in a car borrowed from the aerodrome, with orders to remain silent about what had happened in the desert; and it was hoped that a small sum of money, to enable him to buy food, would show him which side his bread was buttered. Not that there had been much doubt about this, for it was evident from his conversation that his main purpose in life now was to find the man who had left him to his fate; in which case, something very unpleasant was likely to happen to Abu bin Hamud.

Norman had been as good as his word. He had made enquiries, but without much success. All he knew was, the three Arabs were not in Aden. Biggles, who realised that he would have to take this useful man into his confidence, was able to tell him why.

'What I've got to do now is to find this treacherous rascal Hamud,' went on Biggles. 'It's the fact that he's got some seeds that worries me. Our job was to burn the stuff. It's been burnt; but while there are seeds floating loose, we can't call the case closed. It's a queer thought, but if what Raymond says is true the fate of western civilisation may rest on a handful of seeds.'

'I'm afraid you're going to find it difficult to locate Hamud,' said Norman thoughtfully. 'It's pretty certain he isn't in Aden, which means that he might be anywhere within five hundred miles. He might have taken on with another expedition, although I should have thought that I'd have known about it. All I've been able to find out is,

he appeared in Aden a few weeks ago. Then he disappeared again. An Arab I know, who keeps in touch with things, told me that while Hamud was here he was seen with Nicolo Ambrimos. In fact, they went into Ambrimos's office. He may have got a job with him. Ambrimos employs a lot of Arabs in one way or another.'

'Who is Ambrimos?' asked Biggles.

Norman smiled. 'The Sultan. That's his nickname here. He's a very successful business man, a man of many interests, primarily an incense-merchant, but he handles anything in the way of merchandise. He owns several dhows with which he runs a coastal transport service, picking up dates from Muscat, coffee from Mocha —anything that's going, in fact. He carries general freight for anyone, and as he owns one of the few concerns that call at the smaller Red Sea ports, he is really very useful. At one time he was talking of starting an air line between Muscat and Egypt, for urgent mail and small stuff—and he may be going on with it for all I know. He had made a lot of money. The whisper here is, he got his start by dabbling in honey.'

'Honey?' Biggles looked surprised. 'I haven't noticed the bees or the flowers.'

Norman chuckled. 'Honey, my dear fellow, is the local name for hashish.'

'I see,' said Biggles slowly, his eyes on Norman's face. 'Dope, eh?'

'That's only rumour, so don't take my word for it,' replied Norman.

Biggles stroked his chin. 'Hm. I wonder if that could account for the Sultan's interest in Hamud?'

'Could be,' agreed Norman. 'Hamud might be a carrier for him in his spare time.'

'Tell me more about this man,' requested Biggles. 'What's his nationality?'

Norman shook his head. 'That's anyone's guess. Mine is that he's a Levantine of very mixed parentage. He's a charming man, mind you. He speaks English as well as we do. He must be in the fifties. Very particular about his personal appearance—buys expensive clothes and all that. I'd call him elegant. He owns offices and warehouses and lives in one of the best villas in the place.'

'Where does he live?'

'Are you thinking of calling on him?'

'I might.'

'For what purpose? If he had an interest in this new dope, he'd hardly be likely to admit it.'

'He might know where Hamud is to be found. If he knows, there's no reason why he shouldn't tell me—provided he has no personal interest in the man's visit to the Wadi al Arwat.'

'I see what you mean. He'll wonder what you want with him, anyway.'

'I could tell him I'm thinking of organising an expedition to look for oil, and I got Hamud's name, with a strong recommendation, from Dr. Darnley.'

Norman looked pensive. 'You could try it, but it's unlikely that he'll tell you. You don't get straight answers in this part of the world. Still, I don't see that you could do any harm as long as you don't let him spot your real interest. Be careful. The Sultan has spies everywhere, remember. That's in the ordinary course of business.'

'Quite,' murmured Biggles. 'If the secret of the new narcotic leaked out he would be the first to hear about it. And if—I say *if*—Hamud had been one of his hashish smugglers, he'd probably go to the man with the story for the sake of the reward which would be forthcoming.'

Norman nodded. 'There's something in that,' he agreed. 'But watch your step, my lad, or one dark night you'll find a dagger in your ribs. That's what happens to people here if they start asking too many questions. I'll help you as much as I can. Tomorrow I'll take a stroll along the water-front. One of the Sultan's dhows is in. There's a chance that I might pick up news of Hamud.'

'Do you think that's wise?' queried Biggles dubiously. 'If you let it be known that you're looking for Hamud people will wonder why. The man who really knows, and I imagine somebody does know, will hear about it. He may also hear that we've been with you and link the two things together.'

'There's always that possibility, of course.'

'Surely the man to make enquiries is Zahar,' opined Biggles. 'It's known that he has been associated with Hamud, so such enquiries would be quite natural. It's hardly likely that Hamud will have told anyone about what happened in the desert.'

Norman nodded. 'I think you're right. One can't be too careful. How about a drink?'

'I could do with one,' admitted Biggles.

'Iced lemon?' questioned Norman.

'That'll do fine.'

The others made the same choice. Norman pressed the bell and gave the order to a dark-skinned waiter.

'Well, I don't think there's anything more we can do for the moment,' remarked Biggles, as the waiter served the drinks. 'I'll go along and see Ambrimos about some men for my oil prospecting outfit.'

He took a long drink from his glass as Norman signed the chit for the drinks, and the waiter departed.

'I'll send my man along to Zahar right away and say that I want to see him in the morning,' promised Norman.

'What's the Sultan's address?' asked Biggles.

'The Villa el Paloma in the Stretta Fontana. Biggish place, with double entrance gates. Stands back on the left. You can't miss it.'

Biggles lingered a little while over his drink and then

ILLUSTRATED BY
WILLIAM STOBBS

'*As the waiter served the drinks Biggles remarked, "I'll go along and see Ambrimos about some men for my oil prospecting outfit."*'

got up. 'I'll drift along,' he said, and collecting his hat from the vestibule went out into the hot, starry night.

He walked to the Villa el Paloma and found the house without difficulty in the blue moonlight. White-painted and lavishly decorated, it was even more imposing than he had expected. He went up the drive to the front door and rang the bell. The door was opened by an Arab footman in spotless white, who invited him into a hall that was adorned with so much costly furniture that it was obviously intended to impress visitors. The Arab salaamed and beckoned. Biggles followed him to one of several doors leading off the hall, where he was then shown into a room filled with a mixture of European and Oriental furniture.

A man came round a desk, at which he had evidently been seated, hand outstretched. 'Good evening, Major Bigglesworth,' said he, blandly. 'So you are thinking of looking for an oil concession in the district?'

Biggles took the proffered hand hoping that his face did not express the surprise he certainly felt at this unexpected greeting. It had, he realised, been chosen for that very reason; but that did not explain how the man knew his name or business. However, the remark betrayed one weakness in the man—vanity. It flattered him to show off his inside knowledge of other people's business.

'You seem to be very well informed, sir,' answered Biggles calmly.

'A man has to be, in this part of the world,' was the suave reply. 'Please be seated.'

'Your information let you down in one respect,' asserted Biggles. 'Who told you I was a major?'

Nicolo Ambrimos, an elegant Levantine.

The Sultan smiled. 'No one,' he admitted readily. 'But it's good policy to give a man a title above his station. It puts him on good terms with himself.'

'Well, you're frank about it, anyway,' returned Biggles.

'And why not?'

'Why not, indeed?' Biggles spoke cautiously, for his mind was busy trying to work out how the man had forestalled his excuse that he was looking for oil, for he had mentioned this to no one except Norman, who was, presumably, still at the Club. Not only was Ambrimos already in possession of this information, but Biggles had a feeling that the man was expecting him. Clearly, his spies had wasted no time.

'Now, what can I do for you?' said Ambrimos.

Biggles had by this time taken stock of his host, and he saw that Norman's description, while brief, had been apt. An 'elegant Levantine' described him exactly. He judged the man to be in the early fifties, with the unhealthy stoutness that so often goes with that age in the East. His face was round and clean-shaven, with a skin of that curious intermediate tint that is usually the result of a mixture of European and Asiatic blood. His hair was black, and brushed so flat that it gleamed like patent-leather. His dress, in old-fashioned European style, was immaculate. He wore a frock-coat, striped trousers and patent-leather shoes. A massive gold watch-chain hung across his paunch.

'Well, you seem to know my business, so I'll come to the point right away,' said Biggles. 'Did you, by any chance, meet Dr. Darnley when he was here?'

The Sultan pushed forward an expensive-looking box of cigars. 'I know him well. A charming man. I had the honour of helping him to equip his last expedition.'

'I was hoping to find in Aden three Arab camel-men who accompanied him on that occasion,' explained Biggles. 'He speaks very highly of them.'

'But surely you don't need Arabs for an air operation?'

Biggles had not mentioned aircraft but he allowed the reference to pass. 'True,' he agreed. 'But one can't find oil from the air. An air survey may reveal likely areas, and even oil-bearing strata, but at the finish the surveyor must examine the ground on his feet.'

'Quite so. Quite so. Of course. Who are these men you had in mind?'

'Their names were Abu bin Hamud, Kuatim and Zahar,' answered Biggles.

The Sultan massaged his smooth cheeks thoughtfully. 'I remember them, but where they are now I couldn't even guess. I have a vague idea they went off on some business of their own and as far as I know they haven't come back. In fact, I haven't seen them since they returned from Darnley's expedition. May I ask who told you that I might be able to help you in this matter?'

'Certainly,' returned Biggles, realising that it was no use dissembling, for if the man knew about the oil survey he must know where the project was discussed, and with whom. 'I was speaking in the Club with Captain Norman and asked his advice. He told me you were the best-informed man in Aden.'

The Sultan laughed softly. 'He was probably right, too. But on this occasion, I am afraid, my intelligence service has failed me.'

Biggles sipped the coffee that had been placed before him on a small table. It gave him an opportunity to think. He knew that the man must be lying, for according to Norman he had been seen with Hamud when the Arab had returned from the wadi. If he had spoken to Hamud, the chances were that he knew what had happened to Kuatim and Zahar. Hamud supposed his companions to be dead. The Sultan would have the same belief.

Biggles decided to fire a shot in the dark. 'How long is it since you saw any of these men?' he queried.

'Oh, months ago.'

'In that case your intelligence service certainly did let you down,' said Biggles quietly, with his eyes on the Sultan's face. 'You see, there is talk of Zahar having been seen in Aden, quite recently.'

The shot found its mark. The Sultan started slightly. He frowned. For several seconds he was silent. Then he said sharply: 'Who told you that?'

'Somebody happened to mention it in passing,' answered Biggles casually.

'He must have been mistaken,' declared the Sultan.

'Why?' asked Biggles evenly. 'Was there any reason why he shouldn't return to Aden?'

'No—no . . . Of course not,' said Ambrimos quickly. 'I mean,' he corrected himself, 'no reason that I know of. I will enquire into this.'

There was something in the way the Sultan said the last few words that made Biggles regret he had divulged that Zahar had returned. He perceived now that he might have put the Arab in danger. If Ambrimos wanted him dead, the chances were that he soon would be.

Biggles got up. 'Well, I won't take up any more of your time, Mr. Ambrimos. It was kind of you to see me. I shall probably be in Aden for a day or two, so if you should learn anything of these men, perhaps you will let me know.'

'I will, most certainly,' promised Ambrimos emphatically.

He himself saw Biggles to the door, showed him out, and after a final assurance of his co-operation, closed it behind him.

Deep in thought Biggles walked slowly down the shrub-fringed drive towards the gates. He had not learned much, but his time, he felt, had not been wasted. His problem, of course, was not so much to find Hamud, who alone could not do much harm, as the man in whom he had confided his secret. That man, decided Biggles, would almost certainly live in Aden, Hamud's home town, and the place where Darnley had paid him off. The only clue—a slender one admittedly—pointed to Ambrimos, who had seen him, yet now denied it. If Ambrimos had already dabbled in hashish, as rumour alleged, he would not be beyond trafficking in gurra. Moreover, he would have a ready-made organisation for smuggling the stuff into Egypt, or wherever it was going in the first place.

Reaching the gates Biggles stopped to light a cigarette as a new thought struck him. If Ambrimos learned, as he almost certainly would, that Biggles had brought Zahar back in an aircraft, then Biggles's own enquiries about the man would be exposed for what they were worth. The Sultan's suspicions could hardly fail to be aroused. He would find out just who Biggles was, after which his spies would never take their eyes off him. Norman had said that his spies were everywhere and the man himself had practically boasted of it. The waiter at the Club was in his pay. That was certain, for his excuse that he was looking for oil had only been made up on the spur of the moment during the conversation with Norman—when the waiter had been serving drinks.

It followed, therefore, that if Ambrimos was in fact the man who was exporting gurra, then he, Biggles, had un-wittingly put Zahar's life in danger. Ambrimos could not afford to have Zahar walking about Aden spreading the news of Hamud's treachery for this would involve the reason for the trip to the Wadi al Arwat. Zahar must be warned before Ambrimos could get on his track.

Biggles made up his mind. He would go to Zahar right away. He owed it to the man. And there were other reasons why he was anxious that no harm should come to the Arab. Zahar was the only living witness of what had happened at the Wadi al Arwat. He might, when he had fully recovered, recall some remark made by Hamud that would throw light on the case.

But before Biggles had taken half a dozen paces there came a sound from the direction of the big house that caused him to turn his head sharply in that direction. A car door had been slammed. What car? Whose car? Was Ambrimos going out after all, although he had said he was not? Retracing his steps quickly, by the time he had reached the gates the glow of moving headlights had appeared at the top end of the drive. Realising that in another moment they would be on him, and preferring not to be seen, he ducked into the shrubs. And there he crouched while the lights came on slowly, presently to pass within a couple of yards and turn into the main road.

He saw little of the car or its occupants. All he could make out was a big, dark-painted saloon, with a vague figure at the wheel. A curtain covered the rear window.

Biggles hesitated, aware of a sudden sense of alarm and urgency. If Ambrimos was fearful of what Zahar might divulge he would act quickly to prevent it. Whatever he did he could not get to the man's house before the car, if that was the objective for which the car was making.

Sitting on the bank to think the matter over, he estimated that if the car had gone to the native quarter it should be back in half an hour. If the man in it had killed Zahar he could do no more than try to bring the murderer to justice. But it was far more likely that Ambrimos would want to talk to Zahar, if only to find out who had brought him back to Aden. He would be anxious to know if Zahar had told his rescuer about Hamud, and the reason for the visit to the wadi. With this information in his possession the Sultan could liquidate the Arab at his convenience. That would be better than murdering the man in his own home, which would bring in the police.

Feeling slightly better for this comforting thought, Biggles dropped his cigarette and put his foot on it. He still had not worked out how he could see the inside of the car when it returned and, if Zahar was in it, how he could get him out of it. How this was to be done without being seen himself at first appeared impossible.

Still thinking, and regretting that he had not brought his torch, an idea occurred to him. There was, after all, one way in which a light could be thrown on the scene. It involved risks, but since a man's life was at stake they were worth taking.

Moving quickly but quietly, keeping in the deepest shadows, he returned to the Villa, but instead of taking

LIMERICKS

A selection of competition entries from readers.

There is a young lad named Alexis,
Whose chief occupation, to vex is;
This he does with such zest,
He's become quite a pest,
Which is more than his brother called Rex is.

ALEXIS MARESEAUX.

*

There was once a schoolgirl called Rayner,
Who wished that her name had been plainer,
For she found it quite hard
When she acted the bard
To rhyme Rayner, except with tea-strainer.

RAYNER GEIS.

There was a young lady called Jane,
Who one morning slipped right down a drain.
They said ' how peculiar
That a girl should be tubular '
Jane must now have a pain in the brain.

JANE MACBEY.

*

There was once a baby called Beth,
Who said, Mum, ruthkth bore me to death.
With sarcasm, her mum
Said, perhaps you'd like rum?
Beth drew a deep breath and said, yeth

ELIZABETH LORD.

There was once a schoolgirl named Brenda,
Whose skin was decidedly tender.
On the eve of Yuletide,
She was trussed up and tied
And roast on a spit in the fender.

BRENDA MILLS.

*

A cat-loving person named Jennifer.
Of kittens had many too many for
Her mother to house,
And mum's eloquent spouse
Complained, ' Never a meal without any fur.'

JENNIFER WELLER.

'Biggles had his automatic out. "None of that," he snapped. Then to Zahar: "Come on!"'

the carriage-way to the front door, kept to a secondary road which, as he expected, took him to the courtyard at the rear. The double-doors of a big garage gaped like a cavern. There was no one about, although some of the windows of the house showed lights, so without hesitation he went straight over to the garage and walked in. A match, quickly extinguished, revealed three cars. The most convenient looked like a new American Buick. He got into the driver's seat, closed the door quietly and started the engine. The only sound it made to indicate that it was running was a gentle purr. Without switching on the lights he took the car out into the courtyard, turned, and without being challenged ran it down the drive, stopping just inside the gates. Here he put on the hand-brake and switched off, so that the car effectively blocked the drive. Satisfied with this arrangement he got out, and leaving the door open took up a position in the shrubs near at hand. In the darkness the car was no more than a vague silhouette. Not a sound broke the silence of the sultry night.

Five minutes passed. Ten minutes. Then he heard a car approaching the drive, and from the way it slowed down he knew that it was going to turn in. He moved quickly. First, he switched on the lights of the Buick, sending a white blaze straight down the drive. Then, bending low and keeping in the shrubs, he hurried to the gates, a matter of perhaps a dozen paces. By the time he had reached them the driver of the black saloon, confronted by another vehicle which blocked the road, had stopped. He sounded his horn impatiently. As this had no effect, he flung open the door, got out, and walked towards the offending vehicle to see what was happening.

This was the moment for which Biggles had waited. Everything depended on the next few minutes. Stepping out of the shrubs he looked in through the nearest window.

One glance was enough. Three Arabs were sitting on the back seat. The middle one was Zahar.

Biggles went to the nearest door and threw it open. 'Hallo, Zahar!' he said. 'You're the very man I've been looking for.'

'He no come,' rapped out one of the others harshly.

'Oh yes he can. I want to talk to him,' said Biggles curtly. 'Come on, Zahar.'

Zahar moved, looking somewhat bewildered by this unexpected event.

One of the Arabs held him back.

Biggles's manner became brittle. 'Come on, Zahar, I want you,' he said tersely.

One of the Arabs thrust a hand into his *gumbez*, where, Biggles did not doubt, he carried a dagger. But Biggles had his automatic out before he could produce it. 'None of that,' he snapped. Then to Zahar: 'Come on!'

Zahar, looking uncomfortable, obeyed.

As soon as he was out of the car Biggles slammed the door, caught the Arab by the arm and dragged him round the corner. 'Quick,' he muttered, 'those Arabs were going to kill you.'

'But Sahib, they asked me to come with them to Ambrimos, who has *baksheesh* for me.'

Biggles, still walking, answered: 'In that house you would have died.'

Looking back, Biggles could see the chauffeur and his companions standing in the road, apparently at a loss to know what to do. He took a side turning and saw no more of them.

In a way he was sorry about what had happened, for it would inevitably tell Ambrimos more than he was ready for him to know. For that the Sultan was concerned with

Hamud and the gurra racket was no longer in doubt. His anxiety to get hold of Zahar was proof of that.

As soon as he thought they were safe from pursuit, Biggles stopped. 'What story did those Arabs tell you?' he asked his companion.

'They came to me like friends—may God forgive them,' answered Zahar. 'They said to me, our master has heard that you have suffered in the desert and would know the truth of it. For this he will reward you with baksheesh.'

'I have reason to think it was he who sent Hamud to the Wadi al Arwat with orders to collect the gum, and afterwards leave you to die,' said Biggles. 'Doubtless he thought you were dead, for that is what Hamud would tell him; but learning that you had returned he would have questioned you, and when he had learned all that you could tell him his Arabs would have cut your throat so that you could tell no one else about what happened at the wadi.'

'May God punish him,' muttered Zahar fervently.

'I shall be God's willing tool in this matter,' promised Biggles grimly. 'That is, if you will help me.'

'*Wallah!* You may rely on it,' swore Zahar.

'If you will enter my service you will be well paid and there will be no risk of prison at the end of it,' suggested Biggles.

'It shall be as you say, Sahib.'

'Then tell me this,' requested Biggles. 'Have you ever worked for Ambrimos?'

Zahar hesitated. 'Thus was it written,' he admitted sadly.

'What work did you do?'

Again the Arab hesitated.

'Shall I tell you?' murmured Biggles softly.

Zahar looked startled.

'It is said,' went on Biggles distinctly, 'that you carried hashish for him.'

'I cannot deny it,' admitted Zahar. 'But how could you know of this?'

'Never mind how I know. Many stories come to my ear,' asserted Biggles tritely. 'Was Hamud in this business with you?'

'He was, and it is only because the traitor tried to kill me that I will speak, for my lips were sealed,' answered Zahar. 'Always we worked for the Sultan at the time our camels were moulting. We stuck the *kief* on their skins and on it the hair that had fallen off, so that no one guessed what we carried under our baggage.'

'Kief?' queried Biggles. 'What is this?'

'It is the best of all hashish, made from the flowers of the plant and therefore worth most money,' explained Zahar. 'It is true that the Sultan would sell the top leaves of the plant, which is the common hashish, or the gum, which is called *charas*. But the rest of the plant, which here is called *gunjah*, the Sultan threw away, because he wanted only the best hashish.'

'Then the Sultan not only sells hashish but is a producer of it?' prompted Biggles.

'That is the truth.'

'And you would, no doubt, remember the place from where you fetched it?'

'We fetched it from the place where the accursed-plant was grown, O Sahib,' stated Zahar.

'Grown!' Biggles stared, knowing that the cultivation of the hemp plant, from which hashish is derived, is confined mostly to Turkey, Greece and Afghanistan. 'Do you mean the Sultan grows his own plants in this part of the world?'

'He grows it in the country of the Danakali, on the other side of the Red Sea, at a place called El Moab,' declared Zahar. 'There, in a wadi, he has a great store of water saved from the time of the rains, and this makes it possible to grow the plant even in the dry season.'

To Biggles this was news indeed. 'Just where is this place El Moab?' he asked.

'It is in the desert behind Marsa Mekel, which is a small port on the coast, Sahib. From El Moab, most of the hashish goes by camel, but some goes straight to Egypt by aeroplane.'

Again Biggles stared. 'By aeroplane,' he echoed.

'Allah will bear witness to the truth of my words,' said Zahar simply.

'Then there is a place for an aeroplane to land?'

'There is much sabkha, such as surrounds the Wadi al Arwat. Also places were made for this purpose in the war, some by the Italians and some by the English.'

'Such as surrounds the Wadi al Arwat,' breathed Biggles, thinking fast as the significance of this remark struck him. And there would, of course, be old war-time airfields, now abandoned. 'And this aeroplane of which you speak: to whom does it belong?' he asked.

'To the Sultan.'

'Who flies it?'

'I do not know, for I have not been near the man. I only know that he is a farengi.'

'Have you been to this wadi where the hashish is grown?'

'Many times.'

'How far is it from the coast?'

'Two days' march.'

Visualising the atlas Biggles saw that the place must be near the border of, if not actually in, Ethiopia.

'Could you show this wadi to me?' he enquired.

'Without question; but if we are found there by the Sultan's Arabs, or the Danakils, who are paid by the Sultan for their silence, it would be death for both of us.'

'Then we must see to it that we are not caught,' answered Biggles. 'How many men does the Sultan employ at this place?'

Zahar looked vague. 'Many,' was all he could say.

Biggles looked at his watch. 'The hour grows late. We will talk more of this to-morrow. Can you find a place where you will be safe until the morning? For make no mistake, the Arabs of Ambrimos will be looking for you with daggers in their hands.'

'And for you, too, by Allah,' asserted Zahar, making it clear that he had now grasped the situation. 'But fear not for me, Sahib.'

'Then meet me at the aerodrome at the hour of sunrise,' ordered Biggles.

'It shall be as you say,' confirmed Zahar.

With that Biggles left him and strode away towards the Club well-satisfied with his evening's work, for it had borne a heavier crop of fruit than he had expected.

*   *   *

(*Continued on page* 140)

March in the Country

by MICHAEL CHAMPION

Most of the work of spring sowing comes during this month.

The Times

WHEN YOUNG CHARLIE BIGTOE of the stone age wrapped his bearskin around himself, cracked his knuckles and poked his buckled nose out of his cave, first thing at morning, he could nct say to himself, 'Ugh, how I hate Mondays,' or call to his wife, 'Don't forget it's the first of March today, Dearie.'

No! In those days before men could tell the time of year from how the sun rose over a ring of stones, there were no calendars or daily papers from which to read the date. The only way to do it was by simple observations. Falling leaves meant October; the first Speckle-wood butterfly meant the end of April, and so on.

With some practice, anybody can tell the time of year like that. You can. In many cases the signs you see must be the same as those forgotten men saw. Bearskins are not necessary; an observant eye is.

Here are some of the things which mean March to me. It is an easy month to recognise.

Rising over the mill and the bridge and the stream is a beechwood. It grows on the side of a steep hill. At the bottom of the hill the branches hang over the water. At the crest of the hill the tree-tops soar against the sky. In those tops, where the branches are thin and the twigs grow feathery, are hundreds of rooks' nests. Great bundles of twigs they are, black against the sky. Some of them are huge piles after being added to, year after year.

Now at the beginning of March, the splosh-splosh-splosh of the water wheel is joined by the cawing of many rooks. They have come back, as they always do, to build new nests and repair old ones. The air is full of their excited chattering as they quarrel over nests, and wheel in the fresh wind.

All the day long, there is a stream of birds alighting high aloft, with twigs in their bills. Some of these twigs are so large as to be almost branches. Sods of earth, bits of binder twine, all sorts of queer things go to build those ragged piles.

Later in the month the hen birds will be sitting on their four or five eggs. The cock birds will be flying to and fro

Rook   *Crow*

with food for their wives. This is a good time to see the pouch at the base of the rook's bill, which distends and acts as a food store.

In the oak wood where the hazel coppice is grown, the catkins are out. Two inches long, floppy, brilliant yellow with pollen, they hang like the ends of the bell-ropes in the village church. Everybody knows these 'Lambs' tails' which are the hazels' male flowers.

Not so many people know the female flowers. These are small buds, which protrude tiny crimson hairs. They are easy to see on searching closely.

The blustery March wind stirs through the wood and carries the pollen from the catkins to the female buds. One of the pollen grains sticks to a sticky pad

The male (left) and female flowers of the hazel.

at the end of one of the crimson hairs on the female flower. The latter is now fertilised. Throughout the summer a nut will form from this female bud. When ripe it will fall to the ground and help to give some young wood-mouse the hiccoughs.

In this pattern is the key to the fertilisation of many of our forest trees. So why not mark down some female hazel buds, and watch how they develop?

Dusk is deepening over the clearing in the wood. It is late March and primroses show white in the gloom. Suddenly our ears prick up. A guttural churring noise, mingled with a sharp click-click is coming nearer. Three shapes flit past with swift erratic flight. They twist and dive, and all the while emit the quaint 'Tchick-tchick, churr.'

Woodcock! Keep still. Here they come again; right over our heads. This time their rounded wings and long bills are visible. The birds swing behind a clump of sallows, and dash away, outlined black against the orange afterglow of sunset. Still they weave and slant, and call their queer cry. A grand sight.

This aerobatic display was given by two males chasing a female. It is the courtship flight and is called 'roding.' Come to the clearing in a week's time and there will be no roding woodcock, for they will have disappeared under the moon to Scandinavia for the summer.

There are one or two things which always seem very 'Marchy' to me.

Meet t

IN OUR FAMILY, there is a constant stream of new pets coming and going. There have been tortoises, a hedgehog, a pitch black mouse that we called Othello, and a small yellow chick bought in a street market. Only our elderly parrot remains, watching these strangers come and go with complete indifference. He knows he will outlive them all.

The latest addition was a hamster. I found her in the local pet shop—a small, rather flustered, ball of golden fluff from which two enormous black eyes peered out. Whatever was this strange little thing? Never before had I seen a hamster and I was fascinated by what the shopkeeper told me about this unusual, cheap and easy-to-look-after pet.

If you look them up in an encyclopædia you will find that there are ten different kinds of hamsters, that they come from the temperate parts of Europe and Asia, and that they are now used a lot in laboratories for research experiments. The most popular is the 'golden' hamster which comes from Syria. The very first pair to come to England were brought to the London Zoo in 1931, and from these have descended the thousands now kept as pets by many enthusiasts.

They are small, soft creatures, only six inches long or less. Though they look fat and fluffy, as you see in the photographs, their bodies are really tiny underneath their fur—which is so full and loose that it falls in deep folds all round them. Their cheek pouches are enormous and if you give a hamster a big crust or a carrot, he will stuff it all in in one mouthful till his cheeks bulge in a most alarming way.

The hamster is a very friendly little

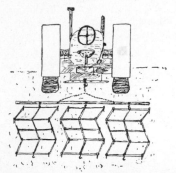

Harrows hammer the clods till they are fine.

How many other signs there are too! First song of the chiffchaff: migrating curlew calling at midnight: tumbling flight of peewits over the ploughland: these and many others, you must find for yourself.

'A bushel of March dust is worth a king's ransom.' That is a proverb which every farmer knows. Do you?

Most of the work of spring sowing comes in March, the planting of barley, spring oats and dredge corn. That is why there are so many tractors humming across the fields now.

Before sowing, the soil must be broken up into a fine 'tilth,' that is into small particles. Seed germinates best when wrapped about with fine earth, moist but not too much so, warm, well aired. It is only in these conditions that the seedling sprouts up as a vigorous young plant.

How does the farmer know how to produce this tilth? How does he know when to harrow, or when not to? It is difficult to explain. Somehow he just 'knows' through long experience.

Land differs from the heaviest clay to the lightest sand. Sometimes fields on the same farm differ. Listen to some of the names farmers call land. 'Wheat and bean land,' 'Sheep and barley land,' 'Three horse land.' In one part they say that all that is needed to plough with is 'Two rabbits and a tooth-pick.' Not very scientific definitions! But farmers know exactly what they mean. In all these different types of soil, the method of working the land varies.

If you take a lump of wet earth and squeeze it, probably it will just 'squish',

Cultivators break down the winter plough.

like a piece of dough. Put it in front of the fire and let it dry. Go on squeezing it gently at intervals, while it becomes dryer. At one certain point, instead of just squishing it will crumble into a thousand pieces. It is when the land is in this stage, such as drying in the sun after rain, that the farmer works the

(*Continued on page* 101)

Donald Brooks

lden Hamsters by ELIZABETH CAREY

Golden hamsters are only about six inches long and are not afraid of being handled.

creature who likes humans and is not a bit afraid of being handled gently. Only if you startle him, or wake him up unexpectedly, will he ever bite. If brought up in confinement, he has no objection to being kept in a box—though ours used to like running about all over the place and would bite her way out of the box if given the slightest opportunity. She had her home on a high shelf in the kitchen and often in the morning we found she had jumped off the shelf (apparently without harm) and was exploring the floor. One day, our electric washing machine refused to work, and when a mechanic came to repair it he was astounded to find that some of the wires inside it had been severed and amongst the machinery was a neat little pile of carrots and cabbage leaves and bits of bread. Our hamster had decided that it would make an excellent new home. So you see, it is not very wise to give your hamster too much freedom.

Hamsters are easy to feed—any sort of vegetables please them (especially turnips or artichokes) and they like nuts, bread, dates, dog biscuits or even grass. They should be offered water or milk too. But you will find that, however much you give them, it all disappears, and their appetite seems endless. If you investigate, you will discover that they eat only a very small part of it all and the rest is carefully stored away in some hidden spot. Our hamster used to carry off her bits and pieces and hide them in a secret place she had found behind a rarely used saucepan on the shelf.

The best home for a hamster is one that he cannot gnaw, and which has no small holes he could crawl through. Metal is ideal, but strong wood will do almost as well. There should be two compartments—a dark one for his bedroom, filled with hay or cotton wool or any similar stuff from which he can make a snug nest; and a playroom adjoining it with either fine wire netting or glass in front so that you can watch him. Give him a small receptacle (like a metal jam jar lid) filled with sawdust and you will find that he always uses this, so that there is no need to clean out his box every day as it will remain clean and fresh. Keep his home in an airy room, but well away from draughts.

If you want to breed hamsters, make sure that there is plenty of bedding in the nest and that the mother gets as much milk as she wants. Generally there are about seven babies in each litter, or, if the mother has had one or two litters before, this number may be increased. But if she has a very large family, she may kill one or two of the young ones as she cannot feed so many. The babies are born very ugly, without fur and with eyes closed, and for about ten days you should not attempt to look at them or touch them, because if you do their mother may refuse to go near them any more and they will die of neglect.

Hamsters are very healthy little creatures and rarely suffer from any disease. Sometimes they get tiny mites on their ears, but this can easily be cured by rubbing with Temosol for a day or two. Occasionally if two strange hamsters are put together they may fight, but on the whole they are most friendly and will not hurt each other. Their average life is two years.

Many pet shops now stock, or can obtain, hamsters. Their price varies according to the shop you go to—mine cost 3s. but I have seen them in a big London store priced at a guinea. They are still unusual enough, however, for shops to want to buy more of them, so if you have a pair you can breed and sell the little ones. If you get really enthusiastic about your new pets you may like to join the Hamster Club.

The Club issues a bulletin of news and advice about hamsters, and a year book; it arranges hamster shows, and its secretary (Mrs. Jean Cook, Glenside, Dukes Hill, Woldingham, Surrey) will answer the queries even of non-members. The subscription is 8s. a year. Mrs. Cook has written a book called 'Hamster Guidance for the Novice' (3s. 6d.) which will give you much more information than this brief article contains.

HOW TO BE A CHAMPION

by Harvey Day

THE RUNNERS come gracefully round the bend for the finish of a hard race. They enter the straight and sprint. Three men fight desperately for first place, and one throws himself forward to win by inches.

As he breaks the tape he is surrounded by friends who shake his hand, clap him on the back and shout, 'Good old George!' People cluster round for autographs. Press cameras click with flashes of light. He is famous.

In the old days—fifty years ago—being a champion athlete was much more fun than it is now. Today competition is so keen that an athlete has to specialise. He or she must pay special attention to diet, training practice, equipment and often climate. To become perfect, first-class athletes work much harder than most boys and girls in school, or for that matter, people in business.

Everyone remembers Don Bradman, the famous Australian cricketer who set up so many records. He could have been either a great tennis player or a great cricketer, but not both. So when he was in his teens, he decided to concentrate on cricket.

Bradman is a little man, but he throws the ball from the farthest corner of the field to the wicket as hard and as accurately as any fielder, and when he hits it, the ball travels like a bullet to the boundary.

The secret of his power is timing; that is, hitting the ball at just the right moment in the right part of the bat. Or, when he throws, letting the ball leave his hand at the correct angle, and at the last moment, imparting just a flick of the wrist which adds speed.

Bradman developed this sense of timing when he was a small boy in Bowral. He had no friends, so was compelled to play alone. For hours each day he would hurl a *golf* ball against a blank wall, and when it re-

bounded, bat it with a gum tree branch no thicker than a hockey stick. In the end he could hit the ball three times out of every four attempts! No wonder, then, that when he faced a bigger ball with a much wider bat he was so much more successful than other cricketers.

One of the differences between just a good athlete and a world beater is that the good player is content when he reaches a certain standard, but the world beater keeps on—always trying to improve. This is just what Denis Compton, our most popular sportsman, is now doing. He is the best batsman in England, and though he also takes lots of wickets in county matches, the other day he went down to Alf Gover's cricket school at Wandsworth and asked to be given a few tips about bowling.

Alf Gover says, 'I don't think I can teach Denis much that he doesn't know already, but I think it's remarkable that a player of his ability should come to me for coaching.'

The superb athlete realises that he cannot rest where he is. He must either improve or deteriorate.

Most of you remember Dorothy Round, twice Wimbledon champion. She is now Mrs. Little and still a first-class tennis player. For years English women's tennis had been in a bad way, for our girls lacked accuracy.

Dorothy Round realised this, so set out to acquire ball control. She got a racket and a ball and clouted it against a blank wall for hours at a stretch. In the end she was so expert that she could hit it to any part of the wall she desired, with any stroke. When she won her Wimbledon titles there were better stroke players opposing her, but none possessed her uncanny accuracy, and Dorothy wore them down. She ran them off their feet by clever placing.

Anyone who tries hard can become a

fair games player; and the boy (or girl) with natural ability, can, if he puts his mind to it seriously, develop into a first class athlete. It may take years, but he will succeed if he sticks to it.

Cecilia Colledge was British and European skating champion when she was only sixteen. She had grit, for she took about ten thousand tosses during training—when practising difficult turns, leaps and other feats. Each time she fell, she risked breaking a bone.

An even finer skater, Sonja Henie, whom you must have seen on the films, was world champion for many years. Like most girls in Norway, she began skating at six, and was junior champion of her country at eight. Although she was so good, her parents made her practise three hours every morning, and two each afternoon. It is little wonder, then, that she became famous.

It is the same in all sports. If you want to reach the top, you must practise, practise, practise. The way the champions play looks easy, but that ease comes only from constant practice.

When Henry Cotton, who is our best golfer, was a boy, he liked cricket. Because he was the smallest member of the team they made him carry the bag. So he took to golf, and decided early to climb to the top of the tree. Today he is reckoned one of the most intelligent sportsmen in the world, and pays tremendous attention to detail.

His doctor told him that he would be better without tea or coffee. So he gave up both. He dieted strictly and did nothing but 'live' golf. Even when on holiday he played golf for at least four hours a day. He was a delicate boy, but developed his muscles by exercise, kept himself fit and became a crack golfer by determination and practice.

This rule holds good for every game under the sun. It does not matter what you play. If you want to excel, you

Fox

Don Bradman's practice in the Nets maintained his unequalled timing and drive.

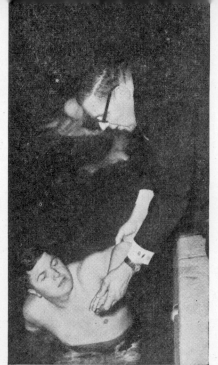

Reuter

Philip Mickman starts a twelve-hour endurance swim under his coach's strict eye.

must work hard, practise for hours each day and give up many pleasures.

Twenty-nine years ago an Englishman named Harris was born amid the smoke and grime of the northern industrial city of Bury. Today Reg Harris is the world's champion sprint cyclist. Till he became amateur champion in 1947 no Englishman had ever won the title.

As a boy he was weak. But he worked hard, cycled all the year and toughened his muscles. When he was 16 he used to cycle anything from 125 to 200 miles *a day on an ordinary push bike*—not a racer, as most boys have. Rain, hail or snow—Harris was out on his machine. A few years ago he was a costing clerk in Manchester, earning £6 10s. a week. This year, when he became professional champion, his earnings exceeded £5,000.

It does not matter what game you play; whether you are a boxer, billiards player, or cricketer; or whether hockey, tennis or swimming is your favourite pastime. You must practise. Stan Matthews is one of the finest dribblers of a football in the world. He used to dribble a ball for hours between rows of bottles, till he could run through at speed without knocking down one. People who watch him, exclaim, 'There's a born genius!' But it isn't true. Matthews was not born like that. He made himself into a football wizard.

Once, he was slow on the ball—so he practised short sprints daily, till now no one in the game is faster on the ball than he. And the secret is HARD WORK.

If you are trying hard, making little improvement and getting discouraged, think of that grand Yorkshire schoolboy, Philip Mickman, who to toughen himself for his Channel attempt, used to plunge into a mill stream near his home and swim lazily for an hour or more every morning in *mid-winter*! Or of Paavo Nurmi, the 'Flying Finn'—now retired —the greatest long distance runner the

Fox

Dorothy Round placing a ball with deadly accuracy achieved by long practice.

Fox

Reg Harris reaches a speed of 80 m.p.h. on his roller bicycle.

world has seen. Every week he ran, watch in hand, hundreds of miles, even when the roads were ice-bound, till he became an unbeatable running machine.

March in the Country
(*Continued from page* 99)

land. If the soil is too wet, implements merely cake the ground into sticky clods. If it is too dry the lumps are hard and unbreakable.

The implements which are most used for forming the tilth or seed-bed are cultivators, harrows and rolls. Cultivators break down the winter plough. Harrows hammer the clods still finer. Rolls crush the lumps into the finest tilth. Once the field is ready, the seed is drilled and covered up with harrows. Finally the soil is firmed around the seed.

It was as he watched the dust swirl up from the roll, as it pressed down the earth over the seed, that some farmer made up that proverb. His eyes saw a fine seed-bed and dust spurting out from the feathers of a shire horse pulling the roll. He imagined in three months' time twenty acres of green waving barley, grown even as a table top. Next to the road where neighbours could see it, too! Then would come August with a magnificent yield of top-price malting barley, worth a 'King's ransom.'

The field pond is not more than four feet deep, but the bottom is not visible, for the water is murky and stagnant. Near the edge, where the water is shallow, you can just see a bed of rotting leaves and twigs.

The surface is still and black. Occasionally a small ring ripples and dies away. That is odd, for there is no sign of anything making them.

Well, anyway, let's do a bit of fishing. It is close season now, but there are no policemen about, so we will risk it!

First we need a piece of string about four yards long; and now a worm. Worms cannot be found without digging? Nonsense! Kick that piece of dry dung over and—Why, there are three of them. Catch one quickly before they dive below, and gently tie the string about the middle of it. Now our tackle is assembled for some strange fishing.

Plop. In goes the worm, at the length of the string from the shore. Pull it in gently, oh, with such tenderness, towards the bank. Now slip one hand into the water with palm upwards and fingers slightly open, and pull the last foot or so of string over the hand.

Here comes the worm. There is something chasing it, too: snapping at it; clinging to it. Now the creature is over your hand. Lift it swiftly on to the bank, and there is a squiggling newt. A good one too, full three inches long. A magnificent catch, sir! You have been initiated into the sport of 'newting.'

The newts have come to the pond to spawn, after lying on land throughout the winter. Their beautiful orange bellies, blotched with black, are their breeding dress.

Some people take newts home in jam jars slowly to die. Having watched them for a while, it is better to put them straight back into the pond. They like it better there, where they can swim up and dimple the surface of the water.

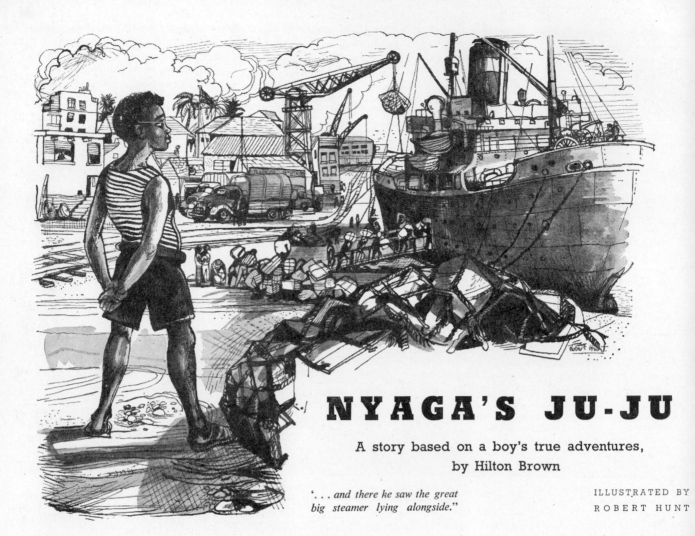

NYAGA'S JU-JU

A story based on a boy's true adventures,
by Hilton Brown

'. . . and there he saw the great
big steamer lying alongside."

ILLUSTRATED BY
ROBERT HUNT

WHY WAS the *Lady of Argyll* wrecked on the Calf of Man one thickish night last autumn? Well, some say one thing and some say another. The Old Man blamed the pilot. The pilot said the Chief Officer —who was on the bridge—had mis-understood his directions, and he wasn't in charge at the time anyway. Everybody said there was a fog and quite a sea running. But nobody *really* knew what caused the wreck except a little African boy from Mombasa called Nyaga.

How *could* he possibly? Well, that's the story.

'Nyaga' means 'ostrich'; but he wasn't called that because he was like an ostrich or to make fun of him; it's just the kind of name the Kikuyu give people. He might as well have been called Snake or Guinea-fowl or Hyena. He might as well have been called Monkey; better, in fact—for that would have suited him.

I said he lived at Mombasa in Kenya. But the Kikuyu don't live in Mombasa much; they come from up-country. Nyaga, being a Kikuyu, was born far inland from Mombasa —somewhere near Fort Hall. But he

came to Mombasa with his uncle after he ran away from the Mission School. Because I'm sorry to say he did run away from it. Which was a pity because at twelve years old Nyaga was a very promising pupil; he could do sums like anything and was even picking up quite a bit of English. He could—nearly—recite 'Mary had a little lamb.' But the fact remains that one day he bolted. He went to his uncle who was then in Nairobi. The uncle had no right to take him in, but when Nyaga came along and said 'I have left the *skuli*' he didn't ask any questions. He wanted a smart boy to do some work while he did nothing. Presently he went away to Mombasa and took Nyaga with him. That's how Nyaga came to be in Mombasa where his adventures really started.

But why did Nyaga run away from the Mission *skuli*? It wasn't like him to do a stupid thing like that when he was getting on so well. No; but he had his reasons. Like Mary, Nyaga had a little lamb; and everywhere that Nyaga went, etc., etc. Or if it wasn't exactly a lamb, it was a ju-ju. Now, as you know, a ju-ju can be absolutely anything; this one, as it happened, was

a bit of wood. It was about the size of, and rather the shape of, a potato, but it had seemed to the African who first found it, or made it, more like a man. Or perhaps something more than a man. Who that African was, goodness only knows; Nyaga got the thing from one of his aunts who believed in ju-jus. 'It is very strong, she said 'It will help you when you are in trouble.' It was a bit of red-wood really, but its successive owners had poured oil upon it and rubbed it and worshipped it until it was nearly black. It had that dull smoky sort of shine you see on a conker or a pair of good brown shoes that have been carefully looked after. Nyaga kept it hidden in the pocket of his coat but he took it out from time to time and talked to it.

That was all very well, but, you see, unfortunately the Mission people didn't approve of Nyaga's ju-ju. It was just the sort of thing they were trying to get out of his young mind. And one day Miss Milligan caught him with it and she said:

'Oh, Nyaga! You should throw that silly thing away.'

Nyaga said immediately that he

would; but Miss Milligan knew what *that* was worth. It was a hot morning and she was feeling cross.

She said, 'Give it to me at once.' Nyaga said nothing. 'All right,' said Miss Milligan, 'I'll ask Mr. Lambert to take it away from you.'

You will, will you? thought Nyaga. And that night he bolted to his uncle in Nairobi. Ju-ju and all.

* * *

After they got to Mombasa, Nyaga's uncle started a business in sweetmeats and nuts. He sent Nyaga out with a basket containing little paper screws of these while he himself sat under a cork-tree and played his marimba. Nyaga was a clever boy; he always sold out his basket of sweets and nuts very early and then he spent the rest of the day talking in Mombasa. It's a nice town—if a bit warm; but it seemed to Nyaga that the people who were doing well in Mombasa, the rich people, were the English and the Indians. That, thought Nyaga, is because they are educated; I too must educate; I must *En'lis* educate. So he told his uncle that he wanted to go to school again, and the uncle said it was a very good idea and went on playing his marimba. Nyaga saw he was getting nowhere and was depressed.

Then one day he went wandering as far as the docks at Kalindini; and there he saw the great big steamers lying alongside and the coolies running on board with loads and running off again. The steamers had wonderful labels on them; 'Seamaster, London'; 'Erbenfels, Hamburg'; 'President Garfield, New Orleans.' And Nyaga saw something else; because as he was gaping at 'Seamaster, London,' a white man in dungarees came down the gangway holding an African by the collar of his coat; and at the foot of the gangway he gave the African a kick and a heave that sent him sprawling on the quay. Nyaga was interested; he said to a bystander:

'Why does the *bwana* beat that boy?'

The bystander said, 'Because that boy is hiding on the big ship. He is trying to steal a free voyage to Capetown.'

'But they have found him,' said Nyaga, tumbling to it. 'They have found him too soon.'

'They have found him,' said the bystander, 'but they do not always find.' He decided to boast a little, African-like. 'A friend of mine, he got to London, England, that way. Never they found him.'

Nyaga thought—*did* he now?

* * *

It was the ship's carpenter of the *Loch Etive* that first unearthed Nyaga; he came on him when they had been three days at sea and he went to get out a tin of paint. The tins had been disarranged somehow and they fell down; and the carpenter shifted a couple of packing cases and lo! there was Nyaga. Said the carpenter, who came from Greenock,

'Losh! here's another o' them.'

Nyaga put his hand very firmly round his ju-ju. He said in his best English,

'Pliss! Is this London, England?'

'Laddie!' said the carpenter, 'It jist is no'. It's the Red Sea. Come you an' see the Old Man.'

The Old Man of the *Loch Etive* was displeased at the sight of Nyaga; but he was also interested. He said, 'An' what are *you* doin' here?'

Nyaga said, because it was the only idea in his mind, 'I want go *skuli*.'

'Ye do?' said the Old Man. 'A very praiseworthy ambition. Ye can start by scrubbin' out the galley.' He aimed a swipe at Nyaga's head that would have knocked him overboard, but Nyaga dodged it. He was used to swipes.

In the galley he scrubbed out beautifully. When it was done, he said to the cook,

'This ship he go London, England?'

The cook, who was a Cockney, said, 'Don' I wish 'e did! Glasgow, Scotland, that's our 'appy 'ome. Non-stop, wot's more.'

Nyaga was disappointed; but he clutched his ju-ju and prayed.

'There is *skuli* in Glasgow?'

'You ask them Scotties,' said the

'Said the carpenter, who came from Greenock, "Losh! here's another o' them."'

cook, 'an they'll tell y' it's the intelleckshual 'ub o' the blinkin' universe.

This, of course, was double Dutch to Nyaga but the tone of the voice sounded satisfactory. He caressed his ju-ju with his thumb.

* * *

They were kind to Nyaga on the *Loch Etive*; he could be a nice little boy when he tried and he did try very hard. The Old Man took quite a fancy to him and gave him a coat and trousers. They were far too big for him but they were nice and warm and the ju-ju liked the new pocket very much. On all possible occasions Nyaga told the ship's company, 'I want *skuli*; I want edoocate; En'lis I want edoocate.' The Scots are a kindly people and set store by education; they approved of his plan and did not wish to disappoint him prematurely. 'Aye!' they said encouragingly; or 'Im-phm!' or 'We'll see, we'll see.' Nyaga saw that his ju-ju was doing him well; he said nothing to anyone about that but kept it carefully hidden. Now and then he took it out and set it on his bunk, when he was quite sure there was nobody about, and worshipped it. One day the carpenter, who moved about very quietly in rope-soled shoes, caught him at it; he was rather disgusted—though he was very far from suspecting what the ju-ju really was.

'Playin' wi' dollies at *your* age?' he said. 'A big boy like you. I'm surprised at ye.'

Nyaga merely grinned. His grin was like a banked coal fire bursting suddenly into flame, or like a volcano suddenly erupting ivory. He was happy.

* * *

Nyaga approved of the Clyde when at last they got there—dark and grey and ugly as it seemed after Kalindini. Quite certainly there would be plenty of 'edoocate' here. But a sad shock awaited him. The Old Man, who was by now besottedly in his favour, took him by the hand and led him in person before the Immigration Officer; and the Immigration Officer was dark and grey and ugly as the Clyde itself.

'Stowaway?' he said, 'I canna think why we're gettin' so many stowaways just now. Why anybody would want to come to *this* country. . . O.K., my lad—back ye go.'

The Old Man said—but rather hopelessly—'He's seekin' to go to school.'

The Immigration Officer intimated quite briefly where Nyaga could go.

The Old Man said pleadingly, 'Ach, Mister Kiddie, cud ye no'—'

'Now, look here, Captain Macvicar.'

for ELEPHANT

These elephants, as you can see,
are an extremely pensive lot
of pachyderms, and that's because
they're trying to remember what
on *earth* it is that ' elephants
never by any chance forget ' !
They know the saying well, of course,
but all the same . . . and yet . . . and yet?
Quiet in their jungle study they,
unmarked by any fretfulness,
graze on their distant memories
and chew upon forgetfulness.

                                    V. G.

said the Immigration Officer, ' Ye know as well as I do that by the law of this land there's just one thing I can do—and that's send him straight back where he came from.' (This was not *quite* true but near enough; anyway, it was the Immigration Officer who had the say.) He turned to Nyaga. ' Here, you! Where's y'r home? '

Nyaga stood speechless with alarm and disappointment. The Old Man said,

' It'll be Mombasa; that's where we picked him up.'

' Then back he goes to Mombasa,' said the Immigration Officer, ' and stays there.' He thought for a minute. ' He can go the week after next. On one o' the Lady boats. I forget which one it is but there *is* one and that's the place for Mister Stowaway.'

Nyaga said, ' But I want edooc—'

The Immigration Officer said, ' Get out!' And the Old Man, sadly, ' It's no good, laddie.' Nyaga burst out weeping; and when an African bursts out weeping—well, ' bursts ' is the right word for it. The Immigration Officer put his hands over his ears.

' Take him away! ' he roared. ' Take him away and drown him.'

The Old Man took Nyaga away, but he didn't drown him; instead he put him in the African Seamen's Hostel till the *Lady of Argyll*—it *was* the

Lady of Argyll—would be ready to sail. Of course Nyaga bolted at the first opportunity; but there was a Policeman at the dockyard gates. Always there was a Policeman; enormous men, Highlanders, gentle but immovable. So *that* was no good.

* * *

Perhaps the Immigration Officer had relented a little, or perhaps Captain Macvicar had put in a word (or perhaps, of course, it was the ju-ju). Anyway, Nyaga was received on board the *Lady of Argyll* like a king. They were prepared to make a pet of him, a mascot, I don't know all what. The Mate said, ' Hullo, Jim Crow! How's Timbuctoo? '—a remark quite incomprehensible to Nyaga but kindly meant. The Second Engineer said, ' Aye, ma mannie; yer mither'll be in a sair state about *you*.' The cook said, more practically, ' Cud ye eat a sausage, laddie? ' Nyaga merely wept—first noisily in great ship-shaking roars and then, as he spent himself, in slow tearing sobs. The crew of the *Lady of Argyll* were much concerned; they followed him about, offering various consolations. This they did for most of the first afternoon out of Glasgow; but as dark began to fall and the sea began to rise, they got tired of it. The Second Officer said, ' Proper little misery— that's what he is '; but the cook, with a better understanding of the young

(he was a married man himself with six children in Leith) said, ' Ach, leave him be. Let him greet hissel' t' sleep. He'll be fine in the mornin'.'

Nyaga, left alone at last, looked round for some place, some dark and secret place, to which he could retire with his sorrows. He found it eventually in the chain locker and there he gave himself up to grief—not British or even European grief but real African end-of-the-world despair. He banged his head on the iron walls of the little room—but Africans have hard heads; all the wretchedness of generations of Kikuyu—hunted by the Masai, eaten by lions, racked with disease and poverty—echoed and resounded. But the cook was right after all ; you can't keep that sort of thing up indefinitely— especially when nobody is taking any notice of you. Also, as I have said, the sea was getting up quite smartly; the *Loch Etive* had had a wonderfully calm voyage and Nyaga was unused to seas; he began to feel qualms and disturbances of a more physical nature. Misery, exhaustion and the rolling of the *Lady of Argyll* at last rocked him to sleep.

He must have slept for quite a time because when he woke it was completely dark; it must have been well on in the night. Nyaga had a look outside, didn't like it and crept back to the chain locker. But his mind

F for FALLOW DEER

Bounding home into the forest
with a coat the colour of fir cones
and dappled with the shadows of leaves,
with twigged branches on his proud head,
and wide eyes brown as autumn pools,
the fallow deer escapes from the hand of
man,
is lost to him in the twilight of the woods,
merges with earth and tree and
mouldering leaf.

Only the crack of a stick and a bird's cry
will show he is there, his heart
thundering as he sniffs the dangerous air,
as he leaps quivering into the heart of
the forest,
his coat the colour of fir cones
and dappled with the shadows of leaves.

V. G.

was working now and suddenly something—now what could that have been?—said to him, 'Is it too late after all? Cannot something be done even yet?' In the pitch darkness of the chain locker, Nyaga groped in his pocket and drew out his ju-ju. He set it up on a coil of anchor chain, wedging it carefully lest it fall; he threw himself down in front of it, flat on his face, his arms and legs spread out as widely as he could manage in that confined space. He began to pray to it.

'Master!' said Nyaga, 'Lion! King! Help me. Do something. Father of crocodiles, lord of elephants, save me. Stop this wicked ship!'

And as he said the words, there was the most appalling, earth-shaking, world-ending crash. Nyaga and his ju-ju were flung clean across the little room and banged against the wall. There were a thousand terrible noises —shouts, yells, the roar of steam, feet running and pounding, a shuddering and grinding that seemed to rise up from the very bottom of the sea. . . .

Well and truly the *Lady of Argyll* had hit the Calf of Man.

* * *

Now, of course, if it had been a real old-fashioned shipwreck, this would have been a terrible tragedy and Nyaga and his ju-ju would have had

a lot to answer for. (Because, honestly, between you and me, if it wasn't Nyaga and his ju-ju, why did it happen? The crew were all alert and at their stations, the chart was all right, the compass was all right; and though it was a roughish thickish night, it wasn't anything out of the ordinary.) But, as some of you may remember, there were no lives lost; nobody was even seriously hurt. The *Lady of Argyll* went on the rocks at the peak of high water; when daylight and low water came round, the Mate got ashore with a ratline pulling a wire and a coil of boat-cover lacing; along this the crew slid comfortably to land in a breeches buoy. The cook carried Nyaga; Nyaga carried his ju-ju. The Port St. Mary lifeboat came along and took them all off; a Liverpool salvage steamer rolled up to look after the *Lady;* within twenty-four hours everybody was back in Glasgow.

And *then*? . . . Well, you know what seafaring folk are. They believe in signs and portents. If there's a little black stowaway and you insist on sending him back to Africa and the ship promptly hits the first rock it comes to—well, *should* you have sent that little boy back? There was quite a feeling in Glasgow that Nyaga had better stay where he was; certainly Captain George of the *Lady of Banff,* who was sailing next week, didn't want him; and neither did Captain Fraser of

the *Lady of Ayr* who was going two weeks later. I don't know what the Immigration Officer said or did this time; but there was a Missionary who had met Nyaga at the African Seamen's Hostel—Nyaga had a lot of reason to be grateful to Missionaries, one way or another—who came forward and said he'd look after him. 'We'll see to him presently,' they all said. 'We'll send him back in a week or two.' Well, of course, when once you begin putting things *off*. . . .

At the present moment, to the best of my knowledge and belief, Nyaga is at a *skuli* in Gourock, having En'lis edoocate; he is getting on very well. What will he become? I wouldn't like to say. What has he done with the ju-ju? I couldn't tell you.

But anyway, *now* you know what did for the *Lady of Argyll*.

THE PILOT'S POINT OF VIEW

by William Simpson

Camera Talks went with Captain Wright, by courtesy of British European Airways to record one of his routine passenger flights to Rome, from start to finish.

1. *Captain Wright plots his course across the Channel and France.*

2. *He examines the brakes on the main undercarriage wheels.*

Most of us have probably felt, as we listened to an airliner roar low overhead or watched it land at an airport, that the life of the Captain of the great silver craft must be intriguing, romantic, and at times even adventurous. And, so it is, although for the most part it seems to him to be a seldom changing routine with a good deal of hard work and responsibility thrown in. Let us see for ourselves by travelling in imagination with Captain E. R. Wright—his friends call him Ben Wright—of British European Airways on one of his routine flights from London to Rome—landing at Marignane Airport near Marseilles in the South of France on the way. We soon discover he is a pilot of considerable experience, with, behind that cheerful face, its expression part hidden by a real R.A.F.-type moustache, a good deal of grey matter tucked away.

He is twenty-seven years old, has a wife and two small children—boy and girl—and is a steady sort of fellow who, nevertheless, knows how to enjoy himself. And, first as a pilot of the R.A.F. Transport Command, and later on Yorks and Liberators of the British Overseas Airways Corporation, he flew for many hours and visited many places during the war—Cairo, Karachi and West Africa for example. So at the end of the war he had a couple of thousand hours in his log book and was all set to become a civil airline pilot. In 1946 he joined British European Airways and flew in command of that Company's airliners speeding to and from London and the Capitals of Europe.

He is a fully fledged airline skipper with two-and-a-half gold rings round his sleeves, some three and a half thousand hours of piloting experience, and is well accustomed to commanding a craft in much the same way as would the Captain of a ship at sea. And among other things he must do before he sets out with his passengers, mail and freight for Rome, is to make quite sure that the weather will be suitable at all points of call and along the route; that all radio and radar aids are functioning properly on the ground; that he will have enough petrol to set off and land somewhere else in emergency; that the aircraft itself is fit in every way to fly, and has been properly fuelled and loaded so as not to upset the balance. His next job is to get across to talk to the 'Met' Officer—the Weather Man as he is often called—highly skilled and qualified civil servant employed by the Ministry of Civil Aviation, owners and operators of the British airports used by national airlines. The are in the meteorological briefing room at Northolt Airport, and as they pore over the weather charts Ben Wright is hearing a detailed account of the conditions likely to be found on the way, at Marignane where he must land to refuel on the way again, and at Ciampino, the airport of Rome, at which he will have to land.

All the detail is there—temperature and pressure of the air at different heights all along the route, as well as the detailed effects they have produced in the way of mist or cloud, haze, rain or snow, and the direction and strength of the wind

3. *Next he makes sure of correct weight distribution between the five separate luggage lockers.*

4. *Captain Wright with his crew, Steward Miss S. M. Cramsie, First Officer R. F. New and Radio Officer I. H. Dalgliesh.*

5. *While the passengers wait comfortably in the airport lounge, the Captain checks with the Tarmac Control Officer that everything is in readiness, the plane fuelled and serviced and all papers in order.*

It has been plotted down in a series of lines, arrows, figures and different coloured marks on the weather map.

It looks all right to the experienced eye of Ben Wright, so off he goes to check over his maps and navigation for the route. You see him drawing a track line on an outline map of part of England and France in *Plate 1*. Of course, he is not going alone, and the other members of his crew have been busy at the same time. For instance there is his First Officer who is also the co-pilot, Second-in-Command of the aircraft, and does the navigation. He sits alongside Captain Wright at the dual controls of the airliner. Then there is the Radio Officer, third member of the flying crew, who by radio-telephone, W/T, and radar keeps in touch with the ground. And finally there is the fourth crew member, the

6. *On busy airports planes may be leaving for widely different destinations, within a few minutes of each other. Signs are put up to help passengers find their particular plane easily.*

8. *Captain Wright switches on the automatic pilot, and enjoys his luncheon.*

9. *The First Officer marks the plane's
position on his map.*

7. *It may be a cloudy day below, but the plane bathes in sunshine above a sparkling
sea of strato-cumulus cloud, stretching as far as the eye can see.*

Steward, who can be either a man or a woman, has a galley aft, and looks after the passengers.

But to follow Captain Wright, you will see how in *Plate 5* he is talking to the officials to make sure that the last-minute preparations of the aircraft on the ground have been made, and Captain Wright is checking that the passengers are waiting in the reception lounge, have had their tickets and passports checked, and will be ready to join the service shortly. He also learns that the aircraft has been fuelled and is serviceable, so he sets out to do his own special checks along with the First Officer—you see them examining the brakes on the port main under-carriage wheel in *Plate 2,* and he will also check the tail and rudder, and other points on the undercarriage.

Next a word with the loaders (*Plate 3*) who are moving the passengers' luggage into the holds—there are five of these in the Viking and the load sheet has to be prepared with great care to make quite sure that every pound of weight is properly balanced and distributed throughout the aircraft. And now, the crew are together on the tarmac

(*Plate 4*), passengers are going up the steps into the aircraft and the loader is removing the signboard 'ROME' (*Plate 6*), and soon we shall be on our way. Last to enter the aircraft is Captain Ben Wright himself who checks the passenger list before walking through and up into his cockpit.

The Captain has started his engines, taxied out to the end of the runway, received permission by radio-telephone for take-off, run up his engines, opened his throttles—and finally takes off and starts to climb up on his course.

It all sounds easy enough, but of course each member of the crew has been busy. The Captain and the First Officer have had every moment of their attention taken up flying the aircraft and watching the slightest deviation from the correct story they should read on the faces of the many clocks, gauges and lights on the instrument panel before them. Now, as they climb up, having set their course, they can relax a little and attend to the many small adjustments which have to be made to keep the aircraft flying smoothly and just as it should. The Radio Officer is thinking about the bear-

ings he may need to take from radio stations on the ground, and the operation of his radar 'Gee' set, an important guide to navigation which was used by Bomber Command during the war, and is established with ground stations in France. 'Gee' will be his stand-by if the weather is bad, and he will have a constant stream of 'fixes' to give to the First Officer who will be doing the navigation. Meanwhile, the Steward will have made quite sure that the passengers are comfortable and started the earlier preparations for serving refreshments and meals on the way.

On the way out to Marseilles Captain Wright will be following the outline of a flight plan which he agreed before he took off. This will entail flying at a certain height which, if the weather is really bad, will have been worked out to give him a safety margin of 1,000 feet vertical separation from any other aircraft likely to be in the vicinity. If the weather is good he will probably fly out at about 10,000 feet, cruising at about 200 miles an hour, which is not as fast as his Viking airliner will go but will allow an economic use of fuel and oil.

10. **Viking Cockpit Controls.** 1. *Throttles and airscrew levers used to control the engines.* 2. *Control columns (dual control, operated by captain or second pilot) control the altitude of the aircraft in flight.* 3. *Auto-pilot ("George") flies the aircraft automatically on the desired course.* 4. *Undercarriage selector used to raise or lower the wheels.* 5. *A.S.I. The air speed indicator shows the speed at which the aircraft is flying, subject to corrections for height and temperature.* 6. *Altimeter used by the pilot to find out at what height he is flying.* 7. *Ignition switches are duplicated as there are two magnetos to each engine.* 8. *Boost gauges show the mixture pressures produced by the engine superchargers.* 9. *R.P.M. indicators indicate the number of revolutions per minute of the engine crankshafts.* 10. *Trimming controls for ailerons, elevators and rudder are used to trim the aircraft to fly straight and level "hands off."* 11. *Undercarriage position warning lights. Green and red indicator lights tell the pilot when the wheels are safely locked "up" or "down" as required.* 12. *Brake levers used during taxying and for slowing down the aircraft on the runway after it has touched down.*

The First Officer can be seen in *Plate 9* marking on a map the position of the aircraft somewhere over the middle of France, and as the ground is completely hidden from view by that lovely bank of strato-cumulus cloud (*Plate 14*), the chances are that navigation so far has been mainly by means of 'Gee,' with the help of a few cross-bearings from W/T stations. Ben Wright, is already begin-ning to settle down into the routine and in *Plate 8* he is sitting for a while in the First Officer's seat with his luncheon tray on his lap and is making a few adjust-ments to the automatic pilot which is now

11. *The 'batsman' signals 'Stop and cut out your engines.'*

12. *The refuelling truck loses no time in getting to work.*

13. *Flying low over the gaunt snow-clad mountains of the Alpes Maritimes.*

14. *A discussion of the route with passengers.*

15. *Circling over the city before coming in to land at the airport.*

in control; he has made his usual tour of inspection to see that all is right in the aircraft, with a word or two of conversation with each passenger on the way.

The Steward has been serving a luncheon box and a cup of coffee to passengers. Already, perhaps, they are thinking of the first landing at Marignane, airport for Marseilles.

Passengers' lap-straps are fastened, cigarettes are stubbed out, the Steward reports to the Captain, the First Officer finishes his log, the Radio Officer is ' working ' the ground and the Captain is waiting for permission to land. Soon

he has it, and throttling back he makes a wide circuit of the airfield, lowers the undercarriage and flaps and makes a fairly flat engine-on approach, finally throttling right back as he runs his wheels along the runway—and *Plate 11* gives some idea of the view he gets of the runway during that last 200 yards.

Down on the tarmac stands the marshaller—or batsman—with a pair of outsize ping-pong bats painted bright yellow, making certain signs to Captain Wright which he interprets as ' Stop, and cut your engines '. The first stage of the flight is over for the passengers, but not

for the crew. They will be busy keeping an eye on the refuelling (*Plate 12*), checking over the aircraft, talking to Customs and other officials, filling in and checking forms, and getting the passengers back on to the aircraft once more.

Of course, it is bound to be much the same on the next lap from Marignane airport to Ciampino airport, Rome. But this time the weather is clear and Ben Wright is flying fairly low over the tops of the gaunt mountains of the Alpes Maritimes (*Plate 13*). In a moment he is over the deep blue of the Mediterranean, hands over to ' George,' the auto-pilot, and leaving the First Officer to keep a lookout he walks back to see the passengers. They have just finished passing from one to the other his last flight bulletin, and he amplifies remarks on it with the help of a map (*Plate* 14).

In just over six hours since leaving Northolt Airport under a grey sky, the twenty-seven passengers on board the B.E.A. Viking are at last in sight of Rome, as Captain Ben Wright circles the city (*Plate 15*) while he asks by radio-telephone for permission to land. It is granted. Once more the same landing routine, with once again the smooth landing at the end of it. And it is a happy landing for Captain Ben Wright and his crew, since Rome is a favourite stopping-place. And in *Plate 16* you see them setting out to see the sights.

Yes, it's largely a matter of routine ..

16. *In the short time before their return journey, the Crew enjoy seeing their destination from ground level.*

EASTER IN ROME

by

J. Hamilton-Dalrymple

[Photo, Paul Popper

The Oldest City in Europe

ROME is called the Eternal City. When you go there it suddenly dawns upon you that this city is a whole generation older than any other in Europe. I do not mean that Rome is all 'old world' and quaint and out of date, because few cities are so up-to-date and modern. I mean that when you are walking through the streets of Rome you may suddenly come across something that was in existence nearly 500 years before London and Paris were thought of. It may be a church built in the fourth century by the Emperor Constantine, like *St. Mary Major's.* This church was old, 800 years old, when our English ruins (like Fountains and Rievaulx Abbeys in Yorkshire), were being built; and to-day it is still filled with people praying and worshipping. Or the *Forum* where are the temples, roads, aqueducts, fountains, columns of the old Romans, and all the other trappings of their civilisation, and above the *Forum* rises the hill of the *Capitol,* the central of the Seven Hills of Rome. Round that hill, centred the old Kingdom of Rome in 650 B.C., in the days even before the Republic. This city, which to-day looks like any other busy twentieth century capital, has roots stretching back far beyond those of our island. If any men existed in England and Scotland then, they dressed in skins and were painted in woad. London and Paris are old and historic cities; but in comparison with them, Rome is eternal.

History in Palaces and Paving Stones

There is mediæval Rome, too, the Rome of the great Popes, like *Innocent III,* who very nearly succeeded in their attempt to bring lasting peace to the whole of Europe. Their Cathedral church is *St. John Lateran.*

It is the period of the Renaissance which leaves most traces in Rome to-day. There is not a street in Rome which does not contain a relic of this tremendously virile period of building and discovery and adventure. Go down the *Corso,* Rome's Piccadilly: it is the old *Via Flaminia* of Ancient Rome, but to-day it is flanked on either side by the palaces of the old Roman families, some of them plain and simple, some ornate and heavy with decoration, but nearly all of them bearing witness to the richness and taste of the Renaissance. At one end is the *Porta Del Popolo,* a fine classical edifice; it is the old Northern Gate of Rome, and through it has entered well nigh every person who came to Rome from the North and England since Roman days.

Although Rome was already 2,000 years old when it began, she did not lag behind her northern sister capitals, Paris, London, Vienna in this new burst of exuberant building. Rather, she began it. You will not properly understand the Italianesque style of our own architects like Inigo Jones, until you have been to Italy and seen those palaces upon which they modelled their art.

The Biggest Church of All

The immense church of *St. Peter's* is hard to describe. Ever since it was built people have been trying to decide whether it was a good thing or a bad thing artistically. Whatever its artistic merits it is certainly far and away the biggest church in the world. Inside it a man feels lost, and outside it, wherever you go in Rome, it makes its presence felt, its great dome riding above the roofs of the city. Whereas most of Rome is situated on the East bank of the Tiber, this great basilica is on the Western bank. It stands apart, as it were. To get to it you have to leave the noise and bustle of the city and strike out across the river to the West, and when you get there, you can look back towards the whole city, because you are on the Vatican Hill; and if you climb up into the dome, you have the Eternal City at your feet—and more than just the city: the whole Roman *Campagna* lies stretched before you, brown and dusty and yellow, hedged in by the *Alban Hills* twenty miles to the South, and the famous *Sabine Mountains,* forty miles due West. Behind your back as you look at those last, will be *Ostia* and the *Mediterranean.*

Pilgrims are called to Rome

This year in Rome 1950, is the Holy Year. This means that all Catholics all over the world will turn even more than ever towards the centre of their Church and its head, the Pope. The Holy Year takes place every twenty-five years, and was founded by Pope Boniface VIII in the year 1300. 1950 is the twenty-fifth to take place. As its name implies, it is a time of special prayer and penance to God, and Catholics all over the world join in it. The Pope has asked that this year be a year of special prayer for peace in the world, and has urged as many Catholics as can to come on pilgrimage to Rome so that they can pray for this object at the tombs of the Apostles. (St. Peter and St. Paul are both buried in Rome.) And naturally Easter, which is the biggest day in the year for Christians, will be the climax of this holy year. In fact, you may take it that anybody you meet in the streets of Rome round about Easter will not be a Roman, and probably will not even be able to talk Italian.

The biggest event in Rome during this fortnight will be on Easter Sunday, when the Pope himself will celebrate *Pontifical High Mass* in *St. Peter's.* If you are lucky, you may be able to get inside the church to attend that, and see all the wonderful pomp and ceremony and hear the lovely music of a Papal Mass. After Mass, the Pope will appear on the balcony outside *St. Peter's.* He will be looking down on the largest square in the world—*Bernini's* tremendous colonnaded piazza, which holds half a million people. Depend upon it, it will be full that day, and if you are there in the crowd, whether you are a Catholic or not, you will find it hard not to join all these Romans in shouting: 'Viva el Papa!' Easter is the day that Christ rose from the tomb in Jerusalem, and these Romans believe that the man they are saluting here in Rome is Christ's representative on Earth. That is why they shout in such numbers; and that is why the Pope when he has said a few words after the shouting has died down, will give from the balcony the most famous of all blessings—the Blessing Urbi et Orbi—to the City of Rome and All the World.

Rome is a city which has many sides to it and which is never exhaustible to the tourist. But during Easter Week there, the visitor will see a side to it which he perhaps never really guessed before. He will realise deeply that Rome has some very sound claim to its boldest boast: that it is the Centre of Christendom.

ROME

AN ARTISTS NOTEBOOK.

The foot of this ancient statue of St. Peter's is worn smooth from Pilgrims' kisses.

The Pope giving his blessing from the 'SEDE GESTATORIA'

A back view on St. Peter's Key, angel & saint from roof of Basilica. Note iron bars supporting huge stone images; compare size to people in foreground.

Vatican railway system is only 100 yards long, can be closed with electrically-operated bronze door.

This is one of the SWISS GUARDS since 400 years the Pope's Army. They still wear traditional costume in blue, red, yellow MEDICI colours

Black marketeers with black cat for bad luck

One of Rome's innumerable queer fountains: a pine cone; others have bees, tortoises, shells and papal crowns on them. Trajanus's column in background.

Traffic Policeman

A Papal Policeman

Tourists around Emperor Nero's circus, the COLOSSEUM, are always besieged by aggressive post-card vendors.

Kids roasting chestnuts

CASTEL SANT'ANGEL once the tomb of Emper Hadrianus, later refuge besieged Popes: a mus to-day.

A Baroque church

Capitoline wolf feeding Romulus and Remus.

Wine from Frascati

White cheese in a bladder

FIASCHETTO

Garland of pork sausages

wreath-shaped bread

Flat sausage

One of Rome's many hungry cats smelling at stuffed pigs foot sausage

Roman almond pastry

The "TORRONE"

Ground red pepper in cellophane bag.

An Egyptian obelisk on a Renaissance fountain

Scared tourists

Pillar of the classical Pantheon

No salami this it is smoked mutton-cheese

Carmelite Sisters

Barrow boys

Policemen

DEL PANTHEON

Balloon vendors are everywhere

A true replica of a galley in bronze. It stands in Vatican gardens and can spout water out of its cannons.

Drawings by G. F. BYRNE

113

BLACK HUNTING WHIP

by Monica Edwards

ILLUSTRATED BY GEOFFREY WHITTAM

PART THREE

NOTHING COULD BE DONE until the next morning because of the rain but Dion and Lindsey both did a great deal of thinking in bed that night, and feeding the chickens in the morning they began at once to discuss the matter as if never having left off.

'How old do you think he was? When did he live here?' Dion was working with the long-handled mixer.

Lindsey scraped dropped scraps from the floor. She said, 'Quite fifteen I should think, and must've lived ages ago because the writing is so formal.'

'Pity he didn't put the year as well as just the day and month. A hundred years, you think? Or more?'

'Did they have shows more than a hundred years ago?' Lindsey measured meal and let it flow into the bucket.

'Might find out, perhaps. Fellow doesn't even give his name, which seems so odd.'

'Only the name of his pony.'

'When we find the whip—' Dion began, bending to finish the mixing with a trowel.

'—Which we mightn't,' Lindsey said.

'But we know where it is!'

'Was,' said Lindsey. She flung the store shed door back into the wind and stepped out among the pushing fowls.

'Well, anyway, when we've found it, d'you know what I mean to do?' They were wading through chickens to the Barn field where the poultry house was.

'Yes.'

'How d'you mean, "yes"?'

'I mean I know, of course. At least I think I do.'

'What?' The bucket was tipped and the fowls' heads went down and tails up like a toy on a string.

'Carry it at Guildford Show.'

Dion stopped scraping the bucket to stare at his sister. He said, 'You're awfully witchery sometimes. It gives me the creeps.'

'I'm not. But it's pretty obvious. I mean that you'd want to try to put history right and all that. To do what that boy and his father both tried to, sort of for their sakes.'

'And to spite the swine of an uncle,' Dion added. They put the bucket away and shut the door.

'Well let's hope we find it,' Lindsey said. 'I'll be in

in a moment but I want to see Moonstone again before breakfast.'

Dion said over his shoulder, 'I saw her when I went to look at Duchess. She was all right and eating hay.'

But Lindsey went on down the yard.

* * *

The kitchen was in a terrible mess. The black range was standing out from its place and mountains of rubble and broken brick and stone stood round it. A wheelbarrow leaned against the cellar door and propped beside it was a mallet, a shovel, a mattock and a chisel. Dust covered everything and the wide inglenook was knee-high in debris, but stretched gloriously across and above the chaos was the long and beautiful arch of two-inch bricks.

'It has a ten foot span,' Mr. Thornton said happily. His hair stood straight up and was powdered with dust and his face was striped and spotted. He was washing his hands for breakfast and Mrs. Thornton was saying that wasn't much good without his face.

Breakfast was fried on a small oil stove carried to the sitting room hearth for the purpose, coffee was afterwards made in the same way and water boiled for washing up. Andrea was excused her usual job of breakfast dishes because it was so difficult doing them in all the mess and muddle, so she joyfully jerked down her riding coat and said she was taking Tarquin to Elstead to be shod as his shoes were so thin and would Lindsey like to come too?

Lindsey said she would, but had things to do. She said Peter was feeding his mice in the workshop and might like to go with her on Red Clover, so Andrea swung out of the door and past the Well House with the bridle in her hands.

Mr. Thornton said that what he would really like would be everyone out of the way while he got on with the fireplace, and Mrs. Thornton said she didn't see how anyone would get any lunch or what she could do about it.

Dion and Lindsey found a spade and a fork in the workshop and Dion went back and took the mattock which was a thing rather like a pick, from the kitchen without being noticed. They began at once on the way black ground beneath the third step of the barn. And when Mr. Thornton came storming down the yard for his mattock they were still digging and scraping and levering and were very hot and beginning to feel disappointed. There was a great hole under the step and a lot of earth and stones all round the doorway.

'What the—' began their father, who was also very hot and rather angry because of hunting for the mattock.

'Digging,' said Dion, explanatorily.

'I can see as much,' his father replied, taking the mattock. 'But what for? And you should ask before you borrow people's tools.'

Lindsey said, 'Sorry, Daddy,' and Dion said, 'Oh, just digging. We thought we might find something. I mean you never know with old places, I suppose.' He sounded apologetic.

'But why there?' Mr. Thornton was mildly astonished as he not infrequently was with his children.

Dion said it seemed as good a place as any and then

father, unconvinced, went back with his mattock to the kitchen.

Lindsey straightened herself and rubbed her back. 'It doesn't really look as if it's here,' she said sadly.

'It must be, the journal says "Under the third step".'

'Somebody else may have found it.' Lindsey began again shovelling loose earth out of the hole. 'He can't have buried it much deeper than this without attracting a lot of attention, can he.'

Dion worked on persistently with the fork, loosening more earth. He said, 'It doesn't *look* as if anyone had dug here for ages, or even ever. There were these biggish elder roots right across, and all those nettles.'

'Elder's awfully quick growing,' Lindsey said, 'and nettles come up in a night almost.'

'Well I still don't think anyone else has dug here for ages. Look how hard the earth is, like iron. I say!' He looked up, struck with a sudden idea, 'I wonder if we've got the right place?'

'Third step of the barn—of course we have.'

'Might not be this barn.'

Lindsey stared at him. 'Really, Dion,' she said in a prim grown-up voice, 'as if there *was* another barn.'

'Well, there might have been—once.'

They looked at each other for a minute and then Dion said, 'Maddening, that the deeds only go back to 1925. I wonder what happened to the earlier ones?'

'They might have told us about the barn and the old wing, too,' Lindsey said.

Dion was staring into the hole. 'Let's shovel all this back,' he said. 'It's nearly lunch time anyway', and the others'll be back from the forge any minute.'

'Too late, they are,' said Lindsey, looking down the green ribbed track to the gate where Tarquin and Red Clover were being greeted by a lonely grey Sula.

They shovelled and forked hastily but Andrea and Peter were through the gate into the yard before they had half done.

'What're you doing?'

'Whatever are you digging for?'

They were off their ponies and leading them across to the barn.

'Oh, digging,' Lindsey said.

'We were,' said Dion, 'but we've finished.'

'Well, we can see that,' said Andrea in a chilly voice, 'but what for?'

'Oh, in case anything might be there,' Lindsey said.

'And what?' said Peter, running his irons up their leathers.

'Oh, bother!' Lindsey was defensive. 'Can't you leave people alone?'

Brother and sister stared at brother and sister. Andrea suddenly said, 'You're keeping a secret from us.'

How true it was! Lindsey thought. And she's right again.

'What if we are? I dare say you often keep things from us,' Dion said.

Peter said *he* didn't but Andrea said nothing. After a moment she said with lightning change of subject, 'We met someone called Ann at the forge. She's frightfully nice and fifteen too.'

'Fifteen-two? Then she must be a horse,' Lindsey said, stamping down the shovelled earth with muddy wellingtons.

'She has a black pony called Pasha,' Andrea went on, ignoring, 'pretty much like Tarquin only no star, and a handsomer head though his hind hoofs are a bit blocky. Otherwise he's good, and he trots out like a thoroughbred.'

'*The kitchen was in a terrible mess. Mr. Thornton said that what he would really like would be everyone out of the way while he got on with the fireplace.*'

Lindsey said she knew that butcher-boy trot, it was all right in harness ponies but bad in saddle animals, so Andrea said Pasha wasn't a bit butcher-boy, and she stalked off to the stable with Tarquin, ignoring Lindsey's parting shot that he was hot round the girths and ears.

Red Clover pulled gently after Tarquin but Peter held her where she was. He said, 'You might tell us what you're digging for.'

'Well, perhaps we might,' said Dion. 'We'll think about it. But not now, we've finished and it's lunch time and we haven't found anything.' He scraped his spade clean with a sharp stone and Lindsey rubbed a sod along the tines of her fork. Then the two of them sauntered up to the workshop.

Peter watched them go, studied the hole very closely for a minute, looked at the barn, then led his pony into the stable.

Lunch was hot-pot and pancakes, all achieved on the small oil stove on the sitting room hearth. The kitchen was in an even worse confusion than before, though the vast ten-foot inglenook now stood almost cleared and very splendid. Large dust-sheets covered the dresser and table and everything else was bundled into the Cream Pan room, which was a beautiful but hybrid little room, being up a very small flight of stairs so neither properly upstairs nor down. At present it was being used as a junk room but was intended as a spare bedroom, when there was time to scrape the fine array of oak beams on its eastern wall, to tile its deep window ledge and distemper the low sloping walls that were partly ceiling. From its casement window there was a perfect view of the old Well House and beyond that the ancient yew tree and the high terraced bank that ran up to the yew tree's roots.

Dion was ferreting about in this room after lunch in the hope of finding his fountain pen which he had left on the smaller kitchen table, when Lindsey came in. She said, 'I've been thinking and I think we ought to tell Andrea. Perhaps Peter too. Four heads would be a lot better than two in finding the black hunting whip.'

'I don't know,' he said doubtfully, then, 'Have you seen my pen anywhere?'

Lindsey said, 'No—What about Peter and Andrea?'

'All right, it might be best. Andrea's frightfully clever though it seems a pity to be always right.'

'But she's much better, I think, since Tarquin came, I mean, it's such an awfully good sign, isn't it, that she should get so fond of an ordinary pony. She was never fond of Moonstone in that kind of way.'

'No-o.' Dion was uncertain about all this.

'She and Peter are scraping beams in our bedroom.'

Dion gave up the hunt for his pen and said, 'Come down to the cowshed first. I want to let Duchess out for a bit to-day, now she knows her place in the shed. She hasn't been out since she came because Jim Faithful says they always have to be kept in for the first day or two in case they try to break out and go home.'

They clumped down the short flight of steps, dashed through the sitting room, snatched coats in the hall and banged out of the front door.

Duchess was delighted to be let out but she was confined to the yard for this first occasion in order to accustom her to her immediate surroundings. She was embarking on a tour of exploration beginning at the pigsties when Dion and Lindsey went into the calf-box with small apples for Moonstone, and she was blowing through the gate at the three ponies when they went back through the overgrown garden to the house. But when they had got to the window of the Priest Hole bedroom, where Lindsey and Andrea slept, she was skipping about

the yard like a mountain ram. Andrea and Peter stopped the excruciating noise they were making with the scrapers and came across to look, and were so enchanted by the sight that they hardly noticed they were being told the deep secret until Dion had got as far as the cupboard in the stone table.

When they really grasped the importance of the matter they forgot the whole existence of Starfleet Countess's Duchess in their excitement about the discovery, and they also forgot about the scraping and later got into trouble with their mother for leaving scrapers in the middle of the floor for anyone to tread on and flaked plaster thick and unswept all round them, because the first thing they wanted to do was to see the cellar.

Andrea was deeply impressed by the diary. She said the first thing to do was to discover if there had ever been another barn, and if so where. She said she had planned to meet Ann Fergusson in the morning for a ride to the Devil's Jumps but she thought she ought to bring her to the farm instead and let her into the secret, because she might be such a help in suggesting the right people and places to go to in the hope of finding out the original layout of the farm.

Peter, who was sitting on the stone table beside the candle, said he thought they ought to try to discover who had written the diary, and Lindsey suggested they might try the church registers for that, and also ask the vicar because parsons often knew pretty well everything about their parish history.

'And we have to get the date if we can,' Dion said, 'because if it was a very long time ago—say two or three hundred years—the whip might have crumbled away.'

Andrea said she knew where to look it up, as there was a history of agriculture in the sitting room, and she thought it couldn't have been much more than a hundred years, if that.

'If so,' said Dion, pushing the diary back into its cupboard, 'and if there was another barn, it must have been there almost in living memory, unless it was already very ruined when the whip was buried, and the diary doesn't give that idea. The great barn sounds prosperous.'

Andrea looked at her watch. She was the only Thornton child who had one, and though it kept rather erratic time it was a help. 'Only half-past two-ish,' she said. 'If we got the ponies and were frightfully quick we've time to do the church before it gets dark.'

Lindsey was poking about in the corner by the steps. She said impatiently, 'Three ponies, four people. Same old bother. How can we all?'

'Drat!' said Andrea. 'Well, I'll stand out if you like. I could find that Agricultural History and see about when shows began and all that.'

Dion said, 'Tell you what. You know the Faithfuls where I'm milking; well, they have a horse. They'd lend it, I know; they said so once.'

'What sort of horse?' Andrea sounded a bit choosey.

'Well, a bit heavy, I'm afraid. He's a vanner really, but they have ridden him and he's quite good, Jim Faithful says, except for with small dogs and he chases those.'

Peter said, 'Oh, come on, Andy, any horse is better than not riding when you might.'

Andrea snapped back not to call her Andy and said all right, she didn't mind trying the animal.

The four Thorntons oozed out of the camouflaged window.

* * *

The Faithfuls' vanner was a stoutly built spotted animal of about fifteen hands and he had very feathered legs. He was called Arthur and he had a docked tail which had

116

grown to an elongated comma, and a long and bushy forelock through which he kept a constant vigil for smallish dogs.

Andrea pretended he was an Appaloosa and wouldn't try to ride him seriously because she thought he looked so funny. All went fairly well until the party was approaching the corner near the church, when Andrea and Arthur just vanished round the corner in a flourish of hairy hoofs and little tail.

'Gosh!' said Dion, steadying the black Tarquin who was taking exception to the disturbance. 'Should you think it's a dog?'

'More probably several,' Lindsey said, trying not to laugh because anything might be happening to Andrea, but she had looked so ridiculous, tearing round the corner like that. She patted dappled Sula who was almost quivering with surprise, and flicked a watchful glance at Red Clover, as yet a rather unknown quantity.

Peter had shortened rein. 'Oughtn't we to go after her?'

'We are,' said Dion, 'though not at the same rate.'

'Andrea's all right,' Lindsey said.

'So long as she isn't being unhorsed in the eye of the village,' Dion began. They rounded the corner and saw Andrea, still sitting on Arthur who appeared to be stuck midway over the church stile. As they rode up they saw what was plainly the vicar approaching her from the other direction, namely, the church porch. All converged at the same time and the vicar, who was quite young and looked exactly like a boxer, said excuse him, but were they looking for anything?

Andrea said she thought her horse was looking for a dog but not with her permission, and now it rather seemed as if he might be stuck. She said she was awfully sorry but he wasn't her horse and seemed entirely indifferent to the aids.

The vicar would have walked round Arthur only he couldn't because of Arthur's being stuck over the stile. Andrea said, 'I think I'd better get off as I can't move him.' She had to step first on to the stile because it came in the middle, and then jump to the ground. But Arthur declined to move an inch when Andrea and the vicar tried to back him out into the pathway.

'Perhaps he'll come into the churchyard,' said the vicar, but Arthur didn't care for that either. Peter, holding fat Clover's reins on the grass patch, said it might help if they showed him a dog and the vicar said that was an excellent idea and Peter obviously a very intelligent child. He said he would go at once and get Mrs. Findlay's pekingese. When the vicar exposed half the pekingese, Andrea had to move extremely fast in order to get hold of the reins at all. She and Arthur travelled irresistibly to the corner but she was able to stop him there because the vicar, having seen what was coming, had taken swift refuge with the pekingese in the boiler room.

A moment later he re-appeared without the little dog and said now what should they do. Andrea said they had really come to ask if they might look at the church registers in order to discover all the people who lived at Punch Bowl Farm before them, but perhaps it would be better to come another day without Arthur.

'Quite unnecessary,' said the vicar kindly. 'There are stables at the vicarage, empty now, and I think you will find your horse quite docile in the stable and we can leave Frou-Frou down in the boiler room. It is both warm and safe for her there.'

'Thank you very much,' said Andrea. 'How do we get to the stables?'

The vicar said the best way for Arthur was straight on through the churchyard but the other three could more easily go round by the lane and meet them at the vicarage.

Andrea shouted these instructions to the rest of her family beyond the stile and led the spotted horse behind the vicar through the churchyard.

At the vicarage the ponies and Arthur were put into dusty loose-boxes out of which a motor-mower, a wheelbarrow, a ladder and a hencoop were first quickly removed by everyone except Andrea and Peter who were holding the ponies. The vicar said he was sorry they had no hay at the vicarage but he gave all the ponies and Arthur some puppy biscuits and they liked them very much. He said that the Thorntons probably knew his name was Findlay and if they would follow him he would be pleased to show them the registers, he had them at the vicarage because he had been engaged on a search for a family who were anxious to establish the date at which their ancestors had first come to Highnoons village.

The winter afternoon was already sinking to a pearly dimness and though it was mild open weather, the fire in the vicar's study was a cheering sight. Peter, who loved cats, went immediately to the hearth where two pure white cats sat regarding the visitors with prim suspicion.

The vicar drew out chairs and then unlocked his desk. Lying open inside it were three heavy registers, their lined pages covered with elaborately perfect copper-plate writing with here and there a large X.

'Baptisms, Marriages and Burials,' Mr. Findlay explained, sitting down in his swivel chair.

'Hatches, Matches and Despatches,' translated Dion, and then suddenly felt that wasn't quite the thing to say to a vicar but Mr. Findlay laughed. 'Before yourselves, of course,' he said, turning pages, 'were the Anstys. You would know that. They came to Punch Bowl, let me see—' he narrowed his eyes in concentration, '—well, not more than fifteen years ago. They are not in any of these registers, having been born and brought up elsewhere, no children, and having moved away from the district last summer.'

'Before them?' queried Andrea, her head on one side in her effort to read the registers from her chair.

'Before them,' repeated the vicar, then with an observing glance over his shoulder, 'Do come and look on, too, if you would like to. Perhaps you, Andrea, would like to hunt through the Burials with Dion? Peter and this child—'

'Lindsey,' supplied the younger daughter.

'—Lindsey, could do the Baptisms and I'll go through the Marriages as they are rather more complicated, involving two addresses each time.'

'Oh, thank you!' Dion and Andrea leaned over the table in the window with the Register of Burials between them, Peter and Lindsey established theirs on the chesterfield and knelt down in front of it.

'Look for the address,' Mr. Findlay instructed them. 'I have only been here for six years myself, so am unfamiliar with the earlier names.'

For a minute or two there was silence except for the turning of pages, the muttering of names and the purring of cats on the dark crimson hearthrug. Then the vicar remarked, 'I have found one entry here, date 1789; Walter Thatcher, bachelor, of Punch Bowl Farm in the parish of Highnoons, to Susannah Jenner, spinster, of Church Cottages, Milford. Any use?'

'Rather early, I should think,' Andrea said, glancing up. 'Are there any more after that one?'

'Oh, you want to locate a special individual?' the vicar said, his index finger running down the written page.

'Well no, not exactly. We just want to find out who was living there, say, about a hundred years ago or thereabouts. But perhaps we ought to make a note of the Walter Thatcher one.'

'Certainly,' said Mr. Findlay, and found her a piece of sermon paper and pencil. While she was writing Lindsey suddenly announced, 'Punch Bowl Farm, Highnoons. That's us. Walter and Susannah Thatcher, a son, Walter, March 17th, 1792. Oh, and they had lots of children because they're here again. A daughter, Mary, in 1794, and here twin sons, James and John, 1797.'

'*And* here,' said Peter, who had turned the page and was pointing, 'A son, Joseph, 1798.'

'That one died,' Dion said. 'It's under my very nose, Joseph Thatcher, Punch Bowl Farm, 1799.'

Lindsey jumped up to look over Dion's shoulder. 'Poor little fellow!' she said in a sudden wave of pity. 'Only a year old!'

Mr. Findlay nodded sympathetically. He said, 'They had large families in those days, but many died young. There was the Plague, to begin with. Lack of knowledge about bacterial infection, and sanitary conditions generally were appalling.'

'And they call them the good old days!' Peter was rather shocked.

'Now here,' said Mr. Findlay, 'is another name for you, date 1831. Matthew Minchin, bachelor, of Punch Bowl Farm, to Sarah Amabel Fletcher, spinster, of the parish of Haslemere.'

Everyone looked up at this and Andrea said that was much more like what they were looking for, except that they hadn't thought there was a wife.

'Perhaps she died, too,' suggested Peter, and Dion went back over the Burials to see if she was there. '1824, 1827, 1830,' he murmured, working down the pages. 'Here we are, she did. Minchin, wasn't it? Sarah Amabel, 1831.'

'But that was the year she was married!' Andrea said, coming over with her sermon paper notes.

The vicar peered into his register again and said, 'The marriage was solemnized in April. The tenth, to be exact.'

'She was buried on May the ninth,' Lindsey said, her finger at the place. 'Quaking Queens, she barely lived a month after her wedding!'

'Then he was a widower!' Andrea suddenly said in a significant voice. 'Did he marry again, please, Mr. Findlay? Does it say?'

There was complete silence for a minute or two while the vicar made further investigations, but this was broken by Dion's announcing that the burial of Matthew Minchin, farmer, was recorded in 1870.

'He had no second wife,' the vicar said now. 'That is, he did not marry again at Highnoons Church.'

'Could he have somewhere else?' Lindsey asked.

'He could.'

'Oh.'

'If that fact is really important,' said the vicar, 'I suggest you get in touch with one of the older inhabitants of Highnoons. It is almost in living memory. Old Joshua Pyecraft, for example, is over ninety and still quite clear in his head. In fact I saw him in his garden yesterday morning.'

Andrea began to scribble. 'Joshua Pyecraft,' she wrote, 'over ninety.' Then she copied from the registers the details about Matthew Minchin and the tragically early death of his bride.

'If he did marry again,' Peter said, still reading down the Baptisms, 'there weren't any children; or if there were they weren't christened.'

'He didn't have any,' Dion said, 'I'm sure.'

Andrea switched the conversation adroitly by saying, 'Well, that seems to be as much as we can find out from the registers. The other thing we want to discover if we can is the original plan of the farm. You see, the deeds only go back to 1925 and no one seems to know anything about it before then.'

'We thought there might have been another barn,' added Dion, as casually as he could.

'Hardly likely, I should say,' Mr. Findlay said, 'with a place of that size. However, you never know, and if anyone does know it would most probably be old Joshua Pyecraft. You should certainly look him up. You know his cottage, do you, just behind the church? It has ivy all over it.'

Dion said they could easily find it, but now they ought to go because it was getting quite dark. Andrea said they would have to hurry and she only hoped they didn't meet any more small dogs on the long lane home.

They thanked the vicar for his help with the registers and he said the pleasure had been his and accompanied them to the stables.

The ponies and Arthur were all glad to be saddled again as, having long since finished the puppy biscuits, they were bored and anxious to be home.

Mr. Findlay helped with girths and the vicarage gate, and wished the four Thorntons a very good afternoon.

There was a white frost when Dion got up the next morning. He was earlier than usual because he wanted to look at Starfleet Countess's Duchess who was due to calve just after Christmas and it was already Christmas Week. The postman came later every day and secret parcels were conveyed from his hands by secretive parents and deposited in forbidden places.

Cows often calved earlier than the calendar date. Just as often they calved later. Jim Faithful had said that an early calf was usually a heifer but when a cow passed her proper date they knew they might expect a bull. Dion hoped Duchess would not have a bull calf, which could not be reared on the farm but must go away to market at a few days old. A heifer calf would crown his hopes and be the foundation stone of the future Punch Bowl herd of pedigree attested Jerseys.

Outside in the slowly growing light the glittering hoar frost covered everything. There was a silence like a holding of breath and the morello cherry in the garden might have burst overnight into astonishing winter blossom from the shower of white that clothed it.

Dion scrunched down the frosty yard to the cowshed where Duchess spent her nights and he heard the rattle and clatter of her chain as she heaved herself to her feet at his approach. He reached a hand over the open half-door to shoot the bolt. Duchess turned her head and regarded him with dark antelope eyes. She was altogether like an antelope, he thought, with her slender black and silver legs and her pale creamy-brown body. No calf yet, and to his inexperienced eye she looked much the same as usual. He wished Holleybone would take more interest in her, but Jim Faithful had promised to come along soon and have a look at her.

Dion took the fork from its corner and tidied up the heifer's bed, putting the soiled straw into the wheelbarrow and taking it across the yard to the dung heap. He offered water in a bucket but she would not drink, so he put fresh hay in the manger and went out to look at Moonstone, it being too early yet to turn Duchess out for the day.

The mare came stiffly across to greet him when he opened her door and he gave her a small handful of dairy nuts from his pocket. She snuffled and pushed for more but he patted her neck and shoulder and spoke to her in a way he would not have dreamed of in front of the others. He was pleased to think that he had visited the mare before Lindsey who was usually there before anyone else was even dressed. He could hear her coming down the yard, her feet scrunching as his had done in the crackle of the frost, the young dog Glen whirling round her in excitement with the sparkle on the ground. She was surprised to see him in the calf-box and looked her astonishment as she came in.

'I was looking at Duchess,' he explained, 'in case she calves early. Holleybone hardly bothers with her at all.'

'And has she?' Lindsey was breaking a carrot with her teeth for Moonstone.

'Of course not.'

Lindsey stroked a gentle hand down Moonstone's face. 'I think she's miles better, don't you?' she said, meaning Moonstone now.

'Yes. You'd never guess she wasn't perfectly normal if you didn't see her moving,' Dion agreed.

'I hope she can have a foal by next year. Do you think she will?'

From the old farmhouse three bells sounded. They were rung erratically, sometimes one, sometimes another, and then all three, and the sound was clear on the cold frosty air.

'Breakfast!' said Lindsey.

'Bet you that's Peter ringing,' said Dion. But it wasn't, it was Andrea. She said, 'Come on, do hurry up. I've got to meet Ann at ten.'

'When the vicar exposed half the pekingese, Andrea had to move extremely fast in order to get hold of the reins at all.'

'Joshua Pyecraft was very active for a man of more than ninety.'

From the sitting room the palate-tickling smell of frying bacon drifted out when Mrs. Thornton opened the door. 'Ready?' she said.

'Ready!' came the answer, and the family crowded from the icy cold kitchen where still no fire was burning, and warmed stiff fingers at the blaze in the sitting room hearth.

It was three minutes past ten when Ann and Andrea met at the top of Kettlebury Hill.

'Hello,' said Andrea, drawing Tarquin to a halt. 'If I'm late we both are.'

'We aren't, very,' said Ann. She was wearing reddish-brown jodhpurs and her dark hair was in a long bob under her velvet cap. Pasha looked a very deep black against a new brown saddle, and Andrea said so.

'Yes,' agreed Ann, 'but I'll be glad when it wears old-looking. New saddles make you feel an awful novice, though I'm fond of this one because I saved up for years and bought it myself.'

'Have you tried banana skins?' Andrea suggested, her hands crossed on Tarquin's saddle bow.

'What, to eat?'

'Of course not. To darken saddles.'

'No, does it really? I've heard of vinegar. Shall we ride on?'

'Well, the point is,' said Andrea, 'would you like to come and meet my family instead? I don't mean just introducing and that kind of thing, but the fact is we've discovered something awfully interesting—that is, Dion and Lindsey have, but we all know about it now and we want to find out more. I thought it'd be an awfully good thing to have you in it too, because you've lived around here so much longer than we have.'

'Count me in,' said Ann, 'and for the love of Mike tell me all about it now or I shall die of curiosity. Which way?'

'Down here,' said Andrea, turning Tarquin on his hocks. Glen was on his feet in a bound and away ahead down the track, and Ann turned Pasha after.

'It began with the gale,' said Andrea, 'when Moonstone was hurt . . . ' Her voice blew away on the cold east wind and the ponies were going down Kettlebury Hill.

Back at Punch Bowl Farm Lindsey was mucking out Moonstone's box. She was hurrying because she wanted to have time to help Dion and Peter cut branches of holly and ivy for decorating the house. She dumped the last forkload of soiled straw into the wheelbarrow and trundled it away to the dung heap. Then she turned the empty barrow on its side against the stable wall, put the fork away in its corner in the cowshed and took the broom to sweep the calf-box floor. Moonstone stood looking out into the yard over her half-door moving stiffly aside to allow Lindsey to pass in and out whenever necessary. Lindsey never did so without a friendly word to the mare, or a touch with a quiet hand.

The next part of her job was the morning exercising of the patient, now part of her regular routine and usually watched over by Mrs. Thornton, as well as the vet on occasions.

This morning Lindsey had the job to herself and when she slipped the leather head collar over Moonstone's ears she was a little awed with the great responsibility. Then, carefully, she led her through the doorway to the yard and, slowly because of Moonstone's limp, to the orchard.

She mustn't go through here, she knew, because of Sula and Red Clover who might tempt the convalescent mare to dangerous excitements, but it was a lovely thing to see the daily greeting between little Sula and her old companion by the gate. Red Clover would come trotting up too, as round and fat as ever, but she had not been Moonstone's closest shadow through years as Sula had, and she would whinny and toss her head at the sight of the elegant stranger. But Sula would make low whickering noises with quivering nostrils and would push her cool muzzle along Moonstone's silky neck, leaning on the gate that stood between them.

Lindsey talked to the ponies and stroked a cupped hand over smooth ears. Then she led the lame Moonstone on across the yard and up the track to Yew Tree field where Dion and Peter were cutting holly branches studded with bright crimson berries.

Ann and Andrea stopped in front of Mr. Capstick's house. Ann was saying, 'He's a most odd person but might easily know things about the way your farm used to be. He's a horse dealer really, and frightfully shrewd, but dabbles in pretty well everything else as well.'

Andrea was sitting on Tarquin, looking up and down the ruinous shack that lay, like an abandoned chicken house, before her. She was about to say, 'You don't mean to say he lives *here*,' when she noticed the orderly row of clean windows in a long, low building at the rear, so said instead, 'What does he keep in the ruined cottage? Feeding stuffs I suppose.'

'No,' said Ann, 'himself. He lives there. That palatial erection at the back is his stable.'

'Cripes!' said Andrea, marvelling, and then Mr. Capstick appeared out of his side door and waddled bow-legged down the path. 'Got the time on you, say?' he shouted as he came.

'He always asks that,' whispered Ann. 'I mean to tell him two a.m. one day. He only says it to start talking.'

Andrea looked at her watch. 'About twenty past ten,' she said and hoped she was right, but doubted it.

'You ought to come in and see my new cob,' said Mr. Capstick.

Ann said thank you, but that they really hadn't time to spare as they were going to Highnoons.

'Oh yes, I can see that, I know that,' shouted Mr. Capstick in the way he had. 'Friend live there?'

Ann said she did, at Punch Bowl Farm. 'We thought that perhaps you might know some things about her farm, the way it used to be, I mean. She's very interested in all that and so are her family.'

'Oh yes,' bellowed Mr. Capstick. He wore a greenish bowler with the brim cut away at the back so that it looked like an antique jockey cap, and he kept pushing it further and further to the back of his head. 'Of course you know there was another barn on your place, time past? You can see that.'

'Another barn—' Andrea's voice rose to a faint squeak with the sudden rush of hope that was in it. 'Do you know where?'

Mr. Capstick picked a twig from his hedge and began to chew it. Then he said that as it was rather before his time he couldn't rightly say, but had they tried old Josh Pyecraft at Highnoons, he'd likely know, considering how old he was and lived there all his life.

'That's the man the vicar said,' Andrea remembered.

'S'right,' said Mr. Capstick. 'Ten past twelve you said,' he foghorned. 'Better get my dinner cooking. A man gotter live.'

Ann and Andrea gathered up their reins, Ann calling Glen from the yard where Mr. Capstick's dog was chained. 'Don't forget to tell us anything else you remember,' Ann called to his departing figure, and they watched him waddle round the corner of his ruin to the stables.

'Another barn!' said Andrea. 'We must tell the others. It makes all the possible difference.'

* * *

Joshua Pyecraft was very active for a man of more than ninety. When the three younger Thorntons rode up to his garden gate he was half way up a step ladder pruning his apple trees. They looked up and saw his fluff of white hair like a halo round his old flat cap, his dark grey jacket with neatly patched elbows and his corduroy trousers tied round below the knee with binder twine.

He looked down and saw the boys and the girl on their ponies. It seemed as if they wanted to speak to him so he came slowly and stiffly down the step ladder.

'We don't want to hinder you if you are busy,' Dion began, but the old man came on down the path.

He was saying, 'No hindrance, young 'uns, no hindrance. I a'nt so good up a ladder as what I was, an' a break don't come unwelcome.'

'Mr. Findlay asked us to come and see you,' Lindsey said. She had dismounted and was checking Sula from eating Mr. Pyecraft's privet hedge.

'He said you knew more than anyone else about Highnoons,' Dion added, 'and we're trying to discover things about Punch Bowl Farm.'

Peter was swinging down from Red Clover's saddle. 'We live there now,' he said to Mr. Pyecraft who replied, 'Thowt there were fower of ye, so they said up the shop.'

'Oh, there are,' Peter told him, 'but Andrea, she's the eldest, stayed at home because we only have three ponies.'

The old man folded up his secateurs and put them in his pocket. 'And what would you be wantin' to find out, partickler?' he inquired gravely, surveying them all with mild blue eyes that were faded and watery with age. 'They took a fine big crop of taties off of that old Little Bottoms field 'bout Armistice year I call to mind, and there was that time in 'ninety fower when the bull what

they had up Punch Bowl broke out and frolicked over Highcomb Bottom with a gate on his 'orns. You never saw the like.'

'Did his horns break?' Peter asked with sudden curiosity, but Dion said, 'It must be wonderful to be able to remember right back to eighteen ninety four; I'm sure I'll never be able to. Can you remember what the farm looked like, Mr. Pyecraft? Or about Mr. Minchin?'

'We-ell,' Mr. Pyecraft leaned on his garden gate and felt for his briar pipe. 'That were a much bigger house, that were. More fell down than what stands now.'

'Did it really fall down, Mr. Pyecraft?' Lindsey said, loosening Sula's girths as she spoke. 'Or did it burn, or what?'

'Time outer mind, that were,' Mr. Pyecraft said, stuffing dark tobacco into his pipe with his thumb. 'Who knows how it went? I bin here fr' nigh ninety year and I never heard nothing about it. But you can see it were a bigger bit what come down from lookin' at the foundationses. Mr. Minchin, now. 'E weren't in my time, see, but I heard me ol' father talk of him. A widder man 'e were. No fam'ly an' 'ad a funny temper, so 'e said. Couldn't keep no labour an' that.'

Dion was leaning across Tarquin's back, his chin on his arms. He said eagerly, 'A widower! We thought so, it really fits in. Do you remember about another barn? There was another barn, wasn't there?'

'Oh, ah, another barn. Truth there were another barn, an' a bigger one than what stands there now. Burnt down it was, the year they made a hot rick inside it. My ol' father told them, 'e did, they'd have trouble an' sure they did. 'Bout ninety eight, that were, if I don't disremember. Folks saw it from Kettlebury, a fine blaze it made. Nothin' left but the tiles an' they broken.'

'Mr. Pyecraft,' Dion was tense with corked up excitement, 'where did the second barn stand? Do you know exactly?'

'We-ell, I can place it meself within a little. 'Twas side the track, see, what goes to the gate. Somewheres atween the house an' the gate, down along the track through the orchard to the lane, if you understand.'

'O—oh,' mixed disappointment and relief was in their voices. They knew something, but how little it was.

'Which side of the track?' Dion asked.

'Now you're arskin'. Reckon it were easterly, but coulder bin west. No-o, east it was. Leastways, I'd bet this pipe er baccy on it, though yer mem'ry plays queer trickses, times. Now if you could get to see some er they ol' mapses, you might likely learn more.'

'What sort of maps?' Dion asked.

'We-ell, there was one useter hang in the schoolroom when I were a boy. Coloured it was, an' give all Highnoons Parish with the farms an' that. Likely it give the lay of the barns an' all but I disremember now.'

The old voice quavered to a standstill and Mr. Pyecraft put his pipe in his mouth and felt for his secateurs.

'We could go to the schoolhouse and ask now, couldn't we?' said Dion.

Mr. Pyecraft nodded, puffing at his pipe. 'Miss Pim,' he said. 'Nice young woman, but not what they useter be in my time. No beatin' . . . no proper discipline . . .'

Dion and Lindsey were mounted in a moment but Red Clover circled and Peter got up at the third attempt. Reins were gathered, Clover's little ears shot forward till they nearly met at the points, Tarquin's white eye rolled, Sula played with her bit.

Dion said, 'Thank you very much, Mr. Pyecraft. We know a lot more now.'

The old man lifted his pipe. 'You're welcome,' he said.

'Goodbye!' said Lindsey and Peter, and the ponies trotted down the lane.

Miss Pim, the 'nice young woman', astonished her visitors by being well over sixty and very managing. She wore her hair on the top of her head like a cottage loaf and had large hips with a very narrow waist. She came to the schoolhouse door with floury hands and waved them at her visitors. 'Excuse the flah on my hands,' she said, 'won't you? But I'm making mince pies and I must have all done in half an ah, so I can only spare a minute.'

Lindsey explained rather nervously about the map, but Miss Pim said it certainly wasn't there now. 'We go in more for brightness at ah little school now,' she explained. 'Flah pictures in bold poster paints, if you understand, and lots of pretty flahs in flahpots. But if you care to call on the retired head teacher, Mrs. Crakethorne, who has a hahse at Churt, she may probably know what has become of it. Now I must go, my dears, I have already put the sah milk in the flah and it will make very sad pastry if I leave it any longer.'

'Could you say what time it might be now?' Dion asked apologetically. 'Perhaps we ought to leave Mrs. Crakethorne till tomorrow.'

Miss Pim said about three, she thought, and Lindsey said that if it was as late as that they'd have to leave it because it got dark so early now, and they still wanted to call at the vicarage.

Mr. Findlay was sawing logs in the stable yard at the vicarage. He put down his saw and came to greet them. They explained about the map but he said this was a thing about which he really couldn't enlighten them as he had no idea where his predecessor's widow now lived, or even whether she lived at all. But he said they should certainly go out to Churt and see old Mrs. Crakethorne because she had just such a map, he had seen it often when he went to call, it hung over a writing desk in the sitting room and he had frequently examined it.

Everyone said thank you. Mr. Findlay said he hoped he would see them all in church on Christmas morning and would they sing very loudly because the new organ drowned the voices of the little congregation, then he waved as they rode down the lane.

On the way back the Thorntons met Ann Fergusson riding home on Pasha. There was a hold-up in the hurrying back because she had been down the secret cellar with Andrea and seen the diary and had to tell about this, and then she had to be told about the barn and the maps and Mrs. Crakethorne, and of course she wanted to be there when the Thorntons rode to Churt to see the Highnoon map. 'What about tomorrow?' she suggested. 'I could meet you on Kettlebury Hill about tennish. I know it's Christmas Eve but she wouldn't mind, would she?'

'Christmas Eve! So it is!' Peter marvelled.

'All right,' said Dion, 'we can all be there.'

Ten minutes later they were back in the lamplight and the firelight, warming fingers and sniffing Scotch Pancakes on a plate in the hearth.

'I made them on the oil stove,' Mrs. Thornton said. She was putting out plates and cups and saucers on a blue checked tablecloth.

'The last time you'll have to,' Andrea said from the sofa where she was still dipping into Early Victorian History. 'Daddy said a cooker's coming tomorrow.'

'This is a wonderful book,' she remarked a minute later. 'I'd no idea history could be such fun. Listen to this, it's a bit about the Eighth Duke of Beaufort and it says, "His children all hunted, though not, as they explained to a visitor, more than three times a week till they were five years old." And Lindsey, there's a bit about a chap who had sheep and showed them, so there must have been shows as long ago as eighteen-thirty.'

(Continued on page 155)

for GIRAFFE

It is both discourteous and idiotic to laugh
too loud at the giraffe;
for though it lacks grace
and has a face
that looks, willy nilly,
pretty silly
stuck up there by itself somewhere near
the stratosphere,
you should realise
that when those goggling eyes
alight on YOU,
you TOO,
standing there below
miles down, somewhere near its toe,
a weeny spot,
a pin, a dot,
are enough to make a cat laugh—
or at any rate a giraffe.

V. G.

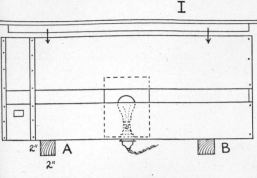

HOW TO MAKE A CHICK BROODER

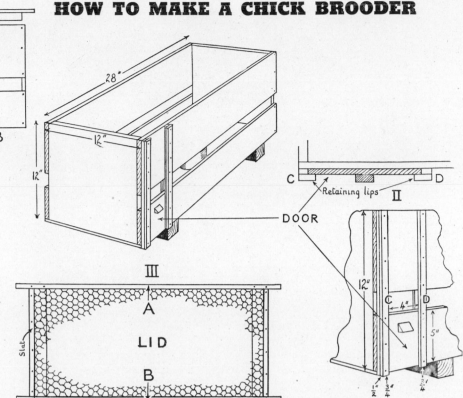

M ANY PARENTS would not object to their children keeping a few hens on a small patch of unwanted ground in the garden, if the initial outlay was not too heavy. Last year my brother and I, aged 13 and 12, with the full co-operation of our mother, successfully reared two batches of day old chicks, 21 in number, having only one loss.

This is how we did it. We purchased: 1. Two orange boxes. 2. An Ostermilk tin. 3. A 5 watt and a 15 watt electric bulb. 4. An electric bracket. 5. A plug. 6. A length of plastic flex. 7. A little creosote (if possible). 8. A piece of ¾-inch wire netting, 28 inches x 12 inches (sold for protecting garden produce).

Take the better of the two boxes and after seeing that you have a good firm base, nail a piece of wood, the width of the box and about 2 inches square at each end. See figs (1) A and B.

Then turn the box on its side and make sure you have about 1 inch ventilation space between the two pieces of wood forming the side 5 inches from the base. Do likewise with opposite side.

Now to make the door, turn the box on the side you want the door and remove the piece of wood nearest the floor. Then saw off a piece 4 inches in length and replace to original position. After that cut two pieces of wood 12 inches x ½-inch x ½-inch and then cut two more 12 inches x ½-inch x ¾-inch. Nail the first two on to each side of the proposed doorway and the second two on to the first two to form a retaining lip to hold the sliding door in position. See diagram (2) C and D.

Now turn the box upside down and draw a circle in the centre just big enough for your light bracket to go through, then burn or cut the hole out.

The next thing to make is the wire mesh lid for as soon as they are big enough the chicks will try to fly out.

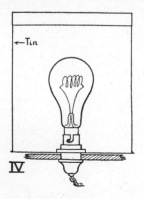

For this you want two pieces of wood 30 inches x 2 inches x ½-inch and two more 11 inches x 3 inches x ½-inch.

Now lay the two pieces so that the distance between them is 21 inches. Then place the netting so that it covers both of them and nail the long pieces A and B in fig. (3) so that they hold the netting in place and the lid together. Now you nail the slat at each end, your lid is complete. It should just sink into the top of the box. See fig. (1).

Then you creosote your floor and let it dry. This is not essential. The last thing to do is to prepare the light which is to be the foster mother to your chicks. In the bottom of your tin, in the centre, punch a hole big enough to take your light bracket and secure it by screwing up the band. See fig. (4).

Then put your 15 watt bulb in and connect the flex to the plug and plug in. The bulb should light up. You then put the lid on the tin, which should have three holes punched in it to let the heat into the brooder. The 15 watt should be exchanged for a 5 watt when the chicks are about five weeks old.

When they reach eight weeks they no longer need the light and they can be put out in a shed.

Now, readers, we come to the part where you need your mother's co-operation, especially if you are like us and have a good deal of Preparation, Saturday school and games. The baby chicks at first must be fed little and often and frequently given fresh water with the chill off. The light must be kept on night and day, and we had one of our camping blankets put all over the box to keep the heat in and kept it like

this in our warm kitchen for the first fortnight. We managed to buy unrationed meal at our corn chandler's and put a thin layer of this on brown paper for the chicks in the brooder.

Now they are a fortnight old we have put them in a shed near the house in the brooder with the heat still on but giving them more room to run about during the day. The floor is now covered with a thin layer of peat moss.

The chicks should be fed at first on hard boiled egg and later on chick meal and potato. They should have fine grit and cod liver oil to prevent rickets.

Well there's your brooder and I wish you the best of luck with your chicks.

RICHARD HALE (14)

THE SEASONS

When I walk down the lanes in spring,
It makes me want to dance and sing.
Primrose and violet are about,
And even bluebells may be out.

In summer the fields are sweet to see,
With poppy and foxglove and buzzing
bee.
The lark and thrush are singing away,
And butterflies floating about all day

In autumn the leaves come falling down,
Yellow and orange and golden brown.
Lovely fruit to pick and eat,
Which when you shake, falls at your
feet.

The first snowflake in winter you see
Reminds you of ice and snow-covered
tree
So out you go and play in the snow,
Coming home to a fire with a warm
happy glow.

JANE ANNING (12)

CASTING IN METAL

by Joseph Natanson

You are wrong to think that striking medals, casting bells or making glorious bronze statues are all beyond you. It is fascinating to find out how these things are done, and realise you can try yourself, within your own home.

FOR A LONG TIME I saved up old bits of lead. After his visit the plumber left behind him almost two inches of the pipe he had cut; the electrician provided me with a length of old wire in a leaden sheath, but the best addition was provided by the builder who came to repair the roof and left behind a lot of cuttings from a sheet of lead. At last I had enough material to start a very tempting experiment: the casting in metal of some little object of sculpture.

You have probably heard about the great art of casting in bronze and how it sometimes takes years to make the preparations for casting a statue or a bell. Even a small statuette in bronze requires enormous skill, and we know from history what a stir Donatello made in the Italian Renaissance when he succeeded in casting the huge statue of Gattamelata in Padua, the first statue of a man on horseback since Roman times.

None of us, of course, can dream of doing anything in bronze, for that requires a very high temperature for melting; but lead, or more probably an alloy of lead and tin from the scraps collected, melts at about 400°F., which is well within the range of the family cooker.

All the same, I would advise only those who are absolutely sure what their hands are doing to follow my experiment, lest they burn themselves or other people in the house. It is better to wear gloves during the casting operation in case you are tempted to touch some bit of metal not yet absolutely cold. And before casting in metal you must be good at casting in plaster.

As the metal can be cast and re-cast indefinitely, it is better to make something quite simple before you begin on the masterpiece which will remain in some museum for ever. Start, for instance, with a commemorative plaquette or a medal. A plaquette is a small sculpture in low relief and, as it has not got two sides like a medal, is easier to do.

Take some clay or plasticine. Make a flat shape (square, oblong or circular). Model any subject you like on it. Round the border write anything you would like to leave to posterity—the title of your work, your name, or the date (in Latin, of course: MCML). Put the whole thing in a box slightly larger and with sides higher than your model, and pour the plaster over it. When the plaster is set, remove it from the box; which will be easy if you have previously smeared the inside with vaseline or any oily substance. Remove the clay or plasticine and when the plaster is dry (which will take a day in a warm place), it will be ready to receive the metal.

Do not use your mother's saucepan to melt the metal. A tin handle with a pair of pincers won't do either. The result of both would be a catastrophe. Buy the smallest saucepan you can. It should have a long handle and a spout (or, if you buy a pan made of thin metal, you could bend it yourself to make a spout) for it is essential to pour the liquid metal with great precision.

Warm the plaster mould on a stove or in the oven, but never on a naked flame, and melt the bits of metal in the saucepan. When the mould is warm, lay it on a stone floor and pour the metal evenly and as thick as you desire. When you turn the plaster mould over, the plaque will fall out on to the stone floor. Don't touch it: in this state it is able to burn its shape into a carpet or the lino, and your fingers are probably even more delicate.

That was easy, as you see. But the second object I made was much harder: a hand-bell. Let me tell you that its sound was neither very pure nor even very bell-like, but it had one advantage —you could ring as hard and as long as you liked but no one in the next room, if you shut the door, would complain of too much noise. It is a pleasant, personal bell to ring for one's self.

Shape the bell in clay, not plasticine. Make it solid. For the time being you are interested only in the inside. Build a cardboard box tall enough to hold it and large enough to make solid walls of plaster. Pour the plaster high enough to cover the bell but leave the top of the handle free. This will make a hole through which you will pour the metal later on. Do not make it too small. Remove the clay very carefully from the mould, without scratching the plaster. Wash it if necessary. Every bit of clay in the mould will make holes in your bell. If you have not done any decoration yet, you can carve anything you

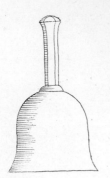
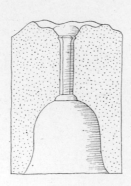
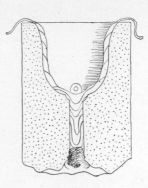
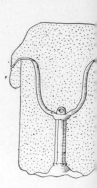

like inside the mould; your carvings will appear in relief later on.

Melt some wax and make a stopper with some wet cotton wool to place in the hole made by the handle. Turn it over and pour the wax on. Move the mould all the time to get an even film of wax inside it, about one-eighth or three-sixteenths of an inch thick. The handle should be entirely filled with wax. Now is the time to make the loop from which the clapper will eventually hang. Make it from wax and stick it well before it is cold.

All the wax parts will ultimately be made of metal. With your finger, level the thickness, round the edges and, last and most important, make the air pipes. Roll some very thin strands of 'spaghetti' from wax and fix them on four sides to the edge of the mould, leading them down outside the mould. Now, still holding the mould upside down, pour the plaster on again, making sure that the top is at least one inch thick over the opening and letting the plaster flow over the sides (rather thick) but leaving the ends of the 'spaghetti' free. Make a flat surface on top. When the plaster is set remove the cotton wool stopper and dry the mould in a warm place. Later on, increase the warmth, leaving the mould in the same position but with a vessel underneath, until the wax melts and completely flows away.

Now stand the mould up and pour the metal through the handle hole slowly but without stopping. Do not be worried if some lead comes through the air pipes. It won't harm a stone floor (though it would ruin wood or carpet) and it will stop eventually. Go on steadily until the mould is full. If you stop, the bell will end in as many pieces as the times you have stopped.

Break the mould carefully, and, even if you can touch the plaster with your finger, don't try to touch the bell. It is still horribly hot. If your bell is a success, you will then know as much about casting as I do.

I also made some figures and heads. If one carefully adds air pipes at places from which air would have difficulty in escaping (in a head, this would be the nose, the chin, long hair, or any part that stands out), it is possible to make a very thin coat of metal and leave the plaster inside. It is as hard and lasting as bronze.

P.S. In my drawings of the plaquette I made a mistake. Can you spot it?

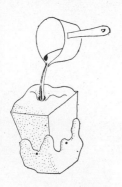

This horse stands eight and a half inches high, and is Italian of the sixteenth century. The mermaid shown opposite was once a door knocker, and was made a century later, also in Italy.

This is the actual size of an Italian 'Mortar' made towards the end of the fifteenth century. These three bronzes shown here are reproduced, by permission, from the originals which you can see if you visit the Wallace Collection, in Hertford House, London.

125

WHO'S AFRAID OF THE DARK?

by AUBREY DE SELINCOURT

ILLUSTRATED BY ROBERT HUNT

ROBIN HAD BEEN SAILING alone because Antony had gone away that morning for a few days. He brought the dinghy to the hard and hopped out on to the slippery stones. Then he hauled her up a yard or two and began to roll up the sail, to leave everything, as he always did, neat and tidy and proper.

Just as he was passing the rope round the sail, he happened to glance up towards the White House (where his friend Elizabeth lived), which was only about two hundred yards away on the further side of the sea-wall.

'Gosh,' he said to himself, 'there's Uncle Lance.'

Robin could see him on the veranda. He was saying goodbye to Elizabeth's mother.

Now Robin particularly wanted a word with Uncle Lance. They had not met for several days, and there was that question of lamp-signalling between the White House and Rose Cottage in Burnham to be discussed.

Robin shouted, but the distance was too great. Uncle Lance didn't hear. So Robin dropped the rope tyre, left

the tidying of the dinghy incomplete, and ran as hard as he could go across the strip of saltings, over the sea-wall, through the tamarisk hedge, and up the broad grass path of the garden towards the house.

He was just in time to catch Uncle Lance, who had seen him pelting up the garden and waited for him. Robin plunged into business as soon as he was within speaking distance, and the matter of the signalling was advanced several stages, further, to the satisfaction of both of them.

Then Uncle Lance went home to Rose Cottage, and Robin went back to the Manor and had what tea he could find, after which he strolled off to the garden room and became deeply absorbed in re-rigging a model boat which he had made some years before. It was a good opportunity to do this, because Antony was away, and Antony had lost interest in model boats.

Almost immediately (it seemed) it was supper time; and after supper, of course, one can never do much because of bed.

126

It is nice to be alone sometimes, however much you like a person; and Robin had enjoyed his day without Antony. For instance, there had been nobody there in the dinghy to ask him what he was thinking about, and then tell him not to be absurd—or to be annoyed if he said he wasn't thinking about anything. And there was the model boat—which *was* fun, whatever Antony might say.

However, as Robin was getting into bed, he suddenly wished that he was not alone. He frowned, compressed his lips—and wanted Antony. Then he turned off the light by the door, glanced uneasily over his shoulder, and got into bed very quickly indeed.

Once between the sheets, all was well; but there was a moment—only just a moment—when things were not well at all. It was just as one was drawing up one's legs to get in. This moment was disagreeable even when Antony was in the room, if it so happened that Antony was in bed first and Robin had to put the light out. But it was much worse when one was alone. How absurd! Yes, Robin was well aware that it was absurd; but . . . it doesn't make a thing less disagreeable to call it absurd.

What was Robin afraid of? Goodness knows. Certainly he didn't know himself. Just *things*, I suppose: nothing definite, but *things*—which quite obviously were not under the bed, or anywhere else, but—might be.

Robin lay deep in his blankets, feeling pretty good and already a little ashamed of having minded that moment, though he knew he would mind it just as much to-morrow. Then, as sleep stealthily approached, he found himself thinking of one or two other things which he always found just as disagreeable as getting into bed: in fact, more so. Cupboards for instance. Especially in large rooms, at night . . . One could never *really* be certain of what might be inside . . . Unless, of course, one looked. But one couldn't look—not possibly. Once, quite a long time ago, he had slept in a room in somebody else's house which had cupboards all round the wall. His father had called it a 'fitted' room, as if, apparently, it was something specially good. But it wasn't. It was vile. There was no telling how deep some of those cupboards were, because no wall was anywhere visible. Nothing but cupboards, and the trouble about *them* was that they were just as disagreeable after one was in bed as when one was undressing. One had to keep a wary eye on them, or on as many of them as possible, all the time until one was asleep.

And then . . . Suppose there was a sudden loud knock on the front door, after everybody else was in bed too, and Robin had to go downstairs to see what it was—or who was there—behind the door. Not that such a thing was likely to happen—but suppose it did. Even at the thought Robin found himself intently listening.

Then, I suppose, he went to sleep. For it must have been hours later that he suddenly sat bolt upright in bed, wide awake. It *felt* late. The house was intensely silent, deep asleep. The sky, framed in the open window, was no longer the bed-time sky, but changed and mysterious. Robin didn't know at first what had woken him, but as his wits gathered, a feeling of urgency came on him. There was something . . . yes, something important. . . .

He had forgotten to anchor the dinghy!

When he saw Uncle Lance, he had been in such a hurry to catch him that he had not only omitted to finish stowing things away, but had forgotten the anchor. How could he have been such an idiot?

He had hauled her up a bit, and the ebb had been running only a couple of hours. She would be all right for a good long time; but when the next tide came, some-time in the middle of the night, she would float off and blow away goodness knows where. She might even be lost—and it would be his fault. What would his father say—and Antony?

Robin swallowed hard, chin on knees, staring out of the window at the strange night. It would be dreadful to lose the dinghy—but it was not that that caused the little chill inside him, and made him long for the continued warm security of bed. It was something else . . .

There was no doubt whatever in Robin's mind about what he must do. Obviously, he must go down to the river at once and anchor the dinghy, unless indeed he was already too late and she was gone. But in any case he must go—and on the way he would have to pass the corner of the wood, just where it joined the garden of the White House, and through the gap in the hedge you could see the potting shed with its half-open door. At least, you could see it in daylight: in the dark you wouldn't be able to—and that would be worse. It was quite a long way to the river, and all of it would be unpleasant; but the corner of the wood would be the worst, much the worst—because of that door.

'What's the time?' Robin muttered. He found himself hoping that it wasn't past twelve, until a far sound in the house made him catch his breath. He listened, holding himself stiff. It was the clock in the hall winding itself up to strike.

One . . . two . . . Then silence again.

'Oh b-bother . . .' Robin whispered, and moistened his lips with his tongue.

It wouldn't have been so bad if it was twelve—if it wasn't the *small hours*. The phrase, in Robin's mind, sounded hollow, like an ache. The small hours . . . they weren't real, like the rest of time; they were a bit of the night slipped in from somewhere else, neither yesterday nor today nor tomorrow. They were much beastlier than twelve.

Robin got out of bed—he had to—put on a few clothes, and stole out into the passage. He moved with the utmost caution, not to be heard by any of the sleepers in the house. Anyone hearing might come out to see what was the matter, and Robin felt that an opening door, even if

'The house was intensely silent . . . Robin didn't know at first what had woken him . . .'

he knew, or thought he knew, who was opening it, would be more than he could bear.

Tiptoeing down the stairs he heard the hall clock ticking loudly, but no other sound, the hall itself a pool of darkness below him.

Suppose, before he could cross it, there was a knock, loud and sudden, at the front door . . . or that whatever was waiting there didn't knock, but let him open the door first, unsuspecting. . . .

'It's all *right*. . . .' He seemed to hear the words, half angry, half pleading, in his head rather than to speak them. But they were false. It was not all right—it was horrible.

Somehow he reached the door, drew back the bolt, undid the chain, and stood for a moment with the handle in his hand, his heart thumping. Then with a wrench he pulled the door wide open.

The golden darkness flowed in, cool and sweet. There was a low yellow moon over the fir trees westward. Robin was so much relieved at having got the door open that he felt better and trotted off across the shadowed lawn.

Indeed, it was not so bad as he had expected, now that he was out of the house, and so long as he was in the open—not too near tall hedges, or concealing walls or the solid black mass of the rhododendrons which bounded the lawn on his left hand—and so long, also, as he could avoid remembering a certain story he had read in a book several years before. *What* story? Well—never mind. It was a stupid story—no sense in it at all. But it wouldn't be forgotten—not quite—and kept popping back into Robin's mind at bad moments. Now, for instance, just when it *was* necessary to pass quite close to the rhododendrons. He passed them at a run, not turning his head, and let himself out through the wooden gate at the east side of the garden, into the fields.

It was not really very dark; it seldom is on a fine summer night. Only the hedges, and the shadows of the hedges, were black as pitch. And of course the wood. The wood lay ahead of him, right in his path . . . and the corner of it, by the hole in the hedge, with the potting shed quite near.

'*Robin took a step or two (limping slightly) towards the hole in the hedge.*'

As he approached, Robin slackened his pace. His heart began thumping again. Once or twice he glanced over his shoulder behind him—then wished he hadn't, because it was necessary (absolutely necessary) to keep his eyes on that corner . . . just in case. At the same time it was horribly difficult not to look back.

The corner was very near. The trees were moving a little, stealthily. Robin's mouth felt dry, and there was an unpleasant tingling at the base of his spine.

'Oh *bother* . . .' he whispered, and stopped dead.

The wood made hardly a sound, only the faintest rustling.

'There's nothing to be frightened of . . .' All the same, he knew there was—lots. It was impossible to advance another step.

'Go away . . . get out . . . !' The words, sudden, loud and in a voice unlike his own seemed forced from him. Horrified, Robin bit his lips into silence.

Then he started to run. He ran blindly, not knowing where. His ears seemed full of the echoes of his own voice—or of the answer to it. He ran himself breathless, then tripped and fell heavily flat on his face.

For a minute he lay, conscious of nothing but pain.

'Oh . . .' he sobbed; 'oh . . .'

The pain eased and he sat up. He got cautiously to his feet. He saw the bit of tree branch he had tripped over, picked it up, and flung it away as hard as he could.

'There,' he said out loud, 'so much for *you*!'

Then he found that he was looking straight towards the corner of the wood and the hole in the hedge where the potting shed was. The yellow moon was visible, in points of light, through the leaves of the hedge hazels. The air was sweet with darkness, and the trees still rustled softly.

Robin took a step or two (limping slightly) towards the hole in the hedge, and peered through.

'Silly old potting shed,' he said to himself. Then he turned and, remembering the reason why he had come out, went briskly on towards the river.

'Oh gosh,' he thought, 'I hope the boat's all right. It'd be awful if I'm too late.'

But he was not too late. The dinghy lay on the edge of the water, not yet quite afloat. Happy that all was well, Robin laid out the anchor, after giving the dinghy an extra heave up the hard. He took off his shoes to do this, and the water was surprisingly warm to his bare feet.

He finished tidying up the sail, fumbling in the darkness; then sat for a minute or two, chin on knees, on the rough grass above the tide mark. The quiet river glimmered under the moon. He could just see *Ianthe*, his father's yacht, lying on her mooring. He glanced behind him at the dreaming windows of the White House.

'How surprised,' he thought, 'Elizabeth would be if she knew I was here.'

He laughed softly, and with a sudden queer rush of pleasure stretched himself prone on the grass, legs and arms straddled wide. For a moment he lay there, happy, and the night folded him in.

Then he got up. On his face was a sort of smile, half pleased, half ashamed.

'Hooh!' he said; 'who's afraid of the dark?'

Then he thought how lucky he was to have been in time to get the dinghy anchored, and trotted home.

On the way he wondered if he should tell Antony. 'Of course' he thought, 'I must tell him about the dinghy—how I forgot the anchor. And I shall tell him I went down in the night . . . Oh yes, I shall tell him *that*. . . .'

But he was not at all sure that he would tell Antony the rest.

SCHOOL IN THE BUSH

PHOTOGRAPHS BY PICTORIAL PRESS

Adani, a Northern Rhodesian schoolboy, steps out proudly for school, leaving his sister pounding maize, while the baby scowls in the bright sun.

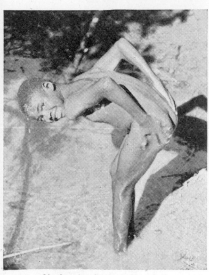

He has his bath on the way.

' Please teacher I can spell it.'

Going to school is a big adventure for an African boy or girl. They may be the first member of their family to have the chance of learning to read and write, so you will realise how tremendously important it is to them. By no means all the African boys and girls can go to school yet, there are nowhere near enough schools, and their villages are scattered often huge distances away from each other and from the nearest road.

More schools are being built all the time, some that can take in boarders. A boy or girl coming from some way off has no school train to catch. Their belongings are tied up in a bundle which they carry on their heads, as they walk bare-footed, over many miles of dusty paths through bush and forest.

Clothes are quite a simple matter for most children. A shirt and a pair of

Under a banana tree Adani and his friends eat their usual meal of ' posho ', a porridge made of maize-meal flavoured with beans or groundnuts.

Carpentry and other crafts are important lessons for African boys, most of whom will have to build their own homes, and make their own furniture.

shorts worn till they are quite tattered may be all a boy possesses, while a girl probably has just one dress and either a cap or bit of material wound round her head.

Some of the bigger schools may have quite simple uniform shirts or dresses made by the pupils themselves.

Very often Africans are not absolutely sure how old they are. It has never seemed so terribly important to them, and they don't trouble about birthdays either—this means you may find that there are boys of quite different ages in the same class. Another reason is that they are tremendously keen to get to school and learn, and quite big boys who have not been able to get to a school before will readily join the lowest Standard and start in on reading and writing.

Trades and crafts are an important part of the school timetable. Carpentry, shoemaking, gardening, farming and many other things will be needed by a boy whether he goes back to his village

These girls are learning to read.

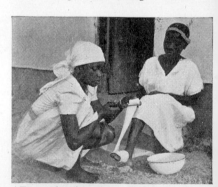

First aid and nursing are very important.

So is the care of babies.

In the school garden, boys are taught to grow fine vegetables, using the implements they would have at home, a hoe and petrol can. These last are used for everything, from water tanks to suitcases, from roofing material to chairs and tables!

to help his people, or whether he takes a job in a trade, whatever it may be. If he is good at his lessons and works up through the school to Standard VI or higher he may become a teacher himself.

It is not all work and no play in an African school any more than it is in ours. Games are very popular, especially football, which they play bare-footed but as fast and as hard as can be. Boxing is also very popular.

On prize-giving day they will have a big show of their work, things they have made and grown, paintings and carvings, and also a football match, and perhaps a P.T. display. Then there is sure to be a play of some kind, for they love acting and are very good at it.

Girls concentrate a good deal more on learning domestic subjects, cooking, sewing, simple nursing and the care of babies. Only very few will reach Standard VI and become teachers or hospital orderlies. The others will go back home, marry quite young and have their own families to bring up.

They play games, too, with great enjoyment, and love country dancing. Their share of the prize-giving display will probably include intricately woven rush mats or baskets of all shapes and sizes, knitting and sewing, brightly patterned beadwork and other handiwork.

Schooldays are happy days in Africa. Many of the ways are unfamiliar, from early morning teeth brushing to meals with variations and extras to their usual 'mealie-meal' porridge. No wonder schoolboys and schoolgirls find it so exciting and are so envied by those not lucky enough to be able to attend a school.

Boys will be boys the world over. A bamboo fishing rod and spear are their sports equipment.

131

THE BLACK WATCH

by Phillis Debenham

ILLUSTRATED BY IRENE HAWKINS

THE BLACKS were a 'birdy' family, root and branch. They always had been. It was in the blood.

This does not mean that they had no other interests in life than birds. They had plenty.

'Dad,' for instance, was a doctor and his patients would give you good evidence that he never neglected them, and that they had every confidence in his skill.

For 'Mum,' too, birds had to be something of a very delightful side-show, for a doctor's wife and the mother of six children, with only a youthful helper at her back, has not many spare moments for hobbies on top of the cooking, cleaning, mending, darning and answering telephone calls which fill up the normal day.

Then to come to the next generation. Deborah was in the Sixth Form at St. Asaph's, a conscientious plodder, though her taste lay more in the domestic direction than in scholarship.

Robert (and here we find the bird expert) had just finished his first term at Public School when my story begins, that school being in a locality which fortunately gave plenty of scope for bird observation, in what time could be snatched from ardent cricket practice.

Then Mary, two years younger, clever, rather quick-tempered, and utterly absent-minded, her pocket and desk filled with half-finished odes and sonnets, but always taking high marks for her imaginative essays and wide historical knowledge.

Then Colin (generally known as the Drummer), freckled and fearless, much given to bicycle accidents going to and from school, resulting in damaged nose and knees, and utterly devoted to Robert.

Then, after a long gap, Lois, an imp of mischief, who was on her way towards mastering the alphabet, under Deb's tuition.

Last, but not least, Augustus, so named by an insistant godfather, who wished to have his family name perpetuated, but who, in the family circle, was generally known as 'the Emperor.'

Dr. Black's practice covered several villages in one of our southern counties. As this is a bird story I shall, of course, keep the name of the county secret. One has to be careful where birds are concerned.

The house was one of the last in the village, and had a long garden, beyond which was a bit of common ground where heather and gorse-bushes grew. Then came a big road leading away to the sea, not many miles distant. This made the common a favourite spot for picnics, and picnickers are sometimes too interested in birds or stupidly indifferent to them, both of which types can be dangerous.

It was the middle of April, and Drummer had taken up his position with the second best binoculars slung on his back, halfway up a pear tree at the bottom of the garden, and was intently watching a gorse bush on the other side of the fence. Robert was due to arrive for the holidays in an hour's time, and Drummer had high hopes of great news for him. An unfamiliar bird had made its appearance from time to time, fluttering above, and flying into this particular gorse-bush. After careful searchings in the bird book he had identified it as a Dartford warbler.

It is not easy for a boy of Drummer's age to hold his tongue over such a discovery, but here was a happening of vast importance and loyalty to Robert and the secretive method he had always taught him to obey where rare birds were concerned made him quite determined that his brother should be the first to be informed.

Drummer slipped down from his perch, his scratched legs trembled with excitement, and repaired to the pump in the backyard to get the worst off his hands before tea. He had heard the church clock strike five, and Robert was due in a quarter of an hour.

Well he knew there would be no chance of a private talk with him till the elder sisters were safe at their homework (their term was not over), Dad in his surgery, and the two youngsters chased up to bed by Mother.

Tea was a lively meal, an extra spread to celebrate Bob's home-coming, everybody talking at once. Dad, late in from his round, was snatching a cup of tea before surgery and trying to get a word in edgeways.

Robert wanted to get his approval for a great plan, a week in Sark with his house-master and five other boys after Easter. This grand chance had come to Bob through one of the selected six falling out with a broken wrist. Thrills of that sort did not come often to the Black family, and if there was a slight sinking of the heart on the part of Drummer, and a little anxiety as to the safety of rock-climbing and bathing on Mother's, it was not mentioned, and all seemed happy about his good luck.

At last Drummer had him to himself as they were hurling Bob's clothes and other belongings out of his suitcase and into their familiar drawers and cupboards. Then the great news was imparted, and the rather sceptical Bob taken off to the point of vantage on the pear tree bough. Dartford warblers were rarities only known by reputation hitherto, and after all, Drummer, though keen, was a beginner in the art of observation. However, a quarter of an hour's watching brought its rich reward. A bird with a quick jerky flight alighted on a bough of the gorse bush, flicked a long tail and disappeared into the middle of the bush, then came out again, and flew away, while Robert's binoculars followed its flight.

'Wait here, Drum. I'm going to investigate,' and he slipped down, and over the garden railings to the bush.

A moment of breathless heart-beats for Drummer, as he saw him peering into the prickly branches. Then his head withdrew, and there was a wink of satisfaction. Over the railings and up into the tree again.

'No mistake, it's a Dartford all right. There's two eggs. Now we must think what to do.'

Drummer's face was scarlet. It was the proudest moment of his life.

'Do we tell the rest of them?' he said in a hoarse whisper.

'Not till we've thought things out. We shall want help, but we must be jolly careful. It's a mercy it's near the garden, but the common's a beastly dangerous place, anyhow, and it'll want watching day and night. We must risk it tonight and get to work tomorrow.'

Between sheets that night an emergency Committee meeting was held—a Committee of two! There is something

'*A figure was to be seen coming steadily nearer. A warning to Drummer, and Bob was off to the telephone.*'

to be said for small committees. They get down to things fast. Breakfast was an early and a punctual meal in the Black family. As Drummer was collecting the porridge plates next morning Robert rose to his feet, and opened a small notebook.

'Everybody,' he announced, 'I have an important statement to make. First you must swear secrecy. It's all fair and square. It's a bird secret. Hold up your hands and say " I promise ".'

The family obliged. Even the Emperor raised some buttery fingers and combed his hair with them, murmuring something, not about promises, but hot pies.

'Well,' continued Robert, 'Drummer has discovered a Dartford warbler's nest in a furze bush just outside the garden on the common. It will have to be watched day and night, and we must arrange a rota of watchers.'

The news was received with breathless 'ohs' of excitement. Even the methodical Deb paused for a moment in doling round the sausages.

'It'll mean sacrifices,' said Robert. 'I mean to chuck Sark, but it's worth it. The Committee suggest moving the tent to the bottom of the garden, in case of bad weather. Dartford warblers will henceforth never be mentioned by name. They will be spoken of as " dish-warblers ".'

Breakfast finished with a hail of questions, comments, and suggestions, and before Deb and Mary had pedalled off to school (the last day but one, Hurrah!) many schemes had been laid.

Dad was good for a night a week, and every Thursday afternoon (provided there were no calls, and that binoculars and an interesting book were allowed). Mum would fit

in whenever she could, and take her darning there. Also she was to initiate Jessie, the 17-year-old maid into the secret, impress upon her solemnly a promise of silence, and arrange for Lois and the Emperor to take their afternoon sleep at the bottom of the garden, while Jessie mended and watched. For safety's sake the name of Dartford warbler was never to be mentioned to her. The mysterious bird was to be for her a 'dish-washer'. Either the boys or Deb and Mary were to sleep under canvas at the bottom of the garden every night except Dad's. They were all old campers, and delighted to have the excuse.

Only on one point was there a short difference of opinion. Mum and Dad were insistent that Robert's week in Sark must be held to. It wasn't fair to let Mr. Austin down when he had been kind enough to invite him, and it was up to the rest of the family to keep watch in his absence. Drummer was eager to second that resolution, and had a constructive plan to propose. He knew just the chap he could rope in to sleep out with him that week, Ken McGee, as safe as a church and a proper bird man.

As the said Kenneth was a patrol leader in the village Scout Company, and son of the Police Inspector, who was also known to be a 'bird man', the resolution was passed, and Robert's objection overcome. Inspector McGee was a 'snake at the game,' Drummer declared. He had caught some brute of a chap with gold-finches on him, and had got him a heavy sentence through his evidence.

The organisation and time-table were soon complete, and Robert's scout tent set up at the bottom of the garden. Through its cracks there was a commanding view of the thrilling furze bush, and the 'Black Watch' started upon its important undertaking.

But do not think, reader, that the faithful carrying through of this job was all 'beer and skittles.' For one thing April weather is proverbially treacherous, and this year was no exception. There were rough wet nights when it would have been rather nice to slip into a warm bed instead of padding down to the tent in a mackintosh. There were cold night frosts, when even sleeping bags and ground sheets seemed a bit inadequate. Then there were tempting invitations which had to be refused if every member of the Black Watch was to be loyal to his or her time-table.

One night when Dad was on duty and peacefully settled into the tent if the telephone didn't ring and down went Mum, complete in top coat, and wellingtons (always ready by her bed) to relieve guard herself, and send him off to the Cottage Hospital to deal with the victims of a lorry accident.

Saturdays and Sundays were specially anxious days, for there were picnic parties and birds-nesting boys to be watched, and even be lured away from the bush on any tactful pretext.

On Easter Monday even the Emperor had to play his part, being moored close to the bush in his pram, and all intruders told that to wake him would have disastrous results.

Of course there were plenty of compensations for these little anxieties and inconveniences, and how well worthwhile they made them—the sudden appearance of a small bird with a slate grey head, and brown back, flicking its long tail on a swaying furze bough, and diving into the depths of the bush with a juicy caterpillar or insect across its bill.

Poor Mary was the only member of the family who was not successful in getting one of these precious peep-shows, but then, as Bob said, you could hardly expect it of anyone who had decided to be a poet. Be that as it may, her eyes never seemed to be on the right spot at the right time, and being too honest to pretend to have seen what she had not seen, she endured a good many pleasantries about 'bat's eyes' etc. However the tables sometimes turn, as we shall see.

Kenneth McGee responded to the call with alacrity, and turned up to time on the evening of Bob's departure for Sark. He and Drummer had planned to share supper in the tent, and were busy devouring cold sausages and mugs of orangeade.

'Father's got his eye on that fellow Barton whose father's at the Bank,' said Ken. 'What do you make of him at school?'

'Can't stick him. He's a cruel beast and a slacker at games.'

Drummer was not given to evil speaking of school-fellows, but his brow knitted at the mention of this undesirable.

Ken nodded his head mysteriously.

'Now we think he's up to a new game. There's some London chap, an egg-collector, who has been busy in these parts lately and he's actually employing boys and paying them to get him eggs. Barton's working for him. By good luck he's been blabbing about it, and now Dad and the Force are watching.'

There was a spice about coming to grips with an old enemy. Ken and Drummer had much to discuss before either of them dozed that night, and Drummer was already picturing an encounter and gloating over the prospect. Oh, if he could catch that detestable Barton red-handed, and hand him over to justice how happy he would be!

* * *

'Someone on the phone for you, Miss Deb,' and Jessie's head looked in at the pantry door, where the girls were busy with the breakfast wash-up.

'It's Daphne Burns,' reported Deb a few minutes later. 'They are going to play on their hard court for the first time tomorrow, and want one of us to make up a four. I've looked up the time-table, and it's really you on duty, but I want to get on with Drummer's sweater, so we'll swap over, and you go to the Burns'. I told her it would be all right.'

Deb was a good hand at inventing reasons why other members of the family should come in for these little bits of fun. The sweater was a useful camouflage, and won the point after a little protest.

Tea and tennis at the Burns' was always good fun, and Mary bicycled off to a jolly afternoon's tennis well content.

On her return journey she was overtaken by another school-fellow going in her direction, Kathleen Barton.

'Hullo Mary, been playing on the Burns' hard court? Lucky dog! They never ask me.'

The remark was not commented on. Kathleen was no more popular at *her school* than her brother was at *his*, and Mary was not too pleased she was to have her company for two miles of her homeward ride.

'I say, Mary, I never saw that prize poem of yours. It seems to have been quite the term's hit. "Swallows and Swifts," wasn't it? I don't know one from t'other, but it would just suit Douglas. He's turned ornithologist all at once. No talk at home now but birds' eggs, till we're sick of the subject. I believe you are great on it too, so perhaps you can help. Do you know anything about Dartford warblers?'

'Never saw one in my life,' said Mary indifferently. 'What about them?'

'Well, from what Doug says, they are very rare, *have* been almost extinct, and now they are supposed to be breeding about here again. Some naturalist that Doug is in with wants him to get hold of some eggs for him. I thought perhaps you'd have an idea. What about your brothers? They are great on birds aren't they, would they know?'

'They never say much about these things, besides the one who knows most about them is in the Channel Islands.' (Mary did not mention that he was coming home tomorrow.) Did you know that the Bird Protection laws are very strict, and that there are heavy sentences for breaking them?'

'O, Douglas laughs at that. He says the police don't care, and anyhow they are old grannies, and you can do things in front of their noses and they don't see them.'

'Well, I think he may find out he's wrong,' said Mary. Her wrath rising, and if it had not been that their ways parted at that moment, she might have broken out beyond the bounds of wisdom.

The incident was an interesting one, and caused much excitement when the family assembled for supper.

'Jolly good thing about your bat's eyes,' remarked Drummer, 'came in useful, didn't they?'

Robert was home next day, and by that time things had reached a thrilling stage in the gorse bush. No one had dared to investigate, but all watchers reported a constant going and coming of parent birds. In the evenings Bob ventured a peep and brought back news of four lively fledglings. Later on, there was a call from the Police Station. The doctor went to the phone but shouted for Bob and passed on the receiver.

'McGee wants your help, old chap,' he said. 'It looks like coming to close quarters with the enemy.'

Bob's consultation was a long one. He hung up the

receiver at last, and emerged full of suppressed excitement. Barton's boss, the so-called 'ornithologist' was said to be at the inn in the next village. He had wind of Dartfords breeding in that area, and was searching every bit of likely country, and questioning everybody he could get hold of as to birds-nesting finds. Barton had been seen at 6 o'clock in the morning hunting amongst gorse bushes. They were combing the ground in a scientific way, he said, which would bring them to our part of the common tomorrow or the next day, and they were at it as soon as it was light, when no one was about.

'We think the safest way to catch them will be for one of us to watch from the pear tree as soon as it is light, and cut for the phone when the enemy approaches. Another watcher will be in the tent, ready for them if they come to the bush. McGee is nuts on a good catch, and will come along at once if we ring. Are you on, Drummer?'

Of course Drummer was 'on,' and the details were worked out in a secret Cabinet meeting. Then the boys relieved guard early in the evening and prepared for a long sitting, with the alarum set for 5.30 a.m. By way of an extra precaution, they pegged a ring of stout wire round the gorse bush, too low to be noticed in the long grass, but high enough to trip up an unprepared intruder. Being ready for anything, our young men were (like Scrooge, on the historic morning when he was expecting the ghost of Christmas Present), by no means prepared for nothing.

A night of unpleasant weather was evidently delaying enemy action. Though the first week of May was nearly over, it was anything but springlike. Cold squalls of wind and rain in the night were succeeded by a sharp thunder-storm as soon as it was light, and there was no sign of visitors on the common. However, a vigilant watch was kept up through the day, and Ken McGee, Mum and even the bat's eyed Mary reported great activities among the parent birds. Mary had got her opportunity at last, and was becoming quite thrilled and alert. The demands of the brood must be getting very insistent, for the insects were coming in in beak fulls every few minutes. Except for this the day passed uneventful and the weather cleared towards evening.

No one would have dared to suggest any night-watchers but the two leaders at such a critical point in the undertaking, but Dad did suggest an early 'turn-in' to the sleeping bags when all fear of an evening attack was over. The previous night, what with the storm and the

'*Bob had vaulted the garden railings to find the two opponents rolling and struggling upon the grass.*'

possibility of early intruders, had been a disturbed one, and blinking and yawns, though unmentioned, had not gone unnoticed.

The next day the alarum roused them both to a clear warm spring morning, and the cuckoo was busy by the time Bob has slipped into his clothes and climbed with his binoculars into the pear tree. He had not more than half an hour to wait. A figure was to be seen peering into the bushes at the further end of the common and was coming steadily nearer. A scramble to the ground, a warning to Drummer, whose head was already through the crack of the tent, and Bob was off to the telephone.

In the meantime Drummer was prepared for action, which came quicker than they had expected. Probably a bird's flight towards the vital spot had betrayed it, for, missing all the intervening covert, Drummer recognised Barton's figure coming quickly towards the danger zone. He was up against the wire, and had tripped over it with a few unmentionable exclamations, by the time Drummer's head appeared over the garden railings. 'Hullo! Barton, you're out early. Had a toss?'

'What's that confounded wire for?' growled Barton, as he picked himself up, and rubbed his knees.

By this time Drummer was over the railings and close beside him.

'What are you here for? That's what I want to know,' he said, striding his legs between the bush and his foe.

'That's none of your business.'

'Yes it is,' said Drummer, 'for I happen to know something about the game you're up to, and the police are watching you. Rare birds' eggs, eh?'

'Take that for your insolence,' said Barton, and struck out savagely at Drummer's head.

Drummer was considerably smaller than Barton, but he was a quick dodger, and escaped him. Barton made a move towards the bush, but Drummer, with the agility of a wild cat, sprang upon his back and sent him backwards, then started pommelling his head vigorously before Barton could get his arms and legs free to kick and hit.

It was at this critical moment that a third party appeared on the scene. Robert had vaulted the garden railings to find the two opponents rolling and struggling upon the grass. Drummer was underneath now, and a violent kick on the shin bone had made him loosen his hold round Barton's neck for a moment.

'Shut up, and get off him,' shouted Bob, dragging at Barton's collar until he had turned his face upwards. He was not a pleasant spectacle. One eye was closed, and his nose was bleeding. Drummer had made the most of his opportunity!

But some more interested parties were converging upon the scene. Dad in pyjamas and top coat negotiating the garden railings, and then the lively jug-jug of McGee's motor-bike coming from the other direction over the grass road over the common.

It is said there is a funny side to every situation, and certainly the Doctor and the big Scotch Police Inspector have had a laugh since at the sight which greeted them.

The combatants were still on the ground, Drummer grinning triumphantly to conceal a wince of pain from his barked shin; Barton, with an angry scowl upon his bleeding face, mopping his bleeding nose with a dirty handkerchief; Bob standing guard over both of them with his arms folded.

But whatever may have been the Scotsman's inward feelings, no smile lighted the seriousness of his broad red face.

'I'm thinkin' the gentleman will be in need of first-aid treatment from you, doctor, before I take this matter in hand,' he said, and the procession moved slowly towards the surgery.

When bathings, disinfectants and bandages had been duly applied McGee cleared his throat for a statement. He showed no inclination to be soft-hearted towards Barton, however deplorable was the culprit's appearance.

'I have a very serious accusation to make against ye Douglas Barton,' he drawled, with rolling r's. 'Ye have been assisting a certain Mr. Leonard Hopkins in illicit practices—no, it would be waste of breath for you to deny it. Mr. Hopkins was caught last evening with incriminating goods upon his person. He had also correspondence from you in his pockets. You will both appear in court shortly for very serious offences, and I have little doubt the sentences will be heavy. I would strongly advise you to go home and hide your bruised face from the public eye, and to make up your mind to give over your cruel evil practices, and learn a little humanity towards man and beast, if it's in you to learn it.'

* * *

This story does not relate anything further of Mr. Douglas Barton's history, so it is unknown if he profited by the excellent advice of Police Inspector McGee. Such things are not impossible, despite the gloomy remarks which are sometimes passed about 'human nature being what it is' etc. Ardent catapultists have developed into ardent naturalists and bird protectionists, trappers into lovers of the beaver folk.

Of the Black family and of their famous Watch I have just this much more to record. The following day was marked by two great events, namely, the fourth birthday of Miss Lois Black, *and an empty nest.*

The brood of young Dartford warblers was launched safely upon the world, and were self-supporting. In the evening there was a great birthday tea-party with an iced sponge-cake and even a box of crackers, salvaged by Mum from the Christmas supply. At the conclusion of this ceremony the heroine of the day was reared to her feet on her high chair by Mary to recite or sing, as pleased her best, a new version of an old rhyme. After due coaxing, it came out in a recognisable and piping tune:—

> 'Hey diddle diddle
> The Black Watch riddle
> Somebody's got a black eye.
> The Dish-washers laughed
> To see such sport
> For the babies are ready to fly.
>   Hurrah!'

'Hurrah! Hurrah!' shouted the Black family. 'Three cheers for Lo. Three cheers for the dish-washers. Three cheers for the Black Watch.'

The Royal Society for the Protection of Birds plays an important part, in real life, in safeguarding rare birds and seeing that Bird Sanctuaries are undisturbed and unmolested. Enquiries are welcomed and if you are interested, you can write for particulars of the Society, whose address is 82 Victoria Street, London, S.W.1.

for HORSE

To every type and breed of horse
    Some man has lost his heart,
The hunter and the percheron,
    The pony in a cart,
The pure white arab with the wind
    Tossing its flowing mane,
The farm horse with a curled moustache
    Drawing the heavy wain,
The racehorse, slender ankled, sleek,
    The shaggy little foal,
The broad and buxom Suffolk punch,
    The horse that brings the coal,
The roan, the chestnut and the black,
    The piebald and the bay,
The cowboy's bucking broncho and
    The tinker's ancient grey.
By beauty, courage, patience, fire,
    By virtue or by art,
The horse has found safe pasturage
    Beside the human heart.

V. G.

The toss—taken against the sun—this is lively and well grouped. Shade the lens with your hand or hat.

SMILE PLEASE

by Adolf Morath

You can find many good subjects for photography in term time. Here are some tips on what to do and what not to do, to get the best out of your camera.

MANY OF YOU will have cameras which you probably use chiefly for taking 'snaps' of your friends. Possibly you just press the 'trigger' and hope for the best. The result may sometimes be just a blur, or a blank, or possibly just the usual posed 'staring at the camera' type of picture. If, however, you try to learn something about the elementary rules of photography and most important of all, use your observation, there is no reason, even if you have only a simple box camera, why you should not achieve really first-rate results.

Most of you will only be in possession of the simple type of box 'Brownie' camera. These cameras are, of course, of quite a simple construction. They have an inexpensive lens with a small opening and a fixed shutter speed of round about $\frac{1}{25}$th of a second. The limitations of these cameras are that you cannot take high-speed action photographs, for example of Football or Tennis. If a picture were attempted, with a box camera, of such subjects when in action, the result would be a blur. This is because the shutter speed is too slow to arrest rapid action. 'Snaps' indoors are also not possible with the box type of camera, because of the small quantity of light which the small aperture lens allows through.

Despite these limitations there are hundreds of subjects open to you with the simple box camera. Pictures of your friends, and landscapes, are all possible. Even Sports pictures are within its scope, providing you do not attempt to take fast action pictures. For example, at a Rugby Match a 'scrum' or a 'line-out' can be quite satisfactorily taken with the slow action box camera providing you choose the moment of exposure when there is the minimum amount of action. The Captains shaking hands at the beginning of any game, is quite an easy subject for the box camera, or a picture of the Goal-keeper waiting to receive a shot.

On Sports Day you could photograph the runners lined up for the start. This will often make a very impressive picture as the runners, with their faces tensed, wait for the word 'Go'. This type of picture is most effective if the camera is operated from the ground level. Instead of standing, lie on the ground and rest the camera on the ground in front of you. Take careful aim in your view-finder and make sure that all the figures are included and the heads not 'chopped off.'

The actual 'finish' will be outside the scope of your camera, but a picture of the winner with a crowd of admirers around him shaking hands is quite pos-

sible and will make a fine picture. Another picture you can take is the winner being 'chaired'. Get a crowd of your friends to lift the winner on their shoulders, then train your camera on the group. Make them laugh and cheer. Don't let them 'pose' and stare at the camera.

Prize-giving, providing it takes place out of doors, is another good subject. As the winner receives the Cup or Prize into his hands, have your camera carefully 'aimed' and press the shutter release just when the recipient is shaking hands with the Prize-giver. If you have your own School Garden, quite a number of good pictures will suggest themselves. Your friends watering the flowers, or setting seeds, or the state of the plot at different seasons. Whatever you decide to take, remember one important point. Always try to get *life* into your pictures.

For example, ask your friends to talk to each other and make a few jokes yourself before you press your camera release. This will all help in bringing animation and life into your group.

Do not pose the Football, Hockey or Tennis Teams in the usual conventional way on a form with a row standing behind. Instead, get the team grouped together in a more or less careless manner, and ask them to look away from the camera. Get some friends to call to the group and encourage the team to chat and joke with those who are calling to them. In this way a perfectly natural group can be obtained quite different from the 'conventional' set group.

A sunny day is much better for photography than a sunless day. This is because sunshine introduces life and sparkle —as a result of the light and shadow areas which are produced. On a sunless day, on the other hand, everything looks a similar tone, because the light falls on your subject more or less from all directions with a similar intensity.

Do not have the sun shine directly on to your subject from behind you, however, because this would give a 'flat' result owing to lack of 'shadow.'

Take up your camera position so that the sun shines more or less from the side of your camera on to your subject. When the sun shines from the side and so gives, as we term it in photography, a 'side' lighting, the shadow areas will, of course, be proportionately much greater than if the sun were shining directly from behind you. It is these areas of light and shade which help to make your picture. Another good direction for the sun to shine is just a little from one side of your shoulder, that is half front and half side light. This is generally the best average position for most subjects.

Into the Sun

Very beautiful effects can be secured by taking up such a view-point with your camera that the sun shines towards you. This lighting gives particularly sparkling and brilliant results. In this 'against the sun' lighting the shadows will project towards you and often a delightful 'halo' effect is produced around the contour or outlines of your subject For landscapes this lighting can be particularly effective. When you take these 'against the sun' studies, a lens hood must be fitted over the lens, so as to shield the lens from the direct rays of the sun. Without such a lens hood or a lens shield, as this is sometimes called, the rays of the sun would 'fog' or 'veil' your film and so your picture would be spoiled. If you are without a proper lens shield or hood, a dark covered book or a hat or an umbrella can be held just above the lens of your camera in such a way that it is shielded from the direct rays of the sun.

The best time of the day for taking your sunny 'snaps' is when the sun is not too high in the sky. In the midsummer months you will get the best results in the early morning, afternoon and evening, rather than at midday. This is because early and later in the day the shadows become longer and the lighting becomes altogether more pleasing.

For portrait studies and groups it is particularly important to avoid a very harsh and glaring sun because this would result in very black shadows and, furthermore, the sun can be so glaring that sometimes the subject's eyes will be half-closed or 'screwed up'. When the sun shines through a very light mist or through some very thin white clouds the light is more diffused and gives a softer light more suitable for portrait studies. Towards the evening the light gets more golden and this, too, can be a particularly suitable lighting for the portraits.

The low evening sun also gives a very beautiful lighting for landscapes, particularly when shining towards the camera—the long shadows projecting forwards can transform a simple theme into a very beautiful picture.

Backgrounds beware

Remember that the background is just as important as the main subject of your picture.

A brick wall, a drain pipe, a dust bin, a display of chimney pots, are amongst the many types of background which have spoiled thousands of what might have been otherwise excellent snapshots. Sometimes a lamp-post or a tree situated immediately behind a group or figure can spoil the whole picture. To be on the safe side, choose a plain background, and allow the background to be some distance from your group. If you are taking your pictures in a field or in the countryside many possibilities will suggest themselves as a background setting. A distant scene as a background can sometimes be very effective.

The sky can form a very simple and natural yet undisturbing background for your portraits and groups. To introduce the sky as a background, take a low position with your camera and arrange your group on a slight elevation—a little hillock, a bank, a wall, or a stile. But have your eyes open that no chimney pots or lamp-posts or roof tops stand out in the rear!

To achieve the best results with your sky backgrounds a light yellow filter should be attached to your lens. This yellow filter, by holding back the excessive ultra-violet rays, will bring out your sky in its correct tone and any picturesque cloud formations will be clearly shown. Because the photographic film is over-sensitive to blue and ultra-violet light, a sky photographed without a filter would be over-exposed and print as a blank white mass. How often have you seen 'snaps' in which the sky has been rendered like white paper? A nice cloud formation can often help in making your picture, which the yellow filter will help to reveal with full detail on your photographic film. Filters suitable for any camera can be supplied by most photographic dealers and chemists, and it is well worth your while to be in possession of one.

Photography—All the Year

Photography can be carried on throughout the year. Even in the winter sunshine pictures are possible with your simple box camera providing you use one of the faster films such as Super XX.

On the other hand, a medium-speed film such as Panatomic X, or Verichrome is preferable in the summer and in the spring, because on a very bright day there is always a possibility of over-exposure with your single-speed box camera.

Those of you who wish to take a serious interest in photography should make a habit of always observing the effect of the sun shining on different scenes and objects. Observe a landscape with the sun shining towards you, then again observe the same scene with a side sunlight, and compare it with the 'flat' lighting given by the sun shining from directly behind you. Study the faces of your friends with the sun shining from different directions, and at different times of the day. By developing and increasing your powers of observation you will soon become 'lighting conscious' and you will then quickly 'see' a striking lighting when out with your camera.

On the more expensive cameras there is as a rule a focusing scale. It is important that this is correctly set. A common fault with some amateurs is that they forget to focus, with the result that the background is sharp whilst the subject or group is blurred.

To ascertain the correct distance between your camera and your subject, just pace the distance out with fairly long steps, starting from your subject and walking to the camera position. Each step can be reckoned as a yard, so that if you take five long steps—this make fifteen feet, which is a good average distance for small groups. Then set your focusing scale accordingly.

There are, of course, other expensive cameras such as the 'Reflex' where you focus on a ground-glass focusing screen on which you see your picture in its full size, and the more modern coupled range camera, where you focus through a range finder. These cameras, are for the more advanced worker.

Those of you with more expensive cameras and with a variety of shutter speeds may be puzzled as to what exposure to give and what lens aperture to use. The faster shutter speeds are useful when you are taking 'action' pictures, or when the light is very bright whilst the open lens should be used when the light is weak. An exposure calculator such as that made by Burroughs Welcome & Co. is invaluable when using one of the better cameras, because then you can calculate just the right exposure for all conditions of light.

As a Career

I started my own photographic career at boarding school at the age of twelve with a 12s. box camera. I at once took a serious interest in Photography and even then produced some lovely pictures

When I left school at sixteen, I soon bought a better camera after saving my first few weeks' wages. To-day I am in possession of some of the most up-to-date cameras. Perhaps some of you, too, may wish to take up a photographic career. It is a fascinating and interesting profession, through which you will learn to 'see' and appreciate the world and its people more fully.

If you do your own developing, printing and enlarging, you will obtain far more enjoyment from your photography. Enlarging your own small snaps is a fascinating process. From your small negatives—if they are clear and sharp—you can make pictures of which you can be proud. Therefore, try and get a dark room rigged up at school or at home.

Mount your 'snaps' neatly into an album and write underneath each full details of the subject and date. Loose photographs are apt to get lost.

In conclusion, don't forget the simplest rule of all, to hold your camera absolutely steady.

Photo: John W. Craddock

Caught napping, but oh ! those huge feet.

Photo: John W. Craddock

Photo: John W. Craddock

Background is as important as the main subject. Notice how your eye is distracted in the first photograph, and how much better the subject stands out in the second.

Photo: John W. Craddock

A ghost horse ? No, the photographer hiccupped.

The conventional school group is dull to look back on, in your album. The team look unnaturally prim.

Photo: John W. Craddock

The result of not winding on.

Three very common errors.

This is more fun. It catches the spirit of success, and you can almost hear the cheers and the jokes.

BIGGLES in Arabia

by Captain W. E. Johns

ILLUSTRATED BY WILLIAM STOBBS

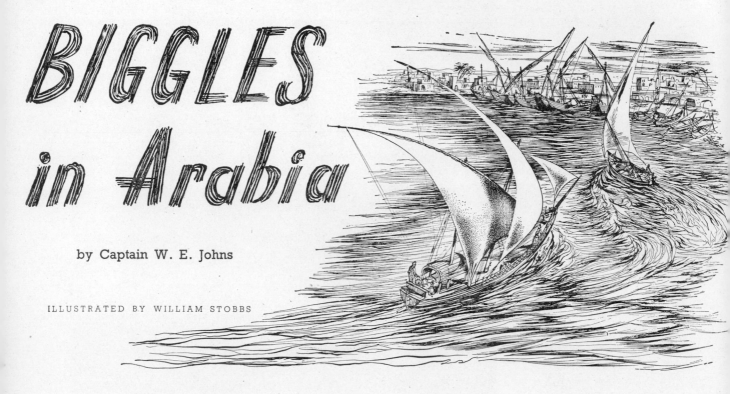

PART THREE

AT DAWN THE FOLLOWING morning Biggles was at the air-field, sitting on a chock, with a map spread on his knees, just inside the hangar in which the two machines had been parked. Ginger and Bertie, on empty oil drums, crouched near his shoulders, following with interest the point of his pencil as from time to time it moved across the map.

Zahar, squatted on the concrete floor gazing with inscrutable eyes across the barren landing-area, hard-baked in the everlasting heat. Except that he was still very thin he showed little signs of his recent ordeal. Nothing of consequence had occurred, except that Biggles had sent a signal home, in code, asking for instructions.

'Of course, as the job we came to do had been done for us, we could have packed up and gone home,' he was saying. 'But the burning of the stuff in the wadi didn't achieve what the Air Commodore intended. In fact, the position is now more serious than ever, because I am convinced that the gurra would not have been burnt unless someone intended growing the stuff elsewhere. And that person now has a supply of seed. When we came here we knew where the stuff grew—or we thought we did. Now we don't know, and our job won't be finished until we do. All the same, I didn't like to carry on without consulting Raymond, and I've switched the responsibility of what we do next, to him. If he says come home, that's all right with me. If he says carry on—well, we'll do what we can to tidy up the business. It isn't going to be easy, though. To march up and down the Danakil country looking for something which may or may not be there, is out of the question. We aren't equipped for such a jaunt, and we should probably end up by being turned into pin-cushions by Danakil spearmen. For that, I believe, is how they discourage tourists. On the other hand, if we fly over we shall certainly be spotted, in which case we might as well go and tell Ambrimos right away what we intend doing. Yet, as far as I can see, there's nothing else

for it.'

'We could fly over and have a dekko at the beastly place,' put in Bertie. 'No need to land, or anything like that.'

'We should have to land sooner or later,' argued Biggles. 'Goofing at the stuff from up topsides, even if we could locate it, wouldn't do any good. I was thinking of looking for it for a start. Zahar may be able to point the place out to us, but I wouldn't reckon on it. It's one thing to know a place from ground level, but another matter to recognise it from five thousand. However, we can but try. As soon as our arrival is reported to Ambrimos by his gang, as it will be, no doubt he'll take steps to make things uncomfortable for us if we try to land anywhere near him—that is, if Ambrimos is the man we are looking for.'

'What about this aircraft Zahar says he's using?' asked Ginger.

Biggles shrugged. 'What about it? He's within his rights in employing one if he wants to. Our only concern is the purpose for which it's being used.'

At this point of the conversation an airman appeared, carrying a small buff envelope. 'From station headquarters, Sir,' said he, as he handed it to Biggles, who tore it open and read the message.

'All right; there's no answer,' said Biggles.

Biggles folded the slip of paper and put it in his pocket book. 'Raymond says: "Go ahead—case now top priority"—from which we may assume that more dope has arrived in London. Let's go and have a look at things. Zahar says he's willing to fly so he'll come with me and Ginger. Bertie, you can waffle along solo to keep an eye on us. If either machine has to land the other will stand by for signals. By the way, in case we're being watched, I shall first trail a red herring by heading east. As soon as we're clear of the area, I shall swing north, and so round to the coast.'

Within five minutes both machines were in the air. Ginger, as usual, sat next to Biggles, with Zahar, occupying the double-seat just behind him.

Automatically Ginger's eyes surveyed the scene ahead, and then dawdled round towards the north. In doing this they ran along the leading edge of the port wing. A slight movement where there should have been no movement, arrested them. He stared. His expression changed and his face turned slightly pale. His right hand groped for Biggles's knee and gripped it. 'Put her down,' he said, in a tense, dry voice.

Biggles asked no questions. 'I can't,' he answered. 'I've only trees and rocks ahead.'

'Then go back,' ordered Ginger, without taking his eyes off the wing. 'Take it slowly.'

As the nose of the machine began to come round Biggles asked: 'What's wrong?'

'There's a hole in the leading edge, and the fabric's trying to "balloon".'

Biggles did not speak again. He knew that if air was getting inside the plane, it would, under pressure, blow the wing up like a balloon and probably rip the entire fabric off.

Having completed his turn he throttled back almost to stalling speed, and losing height gently, headed back for the airfield. Fortunately there was no wind, so it was not necessary to turn again, and a minute or two later he landed practically along the track from which he had taken off.

As the machine ran to a standstill, Ginger drew a deep breath, closed his eyes and shook his head. 'Phew!' he breathed. 'I can't stand shocks like that.'

'What is it?' asked Biggles preparing to get down. He glanced at the reserve machine now landing beside them. 'Bertie's all right, anyway.'

'I don't know,' replied Ginger. 'First I saw the fabric bulging; then I saw a slit in the leading edge, opening and shutting like a mouth. I thought I was seeing things.'

'Let's have a look,' said Biggles briefly, and followed closely by Ginger, jumped down. He went straight to the damaged fabric and examined it closely. 'I'm a fool,' he said bitterly. 'I've made the old mistake of underestimating the enemy. This fabric was cut. Look at it. Cut as clean as if it had been done by a razor blade. The man

who did it knew nothing about aircraft or he'd have cut through the main spar. If he had, it would have been a different story.'

Bertie walked up. 'What's the trouble?' he enquired.

Biggles jerked a thumb at the sabotaged wing. 'Somebody has been busy with a knife while our backs were turned,' he said grimly.

Bertie whistled softly. 'I say, that's nasty,' he said earnestly. 'Who do you think did it?'

'Somebody who wanted us out of the way and was cunning enough to make murder look like an accident. When I say us, I mean me. Presumably your machine is all right? Perhaps the rat who did it thought two crashes from structural failure within five minutes of each other might look suspicious. Let's have a look at your machine.'

They walked over to Bertie's aircraft and examined it closely. They could find nothing wrong.

Biggles lit a cigarette. His expression was grave.

'Well, what are we going to do about it?' asked Ginger presently.

'I'm going on with the job,' answered Biggles. 'In future, we'll mount guard over the machines. I shall have to take your machine, Bertie. You can taxi mine back to the sheds. You'll have to tell the station commander what has happened. Get him to put a patch over the damage. If there's any delay, you'd better wait here for me to come back; but if the job can be done within the next hour or so, you can follow on and try to pick us up. If you don't meet me coming back you may find me in the vicinity of that old aerodrome I pointed out on the map, marked number 137. That's if I decide to land.'

'As you say, old boy,' agreed Bertie.

'All right, let's try again,' said Biggles. 'Get Zahar into this machine, Ginger. Don't tell him what's happened.'

In a few minutes, the transfer complete, Biggles was in the air again, heading east. Behind and below, a trail of dust showed where Bertie was taxying the damaged machine back to the hangar.

Biggles did not cross the Red Sea at its narrowest point, which was somewhere to the south of where they struck it. Instead, he took up a new course to the north-west, which meant that he was flying almost straight up the long, narrow stretch of water, with the coast in sight on either hand—Africa on the one side and Arabia on the other, each protected by numerous outposts of islands. When Ginger remarked on the new course Biggles merely said that as it involved no extra trouble he was doing it to escape observation should Ambrimos have warned his agents to be on the look-out for him.

A few native craft with lateen sails, types almost as old as mankind itself, dotted the glittering surface of the famous biblical sea. In strange contrast, for to the north, making for the Suez Canal and the Mediterranean, a big liner churned a snowy wake and sent aloft a trail of murky smoke to mark its passage.

Biggles did not maintain his course for long. Zahar was asked to watch for, and point out, the minor port of Marsa Mekel, when they came to it. This he was able to do without difficulty, for he had often sailed along the coast in Arab dhows when in the service of the Sultan.

With the port in sight, Biggles flew on a little way before turning to the left towards the land, thus crossing the coast-line some distance north of the area in which, according to Zahar, Ambrimos was producing hashish.

Ginger regarded with interest the territory towards which they were now flying, although as far as he could see it differed little from the land they had just left. There was the same strip of white sand, washed by a lazy surf; the same sand dunes and occasional bluffs; the same monotonous camel-thorn and scrub; the same clusters of tired-looking palms, cacti and mimosa; the same twisting wadis and gorges. Beyond all this was the empty desert, sabkha and stony steppes, backed in the far distance by the vague shadows of the Abyssinian Highlands.

Ginger knew that Biggles had some scheme in mind, although he had not yet divulged it; so, he prompted: 'Are you going to try to spot Ambrimos's place from the air?'

'That was the idea of coming here,' Biggles pointed out. 'But on the way over I've been thinking about it. What I should like to do is spot the exact position from the air without going too near it. Just what's going on below we shall have to ascertain from ground level. So I think the best plan is, first, to locate the place without going too close to it, and then cast around for somewhere to land—not too far away—from which we might make a sortie on foot. I don't necessarily mean that we shall land to-day. I shall be satisfied if we can pin-point Ambrimos's place, and decide on a landing-ground. I'd like to have a look at that war-time airfield marked 137. I'm keeping to the north of the area because that's the direction from which the aircraft Ambrimos is using should come and go. There's a chance we may catch sight of it.'

At this juncture Zahar broke into the conversation. For once he seemed almost excited. Jabbing with a brown finger in a south-westerly direction he cried: 'Sahib! Sahib! That is the place.'

Ginger stared, but could see no conspicuous feature except a glittering streak which he took to be water. Near it there was a vague suggestion of low buildings, but nothing definite.

Biggles, also looking hard, sheered away from the spot Zahar had indicated.

'Try to get a picture of the country in your mind,' ordered Biggles. 'Aerodrome 137 should be a little to the north.'

The finding of the old war-time aerodrome 137 turned out to be a more simple job than Ginger expected. He observed a labyrinth of zig-zag lines that quite obviously had been military trenches. Following the general direction of these with his eyes he picked out a line of old gun-pits, and some way beyond them, near some scrub, three temporary hangars of camouflaged fabric which appeared from the distance to be as sound as on the day they were erected. He pointed them out to Biggles who at once turned towards them.

As the machine, losing height, drew near, it became evident that the first appearance of good condition was an illusion caused by distance and overheated air. One had collapsed, and another had a definite list. From all three, much of the canvas, in easy reach of the ground, had been removed, presumably by natives.

Twice Biggles flew low round the site examining the ground closely for possible obstructions. Then he remarked: 'I think we might have a closer look. That hangar might suit us as an advanced base from which to make a sortie on Ambrimos's plantations. I'm going down.'

Suiting the action to the word, he glided in and landed, afterwards running on to the dilapidated sheds. He taxied slowly into the shade provided by the one in reasonable repair. He then switched off, and in a sultry, depressing sort of silence, Ginger followed him to the ground.

Signs of the purpose for which the structure had been used were at once apparent on all sides. Anything portable or of value had, of course, been salvaged by natives, but there was still a fair amount of junk lying about—empty oil drums, flattened petrol cans, torn canvas, scrap metal, waste packing material, and even a rusty Bofors gun.

Biggles smiled wanly. 'Troops have fought over this ground since history began,' he murmured. 'This is the debris left by the last who passed by. Another year or two and it will be gone with the rest. We could make a dump here and walk over to El Moab. I reckon it can't be more than ten or twelve miles away.'

He turned to Zahar, who had followed them out of the machine and now stood regarding the dismal picture without emotion. 'Have you been here before?' he asked.

The Arab replied that he had not.

'But could you find your way to El Moab?'

'Without doubt, Sahib, God sparing me,' answered Zahar. 'But such a journey should be made by night when the air is cool and the Danakils in their villages.'

'These Danakils, you think, are really dangerous?'

'They are a misbegotten race whom God will one day hold to the reckoning,' asserted Zahar earnestly. 'But they are good fighters, and should they see us they would try to deprive us of our lives.'

'We could perhaps discourage them,' observed Biggles, dryly.

'What is written will come to pass,' averred Zahar, resorting to his fatalistic philosophy.

'Very well,' decided Biggles. 'In that case we will return to Aden and make preparations,' He turned to Ginger. 'I shall have to let Raymond know what we're doing.'

He was about to climb back into his seat when a low cry from Zahar brought him to a stop, and he turned, as did Ginger, to ascertain the cause. The Arab was gazing with shaded eyes through the open end of the hangar at something in the distance. At first Ginger could see nothing for the blinding white glare; but presently he made out a line of heat-distorted figures moving in the form of a column across the arid waste.

'What people are those?' Biggles asked Zahar.

'From the direction they have come, and as they travel with donkeys, they will be Danakils.'

Half-closing his eyes to reduce the glare Biggles gazed at the distant column. Ginger, too, watched it with some apprehension.

'They seem to be in a great hurry,' observed Biggles.

'You have taken the words from my lips,' declared Zahar in a curious voice. 'Wallah! They must have received evil tidings.' He climbed on to an oil drum for a better view. 'Now here is something I do not understand,' he went on. 'The caravan has stopped.'

'So I see,' confirmed Biggles. 'Isn't that a strange thing to do in the heat of the day?'

Zahar did not answer. Suddenly catching his breath he jumped off the drum and, running outside, turned to look at the sky behind the hangar. 'There is no God but God,' he cried.

'What is it?' asked Biggles sharply.

'A haboob is upon us, Sahib,' answered Zahar calmly. 'It is from Allah—may he be glorified! Now the behaviour of the Danakils is explained.'

Biggles joined him and Ginger followed. For a few seconds neither spoke. There was no need to remark on what was plain to see. From out of the north-east, racing towards them from the direction of the coast, and cutting them off from it, came a dark brown wall of sand, thousands of feet high. Above it the sky was no longer blue, but yellow.

'If Bertie got caught in that, he's had it,' said Biggles grimly.

'Couldn't he get above it?' asked Ginger.

'Wallah ! They must have received evil tidings.'

'Not a hope. That grit may go up to twenty thousand feet. An engine sucks it in through the air intake—and if there's one thing an engine won't stand for, it's sand.'

'What are *we* going to do about it?' enquired Ginger anxiously.

'We can't run away from it, that's certain,' answered Biggles. 'It would mean going west, in which case we should probably end up in the Sahara. That sandstorm may travel hundreds of miles before it peters out. We can't travel hundreds of miles; we haven't the petrol. I'd rather take my chance here, where Bertie at least knows where we are. He may not have left the ground yet. If he has, he'll see what's in front of him and turn back.'

'It is the season of *haboobs*,' put in Zahar without emotion.

'It's a bit late to remind us of that,' returned Biggles.

'They come and go quickly.'

'Let's hope this one goes quickly,' muttered Biggles. 'Meanwhile, we'd better start getting ready for it. Hark! What the . . .'

All eyes switched upward as the distant hum of an aero-engine came through the quivering air. It was soon located, a tiny speck that moved against the background of infinite blue some way to the west of the approaching storm. The machine was heading southward, nose down, tail high.

Biggles kept his eyes focussed on the speck. 'That kite looks to me like an old Gipsy Moth. That must be the Sultan's plane. I imagine that the fellow flying it is making flat out for his usual landing-ground at El Moab. He'll probably do it. He hasn't far to go. But come on. Get cracking. Collect all the old canvas that you can find. The important thing is to get the engine covered. Then we'll make a shelter for ourselves or we shall be grinding grit between our teeth for a week.'

Ten minutes of feverish activity followed, with Zahar, who probably knew better than the others what was in store, slashing away long strips of canvas from the walls with his dagger. These were at first dragged over the nose

of the aircraft and secured with thongs of the same material. Then more canvas was thrown over some oil drums so that a space was left in the middle. Sand was piled on the edge of the canvas to hold it down.

The work went on until the first gust of air, travelling on the front of the storm, came moaning across the wilderness. Another gust sent sand flying and set the canvas flapping. Ginger gasped, for the air might have been coming from a blast furnace.

'Inside, everyone,' ordered Biggles, and they scrambled into the cavity they had prepared. Zahar was better off than the others for he was able to wind his voluminous *gumbez* about his face. Ginger, following Biggles's example, tied his handkerchief over his mouth and nose. This done, they lay flat and waited for the worst.

It arrived a few minutes later, and it lasted, at its height, as far as Ginger could tell, about an hour. He had no clear recollection of anything that happened. He certainly did not see anything for he did not dare to open his eyes. The heat was appalling, and breathing a matter of no small difficulty. The world appeared to have turned to sand. It scoured his skin; it trickled down his neck; it got into his ears, his nose, and his mouth, in spite of all efforts to prevent it. It dried his lips and grated between his teeth. Thirst consumed him. The desire to drink became a mania. But at length the roaring tide of sand and grit and dust passed on, and after a moaning aftermath gave way once more to the brooding silence of the wilderness. He fairly gasped his relief, although he knew there had never been any serious danger, provided the hangar did not collapse on top of them, but it was all very unpleasant.

After a while he felt Biggles stirring, so he, too, began to move, carefully, for at every turn more rivulets of sand ran down his neck. He crawled out of the shelter. The air was still laden with sand, and they looked at each other through a gloomy yellow twilight. The sun was a misshapen orange globe. Zahar simply took off his *gumbez* and shook the sand out of it as if the storm had been no more than an ordinary passing incident. Biggles fetched a water-bottle from the aircraft. They all rinsed sand from their mouths and drank with relief and satisfaction.

'And now what?' asked Ginger, when their personal comfort had been more or less restored.

'Do you mean what are we going to do?'

'Yes.'

'That's easily answered,' asserted Biggles. 'We're staying here.' He jerked a derisive thumb upwards. 'I'm not asking any engine to plough its way through that muck. We shall have to wait for the sand to settle, which means that we're going to be here for some time and there's just nothing we can do about it.'

Ginger regarded the outlook moodily, for what Biggles had said was obviously true.

'Bertie will probably fly out to look for us,' went on Biggles. 'But if he's got any sense he'll wait for the

'Collect all the old canvas that you can find. The important thing is to get the engine covered.'

atmosphere to clear. Meanwhile, we might as well make ourselves as comfortable as possible. We're all right for water, so I don't think we have anything to worry about.'

The day passed slowly, with the air clearing somewhat as the storm-tossed sand settled again on the desert from which it had been wrenched. When at length the sun sank into the distant jagged peaks of the Ethiopian Highlands it was in such a riot of colour, due to the dust particles that still hung in the atmosphere, that Ginger could only stand and marvel at it.

Bertie did not put in an appearance. He had, presumably, decided to stay on the ground.

When the moon, a monstrous globe of burnished copper, swung up over the horizon, Biggles served out water and iron rations from the store carried in the machine. While these were being consumed he opened a conversation with Zahar which revealed to Ginger the lines on which he had been thinking.

'There seems to be no reason why we should sit here doing nothing,' he began. 'Sooner or later we shall have to make a reconnaissance from ground level to give this hashish factory the once over. As you say, Zahar, it would be silly to attempt such a trip in daylight. Could you find your way to El Moab without great difficulty?'

'Without doubt, God willing, O Sahib,' answered Zahar without hesitation.

Ginger put in a word. 'What are we going to do when we get to El Moab?'

'That will depend entirely on what we find,' replied Biggles. The only clue we have points to Ambrimos and El Moab, where he already has interests, as the source of supply of gurra. We may be barking up the wrong tree, and if that turns out to be the case we shall have to try somewhere else. One thing is certain. Ambrimos has made it clear that he wants us out of the way. That may be merely on account of the hashish racket. We shall

see. I'm hoping to find a nursery bed of young plants—they can't have grown to full-sized bushes yet.

'And suppose we do find the stuff growing at El Moab?'

'The entire stock will have to be destroyed. If the plants are too small to burn we'll pull them out of the ground one by one. If we leave one plant Ambrimos will save the seeds and start all over again somewhere else.'

'I suppose so,' agreed Ginger moodily.

'The size of the job will depend on the size of the area we find under cultivation,' Biggles went on. 'We haven't much water left as I would like for a show of this sort.'

'In that matter, Sahib, there is no need to fear,' put in Zahar. 'We shall pass a narrow wadi in which there should be water in abundance, a stream that overflows from the lake which the Sultan has made to store water for the dry season. The stream dies at a water hole. You can fill the bottles there.'

'That's good news,' declared Biggles.

'What about the machine?' queried Ginger. 'Will it be safe here?'

'We shall have to chance it. We shouldn't be away very long.'

So it was agreed, and an hour later the expedition set out.

For the first part of the journey there was nothing to break the monotony. The travellers marched almost in silence. The only sound that came from the outer darkness was the occasional ghoulish screaming of a hyena.

Zahar seemed to be in no doubt as to his course although there was no track of any sort. The going varied considerably as the party crossed flat areas of wind-polished stones or zig-zagged up an eminence in which the bedrock lay exposed. Detours were made round patches of scrub, and twice Zahar called a halt while he sought for the easiest way of crossing a wadi. Over all hung a sense of heaviness, a heart-chilling loneliness. There was still a certain amount of sand in the atmosphere which inevitably found its way into the mouth and nose to awaken the demon Thirst.

Knowing the rule about not drinking while on the march, Ginger refrained from touching his water bottle, but he was relieved when at long last Zahar announced that they were approaching the water hole. Presently he asked the others to wait while he went on to confirm that it was not already occupied by travellers who would almost certainly be enemies. Fortunately there was no one there, so they all scrambled down a stony bank to the water, a mere trickle that ended in a stagnant pool perhaps half a dozen yards across. From sheer habit, perhaps, Zahar did not drink. Biggles took a sip and spat it out with an exclamation of disgust. 'I wouldn't touch it unless I really needed it,' he told Ginger, 'you'll probably find a dead camel lying in it higher up.' As a precaution against emergency, however, he topped up his water bottle.

Ginger was too thirsty to accept his advice. He drank a little. The water was definitely brackish, as is most desert water, due to salt in the sand. After he had finished drinking he also discovered that a sweet, musty flavour, was left on his tongue. Actually, however, he swallowed very little, for the most part contenting himself with rinsing out his mouth.

After a brief halt the march was resumed.

It was about twenty minutes after this that Ginger began to feel unwell. For a while he said nothing, hoping that the spasm of nausea from which he suffered would pass off. It did not. On the contrary, it became worse, and so he was at length compelled to reveal his condition to Biggles. 'I'm sorry,' he said, 'but I feel as sick as a dog. I'm giddy, too. I don't think I can go on.'

Biggles stopped. 'That sounds as if you've got a touch of sun,' he diagnosed.

Ginger sank down on a rock mopping cold perspiration from his face. 'I feel pretty awful,' he asserted. 'I think perhaps I'd better start back.'

'Are you out of your mind?' demanded Biggles with asperity. 'What a hope you'd have of finding your way. You'd be lost before you had gone a mile. You'd better stay where you are and we'll pick you up on the way back.'

'Okay,' agreed Ginger miserably. 'Maybe the feeling will pass off when I've had a rest.' And in view of the outcome of this apparently simple incident it must be stated that he really believed what he said. And what was perhaps even more disastrous, Biggles thought so, too.

Even so, Biggles hesitated. 'Maybe, we'd better call the whole thing off and concentrate on getting you back to the machine,' he suggested.

Ginger recoiled from the idea that the sortie should be abandoned on his account. 'I shall be all right,' he insisted.

'You're quite sure?'

'Positive.'

'All right,' consented Biggles. 'But whatever you do, don't move. I mean, if you feel better, don't try to follow us. You'd probably miss us in the dark. Stay here and we shall know where you are.'

'Fair enough,' agreed Ginger weakly.

'We shan't be away long,' said Biggles encouragingly as he turned away. 'We must be pretty close to El Moab. We'll have a quick look round and come straight back. Keep quiet.'

Ginger nodded assent and lay back. The fact was, he was now feeling a good deal worse than he had led Biggles to suppose. He should have made his condition plain.

But he could not bear to think that physical weakness on his part should result in the failure of the expedition.

The moon began to swing about in the sky. The immediate landscape of rock and sand that formed the wadi took on strange colours, and began to pile up before him like a mountain. Time stood still. It no longer had meaning.

He tried to rise, but found that he had lost the power of movement. An icy chill began to creep through his limbs. He was violently sick, and this brought a brief respite. Somewhere near at hand a hyena started its diabolical yowling. He could see the beast. It split into a hundred parts, each part to become another hyena. The moon was falling on him. With an inarticulate cry he scrambled to his feet and reeling like a drunken man blundered blindly into the benighted desolation.

(*Continued on page* 179)

A Meeting of the Birds

THE ORDINARY passer-by would have seen a flock of birds, all shapes and sizes, twittering angrily to one another, and would have dismissed it from his mind after a moment's thought. But it was not something to be dismissed like that! It was an indignation meeting upon the subject of aeroplanes.

'I never, in all my born days,' croaked an old crow, 'came upon such a thing as this. What my great-grandfather would say I do not know. We, up till now, have been the only things that can leave the earth for any space of time. And now these—these monsters'—here he spluttered for breath—'are rushing about the sky.'

'Thinking they can sing, too,' added an old blackbird.

Here the lark interrupted.

'But you forget,' she said soothingly, 'they cannot sing sweetly as we do. They make a harsh, grating sound, but our melody delights the heart of man,' and with that the lark flew from the branch, swelling out her throat in ecstasy, and filling the air with her song. The nightingale watched her for a moment, then he, too, left the branch.

Then the cheeky robin spoke. 'What I think is, that if we could prove to man we were worth more than those—monsters, he would give up the idea of them altogether.'

These were the first wise words the robin had spoken, and the blackbird sang with glee. 'That is a good idea, young-ster,' he said. 'Now—'

But his words were never finished, for at that moment an aeroplane, propellers whirring, sped over the top of the tree, so close that the tip of her wing grazed the robin's beak.

Scared, the birds flew away, wings flapping, eyes bright with terror, and the aeroplane went peacefully on her way.

Felicity Craig (11)

SHEPHERD

Written and illustrated by

Marion Rivers-Moore

FOR THE SHEPHERD this is the busiest time of all the year. Even in the winter he had plenty to do; each day he made a new fold of hurdles for his ewes so that they should have fresh feed to keep them healthy and strong. But now, in this exciting time of the year, he sees the results of his winter's work in what he calls his 'lamb crop'. He wants as many lambs as possible so he is always glad of the birth of twins, or 'doubles' as he calls them.

When the ewes have their lambs the shepherd wants them to be warm and dry and snug and all close together where he can see them and look after them, so usually, especially in exposed, open districts, which is the sort of place where sheep very often are, he builds a special place for the purpose called a lambing pen. He does not need bricks and cement and heavy complicated things of that sort. He only wants to build a temporary shelter which will keep his charges dry and break the winds which sweep across the open country, so he builds the whole affair with hurdles and straw. He makes it, if he can, in a little dip and near a hay stack, for the ewes will need some hay to eat and it is simple to give it to them when it is there already. The outside walls of the pen are often built of two rows of baled straw, one row stacked upon the other like bricks. When there is no baled straw about the wall is made windproof by setting up two rows of hurdles almost touching and stuffing straw down between them. Then the shepherd makes little cubicles all round, carefully roofed with straw, a small private bedroom for each ewe to have her family in solitude and peace.

Every night the shepherd brings his ewes into the pen. Any ewe which he thinks is likely to lamb that night he catches and puts into one of the little pens which he has prepared. He has a place for himself too, his shepherd's hut, a little house on wheels with a bunk and a stove in it. He will not be lying in the bunk very much, for he goes round his ewes many times in the night helping those which are in difficulty and the stove will warm weakly lambs more often than it warms him.

Lambs are rather wobbly on their legs when they are first born but they are soon strong enough to nuzzle about and find their mother's milk and begin sucking. From then on they get bigger and stronger extraordinarily quickly. They are soon frisking about and bunting one another, playing all those tricks which fascinate us so much when we watch them. Sometimes, though, lambs are born which are not very strong and these are the special care of the shepherd. If they are too weak to find their mother's milk he helps them: if they are weak because their mother has not enough milk he either gives them extra milk from a bottle or fosters them on a ewe which has more milk than her own lamb needs, or else on a ewe which has lost her own lamb if there should happen to be one at the right moment. Ewes, just like every other mother, know their own children and will not take easily to others, so the shepherd has to practise little tricks upon them to make them think that the strange lambs are their own. The shepherd rubs the little impostor against the foster ewe's own lamb, or against its dead body if death is the sad reason for the transfer; sometimes he even skins the dead one and sews its skin to the fleece of the living lamb. Then the strange lamb is held to suck and often the ewe will take to it quite easily. If she will not she is tied up in a little pen so that she cannot knock her foster child about and the shepherd helps the poor unwanted child to get the milk from the unwilling foster-mother. Once the milk has passed through the lamb it gives it the foster ewe's smell and from then on she thinks that it is her own and cares for it as only a mother can.

Sometimes there are more motherless lambs than there are ewes which can be used as foster-mothers. These are brought up entirely on bottles of warmed milk. They are called 'pet lambs'. They follow their human foster parent all over the place, if they are not penned up. They need feeding many times a day when they are small so they are often looked after by the farmer's wife or by his children because the shepherd has too much to do already to have time for them. I expect Mary's little lamb was a pet lamb and followed her to school in hopes of a bottle of milk at lunch time.

They Leave Their Tails Behind Them

Lambs are born with long tails and they waggle them like anything when they are having their meals. They wriggle all the way down in a kind of ecstasy; it's quite unlike the wagging of any other animal. Perhaps they look at the short tails of their mothers and realise that they will not be able to wag them for long and try to make the best of the tail wagging time available. Before very long the shepherd takes every one of those tails off with a red hot iron. The iron sizzles through the tail very quickly, it is off before the lamb has time to realise what is happening, and away it runs bleating to its mother. The mothers always look slightly surprised when they see their children looking like that but they are soon quite happy again. That was what happened to Little-Bo-Peep's sheep, I expect, but they didn't give the details in the nursery rhyme. Sheep get very dirty if their tails are not taken off and a dirty sheep houses all sorts of parasites so that it is much kinder to take their tails off than to leave them on. The shepherd takes the tails home and his wife fries them up for his supper. It's funny to have a joint from an animal that is still running about, but you can't

The shearer begins at the top of the head and sweeps round the belly.

The wool-winder ties the rolled-up fleece.

[*Photo, Fox*

do it a second time, for the tails never grow again.

The shepherd is a very busy man. Every season of the year brings its own special job. As soon as the weather begins to be warm, all the sheep, except of course the new lambs, have to be shorn. There is a great to-do when shearing starts. Off goes the dog at the shepherd's command. He circles widely round the sheep and then gradually draws in closer and closer until he has them all together in a close bunch. Then, at a whistled command from his master, or sometimes in obedience to a hand signal, he brings the flock across the field, through a gate, perhaps, and down the road into a pen near the shearing shed. The actual shearing is often done by a gang of men who travel round from farm to farm taking their shearing machines with them. The men who do the shearing keep at it all the time and the sheep are caught and brought to them and even tipped up on their behinds ready for the shearers to begin. A shearer expects his sheep to be ready for him the moment he has finished the previous victim, and woe betide the catcher who is still fumbling for his quarry in the catching pen. The shearer begins at the top of the head, works down the neck, then in sweeps round the belly towards the back on each side. Then he lays the sheep on one side and shears the back, then on the other side and finally over the tail. The astonished animal arises from the yellow white soap-suddy foam of its discarded overcoat very naked and astonishingly skinny.

The wool from the sheep hangs together all in one piece when a good shearer has finished. The wool winder gathers it up and lays it out flat with the outer side uppermost. Then he folds it in on each side and rolls it up; this brings the clean inside part of the fleece outermost. He then puts one knee on the rolled fleece and pulls out and twists the wool of the neck making a long rope of it, as you can see in the drawing. He then winds the rope round the fleece and tucks the end in firmly. If he has done it properly he can pick up the whole thing by the rope like a basket by its handle and carry it away.

One Dip a Year

The next important event in the shepherding year is the annual dipping. To prevent flies and scab and nits and all the various insect pests from which sheep suffer every one of them has to be immersed for one minute in a special bath of disinfectant. This is enforced by law and the local policeman has to see that it is done. He makes an incongruous picture standing in his smart blue uniform beside the dip bath surrounded by bleating sheep and sweating men in overalls. He soon filters off to his other duties and calls back later to collect a form which the farmer has to fill up.

In spite of the dipping the shepherd has to look at all his sheep every day to see whether the small green sheep flies have laid any eggs upon them. If he neglects to do this the eggs hatch into hundreds of maggots and these maggots eat the living sheep in the same way that other kinds eat dead animals. Very soon the suffering animal will leave the flock and creep away by itself to die. Shepherds, like all stockmen, are very quick to notice an ailing animal and a seemingly casual glance around his flock will tell him which sheep need attention.

So the year goes round and the grass stops growing and what little there is has little nourishment in it. Then the shepherd gets his hurdles out again and begins to pen his lambs. They were separated from their mothers in the summer and are quite big and independent now. He pens them on crops which have been grown especially for them, rape, kale, turnips and so on. Each day he sets a new fold and the lambs stream through the open hurdle like a muddy river escaping through a dam and spread out on the fresh new feed. Day by day a new square is eaten out of the field making of it an ever changing pattern from green to brown until the lambs are fat enough to go to the market. When they are gone the shepherd can give all his attention to the ewes again. It is soon lambing time once more and the whole business begins all over again, a year-round effort to give us woollen clothes to our backs and a joint of mutton for our tables.

MAGICIANS AT THE GAME by Neville Cardus

Fox

If he concentrates as hard as this often enough, he may achieve fame, too—who knows?

With a flick of the wrist Ranji would glance a lightning off-break for four to leg.

These are some of Mr. Cardus's heroes, and he knows more than anyone, all there is to know of cricketers, past and present. Will Bradman, Denis Compton and Len Hutton join the ranks of these 'magicians'?

EVERYBODY KNOWS THAT the best stories in the world begin with 'Once upon a time. . . .' There must be past as well as present-history. Nothing can happen *now*; the event follows from what has been done before—and it 'will be continued in our next.' If you score fifty in a match today, you will at once begin to compare it with an innings you played last week; probably a better innings, too, though your total was a beggarly fifteen. We can't tell the value of anything until we have weighed it in the balance with something else. If you are given a cricket bat for a present next birthday, you will at once hope that it is a better one than anybody else's in the team. And, by the way, don't worry if the blade isn't pure white like the driven snow. A 'grain' in a willow blade doesn't mean there's something wrong with it.

By measurement we arrive at values. So it isn't enough just to *think* your favourite cricketer is the greatest player of your or any other time. And you can't go by averages. For instance, Bradman scored many more runs in Test matches than Ranjitsinhji at a vastly higher average; but figures will no more prove that Bradman was a finer batsman than Ranjitsinhji than figures will prove that Wagner was a better composer than Mozart merely because he often wrote more notes to a square yard of paper. None of my readers will be able to imagine what Ranjitsinhji was like: an Indian Prince, lithe, supple, his dark skin in contrast to his silk shirt, which always seemed to ripple unlike anybody else's cricket shirt, as though not only a breeze were making it flutter but something coming from his body and spirit.

He was a magician. A bat in his hands appeared to be flexible, a wizard's wand. He stood quite still when the ball was coming to him, never making a movement until the last second, then the bat went to the ball—I can't say that 'Ranji' even struck the ball; it was like a mesmeric wave, or gesture. Sometimes a terrific fast one—from Tom Richardson, a mighty fast bowler in the 1890's—pitched on the middle stump. 'Ranji' put his left leg across his right, and with a flick of the wrists, he glanced a lightning off-break for four to leg—and it was as swift indeed as lightning.

George Giffen, a famous Australian captain, once denied that Ranjitsinhji was a batsman at all—'No,' he said, 'he's no batsman, he's a blinkin' conjuror!' 'Ranji,' in fact, expressed his Oriental personality through our English game of cricket: he was marvellous, and we will never look upon his like again.

There are great cricketers whose scores and style we can understand; we can see 'how they do it,' and we can learn from them. They obey the rules and grammar. But nobody could learn safely from 'Ranji'; he was a law unto himself. But no—to speak of law in connection with 'Ranji' is a sin of matter-of-factness. He swam into our ken like a new comet.

There was G. L. Jessop, too, another batsman of originality. He is sometimes ignorantly described as a 'slogger.' No cricketer could year after year make hundreds of runs against the best bowling ever known—as

'The greatest of the Kings of Cricket.' Dr. W. G. Grace.

G. L. Jessop's secret was rapidity of eye and feet.

Jessop did—if he were only a crude smiter. Jessop was a logical, even a scientific, hitter, always finding the ball with the middle of his bat, always with his feet near the line and the pitch of it. His secret was rapidity of eye and feet. And he could cut, which meant that bowlers daren't drop short ones to him. They had to send them fairly well up to him—and then he drove them on the half-volley, often out of the ground. When you read in *Wisden* that Jessop hit sixers, don't imagine the strokes fell in the crowd over the ordinary boundary-line. In those days a six meant a hit clean out of the ground, out of the premises, into the streets. Once when Jessop was playing at Scarborough, he drove a ball into Trafalgar Square, situated outside the grounds. When somebody told an old lady about it—she was an enthusiastic lover of the game—she said, 'How splendid of him! And was he batting at Lord's or the Oval!' Jessop was called 'The Croucher' because he bent low over his bat when the bowler began to attack. But at the right moment he leaped upright, like a panther on the kill. In 1902, England had lost five wickets for forty-eight against Australia. Jessop came in and made 104 in an hour and a quarter, and changed apparently certain defeat to victory. That is the sign of genius—to bend dire circumstance to your way. You can't measure *that* sort of cricketer by his average.

If I were to be asked to choose an eleven of the most original cricketers I have ever seen, men of character, personality, who played in a way of their own, each making a contribution that nobody else could imitate, I might name the following: W. G. Grace, V. Trumper, Ranjitsinhji, George Gunn, Denis Compton, G. L. Jessop, Johnny Briggs, J. M. Gregory, Maurice Tate, A. A. Mailey and Duckworth. I'm sorry to leave out Patsy Hendren, Jim Sims, Emmott Robinson and many others; but there are only eleven places.

George Gunn was perhaps the most individual of them all. If he had tried to get runs every innings, the average would have been immense. He played according to private humours of his own, or to the state of the game. On a hot morning at Trent Bridge, Nottinghamshire won the toss and began batting on a perfect wicket against a county that was weak in bowling. It was a sure case of 'runs for nothing.' George Gunn went in first as usual, with Whysall, and he wore a beautiful new panama hat for the occasion. In two overs or so he helped himself to three or four fours, sauntering down the pitch to fast bowling, and not so much hitting the ball as 'pinking' it, much as a man in a park picks up litter. In five minutes George scored twenty. He then suddenly returned a simple ball to the bowler and retired 'c and b'. As he was walking up the pavilion steps, his captain thrust his head through the window of the amateurs' dressing-room and said: 'Why in the name of goodness, George, did you get out in that silly way, to *such* a stroke?'

And George replied: 'Too hot, sir.' The averages are unable to cope with a batsman of Gunn's genius. There was also Albert Trott, who came from Australia, and played for Middlesex and was as popular at Lord's as anybody that ever delighted the crowd near the Tavern. Albert Trott one afternoon drove a ball clean over the top of the Pavilion at Lords. And in his benefit match he took four wickets in four balls, then in the same innings, he did the 'hat trick.' The match was over in two days, so Trott in the coils of joy of his own art, may be said to have bowled himself into the bankruptcy court.

No; you can't measure greatness in cricket or anywhere else, by statistics.

Photographs by courtesy of Mrs. G. W. Beldam. Those of Ranjitsinhji and Jessop were reproduced in 'English Cricket' by Neville Cardus. (Britain in Pictures. 5s.)

I WANT TO BE AN ARCHITECT

'I WANT TO BE AN ARCHITECT!' So said David, a friend of mine, the other day. He thought it was time to decide on a career. What was architecture like? What did architects do?

I told David all I could about architecture. In fact we talked about it for a whole afternoon. In the end, he went away with an armful of my books and a promise to think very carefully before he made up his mind. When I met him last week he said, 'I'm *going* to be an architect!' And I think he will be a very good one.

David asked me how I first became interested in architecture. A couple of years before I left school, our art master decided we were to plan a house, build a model of it, and then furnish and decorate it from top to bottom. We had to decide on colour schemes, design and paint the wallpaper, make miniatures of all the furniture and complete the whole thing in time for the school exhibition at Christmas.

Well, Christmas came and the models were shown, and for most of us, that was the end of playing at architects. But not for me. I lost my interest in aeroplanes and polar expeditions. My stamp album lay neglected in a drawer. I was only interested in designing things. That brief glimpse of architecture decided me once and for all.

In the next couple of years I read every book on the subject I could find. Some I couldn't understand at all—but that only made them more fascinating. Others had pictures which set me longing to design huge skyscrapers and towering cathedrals. In the end, I left school and was lucky enough to become a pupil in an architect's office. After only a week, I knew that architecture was the finest job of all.

First of all architects do *not* sit about drawing pretty sketches all day long. Next, you do *not* have to be very, very good at drawing. I don't like to think how many fine architects have been lost to the world because someone said to them, 'Oh—but you can't draw!' There's much more in architecture than just drawing. If you are good at making things with your hands; or writing a good essay; or organising in any way— whether it's a stamp club or a picnic— why then, it is quite likely that you will make as good an architect as the best artist in the school. For architecture is simply a matter of getting things organised. When an architect draws a plan,

Planning and making a model house for his School Exhibition, fired the author, James Cheetham, when he was a boy, to become an Architect. He describes here what his job is. Being good at drawing is not the most important qualification for becoming an A.R.I.B.A.

Camera Talks

he's really only organising his ideas—and drawing is simply a kind of shorthand which helps him to do this. It helps him to show those ideas to other people, so that they can carry them out.

Suppose a rich uncle has left you a fortune, and you want to build a house. You have all kinds of ideas which you

want to incorporate in the plan. A swimming pool on the roof, for instance, and an aquarium for tropical fish in the basement. And, of course, there's a darkroom for photography, and a workshop, all to be included.

So off you go and see your friend the architect. You tell him where you want to build the house, and describe all the special rooms and fittings which you must have. The architect nods, and writes it all down. Almost before you have finished telling him your requirements, he has begun to plan.

He will ask you, very tactfully, how much money you wish to spend. Perhaps you hadn't thought of that? Oh well—say ten thousand pounds. And with a wave of the hand off you go. The architect writes it down—and gets to work. In telling him what you need, and giving him the cost, you have presented the architect with what is called a 'programme.' That is what starts off the design. While you are dreaming blissfully of your wonder house-to-be, the architect is wrestling with all kinds of difficult problems—all brought about by *your* programme. How can he stop the vibrations from the workshop machinery from startling your priceless tropical fish? And that swimming pool on the roof! Something special needed there, or the water will pour through into your bedroom.

There will be these, and a thousand other problems to be solved before he rings you up one day to say that the first sketch-plans are ready, and can you call to see them. Those first sketches are always exciting, both for the architect and his client. (That's *you*. Architects don't have customers, only clients.) Drawn out on nice thick paper is your house. Everything is to scale. Plans of the different floors to give you an idea of the positions of all the rooms. Pictures—we call them elevations—of the front and back, all coloured exactly as the finished building is to be. And probably a freehand drawing of the whole

thing, with a sketch of you on the high diving board, ready to do a jack-knife into the swimming pool.

You have a good look at the plans, and decide that you like them. There may be one or two small alterations to be made, but on the whole, the house is just as you wanted it. Right. Now the architect can really get to work. He must now make what are called working drawings. These are far more complicated than your simple sketch plans. They must be so accurate and so detailed that they can be handed to a builder with instructions to go ahead with the job. These drawings show the exact sizes of all the rooms; the thicknesses of walls and floors; the way the roof is constructed; the position of the drains; the height of the chimneys—scores and scores of things like that.

When all these drawings are finished, they have to be sent in to the local council to be approved. The council has all sorts of rules and regulations which must be followed, and it's no use trying to build anything unless the drawings have been examined by the authorities. If you *do* try it, you'll find that your fine new house may be pulled down again. Horrible thought!

With the drawings safely out of the way, the architect now does quite a bit of writing. He sits down at his desk and composes a very long and very boring essay called 'The Specification.' This is really a full description of every single bit of material in your house. If you look at it, you'll find that the specification gives full details of the bricks to be used; the quality of the sand; the various types of timber; the sizes of the various beams and girders; the colour of the paint. The list is nearly endless, but it's very necessary. If there *were* no specification, and the builder were dishonest, he could put all sorts of shoddy material into your house, and the architect could not do anything about it.

By the time the specification is ready, the drawings will be back from the local council—and you are nearly ready to begin the actual building. The architect now asks several builders how much they will erect the house for. After they have studied the drawings and specification for a week or two, back come the answers. One builder will put up your house for nine thousand pounds. Another wants ten thousand, and still another eleven. So the architect says to you, 'This man who has sent in the lowest price is a good builder. I think we should let him carry out the job.' Being wise, you take the architect's advice, and at last—at long last, the work begins.

Now things really begin to move. Hordes of workmen appear on the site as if by magic. Lorries arrive every few minutes with sand and cement and bricks and timber and beams and tiles—there are so many different materials lying about that you can hardly see the ground. And all the time, the workmen are busy digging trenches and great holes; and rushing about under tremendous loads of bricks and cement. As the weeks pass, your fine house begins to take shape. With your copy of the plan spread out on an upturned barrow, you can see everything becoming real, before your eyes. There is the workshop and the aquarium. And there, nearly finished up on the roof is your special bathing pool. It's tremendously exciting to see something you have always dreamed of coming true. But how much more exciting for the architect, who has created it all! That first idea of his has grown in his mind, developed and expanded, until here it is—come to life! And although it will be *your* house; although your money has paid for it, your house will really always belong to the man who designed it. It's the same whether he designs a house or a fine church. Buildings always belong to their architects.

Well, here you are with the builders nearly finished. All the time the work has been going on, your architect has been busier than ever. Every few days, he will have been down to see what is happening. The foreman in charge of the builder's men has to answer dozens of questions at every visit—and woe betide him if he has not made a good job of things! The house must be properly built, or the architect will know the reason why. He has been everywhere; from the chimney tops to the foundations. No shoddy work for you!

At long last, the day comes when you move into this brand new house. Everything is clean and shining and polished and perfect. There is no other house like yours in any part of the world. It is unique, and in its way, it is a work of art.

Perhaps you are thinking that now the architect's work is finished too? Oh dear, no! There's still a lot to be done before he puts all the letters and papers and drawings connected with your house away for the last time. When buildings are completed, they are new. They have to get used to their surroundings, just like people do when they move to a new town. And while buildings are settling down (they do, you know) all kinds of things happen. Little cracks appear in the plaster; a spot of paint is rubbed off a door. So for six months, the architect

'What care I for a goose-feather bed,
With the sheet turned down so bravely, O?

For to-night I shall sleep in a cold open field,
Along with the wraggle-taggle gipsies, O.'

The architect has not gone mad. He has studied his clients' special taste very closely. They just happened to be the Penguins at the Zoo!

looks after your house, and watches to see what happens. At the end of that time he calls in the builder once again, and instructs him to 'make everything good' as the saying goes. And the builder does so and goes away, and this time it really is the end.

To finish off, the architect writes out what looks like a difficult exercise in arithmetic, and sends you a copy of it. This is called the 'final account' and shows to a penny how all your money has been spent.

Your adventure in building has shown you what an architect has to do for a living. But houses, as you can imagine, are quite small buildings compared with some that architects have to carry out. Think of shops, cinemas, offices, flats, factories, garages, theatres, schools, banks, hotels, farms—in fact almost every kind of building you *can* think of, and you can understand how complicated, how difficult—and how very interesting the work of the architect is. If he designs a factory, he has to study the methods of production used in that particular industry. If he designs a hospital, he meets doctors, surgeons, nurses—even the patients—to make certain that his new hospital is going to be the best of its kind. He may visit Sweden, to have a look at a special method of constructing

buildings in timber; or he may take a trip to America to see the latest developments in factory design. The possibilities are endless. You can see that the drawings of plans may take up only a very small part of his time.

Now perhaps you would like to know how one becomes an architect. There are two main methods of training. The first—and best—is to go to a school of architecture, most of which are attached to universities. The second is to become a 'pupil' in the office of a local architect. In both cases, you can qualify as an architect, and eventually set up an office to practise yourself. A school or university course in architecture takes about five years; to qualify from an office usually takes longer—six to seven years is a reasonable average. This may seem a long time, but you should remember that an architect has a very complicated, and very responsible job. Throughout his life he is using other people's money

to erect buildings for them, so obviously, he must be thoroughly trained.

Before you can call yourself an architect, your name has to be placed on the National Register of Architects. And before that can happen, you have to sit for (and pass!) quite a stiff examination.

Nearly all architects today apply for membership of the Royal Institute of British Architects as soon as they have passed the necessary examinations. If accepted the architect is entitled to the use of the letters A.R.I.B.A. (Associate of the Royal Institute of British Architects) after his name and may also refer to himself as a Chartered Architect.

The R.I.B.A., as architects call it, was founded in 1834 to take care of the interests of architects, and it sets a very high standard of conduct among its members. Next time you are in London, have a look at the R.I.B.A. building at 66 Portland Place—near Broadcasting House. There you will see a building designed by an architect *for* architects, and a very fine example of architecture it is.

To become an A.R.I.B.A., you have to pass two separate examinations, called the Intermediate and the Final. If you are studying at a university, you take these examinations as normal tests at the end of the third and fifth years. If you

The 'working drawings' must be accurate and detailed. They are the builders' instructions.

are working in an office, and have to study in your spare time, you have to sit for similar examinations in London, or one of the large provincial towns. In either case, you must first become a *Probationer* of the R.I.B.A. To do this, you really need School Certificate with a credit in Art. If you have a certificate without the necessary credit, then it is necessary to do some freehand drawings and send them in with your application.

Until a few years ago, school training in architecture was unknown. Architects were trained by becoming 'pupils' in private offices, gaining their theoretical knowledge by spare-time study. Nowa-

days, things are different. If you can possibly attend a school, you should certainly do so. The training is better and more regular than can be had in an office. The very names of the subjects taught in the university 'school of architecture' are fascinating. Among them are Theory of Design, History of Architecture, Surveying, Colour and its Uses, Construction, Hygiene and Sanitation, Acoustics, Furniture and Decoration, Specifications, and Professional Practice. And these are not all, so you can see how much you have to learn before you can be a real architect.

For five years, you will not only study

these things in theory; you will put them to good use by actually designing buildings, simple ones at first, then gradually more difficult, until at the end of your course, you prepare your 'thesis design' —a complete set of designs and constructional drawings for a large building of your own choice—it may be a hospital, or a theatre, for instance.

As a pupil in an office your studies will cover much of the same ground. But since you can only study at home, it will naturally take longer to prepare for the examinations. However, if you leave school and start work in an architect's office right away, you have one big advantage over the university student. You are engaged in actual building work from the start, while he has to wait nearly five years before getting any practical experience.

So you see there are advantages in both methods of training. Space does not allow me to give a list of all the schools of architecture available. You will find, however, that nearly all the universities have a Department of Architecture, to which you should apply for full particulars. In addition, there are many schools and technical colleges which give part-time training, and these are very useful for the student who is working in an office. If you wish to enquire further, write to the R.I.B.A. for a copy of the pamphlet 'Membership of the R.I.B.A.' which gives details of training and examinations. You may also be interested in the Ministry of Labour's 'Careers' booklet No. 4, entitled 'Architecture,' which gives you all kinds of interesting facts and figures.

You may be thinking 'This is all very

well for those who can go to a school of architecture. Suppose I can't. What then?' In this case, your best plan is to try for a post with an architect who has an office in your locality. If they are approached in the proper way, you will find practising architects very ready to listen to your problems, and if possible they will help you. Of course pupils receive only a small wage—that is only right—for in an office, you are being taught your profession just as much as your friend in the university. And some architects ask what is known as a 'premium' for taking a pupil—that is a sum of money, in return for which you are 'articled' or bound to your master for three or five years. This practice is, however, not usual today.

So far, I have mentioned only the architect who is in private practice. That is the man with an office of his own and a brass plate outside, ready to tackle any and every job which may come along. There are, however, many thousands of architects who will never practise on their own. They are employed by local councils, government offices, large firms, hospitals—all kinds of official departments. They work in just the same way as the private architect, but they are paid regular wages and simply carry out the various schemes of their employers. Many architects prefer this type of work, and many try all kinds of work before they finally settle down to one particular job. Again, most private architects employ a number of assistants, who carry out a good deal of the routine work of the office. Whatever the job, it is always necessary to have a few years' experience of actual work before finally setting up for oneself.

There are many things I haven't even mentioned. The great architectural competitions which are open to all architects. This is how many young and unknown architects have leapt to fame overnight. Sir Giles Scott won the competition for the new Liverpool Cathedral when he was little more than twenty. That was fifty years ago—and the cathedral is still in building!

And then there are sketching holidays, and fine old buildings to be measured and drawn, and new friends to be made among all sorts and conditions of men. And there's always something new and exciting about to happen, and every day's work is different from all the others. And there is always the strange fact that you are being paid to enjoy yourself.

By the way—someone is sure to ask this one: Can girls become architects? The answer is a large YES. More and more and more of you!

Good luck!

It has of course not been possible to give anything like full details in this short article. Any boy or girl who thinks they might like to become an architect should send to the Secretary, Royal Institute of British Architects, 66 Portland Place, London, W.1, for further information.

BLACK HUNTING WHIP

by Monica Edwards

ILLUSTRATED BY GEOFFREY WHITTAM

'A heifer it was, and as pretty as a fallow deer fawn.'

PART FOUR

BY TEA-TIME Lindsey had finished the small breast harness and the withy snowshoes' framework. Peter, coming in warm and red from sledging down the slopes of Barn field, was helping her with cutting out the rabbit skins, and Andrea, glad to be able to work again in the room she shared with Lindsey, now Lindsey was no longer in bed there, was brushing brown solignum into the clean-scraped beams of the walls.

Mrs. Thornton had been making jam tarts and biscuits for tea and Dion and his father were bedding down ponies for the night, winding water up the well and filling buckets for the house, the animals and chickens.

The well was an enchanted place in the stark gripping coldness. Icicles hung round the rim where the brimming buckets splashed as they were handed to the pathway. Dion was fascinated by the sickening black drop, the slip-slap-slop of the rising bucket, groan and creak of the windlass on which his father strained, and the writhing, wreathing twists of steamy vapour that floated out on the dim daylight. He felt the strange witchery of the place, and was glad when the heavy wooden lid was slid back into place and the fresh drops left to freeze on the ends of lengthening icicles.

In the cowshed, feeding the Jersey heifer and tidying her bed for the evening, he was struck by a queer uneasiness in her behaviour. He leaned on his fork for a moment staring thoughtfully at Duchess, and her large antelope eyes stared back with a troubled foreboding. She moved restlessly in her deep straw and made a long soft lowing noise as she sniffed among her bedding.

Dion propped his fork against the wall and went outside into the yard. 'Dad!' he called, and his father answered from the Barn field where he was shutting up the chickens. 'Do you want me?'

'Can you come and see Duchess? Now?'

Father and son stood together and looked at the Jersey. 'Can you get Jim Faithful, do you think?' Mr. Thornton said. 'Holleybone goes home at five and in any case he won't handle Jerseys.'

'I think so,' Dion said, 'yes, I'm sure he'll come. Is it the calf d'you think, Dad?'

'I think so.'

'Shall I get Jim in time?' Dion was anxious, uncertain, before the unknown mysteries of birth.

'In time? Of course!' Mr. Thornton said. 'She'll be hours yet. I'm not the farmer you'll be, son, but I know you can have your tea, then take the lantern and go for Jim, and then most likely have a good night's rest before you see your calf.'

'Oh.' Dion looked doubtfully at the heifer and then said, 'Well, I suppose I'd better get on with her bed. And can you give me a hand with a bale of hay now you're here? '

Jim Faithful said it was the calf. 'And much better,' he said, 'to give her a look-over every two hours or so through the night, being a first-calver and a pedigree too. Look, I'll tell you what, I'll come along myself about nine and get a little shut-eye in the straw here. No trouble, and she might want a hand. You never know with heifers and I don't reckon these high-bred cattle have the stamina they might.'

'That's really handsome of you, Jim,' Mr. Thornton said. 'But you have to be up early in the morning and work hard all day. I'll stay with Duchess and keep an eye on her while you get some proper sleep, as far as you can in the straw, and wake you if need be.'

'We-ell, if that's all the same to you, sir. But we're used to missing a night now and then you know, with cattle. It's all in a life-time is what I say.'

'Dad!' Dion suddenly swung round. 'Dad! I could do that! Let me keep watch, I could stay awake easily. In any case, I'd never sleep in the house when I knew Duchess was having her calf and me not there.'

Mr. Thornton looked doubtfully at his son. 'I don't know what your mother would say—' he began.

'I know she'd say yes if you did. And after all, if I'm going to farm this place when I'm older I *ought* to learn everything I can, right from now.'

Dion had his way, and when the farmhouse was a dark, blind shadow below the great yew tree he was sitting on a bale of straw beside Starfleet Countess's Duchess, listening to the deep heavy breathing of Jim Faithful in the next stall, buried up to his neck in straw and blankets.

Dion wore his warm great-coat and had two car rugs wrapped around him where he sat. He leaned back against the partition of Duchess's stall and stared up into the shadowed rafters of the roof, down at the yellow flame of the hanging lantern and lower, at the fitfully dozing heifer, tawny yellow in the golden yellow of her bed.

He mustn't get too comfortable in case he fell asleep himself. There might be hours ahead of him yet and he would never live down the shame of sleeping at his post.

He went to the cowshed door. Pushing the top half open he leaned out and stared for a long, long time into the frozen starry night. He heard a fox bark away in the wild valley beyond Lower Naps, the sound so clear and sharp on the crystal air that it might have been in the garden. Owls down in the orchard and up Rocky Lane; Tawny, with its high, 'Gee-wick!' and the white Barn Owls, screeching like lost demons in the petrified trees.

Duchess moved suddenly in the straw and the boy turned round. He stared intently for a minute and then went quickly to the further stall. 'Jim!' he said. 'Jim! Can you come? '

In a moment Jim was awake, already clothed and booted, no sleep in his eyes and his wits about him. This was the way a man should wake, Dion thought. No lazy yawn and stretch, rubbing of eyes and slow tired movements. He came with Dion to the heifer's stall and looked her over with the eye of understanding. 'She's near enough,' he said, 'and late enough. You'll likely get a bull.'

By Dion's watch it was a quarter past midnight when Duchess's calf was born. A heifer it was, and as pretty as a fallow deer fawn. Duchess was so proud of her first child that it was delightful to watch her, so motherly she was and so gentle; licking the small calf all over with her long black-and-pink tongue, nuzzling it against her side when it rose precariously on slender wobbly legs. Dion and Jim stood watching for a while, Jim saying he was properly amazed it was a heifer, and Duchess so late

in her time. Dion pondering already on the name. 'Jim, he said, ' what shall we call her? '

Jim Faithful took off his flat cap and scratched his head 'We-ell,' he said, 'Bluebell's a good name for a cow. Then Buttercup, our best milker was called Buttercup. 'Course for a calf that colour you might like Primrose better.'

'But Jim,' Dion said, 'I'd want something quite unusual for our very first calf. I mean, she must have a name no other calf is likely to have. And in any case, she isn't really primrose colour, is she? Except for her middle Her legs are quite black and so is her face and tail, and her eyes are as dark as midnight.'

'Ah, you want something fancy.'

The little calf uttered a thin moo and shivered in the cold. Duchess fussed over it with her shapely dark muzzle and Jim Faithful bent to build the soft straw higher round the tiny form.

'I've got it! I shall call her Punch Bowl Midnight. I was nearly midnight when she was born and look at her eyes.'

The man straightened himself and looked down at the boy. 'Mm,' he said vaguely, 'Ah.' This was bursting into wholly unturned ground, this was. Punch Bowl Midnight! 'We-ell,' he said uncertainly, 'you could always call her Midden for short.'

Lindsey was allowed to make her first venture out of doors to see Punch Bowl Midnight in the morning. A crowd was not allowed in the cowshed to disturb the peace of mother and daughter, but one by one they all came down to admire and smile and gaze. Even Holleybone grudgingly, came to glance over the door and said all seemed well enough, though he didn't believe in fancy cows and no good could possibly come of it.

It was difficult to keep Peter from the cowshed. Whenever Dion passed him with water, straw or hay he would call out conversationally.

'When are you going to milk Duchess? '

'Three days.'

'Why? Why not now? Hasn't she got any yet? I thought you milked twice a day.'

'You do, but Midnight has it all for three days.'

Then later, when Dion was wheeling muck to the dung heap, 'What does Midnight have after three days, then? '

'Milk of course, chump. But out of a bucket and we measure it. The rest's for the house.'

'Oh. Will it be much? '

'Enough. She's got a good bag.'

'Golly! I shall drink pints and pints.'

'Well I hope you're sick.' Dion pushed the wheel-barrow up against the barn and went into the stable with a broom.

That afternoon Lindsey floundered on her snowshoes, falling into drifts, losing her balance, falling, even, over her own spreading snowshoes. She had barely begun to feel an improvement when again she had to come in and ' do something restful.' The crowning disappointment was when Jim Faithful came out just before tea-time and said the lane had been cleared enough for walking, there would be letters in the morning and he would be able to get his milk into the village again. ' But you can't run a car down there,' he said. ' We've had to put runners on an old cart we've got and it'll take three of us to get it to the village.'

' If it isn't clear for cars there still won't be any groceries,' Lindsey said hopefully, 'so even if the snowshoes aren't any good now, we'll need Glen and the sledge for supplies.'

Andrea came in with six eggs in a tin. She said she knew a very good use for the snowshoes if Lindsey would lend them.

' Hi, Missy ! Hi, Missy Lindsey ! Jus' a minute, can you ?'

' Well, I might,' said Lindsey, ' Why? '

Andrea was pencilling the date on the eggs. ' To go over Kettlebury to Ann's,' she said. ' It's the only way while the snow lasts.'

' All right. But you'll need a terrible lot of practice.'

Andrea said she would see to that, and put the eggs away into the larder.

When Lindsey set out in the morning for the village with Glen and the sledge, a long list of groceries, some letters and some money, Andrea was still ' seeing to that' in the orchard and Hanger field. Lindsey's last glimpse of her as she shut the farm gate was her ankles and the snow-shoes waving dauntlessly above the deep snow. Lindsey chuckled to herself, knowing well how Andrea would ache by bedtime and how slowly progress would be made.

In the village, Lindsey and her dog-drawn sledge aroused much curious interest. Glen, for all his silly reputation, behaved in harness as if born and bred to it. He even stood quietly outside the shop while Lindsey collected her supplies, and when the sledge was loaded he threw himself into his harness like a seasoned plough-horse.

Lindsey had tied a spare rope to the sledge and she pulled on this, herself, to help the dog on the hill going up through the village. She had barely passed old Mr. Pyecraft's cottage when she stopped at the sound of her name. ' Hi, Missy! Hi, Missy Lindsey! Jus' a minute, can you? '

Turning, she saw Mr. Pyecraft hobbling carefully down his slippery path, and she turned Glen and the sledge and came back to his garden gate.

' 'Bout that 'ere barn, now,' the old man began at once, a little wheezily. ' I been and called to mind a thing about it, what I thinks your brother might happen like to know.'

' Oh, yes? '

' This yur barn. Told you I sawed it when I were a little 'un. Now I remember I been in it, see, an' I remember somethin' more. In your orchard, now, have you still got the wide old spreadin' fig tree? '

Lindsey frowned for a moment of deep thought. ' Fig tree? ' she said. ' I don't think so. Where was it? '

' Couldn't miss it,' Mr. Pyecraft said as he stamped his old feet in the snow. ' Stood right atween the track and Hanger field. A vast great tree, I tell you.'

Lindsey looked into the corners of her mind for a picture of the orchard. ' Well it isn't there now,' she said at last. ' Though there is a very big stump about there.

I know because it's rather in the way when we want to canter through from Hanger to the stable.'

' Ah! ' said Mr. Pyecraft. ' That's 'er. Now listen and I'll tell you how to find the place whur the great barn stood.'

Lindsey's ears almost swung forward at this.

' I were only but so high,' the old man's wavery voice went on, ' when me father took me out to Punch Bowl one mornin', time he were workin' in Hanger on turmut singlin' there. You understand, it waddn't always pasture. Now 'twas then I saw about the fig tree. I tell you, I couldn't see a thing of Hanger field when I wuz in the barn. Thur was them high hedges, an' then the fig atween me an' the gateway. You see what I'm gittin' at? '

Lindsey's face had a faraway look. She said slowly, ' Yes, I see what you mean. If we get the bole of the fig tree in line with Hanger field gate, we're somewhere in a line with the door of the great barn.'

Mr. Pyecraft nodded respectfully. ' You gotter brain,' he said. ' Now you tell that boy Dion what I told you, see, an' you got him onto somethin'.'

' I will. And thank you very much. Oh, I do hope the snow will go soon so's he can start! D'you think it will, Mr. Pyecraft, please? '

' Aha, now! Who can say? Wind's in north-east, sky middlin' clouded. Can't be too hopeful. But it'll do the ground good, you know. Kills off they pestes in the soil, see, an' some say the snow's as good as dungin' fer the land.'

' I'll go straight back and tell him now,' Lindsey said, and took a turn round her hand with her rope. The dog bounded up to his feet, his plumed tail swinging, tongue out and eyes on Lindsey's face.

Old Mr. Pyecraft raised his hand again in sad farewell and was hobbling back along his path. Lindsey watched him, half uneasily, but she couldn't know that it was the last time anyone would ever see him alive.

School had already begun, but not for the four Thornton children. Snow still blocked the wild valley and the tracks through the Punch Bowl, but Holleybone thought there was a thaw in the air. Dion walked down the dug pathway to the cowshed, very early one January morning. Darkness still curtained the valley and he carried a hurricane lantern in one hand. The other held his milking pail and an old tin kettle of hot water for washing Duchess's udder. Tucked under the lantern arm was a large bowlful of mixed oats and dairy nuts which was kept and measured in the outside cellar because of the night raids of rats.

Duchess's chain clanked and jingled as she rose to her feet at his approach. The cowshed was shut right up against the bitter night frost and Dion put down his lantern, pail, bowl and kettle to open the doors. Duchess was half turned to watch him, standing in the delicate halo of her own air-borne breath.

The first thing Dion did, after hanging the lantern on its hook, was to feed the robins which had invaded the cowshed to find refuge from the snow. There were three of them and they watched him with round black beads of eyes from the cross-beams under the low rafters. In the end stall, where hay and straw were kept with the broom, fork and shovel, was a churnful of water which Holleybone was encouraged and almost driven to keep filled with water for Duchess. Dion ladled a bucketful out for the heifer, replaced the flat lid and then, taking a slice of bread from his pocket, crumbled it on to the lid. Down came the robins with a quick whisper of wings, before the boy had moved more than a yard.

Duchess drank deeply, finishing the whole pailful while Dion forked her bed over before milking. In the far stall of the adjoining stable Punch Bowl Midnight had heard the noises in the cowshed and called plaintively for her mother. Duchess's large dark eyes dilated as she called back to her calf and Dion felt a sudden wave of pity for them, that they had to be kept in separation. But that, he knew, was the only way milk could be obtained for people's use. Midnight could have all she needed and still there was plenty to spare.

Dion washed the heifer's udder, poured the water away and began milking. He pushed his cold toes into the straw and felt the spreading warmth of the teats in his stiff fingers. He hoped Duchess didn't mind the coldness of his touch but she didn't draw away and he settled to his milking. First the strong double stream hit the bottom of the pail with a high musical pinging noise, then, as the rich milk deepened and a froth foamed over the surface, with a steady low hiss.

Gradually, his wrists and fingers tiring, the pulse of his milking slowed down, 'Swish-swi-i-sh. Swish-swi-i-sh.' What a long time he still took to milk. Seven minutes, Jim Faithful had told him, was the proper time to take over one cow. Dion thought he must be taking over twenty. The robins had cleared up their crumbs before he had started the two hind teats and Duchess had finished her bowl of concentrates and was nosing about in her hay. Sometimes she would raise her head, listening, then low to her calf down in the stable with the ponies. She would lick her salt-lick, slowly and with appreciation, then back to her hay again, looking round now and again at the boy on his stool who did queer things to her udder. But she knew the letting down of her milk was a relief to her tight fulness and she stood quietly to let him continue.

Dion's wrists were aching now and his milking was very slow and laboured. His mind was on the hunting whip and the prophesied thaw. He knew, now, where to dig. He and Lindsey had drawn a long line in the deep snow, between the fig tree bole and Hanger gate. They had carried it on across the orchard to the track, and somewhere below it, they knew, was the place where the great barn doorway had hung. Where the steps were, up to the flooring and, he was sure, where the old black hunting whip still lay hidden under nearly a hundred years of blown dust and soil.

No one had been down in the lost cellar since the snowstorm began, because of revealing the place where they made entry. The diary was still in the cupboard of the big stone table, but much of it Dion knew by heart and he thought about it often.

The top of the cowshed doorway swung open and Lindsey's oval face looked in at him from the darkness. 'Nearly finished?' she said.

'Just stripping,' said Dion.

'Got much?' Lindsey came in with the stable lantern and looked. 'Oh, heaps,' she said, 'and isn't it *yellow*.'

'Always is with Jerseys,' Dion said. He was running his thumbs and forefingers down the teats to strip the last drops. The cream came last, Jim Faithful said, and those who didn't strip didn't get it.

'I'm going to Moonstone first,' said Lindsey, 'but let me know when you're ready to feed Midnight.'

Dion rose to his feet with his bucket and stool, put the lid on the bucket, picked up the kettle and bowl and lantern and went up to the house to measure Midnight's three-and-a-half pints and the half pint of hot water he mixed with it.

Punch Bowl Midnight had heard him coming down the yard with her bucket and was calling loudly from her partitioned stall in the stable. Lindsey heard him too, and came out from Moonstone's box to open the stable door for him. All the ponies turned and whickered as they came in with the lanterns but Midnight bounced about stiffly on long black legs and said mu' mu', very shortly and often. Lindsey took the bucket and climbed over the partition. The small calf bunted and butted at her side with a wet cold muzzle when she offered her the bucket. Lindsey dipped her fingers in the warm milk and held them out for the calf to suck, then she lowered them under the milk, the calf's muzzle coming with them till there was a spluttering and blowing in the milk and Midnight was sneezing loudly with a white milky muzzle.

Soon the calf was drinking eagerly alone, her large round ears flapping over with every gulp and her woolly black tail wriggling ecstatically all the time.

In the farmhouse Andrea was measuring and filtering the milk. It ran through the triple filter into the shining milk bucket with a noise like the tearing of silk. Mrs. Thornton was busy at the Christmas cooker frying bacon, eggs and squares of bread, and Peter was out with his father feeding the hens. The winter dawn was just breaking and the grey daylight mingled in the big low kitchen with the yellow light of the oil lamps on the table.

'Holleybone said it might thaw to-day,' Andrea said.

Mrs. Thornton said she would be glad to see the end of the snow this time: she had never felt tired of it before but this year it had been altogether too much and too long.

At breakfast Mr. Thornton said, 'You know, it's started. I can smell it.'

'Smell what?' Peter said, only smelling his bacon and egg.

'The thaw. It's coming, you'll see.'

If the thaw came Dion would go out with his father and Glen and the guns, down into the wild valley where fallow deer came. If the thaw came, too, he would find the black hunting whip. He knew he would find it. That was what they had come to Punch Bowl for, to right the old wrongs. Everything had a reason, and it was so odd, the way the farm had fallen into their hands, almost by chance it might seem, but he knew it wasn't that.

If only he had a really good pony, a 'lepper' such as Blackmail had been. Sula jumped well enough but not really up to show standard and he was getting rather heavy for her. But Clover was much too small, Tarquin didn't really jump at all and Moonstone—she was out of it for ever. 'Dad,' he said, 'do you think we might go shooting when it thaws? The deer are coming quite near the farm since the snow. Holleybone says he's seen their slots in Rockfield Lane.'

'If you shoot a deer,' Lindsey said, the honey dripping from her toast, 'I'll never speak to you again. It's bad enough having to take a tiny calf away from her mother at only three days old, without bringing misery to the wild animals too. I sometimes think farming's horrible.'

Lindsey was pouring cream on her porridge. 'You shouldn't really eat *that*, if you think farming's horrible,' Andrea told her.

Mrs. Thornton smiled. 'I should eat it,' she said. 'In less than a week the cow and calf will both be happy; they forget so soon. You mustn't be too soft when you're farming.'

Lindsey picked up the cream jug and went on pouring, though uncertainly. 'But deer,' she said, 'are quite different.'

The thaw came so quickly with the sun and a soft wind veering southerly.

Everyone was glad to see Ann again after the long isolation of the snowstorm and she was a welcome and willing extra hand in watering, feeding, exercising and mucking out the animals still housebound by the snow.

The sun gained hourly in warmth and brightness. The warmth made everyone shed jerkins, scarves, and gloves all over the buildings, and the brightness was a dazzle to the eyes on quickly melting snow.

Joyfully the stabled animals were turned out, all except Moonstone and Midnight. The ponies went absolutely crazy with delight. Here were their glorious green fields again, after long dark days and nights in stables. Madly they galloped round their territory, from one favourite place to another, slithering in the wet slush, neighing their delight, wet mud thrown from flying hoofs, the winter sun glinting on the flash of upturned shoes.

Starfleet Countess's Duchess was a sight. She came to her doorway, lifted her pretty head and smelt the air. She came into the yard with skittish jumps and skipped comically round and round the dung heap. She was like a very large, very matronly looking baby fawn, and she tossed her head and swung her curving horns. Excited by this preliminary canter, she attacked the dung heap fair and square, horning showers of it up into the air. Long straw hung on her horns like feathers.

When she had settled to her grazing among snow patches in Barn field, Dion, Peter and Lindsey began the serious work of cleaning out stables, calf-box and cowshed, and exercising Moonstone. Ann and Andrea had promised to make butter and got busy in the kitchen with the churn.

The thaw was a joyous occasion, though bringing with it as it did, the swiftly approaching certainty of school. Dion in particular was elated as he looked out his mattock and sharpened the edge of his spade. This afternoon he would dig.

As it happened, everybody dug. All the children that is, the parents having early departed for a long delayed shopping expedition with lists of farm and household requirements and last minute instructions about oil lamps, fireguard, chickens and water, in case they didn't get home in time for tea.

Lindsey was the first to be fired by Dion's enthusiasm and got her fork and joined him. Ann and Andrea heard the shout that Dion sent up and ran to see what was happening. Dion, Peter and Lindsey were all bent double and all were digging like machines.

'What's up?' Andrea called through cupped hands.

'Come and see!' Dion called back, and Peter squeak-shouted, 'He's found it!'

Ann and Andrea tore through the gate and down the orchard track. 'Found what? The hunting whip?' 'Where is it?'

'Of course I haven't,' Dion said. 'But if I haven't found the steps I'd like to know what this is.' He was scraping carefully with his spade along the surface of a dark piece of buried planking. It was about three feet long by one foot wide and was rotting in the damp earth.

Ann and Andrea stared at it, wildly speculating. Peter and Lindsey feverishly scraped and dug on either side of it. The plank began slowly to emerge from its long dark grave and, showing now the fragments of what were once connecting side pieces, proclaimed itself indeed a wooden step.

Ann and Andrea said, 'It *is* the steps!' and 'I'm going to get a fork. Coming, Ann?'

Lindsey stood in the sodden grass and stared in awe-struck silence while Peter danced crazily round and round the excavation with loud whoops of triumph that sent the three ponies streaming fearfully up the bank and into Hanger field again. Only Dion worked on. Nothing mattered at the moment but the finding of the very bottom step. From that he could see at once which was the third, and then all that would lie between him and the whip was the cold wet earth of the orchard.

Lindsey said wonderingly, 'In a dead straight line with the fig and Hanger field gate. Old Mr. Pyecraft stood just here, perhaps where I am now, when he was only so high.' A second step was under his carefully exploring spade and his next scrape revealed the wood of it.

Dion was puzzled by the apparent non-existence of another step, and yet there must be at least three, the journal had said so. The whip was buried beneath the third step.

Then suddenly the thought occurred to him that the second step he had uncovered was probably the first step of the flight, in which case only two were still in existence and the third one had crumbled, burnt or rotted right away with any others formerly above it.

It would have come about *here*. He held the edge of his spade above the ground for a brief moment, then quickly he thrust the blade downwards and into the wet earth beneath the vanished third step.

His spade struck iron. He took his mattock, prising and levering in the bottom of the hole. Not enough earth out, he must shovel some more. Then, the level iron surface exposed, he took the mattock again.

Working the strong edge of it underneath the black lump, he threw the whole of his weight on the handle, and with a loud sucking noise the lump came up into the daylight. Dion's hands were on it, rubbing off the sticky earth. It was a long iron box, light of weight and very narrow. He knew, without giving it a thought, what he had found. Where was the catch? There wasn't one, the lid was rusted down upon its box, stuck hard and fast and unresponsive to his fingers. He threw down his gloves and tried again but only took the skin from two bare finger tips.

Putting the box down on the ground he took his mattock and struck a neatly judged blow upon the lid's edge. With a clatter the iron box fell apart, and under the leaping certainty of Dion's gaze the black hunting whip lay suddenly revealed.

*   *   *

Through all the rest of that winter and the loveliness of spring Dion was a person with one purpose. His main and dominant interest, the farm, was in temporary submission, and when he milked Duchess in the early mornings before school, or fed the ever ravenous chickens,

159

'I wonder if you would mind,' said the boy with stiff courtesy, 'If you could possibly lend me your whip?'

or saw to the welfare of the swiftly growing Midnight, he did all these things efficiently and well. But the long dead boy and his black hunting whip were never far away from his mind.

He knew with a cool certainty that he had a mission to accomplish. Almost a crusade it seemed to his chivalrous nature, to carry a whip to victory for a boy who had tried to do this in memory of his father. Dion knew that this was what he must do, and somehow he would do it. The boy and his whip came first and to Dion this was perfectly in order. The farm would wait.

How he could encompass victory on little bouncing Sula he couldn't well imagine. But if he was meant to do it, most certainly it would happen.

Meanwhile, through the lengthening, softening days into the green flood of spring he schooled and trained the pony.

In the quick surge of spring when the lush grass brought a deep yellow colour to Duchess's rich milk, Sula began to get fat as she was prone to. Dion brought her in during the daytime through the Easter holidays so that she could not keep on eating.

The black hunting whip itself still lay in its iron box, untouched, but it was placed in the hidden cellar in the stone table cupboard with the journal, and there it awaited the day in early June when a boy would carry it for a chivalrous idea.

That spring was a long golden pageant of scented coloured days. Instead of dead leaves and lichens and mosses in the rain water for washing, there floated now the white fallen petals of the plum blossom, or curly catkins of the tall oak.

Riding Sula, or more often now, Red Clover, Lindsey knew it was spring by the fine triple vein that ran up behind the pointed ears. In the winter she had never seen it for the thick cover of the warm winter coat.

She knew, as indeed did all the household, by the night-and-day-long ecstasy of nightingales, all around the farmhouse, in the valley. All day they sang, with a brief midday silence, and, it seemed to Lindsey, all the long night too. Often she woke up for a drowsy moment in the dark and almost always she heard the bubbling, thrilling liquid song come floating through her open window.

Moonstone, it was hoped, was now in foal to an Arab stallion and spent her days browsing peacefully in the orchard, her milky coat as white as the plum blossoms that fell and lay upon it. She was the pet and favourite of the family and especially loved by Lindsey, who, when bereft of Sula because Dion was schooling over jumps, would spend hours grooming her and talking to her out in the orchard among the dazzle of the white clouds and blossom.

Lindsey would not go to the show. She said she was 'all little wheels inside' because of Sula and the greatness of her task. She said she couldn't bear to watch her, and she stayed behind and with loving care prepared a dish of diced young carrots, sugar lumps, apple slices, dairy nuts and oats, such as a very hungry, very dieted little pony would adore.

Poor little Sula! Beautiful, courageous and so sensible. She had no possible chance against so many and so great, but Dion was a person with a purpose, a knight on a crusade, and nothing would have turned him from his path.

On the showground Dion was cool and quiet. He had no sense of futility, no nervousness or stage-fright. He had come because he had to, and he wasn't the one to question why. What he must accomplish he would accomplish and he had himself done all he could towards it. His father and mother had been puzzled by his deter-

mination to jump Sula, who, though good was not outstanding. Dion could see them sitting together by the second ring.

Standing with Sula near the collecting ring because the Children's Jumping was the next but one event, he almost felt the black hunting whip burning into his hand as he looked curiously about him at the ponies who would probably be competing in his class. Five, he thought, were probably not much better than Sula if looks were anything to go by, two far worse. Three would almost certainly be very much superior, one of these especially, a bright chestnut with strong quarters and great jumping hocks.

If Sula could only get placed it would be something, and perhaps the long-ago boy would rest content with so much, or so little of a victory.

The first jumping children began to look to their girths and get ready. Dion mounted his pony and moved up into the collecting ring among the other competitors, noting each one with a look of careful judgement. He would have liked to carry the whip well, to win for its sake a first or second place. But, knowing Sula and seeing what he was up against, he knew he would be hard put to it to gain a mere reserve.

The minutes were fast slipping away when the boy on the black pony came cantering into the collecting ring and quickly looked around him. Not much older than I am, Dion thought, but a much better rider and the pony is superb.

Dion, with his horseman's eye appraising the little black, did not realise at first that the rider's eyes were on himself. But when the pony turned towards him he quickly raised his glance and caught the strange intentness of the rider's eyes upon him. Returning the look with a swiftly growing interest, Dion waited for the boy to come up to him and then waited for him to speak first. It seemed to him that everything now happening was urgently important, most significant, but he could not have said why.

'I wonder if you would mind,' said the boy with stiff courtesy, 'If you could possibly lend me your whip? My pony does not go so well without the little touch behind the girth, and I have not brought my own.'

The sudden angry refusal sprang to Dion's tongue but stayed there. He looked at the stranger with hostility but said nothing. He dropped his glance to the proud black pony and hostility changed to unwilling admiration.

'I would be most grateful,' said the stranger quietly.

Then suddenly crept into Dion's mind a new idea. If he really only wanted the victory for the hunting whip and for the boy who used to own it, not for Sula or himself, then who better, who more certain to carry it with credit than this boy on his incomparable pony?

'Number Forty-Seven,' called the secretary through his megaphone, and it was Dion's number. He held the whip out to the stranger and heard his own voice unaccountably saying, 'Yes, certainly, you can take it now. I can manage better without it,' and cantered slowly into the ring. Sula had nine faults, mostly due to failure in drawing up her hocks. Dion made much of her when he dismounted but her performance was no longer the most important one to him. Eagerly he watched while the other ponies jumped, the bright chestnut leading easily with only one and a half faults until the last competitor came in. This was the one that he had waited for, the stranger who carried the black hunting whip.

It seemed to Dion that it must have been inevitable; the faultless, perfect round the stranger's pony completed. Almost soundless he was, as he rose and stretched to each

(*Continued on page* 164)

Chu Ching and the Talking Fish

By Meryon Vance

ILLUSTRATED E
JOHN ROBINSO

ONCE LONG AGO, in the Province of Kiang-su, there lived a poor fisher-boy called Chu Ching.

Now, Chu Ching seemed an unlucky boy. Because he was kind and slow people and animals took advantage of him; his Cormorants brought him the littlest fish, his Master's Customers got the best of the bargain, and whatever he picked up seemed to fall from his fingers.

His Master often thought, 'I must get rid of him!' but Chu was an honest boy, so he kept him at some loss.

One evening, when fishing from his Master's Catamaran, a Cormorant brought him a larger fish than usual, a beautiful fish, all silver scales. It slipped through his hands to the bottom of the boat. Chu bent down to examine it, when the fish opened its mouth, and said in a clear, tiny voice:

'O kind Chu Ching, put me into water please, and spare my life!'

There was an old pot, used for fresh water in the stern, so Chu slipped the silver fish into that. When the raft returned to her moorings, Chu carried the pot and the fish back to the shed where he slept.

'I shall now make my fortune,' he said, 'everyone will pay to hear a talking fish!'

The silver fish said nothing. It had other ideas. In the morning, Chu shouldered his baskets, loaded with fish, to go round his Master's Customers, when the fish put its head out of the pot, and said—

'Honoured Chu, bring me home a green dress and yellow jacket, please!'

'What can a fish want with a green dress and yellow jacket?' said Chu.

'You will see when you bring it,' the fish replied.

'Am I a rich merchant or mandarin to buy dresses for fishes?' said Chu.

'Only a little dress, a doll's dress!' said the fish.

'Alas! I have not one cash of my own, and the fish I sell is my Master's.'

'Perhaps you will make some money yourself to-day,' said the fish, and dropped back into the jar again.

Oddly enough, Chu did make some money. He exerted himself, and drove some good bargains, and his Master, pleased and surprised at his efforts, gave him some cash for himself. With this, Chu purchased a doll's dress and coat, and when he returned, placed them on the handle of the jar and commenced his cooking.

'O thank you, kind Chu,' said the fish. Its voice sounded clearer and stronger, and looking round, Chu saw a charming little lady seated on the jar, dressed in the green dress and yellow jacket. She was perfect in every way, except where her feet should have been was a silver fish's tail.

'Now that you are half mortal, your honourable self will require some supper,' said Chu.

'Indeed, it smells good,' said the Mermaid, 'I should have been honoured to prepare it for you, but I must keep my tail cool in this jar.'

'It is no trouble at all,' said Chu, 'I can see we shall both make our fortunes. At the feast of Ming-Ting what will not people pay to see a live Mermaid?'

The Mermaid did not answer this, for truth to tell, she had other ideas.

The next day, Chu shouldered his baskets to commence his round, when the Mermaid inspected his catch with some interest.

'This is good fish,' she said, 'and a beautiful choice. Why not take it up to the Ogre's Castle! You will do very well there.'

'The Ogre is not one of my Master's Customers,' said Chu, 'And I have not time to climb there.'

'It would pay you,' said the Mermaid, 'I happen to know that his daughter has no fish-man at present. She is a good cook and pays well.'

'I certainly shall not go,' said Chu, 'why should I put my head in the Ogre's mouth?'

The Mermaid began to cry, and said imploringly:

'I entreat you, Master Chu, to go up to the Castle. The

Ogre is away on Wednesdays, and his daughter will give a good price. When you have put her in a good temper, ask her what became of the three little rings her father took from the Fairy Ah Shiu.'

So, in the end, Chu shouldered his baskets and went up to the Castle.

The Ogre's daughter came into the courtyard, to see the fish for herself. She was the ugliest girl Chu had ever seen, but handsome is as handsome does, and she paid him well for the fish. When the usual compliments had been exchanged, Chu still lingered, and the Ogre's daughter said—

'Is there anything on your honourable mind?'

'If it is permitted to ask a question,' said Chu, 'I should like to know what became of the three rings of the Fairy Ah Shiu?'

'O that,' said the Ogre's daughter laughing, 'I can easily tell you that. My noble father was so angry, he threw them away as far as he could. One fell in the Sing River, one in the trees of the Pine Grove, and one in the sand-pit by the road.'

'May one ask, why your noble father was angry, lady?'

'You may well ask,' said the Ogre's daughter. 'The Fairy Ah Shiu insulted my father. She showed him his face in her own mirror. Such a thing is not done in Ogre Society. We prefer our own mirrors, which, of course, are the very best made, and always ensure a charming reflection.'

Chu thanked her for her information and started briskly for home, but he was not allowed to return home easily.

On the road he met an old badger.

'Kind sir,' said the badger, 'I see you are young and supple whilst I am old and stiff. Will you assist me in turning and airing my bedding?'

The badger was so old and grey, Chu felt he could not refuse, so he helped him spread out his bedding in the sun. The badger thanked him and he hurried on.

Presently the road passed through a pine grove, and an ape, high up in the branches called to him,

'Honoured sir, will you pick up my Persimmon fruit, it has dropped near your feet. Please throw it up.'

'What a nuisance the animals are to-day,' thought Chu, 'ordering me about.' But, as the Persimmon fruit was just at his feet, he could hardly refuse.

He tossed it to the ape, who caught it deftly. Chu hurried on. 'I shall never get home to-day,' he thought.

But he had not finished yet.

By the humped bridge, over the Sing River, a duck on the roadside called out to him:

'Good sir, pray pick me up and carry me over the bridge. I have sustained a great misfortune, and am lame. If you put me down near my home, I will give you a thousand thanks.'

The duck's feet were bleeding, so Chu picked her up and carried her over the bridge, putting her down in the place she directed. He also bathed her feet, and she gave him a thousand thanks. At last, Chu was allowed to make his way home, where he told all that had happened to the Mermaid.

'Now, please don't ask me to do anything else,' he said, 'my feet are heavy as barges, and I still have the rest of the fish to take round to my Master's Customers.'

But the Mermaid had other ideas. She allowed him to fish all the following day, but the day after that, when he was about to set out on his rounds, she said:

'Honoured Chu, I must tell you I am the Fairy Ah Shiu, as you might have guessed, had you been a little bit clever. My home is in the Moon, where I sit under the Cassia Tree, combing the hair of the Rabbit of Yin, as he pounds the drugs of Immortality. Alas! his coat has not been

brushed or combed for seven weeks, doubtless it is in tangles!'

'It is all very sad,' said Chu, 'but, I cannot do anything about it.'

'Ah! but you can,' said the Fairy Ah Shiu, and tho' he fidgeted, she continued, 'I was sent by the Rabbit of Yin, to obtain more cinnamon bark for him. The Ogre found me combing my hair. He looked over my shoulder and saw his face in my mirror. He saw himself as he really is, and the sight enraged him.

You must know, Chu, that Ogres, like many people, prefer to use their own mirrors and flatter themselves.

In his rage he caught me and threw away my three magic rings, so I was helpless. Then he hurled me down to the Realm of Fishes, where you caught me. Your kindness, Chu, has restored all but my feet. Will you not complete the good work and find my three rings?'

'I see I shall have no peace till I do!' said Chu.

'Why not go to the Castle again with your fish? The Ogre takes carriage exercise on Fridays. Look for my rings on the way.'

'How can I find them in such impossible places?' said Chu.

'Don't make excuses. Perhaps someone will help you. Meanwhile, the Ogre's daughter pays well, and I want new shoes.'

However can someone without feet want shoes? thought Chu. However, he set out again for the Castle, and who should he meet by the humped bridge, but the duck, to whom he told his troubles.

'I will look for the ring in the river,' said the duck,

'The Ogre's daughter came into the courtyard to see the fish for herself.'

'there is nothing I like better than dibbling in the weeds. I'll meet you here on your return.'

When he came to the pine grove he met the ape.

'I'll swing along the tree tops,' said the ape, 'there's nothing I like better. I'll have the ring here on your return.'

By the sand-pit he met the old badger.

'There's nothing I like better than tunnelling in sand,' said the badger, 'I'm pretty sure to find your ring, and I'll bring it you on your return.'

'Your kindness, Chu, has restored all but my feet.'

At the Castle, the Ogre's daughter was all smiles.

'Your fish was delicious,' she said, 'My noble father has appointed you his own Imperial Fish-man,' and she paid him handsomely.

On the way home the badger, the ape, and the duck met him with the three rings, and with the extra cash the Ogre's daughter had given him for himself, Chu bought two tiny embroidered shoes.

The Fairy Ah Shiu was delighted. She put on her three rings at once. When she had done so the scales of her tail fell in a little silver heap on the floor, and she held out her tiny feet for Chu to put the embroidered shoes on.

'Now I hope we shall make our fortunes, at last,' cried Chu. 'What will not everyone pay to see a Moon Fairy—'

'You will prosper, Chu, as you deserve,' said the Fairy. 'But I must go back to the Moon. The Rabbit of Yin needs me, and you do not any more!'

'O but I do, you must stay,' said Chu.

'You have learnt to make a good bargain and to persevere,' said the Fairy, 'and nothing has slipped through your fingers for a week!'

'Do you mean you came to help me,' said Chu surprised, 'I thought you came for the rabbit's cinnamon bark.'

'One thing leads to another,' said the Fairy. 'The Threads of Life cross in many ways, but, good deeds work together for good. You will make a fortune, Chu, tho' not in the way you supposed.'

Light from the Fairy illuminated the hut. She glistened like a star. Chu cried 'Stay, O stay—!' but she rose in the air, and was gone. From the roof, something fell softly, as autumn leaves, at Chu's feet. The doll's green dress and yellow jacket, and the little embroidered shoes.

Chu kept them always, in a case, by his bed-side.

Soon the Fairy's words came true. His Master took him into partnership, and later left the business to him. All that Chu touched, prospered, and he became the most honoured and respected Merchant in the Province of Kiang-su.

Black Hunting Whip—*Continued from page 161)*

jump. Beautifully collected, absolutely calm. He cantered out to a sudden swaying roar of clapping and Dion too was clapping as if he had been a brother.

Afterwards he hunted for the stranger, anxious for his hunting whip. But he couldn't find the boy or see the pony. He asked people up and down the field if they had seen him but no one remembered doing so since the jumping. Perplexed and a little worried, Dion went to the secretary's tent and enquired there.

'Well, he was a gate entry, of course,' the secretary said, moving papers on his table. 'Rather a last minute one, in fact. I took the details down somewhere, not in the proper book because I was just leaving the tent, but on a scrap of paper. I thought I had it in my pocket but it doesn't seem to be there.'

'You don't happen to remember his name or anything, do you?' Dion asked him.

'I'm afraid I can't say I do. I'm sorry. I do remember the pony's name but that would hardly be any help, I suppose.'

Dion stared in a puzzled way through the open tent door. 'No,' he said, 'I don't suppose it would. You see, I lent him my whip. He looked straight and honest—and the whip was rather special.'

'Oh,' the secretary was suddenly interested. 'You are Dion Thornton, then? I have your whip here for you. The boy handed it in immediately after the jumping. He said you would call for it and would we tell you he was grateful. If you had mentioned it at first I could have been more helpful. The boy also asked if you would collect his prize for him as he must go at once. He said you would understand.' The secretary took a whip from the end of the bench and handed it to Dion who stared at it in wonder.

'But this isn't my whip! Mine was a black hunting whip. Not a bit like this one!'

The secretary looked nonplussed. 'This is the one he gave me,' and he said you would be calling for it.'

Then, as Dion still stared, 'It's a very good whip. Silver bands and the handle's ivory, I think. I should have it if I were you, and say nothing.'

The boy turned it over in his hands and then suddenly looked up. 'I think,' he said slowly, 'I would like to know the pony's name after all, if you don't mind.'

'Why certainly,' said the secretary, 'and a wonderful pony it was. I remember the name perfectly, it seemed to suit the animal so well. The pony's name was Blackmail. But I'm sorry I can't help you more about the owner.'

'Thank you, sir,' said Dion. 'You have told me all I want to know.' And, taking the unknown whip in his hand, he swung across the ground to find Sula.

All things were well with him, old wrongs were righted, old sorrows put away, the spirit of Punch Bowl Farmhouse was at rest—and the farm had waited.

THE END

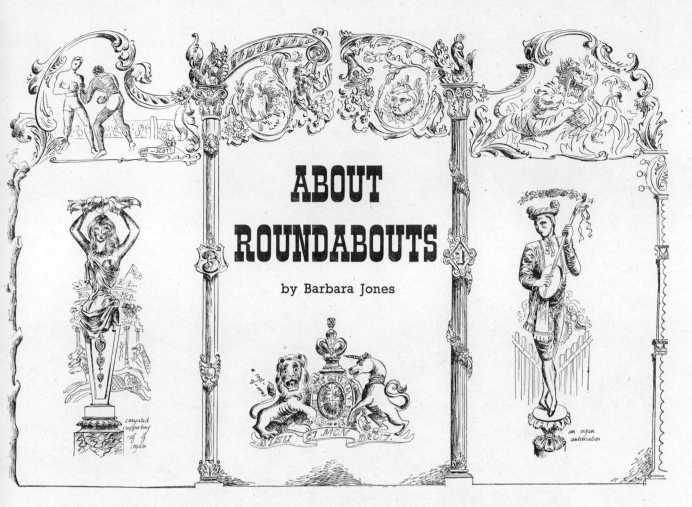

ABOUT ROUNDABOUTS

by Barbara Jones

**In all the noise and bustle and twirling of the Merry-Go-Round at the Fair, you
are not in the mood to examine the carvings or reflect on what they may mean.
Here is a description that will make your next visit to the Fair even more fascinating.**

THE CENTRE of any good Fair, however
tall the slide and however colossal
the Great Wheel, is the carved and
gilded roundabout.

The roundabout's effect of dazzling
riot, is produced mainly by the paintings
on the flat wooden panels between the
carved curly-cues. Most showmen are
competent artists, and repaint to keep up
with changing fashions. The nineteenth
century liked apes and parrots, lions and
bears, nowadays portraits of filmstars,
dirt track riders or Generals Montgomery
or Stalin have taken their place. Change
in the carved parts is slower, but racing
cars and motor bikes are sometimes to
be seen chasing a horse round the platform while escaping themselves from the
outstretched beak of an ostrich. The
origin of the elaborate ornament on
roundabouts, must have been the Italian
theatre in the sixteenth century, when
the wonderfully elaborate stage settings
were then models for the whole European world. Within the limits of a
circular structure, you can see all the
devices that designers then used on the
stage.

Round and round, up and down, the
weaving surging motion is so exciting
and the organ music so deafening, that

it is difficult when you leave the fairground to remember what a roundabout
really looks like. The best thing to do is
to go back to the fair early one morning
when everything is still and quiet, and
then you can walk round the rides and
see how they are put together.

The platform cannot touch the ground,
so the whole structure hangs from a
turret built above the central engine.
From this radiate the 'swifts', with their
ends tidily encircled by the ornate
'rounding-board', itself sometimes enormously heavy and always painted with
the name of the owner and a description
of 'The Fastest Stud of Galloping
Cossack Horses in the World. Safe
Riding for all Classes'. The horses hang
from metal stays radiating alternately
with the 'swifts', and the platform is also
suspended on iron bars as it revolves
under the horses' hooves. The people
riding on top of all this, weigh perhaps
five tons, and when you remember that
it is all prefabricated and can be taken
to pieces in a few hours, how it holds
together becomes a permanent miracle.
The great engineering skill used during
the nineteenth century to build so many
of our bridges and railways was equally
carefully employed on their steam

roundabouts, some of which are still
travelling today.

Among the gallopers, as well as horses
you will find ostriches, turkeys, dragons
or cocks, in any variety or wildly inter-
mixed, but always, on a good roundabout, most beautifully and richly
carved. The carving is less deep on the
off-side where the only man to see it
has already paid his sixpence, and the
inside animal of these which prance
abreast, has very little ornament indeed.
The traditional colouring for horses is
cream with scarlet nostrils and bright
manes and harness. Birds usually have
yellow beaks and legs, and a red head
shading down through purple into a blue
body. The best animals have glass eyes,
most of them have fearsome expressions,
probably to give their riders a feeling of
having subdued something fierce.

In the mornings, and all day on
Sundays, the delicate French-Italian-
made organ is kept carefully muffled up
against the English damp. It travels on
a wagon of its own and is drawn up
beside the engine in such a way that its
gay front is open so that all the pipes
are visible, gathered in groups according
to size and painted. Before the pipes
on little platforms stand the members

of the orchestra, staring before them with tight-lipped dignity, moving their chamois-jointed arms to strike a bell or a drum.

The very expensive, hand-made music is played on the 'mechanical box' attached to the side of the organ. The music is drawn on a long roll of thin card, but the 'notes' are horizontal slits. The roll is fitted over a platform which has a row of steel teeth standing up at one end. The music is fastened down so tightly that all the teeth are pressed down by it, and a pair of revolving rubber rollers draw it across them. While the teeth are all down, the small valves under them are closed but as the holes in the music come along the appropriate teeth are released so that the small valves open to let the air into the organ pipes, and out comes the sound, flute, violin, 'cello.

Usually the whole roundabout is festooned with electric light bulbs which have replaced the roar and flicker of naphtha-flares. But the general glow of the whole elaborate machine, is still very mellow. This is because showmen varnish everything frequently to preserve it from bad weather, and their many coats of varnish produce an effect like the patina of age on an 'Old Master'. On a merry-go-round you ride in a rich golden world which is strangely like being inside an old painting. But more noisy.

Pay-box

revolving pillar

rounding-board

hybrid bird, horse, and dragon

Barbara Jones

RAFFLES OF SINGAPORE

Malaya House

By JOSEPHINE KAMM

THE NEXT TIME you go to the London Zoo, look in the Lion House for the marble bust of the founder of the Zoological Society, Sir Thomas Stamford Raffles. You will see the head and shoulders of a man with a firm face, a broad forehead, and finely carved lips which give the whole face a kindly expression. A painting of Raffles in the National Gallery shows him dressed in the dark coat and knee breeches and the high white stock which were fashionable in the early part of the nineteenth century.

If Raffles had done no more in his life than found the Zoo we should have reason to be grateful to him, but in fact he did very much more. He was born in 1781 in the reign of George III. His father was the master of a merchant ship which plied between London and the West Indies, and his mother must sometimes have joined him on the long sea voyage, for the baby was born on board ship just off Jamaica.

Young Thomas Raffles (or Stamford, as he came to be called) spent his childhood in London with his mother and elder sisters while his father tried, without success, to make a living for the family. For a short time the boy went to a boarding school in Hammersmith. But Captain Raffles could not afford to keep him long at school and before he was fourteen the boy had to start earning his own living.

The job which the elder Raffles found for his son was a humble one, as a very junior clerk in the London office of the East India Company; but if the job had been anywhere else the whole story of the British Empire in the Far East might have been different. The East India Company had already had a long and important history. It was founded in the reign of Queen Elizabeth for the purpose of trading with India and the islands of the East Indies. In order to guard the trading posts it had set up, the East India Company began to take over more and more strips of land, mostly in India. This meant that some of the men sent out by the Company to the Far East became the rulers of large areas of

land and of the native people who lived there. In the end the British Government took over control of the Company's lands in India and elsewhere, but this did not happen until many years later.

When Stamford Raffles started work with the Company he was kept closely to his office desk all day. But he was determined to make up for the schooling he had lost and so he spent every minute of his spare time in study. He taught himself French until he could read it as easily as English, but his special interest was Natural History. We can picture him reading far into the night, grudging the hours that went in sleeping or eating; and getting up early each morning to go to his day's work in the City. But his home life was not a very happy one, for his parents' poverty weighed heavily on him; but, whatever the cause, he certainly overstrained himself. He cannot have had many holidays but on one occasion he was so ill that he was ordered to stay away from the office for a fortnight. Instead of resting, he set out to walk to the Welsh mountains and, after covering thirty or forty miles every day, came back in the best of health.

Eastward Bound

Meanwhile he had made so much headway with his office work that he was promoted to a better job and in 1815, when he was only thirty-four he was given the first important post of his career. At this time the East India Company were setting up trading posts for their ships to call on the short sea route to China which passed through the Malacca Straits, and Raffles was ordered to the island of Penang, off the west coast of Malaya. His salary was large enough to keep his family in comfort and also to allow him to get married; and so a few months later he and his wife set sail for the East.

The voyage was a long one, for sailing ships took several months to make a journey which now takes only a few weeks (or a few days by air). It was uncomfortable, too, for in those days there were no refrigerators to keep the

food fresh or electric fans to cool the heat of the tropics; and with every wave the little ship plunged or rolled. But Raffles must have noticed very little of this for he was busy learning the Malay language, to such good effect that within a few months of his arrival he could speak and read it with ease. This meant that he was able to make friends with the people, who are usually very shy and reserved.

The Malays, men as well as women, are fond of wearing bright colours, and with their olive skins, smooth black hair and large expressive eyes they must have looked like butterflies compared with Raffles in his dark London clothes and his wife in her pale muslins. He liked them at once, they liked him and he soon had many friends. The most devoted was his secretary, who was called Abdulla. We know this because later on Abdulla wrote the story of his own life and in it he praised his master for his kindness, his friendliness and his courage. 'He spoke in smiles', wrote Abdulla, and 'always had a sweet expression towards European as well as Native gentlemen.'

Raffles spent most of the remainder of his life in the East. He held a number of different posts under the East India Company and rose to the rank of Governor, the highest honour he could gain. And he worked harder than ever. In his office he reckoned that there were three times as many letters to write as there had been in London, quite apart from everything else he had to do. But he managed to deal with it all and also to find time to learn a great deal about the Malay people and the Natural History of their country. Visitors flocked to see him and he took frequent trips on the mainland to see conditions for himself.

He found plenty to worry him. The coasts of Malaya were infested with pirates, who lived by plunder and murder. Inland, the country was divided into small states under native rulers who were always quarrelling and fighting among themselves; while rich men added daily to their wealth at the expense of

167

Sir Thomas Stamford Bingley Raffles, better known as "Raffles of Singapore" and Founder of the London Zoo

the down-trodden poor. One of the worst evils that Raffles found was slavery, which flourished in the cruellest manner. A poor man who found himself in debt (as poor men only too often did) was forced to sell himself as a slave to the man to whom he owed money. If he committed a crime and was sentenced to death, his innocent wife and children were sold into slavery for life.

These evils could only be attacked in the districts held by the East India Company. And so, wherever he was posted by the Company, Raffles set himself to stamp out the buying and selling of men and women as slaves, to set up a wise and just form of government, and to make life safe for the people. When these things had been done, he saw to it that schools were opened for the Malay children, for he had never forgotten that his own school days had been far too short.

His Dream City

But his greatest work was still to come. He believed that if a British port could be built in Eastern waters which should be free not only to British ships but to the ships of all nations, then trade would be enormous and prosperity certain. In search of the ideal spot, his thoughts turned to an island at the tip of the Malay Peninsula, swampy, unhealthy and haunted by pirates. The island was called Singapore, and Raffles saw beyond the disease and poverty of its few inhabitants to a glorious future.

He had less than a year to establish the new town, for his career in the East was coming to an end; but with lightning

Raffles' dream come true—Singapore—in his day a swampy island haunted by pirates and disease

speed he put down slavery and other evil practices, gave peace to this former nest of pirates, and opened schools and a college for the study of Eastern languages. The port brought trade, as he had known it would. When neighbouring peoples heard of the island's prosperity, they flocked to settle there—Europeans, Chinese traders, and Arabs as well as Malays. And this growing prosperity spread beyond the island into Malaya, for the people found that the tin and other products of the mainland could be shipped from Singapore to the world. By the time Raffles left the island more than 10,000 people were living there instead of a mere handful, and this number grew later to three-quarters of a million.

Meanwhile, Raffles was thinking out an entire set of laws for the people, and planning a Council of the people's representatives to see that the laws were kept. These laws were made in 1823 and put into use before he left. Until 1942, when Singapore fell to the Japanese in one of the darkest moments of the 1939-1945 War, Raffles' laws were kept with only a few small changes. Today, life in Singapore is being rebuilt according to his ideas. 'I have had . . . to look for a century or two beforehand', he wrote early in 1824, 'and provide for what Singapore may one day become. And it would have been a proud day for him if he could have revisited the island on April 1st, 1948, to watch the opening of Singapore's peacetime Council, and see British, Malay, Chinese and Indian members (elected by the people to represent them) take their seats in the Council Chamber.

In the few months which he spent on the island Raffles worked even harder than before, for he felt that nothing was too good for his 'political child', as he called Singapore. It was almost his only child, for the unhealthy climate, which had wrecked his own health, had killed all but one of his real children and also his wife. During a short visit to England (when he had been knighted by the Prince Regent for his services) he had married for the second time. Now he and his wife were going home, taking with them a most valuable collection of drawings and maps; Raffles' own notes on history and natural history; and a large collection of animals, birds and plants.

Noah's Ark Alight

Scarcely had the journey started when the ship caught fire. All the passengers were rescued, but everything else was lost. 'There was scarcely an unknown animal, bird, beast, or fish, or an interesting plant, which we had not on board', wrote Raffles about his loss. 'A living tapir, a new species of tiger, splendid pheasants, etc., domesticated for the voyage; we were, in short in this respect, a perfect Noah's Ark.'

After a nightmare voyage, with a terrible gale blowing for three weeks on end, the passengers reached Plymouth in the late summer of 1824. Raffles was only forty-three, but he looked (to use his own words) 'a little old man, all yellow and shrivelled' with his 'hair pretty well blanched.' He was a sick man too, always in pain, but he refused

to rest. 'I am much interested at present', he wrote, 'in establishing a grand Zoological collection in the metropolis, with a Society for the introduction of living animals.' And so the London Zoo was planned, and Raffles became the first President of the Zoological Society in 1826.

He had planned, too, to go on with the writing work he had started, and to live outside London at Mill Hill, which was then in the heart of the country. He had chosen Mill Hill because one of his best friends was going to live there and the gardens of the houses which they bought joined one another. Raffles' friend was another great man, William Wilberforce, who was nearing the end of a long and gallant fight against the African slave trade.

Raffles was the first to move into his new house; but he did not live long enough to enjoy his friend's company for more than a few weeks, or to see the success of the Zoological Society. In England, for every ten people who know Raffles as the founder of the Zoo, there is perhaps one who knows him as the founder of Singapore. But on the island itself his memory was honoured by the naming of Raffles College (soon to form part of a new University), Raffles Museum, Raffles Quay, Raffles Place, Raffles Hotel. At the edge of Raffles Plain a statue was unveiled many years after his death, when Singapore had become a British Colony and his dream of an Eastern Empire had come true. And at the unveiling ceremony some very true words were spoken: 'In Raffles, England had one of her greatest sons.'

MONKEYS AND MEN

by Lorna Lewis

MONKEYS AND MEN both belong to the most highly developed group of all the living things that make up the animal kingdom: the Primates, so-called from the Latin word for Principal. In this group, man is ruler, apart from the fact that he has a soul, because he has the best intelligence, including the power of reasoning. The monkey shows signs of intelligence of some kind; for this and other similarities we have to look on him as our closest four-footed relative.

The other points of similarity are mainly physiological. Look at a monkey —especially at a chimpanzee—and see the strong resemblance between human and monkey body: the way the legs and hands fit on and work, the way they both walk on their back legs easily, the shape of their faces. (This latter enable monkeys to drink as well as suck, where as other animals can only lap and suck. Look at the big toe of each—it is buil for gripping; and each can use hi 'hand' as a definite holding instrumen not just as a foot which can sometime do a bit of non-foot work when it isn' being walked on.

Humans have lines on their hands— so have monkeys. The chimpanzee ha different lines on his right and his lef hand, as do humans; but these fade as h gets older. Most monkeys are sociabl and chattering, some are non-stor howlers, some seem morose and onl grunt occasionally—quite like humans.

The many families of monkeys, from twenty-stone gorilla to tiny marmoset vary greatly among themselves, for in stance, in their ways of springing, climb ing, swinging; in their facial appearance (think of the half-human squirrel monke from South America and the distorted highly-coloured face of the mandril) Their tails range from very long to n tail at all, and of these tails, some ar prehensile (usable for climbing), som are non-prehensile.

To return to the chimpanzee, mos developed of monkeys. Some say tha he can actually think—certain chimp have in fact learnt to count up to a fev figures, smoke a pipe, ride a bicycle thread needles, sweep the floor, and s on. Others say that this proves nothin; about chimps in general and does no even prove *reasoned* thought in individua animals. A study of *Jubilee*, the famou chimpanzee who was born and brough up in the London Zoo just before th war, showed that as a baby she behaved very much like a small human. She la in her mother's arms, she played with he keeper, dancing round him, clutching a him, begging him by her movements an expressions to pick her up and toss he high as he did his own little girl at home But about three years later, learning wit other young chimps not bred in captivity all of whom were being trained for th Chimpanzees' tea-party, she had becom quite definitely just a young anima *learning to behave like a young human*

Chimpanzees' so-called intelligence i fact decreases as they grow and get full developed physically (at the age of abou seven); this is the reverse of reasonabl thinking humans, or should be.

Photo: Paul Popper

Jubilee, who was born at the Zoo, behaved very much like a small human.

HOW HILDEBRAND BECAME A HERO

by John Thorburn

ILLUSTRATED BY PETER BIEGEL

H ELEN FELT CERTAIN, as soon as she woke up, that it was going to be an exciting day: Henrietta was still asleep, she always seemed to wake up a quarter of an hour after Helen. Usually there was a book to read but on this occasion Helen lay on her back wondering.

First of all she wondered what had happened to Hildebrand, it seemed ages since she had seen him. Hildebrand had been a great friend of theirs, a piebald horse, black at both ends with a white stripe round his tummy, like a piece of chocolate cake with cream in the middle. That reminded her that she had left a bar of chocolate cream under her pillow the night before. It must have been a very hot night but, perhaps, she could remove most of the mess with a sponge.

Then she wondered what had happened to Horace the Horsedealer, to whom Hildebrand belonged. What a funny couple they were! Hildebrand, after that trouble at his christening with one of his godmothers, a horrible Nightmare of a horse called Sal Volatile, had only been able to eat things that started with an 'aitch'. This had been an awful nuisance until he discovered that most of the nicest things to eat were called 'hextras' by Horace. For Horace was always having trouble with his aitches. He used to say such things as 'Hildebrand is an hintelligent hanimal and it is unfortunate that we have so many haccidents in the 'unting field.' Horace seemed to fall off a great deal.

And then she wondered about Miss Prisms, their governess, who had gone off to marry the Colonel of the Piccadilly Yeomanry. Annie had told them that they had not got married after all, the regiment having been ordered to Poona. Annie said you never knew where you were with a soldier. Helen wondered whether the tip of Miss Prisms' nose still wobbled when she was angry and whether she had bought another straw hat to replace the one which Hildebrand had eaten, thinking it was made of hay.

By this time Helen was getting tired of wondering and, seeing that Henrietta had woken up, she threw her pillow on to the other bed.

* * *

When they arrived down to breakfast Mummy was reading a letter and Daddy was scraping the butter off the back of the *Times*.

Helen peeped under Mummy's letter to see if she could recognise the writing.

'Oh! Henrietta,' she called out, 'Mummy's got a letter from Primmy. Has she got married, Mummy, after all?'

'No,' said Mummy, 'I'll read you what she says.'

'"Dear Mrs. Underwood, The gentleman to whom I was betrothed sent me a cablegram from Poona to say that India was no place for young ladies and to offer to release me from the engagement. I immediately cabled back,

"Willing share your lot wheresoever king and country need you,' to which he replied, 'Haven't got a lot. King doesn't care a jot. Sell ring. Remit proceeds,'

"I have consequently decided to offer you my services to continue the education of your two daughters, and I am prepared to come as soon as you send for me.
Yours sincerely,
Prunella Prisms."

The faces of the two little girls fell.

'Oh! please not,' pleaded Henrietta, 'can't Daddy go on teaching us? It's much more interesting.'

'And less 'spensive," added Helen.

But just at that moment Annie came into the dining room, holding up Helen's pillow case for her parents to see and, a minute or two later, Giles, the gardener, came to the French windows to say that somebody had left the gate open and the rabbits had eaten all the lettuces.

Mrs. Underwood gave her husband a meaning look and he sighed and nodded his head.

'I shall send Miss Prisms a telegram immediately,' said Mummy, 'asking her to come by the afternoon train. Helen and Henrietta can go and meet her. Now run along both of you and help Annie to get her room ready. And, Helen, go and pick some flowers and put them in a vase on her dressing table.'

Helen went into the garden trying to remember the particular flowers which gave Miss Prisms hay fever.

* * *

After lunch the two little girls set out for the station. 'Let's make up a song of welcome,' suggested Helen, when, all of a sudden, they heard a loud wailing noise that went up and down in a series of mournful screeches.

'Oh!' cried Henrietta, 'it must be an air raid; can you see any aeroplanes Helen?'

'Don't be silly,' rejoined Helen, 'it must be a fire. The sirens always go off when there's a fire, to tell some of the firemen who are working in the village to run to the Fire Station and get the fire engine. Giles is a fireman. He says there hasn't been a fire for months. Look! There he is running along the road now. Come along, Henrietta, hurry up! There's the Fire Station over there with the red doors. If we hurry we'll see them turn out and follow them to the fire. Perhaps the railway station's on fire, or Primmy's train.'

They scampered across the street and when they got to the Fire Station there seemed to be an extraordinary commotion going on inside. There were rattles and clanks of things falling behind the red doors, which were still shut, and a lot of bad words. Then they heard the clop, clop of horses' hooves.

'I remember now,' cried Helen, 'Giles told me the fire

171

'The soap has started to melt. Come and carry me down at once.'

engine was pulled by a horse because the village couldn't afford a motor car. I wish they'd open the doors.'

The commotion inside increased but a voice near the door could be heard quite clearly.

'It's no good putting on the harness back to front because I'm not going to PUSH the fire engine. I'm not sure if I can even PULL it because I haven't had time to finish my lunch. And, if you don't hurry, there won't be any fire left to put out.'

Helen and Henrietta gave a shriek of delight. 'Oh! hurrah! it's Hildebrand—we've found him again at last.'

There was a shout from the upper floor.

'Look hout below, I'm coming down,' followed immediately by a loud splash. For a second there was a pause.

'And Horace too,' cried Henrietta.

'How hoften 'ave I told you not to leave the water carrier hunder the pole I 'ave to slide down,' came the indignant voice of Horace.

'Never mind,' said Hildebrand's voice, 'you'll be able to roll on the fire now and put it out yourself. No need for me or the engine or anything else. Isn't it about time somebody opened the doors?'

There was more clatter as the doors opened to reveal a scene of great confusion. Horace was standing on his head trying to get the water out of his boots. Giles, wearing a brass helmet and a blue fireman's tunic was trying to sort out the harness which seemed to be in a dreadful muddle. Another fireman was pouring buckets of water into a large tank mounted on wheels and with shafts attached. Behind the tank, and attached to it, was a bright red trailer pump which was used to pump the water to put out a fire. Coils of canvas hosepipes, most of them half unrolled, lay all over the floor and a fourth fireman

was trying to roll them up and put them on to the trailer pump.

Hildebrand was the only one who seemed perfectly calm. He was standing with his eyes half shut singing to himself:

> 'London's Burning
> London's Burning
> Fire! Fire!
> Fire! Fire
> Call Horace, Call Horace
> He's swallowed all the water.'

'Hildebrand!' yelled the two little girls, 'Look, it's us!' Hildebrand opened his eyes.

'Oh! Hullo,' he said, 'fancy seeing you here! Nice to see you. Brought any "hextras"?'

By this time, Giles seemed to have the harness sorted out.

'Where's the fire Sid?' he called out to the second fireman.

'Where's the fire Bert?' called out Sid to the third fireman.

'Where's the fire Mr. Horace?' called out Sid to Horace.

Horace turned himself right way up and felt in the pocket of his fire jacket.

'Hi wrote it down on a henvelope when I hanswered the 'phone,' he said, pulling out a sodden bit of paper, 'but the water has made it hillegible.'

Hildebrand started to walk away in disgust.

'I may as well go and finish my lunch,' he said. 'Come and talk to me Helen and Henrietta.'

But just at that moment a policeman walked up—he was very nearly running, but policemen never run.

'Who is the officer in charge?' he asked.

Horace drew himself up:

'I'm the Chief Hofficer,' he said importantly.

The policeman opened a thick, black notebook and started to read.

'On Tuesday, April 24th, in the course of my duties I was proceeding along Meadow Lane when my attention was drawn to a smell of burning. Investigating further I noticed smoke issuing from a window of premises known as Meadow Court, the property of Lady Lochness. I proceeded up the drive. . . .'

Here, Giles interrupted him.

'So that's where the fire is. Come on Sid, come on Mr. Horace, come on Hildebrand. Off we go.'

And they all put on their brass helmets and scrambled on to the seat in front of the water tank. Giles, who was driving, gave Hildebrand a flick with the whip.

Hildebrand started off, but as they had forgotten to fasten the traces on to the water tank there was nothing to pull. So he stopped and looked round scornfully.

'I thought you were coming with me,' he grumbled. 'If you wanted me to go alone why did you put all this beastly harness on me?'

Giles climbed down and fastened the traces on to the hooks. Hildebrand put his head down and whispered to Helen and Henrietta.

'Quick, get on to the pump at the back, you simply must come too.'

And at last they really started. Hildebrand galloped as fast as he could and the four firemen and the two little girls had to cling on to prevent themselves from being flung off as they went round corners. Everybody in the street cheered as they flew past. Horace actually did fall off as they turned into Meadow Lane but a man on a motor bicycle picked him up and brought him along, so there was no need to stop.

When they reached Meadow Court, smoke and flames were shooting out of most of the windows. Many of the smaller pieces of furniture, pictures, rugs and articles of clothing which the maids and gardeners had rescued, were strewn over the lawn.

'Hurry hup, Sid,' panted Horace, 'start hup the pump, run out the hose, get a ladder hup to the windows.'

'Horace seems to have got hiccups,' said Hildebrand.

Sid wound away at the starting handle of the pump but nothing happened.

'She don't seem to have no petrol in her,' grunted Sid. 'Didn't you borrow the petrol, Mr. Horace, when you hired a car to take your lady friend to the races?'

Horace remembered that he HAD borrowed the petrol, and blushed, but his face was so red already that it made no difference. However, before he had time to think what to do an angry face appeared at one of the few windows which the fire did not seem to have reached.

'Oh! goodness,' cried one of the maids, 'it's Lady Lochness, we've forgotten all about her. She was having a bath when the fire started and she always falls asleep in her bath.'

Lady Lochness opened the window and indignantly surveyed the scene beneath her.

'What are all these people doing here?' she inquired. 'My garden party is not until next week, Mr. Horace, and I do not like the hat you are wearing, it is most unsuitable. And what are my underclothes doing on the lawn? And somebody seems to be smoking the most disgusting cigarettes. Please, all of you, go away at once. If that red thing is a vacuum cleaner I do not want one and, in any case, I never buy things from pedlars.' And she slammed the window down.

Horace became very agitated.

'We must rescue her himmediately,' he cried.

'She'll be boiled in her bath,' gasped Helen.

Sid and Bert were fumbling with the ladder fastened to the side of the water tank. At last they got it off and put it up to the window. Lady Lochness opened it again.

'I told you to go away,' she croaked furiously, 'what DO you want?'

'The house is on fire, your ladyship,' called up one of the maids.

'Well why did you not say so before,' said Lady Lochness. 'Send for the fire brigade at once.' And she slammed down the window again.

'Somebody had better get up that ladder pretty snappy,'

'Lady Lochness was wearing two firemen's tunics, one as a coat and the other as a pair of trousers.'

commented Bert, 'the bottom part's beginning to catch fire from the flames out of the downstairs windows.'

Nobody seemed anxious to go so Horace suggested they should play 'Heeny, Meeny, Miny Mo' to decide who it should be, but, before they had finished, the window opened again. Lady Lochness seemed to be more exasperated than ever.

'Yes,' she cried, 'the house really does seem to be on fire. The soap has started to melt. Mr. Horace, I must ask you to rescue me. Come and carry me down the ladder at once.'

'I can't, your ladyship, the ladder's on fire.'

'You are a coward,' cried Lady Lochness.

'I must think of my wife and children.'

'You are not married,' cried Lady Lochness.

'But I hope to be one day,' replied Horace, 'and I don't want my children to be orphans.'

'Stop quibbling,' said Lady Lochness furiously, 'the bath has started to boil, my patience is exhausted.'

All this time Hildebrand had been thinking very hard.

'There's only one thing for it,' he announced, 'she'll have to jump. All of you hurry up and collect all the soft things you can find, such as cushions and rugs and grass mowings and all your coats and waistcoats and make them into a heap under the window. Horace is probably softer than anything,' he added, 'but she might think it beneath her dignity to land on Horace.'

Everybody thought this a very good plan and they all took off as many of their clothes as seemed polite, and fetched all the soft things from the lawn. And the gardeners brought barrow loads of lawn mowings until they had an enormous pile.

'Now, your ladyship,' called out Horace, 'hall you have to do is to jump down on to that henormous cushion.'

Lady Lochness contemplated the 'cushion' and looked round at the crowd which, by this time, numbered over a hundred spectators.

'I make one condition,' she said sternly. 'Everybody must promise to turn the other way, close their eyes and count fifty slowly before opening them again.'

Everybody promised and turned round. There was a pause and then a dull thud, then a longer pause while everybody finished counting fifty. When they opened their eyes Lady Lochness was standing there wearing two firemen's tunics, one as a coat and the other as a pair of trousers. She turned to Hildebrand.

'Thank you horse,' she said in her most gracious manner, 'you saved my life. You are a hero.'

And, with a look of scorn at Horace, she marched sedately to the summer house and closed the door.

Helen patted Hildebrand on his neck.

'She ought to supply you with "hextras" for ever and ever,' she said. 'I wonder why we had to count fifty.'

'I expect she'd forgotten her bath towel,' said Hildebrand.

* * *

It was long after tea-time before Helen and Henrietta left the smouldering remains of Meadow Court.

When they reached their garden gate Henrietta stopped and seized Helen by the arms.

'Oh! Helen,' she cried, 'I knew we'd forgotten something. We never went to meet Miss Prisms. Mummy will be furious.'

There was a loud sneeze from one of the upstairs windows.

'Anyway, I picked the right hay-fever flowers,' said Helen.

HAYMAKER

Written and illustrated by
Marion Rivers-Moore

FARMERS GROW all sorts of different crops in their fields; corn both for human beings and for their animals, root crops for humans and animals; things like cabbages and potatoes, also for us as well as beasts; but there is one crop which many people do not think of as a crop at all, which is grown only for animals to feed on. That crop is grass, and in spite of being for animals only, it is the most important crop of all. Although we do not sit down to the table and champ it up by the plateful we do eat grass indirectly, for it has been manufactured by the animals which ate it in its grass form into a form in which we can eat it—milk, butter, meat and so on. That is why grass is so important.

Good grass does not just 'happen'. Those of you who have anything to do with tennis courts will know that. Tennis courts have to be rolled and raked and dressed with lawn sand and you have to crawl about on them digging up dandelions with one of those funny little spuds. Good farmers look after their grass just as carefully. It has been said that a good farmer is a man who 'makes two blades of grass grow where one grew before' and it is very true. He rolls his meadows in the spring; he harrows them to drag out all the moss and coarse dead grasses and he dresses them with fertilizers. He grazes them very scientifically, putting his animals in at just the right time and taking them away to another field as soon as they have eaten the grass close enough. He also grazes the fields with the right kind of animal or mixture of animals. If the grass is tussocky and coarse, cattle will whip their long tongues round it and tear it off so that the new young grass and clovers can come up. Sheep on the other hand, graze very closely with their lips. They will eat a meadow so short that it looks like a lawn, but they must not be left long enough to eat out the hearts of the young clovers which they are apt to do if they gnaw too close. Horses are very bad grazers and fields grazed only by them soon grow rank because they always dung in one place and will not eat the grass there so it soon grows into tough, unappetising tussocks. That is why they keep cattle at horse breeding studs, for they will eat what the horses leave and so keep the paddocks sweet.

Early in the spring the farmer shuts up some of his meadows for hay, and woe betide anyone who goes and romps or plays cricket in one of them! The animals are taken out and the grass is left to grow long. By May it is lush and green and tempting but gradually a silver shimmer spreads across the field as the flower heads of the grasses emerge through the green leaf. When the grass is in full bloom it is ready to be cut. This is usually in early June, the month which we all associate with haymaking. If the weather is kind, in goes the mowing machine, for grass left too long becomes old and tough and the feeding value of the resulting hay will not be so high.

Drawn by horses or tractor, the mower goes round and round the field leaving the grass lying in long ribbons called 'swathes', behind it. There it lies at the mercy of the weather. Will the sun come out and turn it into a sweet-smelling meal fit for the farmer's dairy cows or will it rain and rain and make of it a sodden mush which has to be turned and turned and turned again, giving after all that extra labour, a hay which only really hungry animals will eat at all?

If all goes well, and the sun does come out as it should, the hay will soon be ready for turning. People who have never gone haymaking usually think of it as a serene, picturesque, peaceful occupation. Do not believe a word of it. It may have been so in the days when rows of women in pretty cotton sun-bonnets turned the sweet-smelling swathes with

The farmer's concern is to get the hay into a stack before a heavy shower of rain spoils it. Photo : The Times

those delightful hand-made wooden rakes. Now it is all hustle, bustle and dust and the smell of paraffin and diesel oil is more pungent, though less pleasant, than the smell of the sun-baked herbage. Instead of the picturesque line of women, we see one man with a clever device called a 'swathe-turner'. It consists of a series of rakes mounted on large discs at each end. As the machine is drawn along the discs revolve, causing the rakes to travel sideways, rolling the swathes of hay over as they pass. This, of course, exposes what has formerly been the underside of the swathes to the sun and air, and if the weather continues fine the hay is soon made.

It is now that the hustle and bustle begin. The hay is fit but it is not yet safe and a heavy shower of rain may yet spoil it all. The farmer's concern, therefore, is to get it into a stack as quickly as he possibly can. It is definitely not the moment to call to see him about trivial matters nor to keep him in idle conversation. He would not stop if you tried. As soon as the dew is off the ground he is out in the hay field, and he and his men stay there until dark.

If the weather has been good enough to make the hay properly, there is a better chance now than there used to be of getting it harvested before the rain can spoil it. With modern machinery it does not take long to collect the crop from the field. The latest machine made for this purpose is the 'pick-up baler'. When this is used no rick is built and the whole job can be done by only two men; one drives the tractor which draws the baler round the field and the other comes round with a lorry or tractor and trailer and collects up the bales. The

baler moves slowly along the swathes picking the hay up as it goes. The hay is compressed into long shaped blocks tied with string and pushed out onto the ground leaving the field looking as if some monstrous child playing with bricks had left them strewn about. There are obvious advantages in this method but there are disadvantages too. Unless the hay is absolutely dry it is apt to go mouldy in the tightly compressed bales, and if it is dry enough not to do that it is so brittle when it is picked up that the baler knocks off a lot of the leaf which is the most valuable part of the hay. So you see that there are difficulties even in what looks like a fool-proof job.

Before mechanisation hay used to be collected with forks into cocks and each

cock was pitched by one man to another man on top of a horse-drawn waggon which moved slowly all day long from cock to cock. There is no doubt that hay collected by this laborious method retained more of its leaf and produced a superior sample to most of that made now. But there is not enough labour on the farms today even if the farmer could afford this costly method, so on most farms the hay is brought to the rick by a gadget called a 'hay sweep'. It is attached to the front of a tractor or old car. It has long wooden tines

protected at the ends by metal tips. If you lay your hand on the ground palm upwards, spread out your fingers and push your hand along, you will get exactly the idea of how a hay sweep works. The hay all collects on the tines as the tractor is driven along the swathes. When the sweep is covered the driver takes it to the foot of the elevator at the stack. When the tractor is reversed the tines are drawn out from under the hay and the men by the elevator, fork it in and up it goes to the men on top of the stack. By the time that lot is nearly cleared the tractor and sweep come up with another pile and so it goes on until the field is cleared but for a few little odd bits. To save these bits from being wasted a monstrous rake is drawn up and down over the field. (You can see one in the background of the picture, drawn by a horse.) At regular intervals the tines of this are raised and its load of hay is dropped out. When the rake draws level with the same spot again on its way back across the field, the tines are raised again and in this way the hay is deposited in a long row across the field. Along comes the tractor and sweeps down the row, then up to the elevator once more and the job is done. The rick builder rakes down the sides of his rick and finishes off the top with the odd pitches of hay. It is now ready for the thatcher who will see that it keeps dry so that the animals on the farm have good feed for the winter when the days are cold and short and no grass grows. A bad hay season means a hungry time for them and a worrying time for the men who look after them. No wonder they all work so hard in June and look so anxiously and often at the sky.

Green and White

OR

Red and Blue

by Joseph Natanson

Black is Black and White is White. Stop. You are wrong! A hundred years ago artists discovered that black does not exist, and white is made up of almost any colour. Painting calls for a skilful use of optical illusion.

Blues are most important in this Renoir, 'La Première Sortie'. Reproduced by kind permission of the Tate Gallery.

'Two Little Circus Girls,' by Renoir, is bathed in a glowing golden light. Reproduced by kind permission of the Art Institute of Chicago.

I WAS STILL a small boy when I made the important decision to become an artist. The only one, I think, who was truly pleased about this choice of career was my great-uncle, who rather disliked me. He thought—and, what is worse, never kept this thought to himself—that nothing good would ever come of me anyway.

It was he who, with his usual sneer in my direction, told the story about a painter in Paris, who seeing his white clad son playing in the garden, shouted at him: ' Don't sit on the grass. You will smear the blue of your pants with red! '

' Ha, ha, ha! All artists are mad! ' laughed my uncle.

As my uncle was famous in our family for a complete lack of humour it was not the first time that he laughed alone at what seemed to him an excellent joke. Only when, years afterwards, this little story came back to my memory, did I understand what it was all about. I did not go so far as to think that it was very, very funny, but it was amusing in some way, if only because it was an ' antique ' amongst jokes (jokes become antiques much sooner than furniture does), and I could date the joke just like a work of art.

My great-uncle heard it in Paris about 1870-80 when a group of artists, who had just held their first public exhibition, were being attacked by critics, other artists and the public, who at first laughed at them and later became very angry indeed.

One of the artists had chosen a railway station for his subject. He made a very colourful affair out of it, full of sunshine coming through the steam, and called it ' Impression '. Soon the whole group of artists were scornfully labelled ' Impressionists.'

One has to go deeply into the history of art in the nine-

*Seurat painted this picture entirely with masses of dots, including the border round the edge. It is
'Entrance to the Harbour at Gravelines,' and is reproduced by kind permission of Mrs. R. A. Butler.*

teenth century to understand what all this battle was about. But the really important thing was the fact that the Impressionists won—won because they were Manet, Pissarro, Sisley, Monet, Renoir, Degas, and later on, Seurat, Gauguin, Van Gogh and Cézanne. Everybody knows these names, for they are the greatest painters of the nineteenth century, and some of them are amongst the greatest artists who ever lived. It is also important to us that, for the first time in history, artists stated openly facts which, although they shocked their contemporaries so much, were known a long time before by the great masters.

They stated that the subject in itself cannot be good or bad, beautiful or ugly. Only the result—the painting—can be good or bad. For instance, it does not seem very logical to choose a foggy day on which to go with canvas and easel, paints and brushes, to the riverside to paint a panorama of a town. And yet it was in such conditions that Monet made a view of the Thames with Charing Cross Bridge which gives the most convincing sense of reality, even though all the forms are blurred in the fog. Moreover, the fog, far from being dull and grey, is in all colours, made from the vibration of clear blues, greens, pinks, purples and yellows, dabbed energetically all over the painting.

The Impressionists believed that there is no local colour in nature. Even if there is some—because when we say, 'Jean has a red frock,' we know very well what we mean, it cannot be represented as such in painting because Jean's red frock is in reality red plus all the light playing

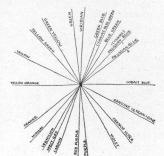

on it from all sides over the folds. As a painter has only the resources of his flat canvas, on which the light falls evenly, the frock will, if painted in one shade of red, be dull and flat. To give the red life, he has to create a vibration either by different colours in the red itself or by contrast with other colours close to it.

What all the Impressionists did by intuition and sensitivity, Seurat worked out as a scientific theory. I have copied for you in English his 'wheel' of complementary colours, which gives automatically on each line crossing the centre those pairs of colours which when contrasted show the maximum intensity. With amazing precision Seurat covered the whole surface of his canvas with minute dots of pure colours, which at a distance merge in the eye of the spectator and create an impression of colour and light.

In the painting reproduced here there is not much to look at when it is printed in black and white. Half of it is sand and the houses are not very spectacular. Yet this is a very wonderful painting in original. As you can see the dots clearly, you can imagine the rest and understand Seurat's technique. Each dot is of a very pure colour, and all of them together make the sand and the houses and the sky glow with sunshine. One almost has the impression that the air is moving, as it sometimes does on a very hot day. Seurat was so conscientious in making every inch of his painting fully active in the general effect that he usually painted a narrow border around it so as to prevent any accidental vibration between the edge of the painting and a frame which might be 'out of tune.'

This border is also, of course, composed of small dots which merge into a general effect of blue, but when seen closer its composition changes as we follow it around the painting. Against the yellow of the sand there are different

You can almost feel the sun and smell the sea, yet how simply has Manet achieved this using shadows and contrasting tones. Reproduced by kind permission of the Hon. Mrs. A. E. Pleydell-Bouverie.

tones of blue, against the grass (in the left corner) there are red dots amongst the blue, which disappear when the border touches sand again. Then green appears when we are in the vicinity of the houses with red roofs, and yellow dots are in great number when the border is near the blue sky. As you see, Seurat was following his wheel exactly.

The Impressionists believed that black does not exist in nature and therefore they removed black from their palettes. Similarly, white is rarely pure white in nature as it absorbs and reflects all other surrounding colours.

The public, accustomed to the very detailed and smooth paintings of academic masters, were naturally shocked by the rough surface of the Impressionist paintings and surprised to find, when looking closely at the painting, so much red in the green of the grass and so much blue in the white of a child's dress. Now you see the explanation of my uncle's antique joke.

MID-JUNE

Mid-June is the lucent
  And cool time o' year
When ash is in full leaf
  And barley in ear,
And roses in full-blow
  And every ash-wand
The greenest, the greenest
  In all the woodland.

The nightingale sapphired
  Dark mid-nights of May,
But black-caps remember
  And flute all the day;
The ash takes her own time
  To come to full green,
And all the proud courtiers
  Must wait on the queen.

The cuckoo's throat alters,
  Her going is near
When ash is in full-leaf
  And barley in ear,
And black-caps in full song
  And every ash-wand
The greenest, the greenest
  In all the woodland

S. OAKLEY HEATHCOTE

The moral of the Impressionist story is far more important than the usual story of the public who cannot immediately understand the natural originality which is the attribute of the great artist.

Even though it will soon be a hundred years since the movement started and it is time to treat Monet, Renoir, Cézanne and Van Gogh as old masters, nobody seems to call them so and still there are many people who consider them modern.

After all, they are still very modern, as all contemporary art sprang out of their creative activity. Whether you wish to be an artist or only to understand art, you have to learn the teaching of the Impressionists who, at the time when photography was born, discovered that colour and the vibration of colour can produce a much more convincing reality than mechanical reproduction does.

At first, drunk with the joy of being able to capture the most subtle moods of nature, they painted sunshine and fog, spring and winter, reflections in the water, and passing clouds. Visions of great beauty lasting for only a moment were held on canvas for ever. Recreating the world all over again, they could not leave man out of it, and human beings appear in the impressionistic landscape to live their lives of colour and light. The artist followed the man into his house, into the street, into his everyday life. He was with him, too, when he was enjoying himself in the theatre, in the circus. . . .

Whatever he paints, the contemporary artist remembers, as the Impressionists taught him, that the paint on the canvas itself gives us immense pleasure according to the way in which the colours are distributed, in harmony or contrast, spread smoothly, or dabbed on vigorously to make a rough surface as pleasant to the eye as a carpet. He knows that he will arouse our interest by unexpected colour 'situations' and a 'plot' of the forms which make his composition. And at last he knows that we are much more interested in his vision which can make us see things that we would otherwise never have noticed or thought of, rather than in his mechanical ability to reproduce what we can see for ourselves and record with a camera.

ILLUSTRATED BY WILLIAM STOBBS

BIGGLES in Arabia

by CAPTAIN W. E. JOHNS

PART FOUR

UNAWARE of Ginger's desperate plight Biggles walked on, keeping close behind Zahar who automatically took the lead. They kept to the bottom of the wadi, which now became broad and shallow, rather than risk exposing themselves now that they were drawing near to their destination. The Sultan's men, said Zahar, might be moving about, collecting fodder for their animals, or perhaps looking for one that had strayed.

Several times as they advanced Biggles passed his tongue over his lips, puzzled by a slight stickiness that formed on them. This had, moreover, a peculiar spicy taste, although not altogether unpleasant. Curiously enough, he did not connect this with the water he had tasted. Even when, a little later, he experienced a momentary twinge of nausea, he put it down to an adulterant in the condensed meat paste, a tin of which he had opened from the store carried in the aircraft. He recalled that Ginger had eaten rather more of it, while Zahar had had none, such viands being forbidden by his religion. The implication was too obvious to be overlooked. Ginger, he was now convinced was suffering from food poisoning, and he regretted that he had left him. Indeed, for a moment or two he contemplated going back, but having got so near the objective it seemed a pity to return without so much as a glance at the enemy camp. Rather worried he walked on, wishing that he couud move as silently as did Zahar over the loose stones.

The first sign that they were nearing their journey's end came when, from no great distance ahead a donkey brayed.

'We have arrived at El Moab.' announced Zahar in a low voice. 'What is your intention, Sahib, remembering that we are now in the hands of Allah—may he be glorified?'

'My intention is to find out what happened here,' answered Biggles. 'In particular, I would know if it was to this place that Hamud brought the seeds that were gathered in the Wadi al Arwat. If there is danger I will go on alone, so that should evil befall me you can go back and carry the tidings to my friends.'

'Wallah! Am I a jackal to be hiding in a wadi when there is men's work to be done?' protested Zahar. 'I know my way about this place, so surely it is better that I should go with you?'

Biggles did not argue the point. 'As you wish,' he agreed. 'Upon your own head be it.'

'May my face be blackened if I fail you,' said Zahar. 'Let us go on. This is a thing to be remembered.'

'You never said a truer word,' averred Biggles, whose feet were aching from the rough going.

He made his way cautiously to the lip of the wadi and looked over. From the elevated position thus gained he could see a good deal more than had been possible from the depression, for the wadi took a sharp turn, so that he was on a sort of saddle-back, with the ground falling away both behind and in front of him. It seemed that the wadi, as it made the bend, also opened out somewhat, and it was in the shallow basin thus formed that the huts and tents of El Moab had been erected.

Biggles spent some time studying the lay-out of the place. There were two or three huts in the manner of a small military camp. One was fairly large. It was, explained Zahar, who had joined him, the house in which the manager lived. A huddle of black native tents stood a little distance beyond. Here, too, were some camels and donkeys, not tethered, but wandering at will. What lay beyond the basin was not evident, for the wadi closed up again to a narrow rocky defile. It was across this, apparently, that a dam had been built, for above it, through a low place in the bank, moonlight glinted on a fairly extensive sheet of water.

Having completed his inspection of the general features of the place, Biggles moved on again, now with the utmost caution, with Zahar, dagger in hand, close by his side. Gradually the picture became more clearly defined. A smouldering camp fire came into view as someone blew on the embers, making it possible to see the outline of some natives who were seated around it. Others moved dimly in the background, near the animals. Moonlight revealed an object which, had Biggles not been prepared for it, would have caused astonishment. It was an aircraft which he identified as a Moth, presumably the one that had been seen in the air. It now had a cover over the engine cowling and the wings and tail had been anchored with sandbags. In that position, apparently, it had weathered the *haboob*. A faint, rather sickly yet aromatic aroma had become perceptible.

Biggles touched his companion on the arm and said softly: ' What can I smell? '

ROGER BACON

by Nicholas Woolley (10½)

Roger Bacon
Was terribly clever.
People who knew him
Said ' Well I never.'
His friends and relations
Were sorely perplexed,
For no one knew what
He'd be thinking of next.
Day after day
He'd be scheming, devising
And thinking of stunts
That were new and surprising,
His workshop was littered
With test tubes and phials
And corks without bottles
And clocks without dials.
He collected the gas
That escaped from the meter
And mixed it with sulphur
And sand and saltpetre.
And if, as oft' happened,
One fine summer morning
His neighbours were wakened
Without any warning
By bangs and explosions
That deafened them (nearly)
And broke all their chimneys
And windows, they merely
Said ' Very unpleasant
But no use lamenting
It's just Roger Bacon
He's busy inventing.'

' Hashish,' answered the Arab. He pointed to a long low hut that stood beside the rivulet that meandered down the centre of the wadi. ' That is the house where the hashish is made,' he went on.

As the camp seemed to have settled down for the night Biggles went on again, warily, with eyes alert for danger. He did not at first go down into the wadi, but remained just below the lip, taking care not to show himself against the sky-line. The lake that was the reservoir came into view, and, at the nearer end, the dam that held the water in check. This was higher than he had supposed it to be, a matter of nearly twenty feet, which gave a clear indication of the considerable amount of water thus made available, although this would naturally diminish as the dry season advanced. The irrigation channels that carried the water to the land under cultivation could also be seen. This comprised most of the ground in the bottom of the wadi not occupied by buildings.

Towards this area he now made his way, although as far as he could see there was not a crop of any sort. In a whisper he asked Zahar what he thought about it.

The Arab said that he thought there had recently been a crop of the hemp from which hashish is derived. This had been cut, and was now, judging from the smell, in the drying-room. No doubt the aeroplane had arrived to transport some of the finished product to Egypt.

Biggles soon learned all he needed to know. The hemp crop had been harvested. That is to say, the leaves had been gathered and the unwanted stalks left on the ground. In one place, however, the earth had been cleared, tilled, and close investigation showed that a new crop had just been planted. The plants were small, and they were not hemp. They were gurra, in the form of seedlings a few inches high, about a foot apart. Biggles pulled up one of the seedlings and held it to his nose. That settled any doubt. The area concerned covered perhaps half an acre.

Now the difficulty of destroying such a crop was at once apparent. The plants were too spindly to burn collectively as they grew, even if they had developed enough rosin to make them inflammable. The alternative appeared to be, as he had said, to pull them out of the ground one by one; but it was unlikely that such an operation could be carried out in one session. Many hours of time would be required.

Considering the matter, it occurred to Biggles that cultivation in the wadi could only exist by irrigation. It followed that if the water supply failed the ground would dry out in a few hours, and the burning sun would consume the seedlings as effectively as if they had been thrown on a bonfire. The thing to destroy, then, was the water supply, and this appeared to offer no great difficulty. One well-placed charge of explosive in the dam would do all that was necessary. Even if the dam were repaired it would take a long time for such a quantity of water, as was now in the reservoir, to accumulate again. Discussing the matter with Zahar, the Arab gave it as his opinion that the trickle of water in the bottom of the wadi would dry up altogether before the end of the hot season. The rains were now past. It would not rain again for many months.

That, really, was as much as Biggles wanted to know. It was Nicolo Ambrimos, the Sultan of Aden, who was trafficking in the new narcotic. It must have been he who had sent Hamud into the desert to collect seeds of the plant, and murder his companions so that there could be no witness. It was he who was now growing a large stock of gurra at El Moab. All Biggles wanted was the explosive, and that could soon be obtained in Aden, or from the nearest Royal Engineers' Depot.

Well satisfied with his night's work he crept away as silently as he had approached. All that remained to be done was to collect Ginger and get home.

If it turned out that Ginger was really ill, a serious complication would arise, for it would be no easy matter to get him back to the aircraft. With this thought on his mind it was almost at a run, that, once clear of the camp, he returned to the spot where Ginger had been left. Reaching it he stopped, looking about him.

'Ginger,' he said quietly.

There was no answer.

'Ginger, where are you?' he said again, raising his voice slightly.

Still no answer.

Biggles looked at Zahar. 'This is where we left him, isn't it?'

'This is the place,' confirmed Zahar.

Biggles made a swift circle round the area, calling Ginger by name. But there was no response. He returned to Zahar. 'I don't understand this,' he said in a puzzled voice.

'He is not here.'

'I can see that.'

'He went away.'

'He would not go away because I told him to remain here, and he obeys my orders,' declared Biggles.

'Then he was taken by force,' stated Zahar.

'But that could not happen without noise. If he were attacked he would fight. There were no sounds of fighting.'

'He may have been captured while he slept,' offered Zahar.

'In which case, surely he would have been taken to El Moab, and we should have heard talking and shouting?' argued Biggles. He bit his lip, utterly at a loss to understand what could have happened.

Zahar dropped on his hands and knees and began examining the ground closely. He found the place where Ginger had lain, and a moment later sucked in his breath with a sharp hiss. 'There is no God but God!' he gasped, in a voice of wonder.

'What is it?' asked Biggles tersely.

'Here he was sick.'

'What about it?'

'He was sick because he had eaten hashish,' declared Zahar.

Biggles did not answer for a moment. 'Nonsense!' he exclaimed.

'He had eaten hashish, Sahib,' repeated Zahar. 'I know this because I smell it. It is a smell not easily forgotten.'

'But where could he get the stuff?' asked Biggles, in a voice not far from exasperation.

'God is the knower.'

Zahar was still prowling about. 'That is the way he went,' he averred, pointing a brown finger towards the desert. 'I see his footmarks. The sands cannot lie. The hashish had deprived him of his senses.'

'But tell me this, O Zahar. Where could he get hashish?' cried Biggles desperately.

Suddenly Zahar stood erect and slapped a hand on his thigh. He went quickly to the water hole, and, plunging in his hand, raised the liquid to his nostrils. 'It was here,' he said simply. 'He drank hashish.'

'You mean there's hashish in the water?'

'Without a doubt. This water passes through El Moab. In the water has been washed the sheets on which the hashish was dried. That is the answer.'

'So that's it,' agreed Biggles wearily. 'I drank a little

'Pistol in hand, Biggles rose slowly to his feet, ready for action.'

and it made me feel sick. He drank more. What would be the effect?'

Said Zahar: 'For a time he will feel ill. His brain will be in two pieces. He will wander about. Then he will fall down and sleep for many hours.'

For two hours or more they searched diligently, but without success, or any hope of it. The moon set, and utter darkness descended on the wilderness.

Biggles pulled up, baffled, impotent. To find an unconscious body in such country, in the dark, was manifestly a hopeless task. 'There is only one way I shall be able to find him,' he decided. 'I will return with the aeroplane. When daylight comes, by flying low and covering much ground quickly, I shall see him.' He could think of no alternative, although such a course would, he feared, ruin his plan. It would be impossible to fly so near El Moab without being seen, or at any rate, heard. That, inevitably, would put the camp on the alert. But there was no other way. Whatever the result, he could not abandon Ginger.

'There is nothing more we can do here,' he said. 'Let us go.' He turned his face towards aerodrome 137.

It was a long walk back. The night died with tardy reluctance. Just before dawn, although he did not see it, he heard a light aeroplane purring its way overhead. Its course was from south to north, so he concluded that it was the Moth, now on its way to a rendezvous with a load of hashish. At length the night died. Dawn became day. They plodded on. The sun rose higher and resumed its relentless scorching of the tired earth. Zahar said not a word. It was life as he understood it, and, doubtless, life as God wished it to be.

With the airfield almost in sight the silence was suddenly broken by a shot and a bullet kicked up the sand a yard in front of Biggles's feet. He dropped flat instantly, as did Zahar, for the attack was entirely unexpected.

He was by no means sure of the direction whence the shot had come. Neither was Zahar. When it was not repeated, Biggles crawled to the top of the nearest rise. Not a soul was in sight! On all sides lay the wilderness, dreary and forlorn in its dark sterility. Pistol in hand,

'With a quick intake of breath, he whipped out a revolver and fired over the top of the fuselage.'

Biggles rose slowly to his feet, ready for action. Nothing happened.

'Come, O Zahar,' he said in a tired voice. 'Let us go on.'

In the meantime, while events had been shaping themselves around El Moab, Bertie had not been free from anxiety. He was afraid that Biggles and Ginger had been caught by the *haboob*.

There had been no difficulty about getting the sabotaged aircraft repaired and he had no intention of being left out of anything that was going forward on the other side of the Red Sea, over which he was soon flying with a song on his lips.

The ditty died abruptly when he observed the sandstorm sweeping across his front, blotting out both land and sky. He was too experienced a pilot to commit the folly of trying to fly over it. So for a time he flew up and down, keeping at a safe distance from the storm, watching the sky for Biggles's machine, which he fully expected to see coming back. His anxiety grew as time passed without any sign of it, and he was at last compelled reluctantly to accept the explanation that Biggles had been caught on the ground, too far inside the path of the storm to escape from it. There was nothing he could do about it while the sand persisted in the atmosphere, so as his petrol was running low he had no choice but to return to Aden.

Thereafter all he could do was kill time on the aerodrome until the atmospheric conditions returned to normal. That Biggles was down was now certain, for he had long exceeded his petrol capacity. Bertie was concerned about the safety of Biggles and Ginger but he was not seriously alarmed.

With the sabotaging of Biggles's machine still fresh in his mind he decided to spend the night in the cockpit rather than risk a repetition of the trouble. And in view of what happened it seemed likely that such a plot was projected. Having dined in the R.A.F. mess as a guest, during which time he thought the machine would be safe as there were still airmen moving about, he returned to the hangar in which the machine had been parked for the night. There he sat down to wait for the morning.

After the airfield had settled down for the night he moved his position to a softer seat in the cockpit. He knew, of course, that a headquarters guard would not prevent a determined intruder from getting in. As the war revealed, to guard an entire airfield against trespassers, by reason of its extent, requires more men than can normally be made available.

The machine was parked facing the open entrance, which he was thus able to watch. The time passed slowly, as it always does in such circumstances, and he was half regretting that he had imposed upon himself such a tiresome task, when, just before dawn, silhouetted against the moonlight, he saw a native figure slip silently and stealthily round the corner. The inside of the hangar was, of course, in pitch darkness, so that it was not possible to see what the man was doing. Afraid that some mischief might be done before he could prevent it, Bertie started to get out; but the Arab must have seen him, or heard a movement, for he bolted. He hurried to the entrance but the intruder had disappeared.

The stars were now paling in the sky so Bertie made no attempt to rest for fear of oversleeping. In any case, his anxiety about Biggles and Ginger was such that he was in no mood to relax. So he made ready to take off.

By the time the false dawn was lighting the east with its pallid glow he was in the air, on a course for aerodrome 137, the only definite objective that he knew. Crossing the narrow arm of the Red Sea, he began in the growing light to scan the ground in case Biggles had been forced down by engine trouble, a likely enough event should the machine have been exposed, even for a short time, to the dust laden air. But he saw nothing of it, and in due course made out the weather-worn fabric hangars of the abandoned airfield. After flying round it once or twice he landed to see if there were any signs of Biggles's occupation. He observed that two of the hangars were pretty well flat, so he wasted no time on them. The other was somewhat askew, but he taxied his machine into it to keep out of sight while he looked around.

All he found was the stub of a recently-smoked cigarette, of the brand which Biggles habitually used. It was not much, but it did at least tell him that Biggles had landed there; and had, moreover, been there after the

(Continued on page 197)

Penny and The China Dog

by SHEILA M. GODFREY

ILLUSTRATED BY J. M. FRENCH

EVERY DAY on her way home from school Penny paused at the corner of the High Street and gazed into the antique dealer's. It was dark and gloomy, with odd pieces of furniture and piles of dusty books. Old-fashioned paintings lay propped against the walls, and the window ledge was crammed with knick-knacks and ornaments of all kinds. But Penny was only interested in the China Dog.

He sat alone, with pale sad eyes, and looked so miserable and forlorn that she longed to take him in her arms and comfort him, and smooth away the dust that lay upon his painted red-gold hair. Sometimes she tried to cheer him by whispering through the window, but then the glass would grow steamy where her small nose pressed against it, and she would lose sight of him completely.

Then Penny's big brother had his 15th birthday, and went to work in the greengrocer's. At the end of his first week, he proudly presented her with two shillings.

It was a great day for Penny. She had never owned so much in her whole life. She went straight to the antique shop and ventured inside for the first time. The antique dealer was about to go home.

'Oh no! Not you again, is it?' he asked wearily, shaking his head. 'Why don't you go home and play with your dolls? You'll have people talking, you know—always round here. It isn't nice.'

'I haven't any dolls,' said Penny timidly. 'Please, I've come to spend this.'

The antique dealer roared with laughter. 'Lor' bless my soul,' he cried, 'and what do you think you can buy with that?' Then, as Penny's face dropped, 'Here, you run along.'

But Penny shook her head miserably, and two large tears began to trickle down her face. 'It's him,' she said. 'I don't want anything else.'

The dealer picked up the China Dog by the neck and turned him upside down, so that Penny caught her breath in alarm.

'Genuine antique,' he said. 'Worth quite a lot of money.'

Penny took the China Dog and held him cold against her flushed, burning face. And she sniffed audibly. The dealer was moved, and hated himself for it.

'Here, give me the two shillings,' he said crossly. 'And if you ever come round here again, I'll fetch the police to you. And you can tell your mother I said so.'

Without a word, Penny fled.

'Coo, what a waste!' said her big brother. 'You won't catch me giving you money again. It's even got eyebrows! Whoever saw a dog with eyebrows!'

But Penny did not care. She rubbed her cheek tenderly against the China Dog and told him not to listen. 'You're the most beautiful dog in the world,' she whispered. And she was almost certain she heard him chink with gratitude.

Every night after that Penny took the China Dog to bed with her, and hugged him until he was quite, quite warm.

Before she went to sleep Penny told the China Dog all that had happened during the day: what she had done at school and what she had seen on her way home. And gradually the China Dog began to talk back, and his eyes grew less sad and lonesome. He told her wonderful tales of the antique dealer's—how each night the copper kettle used to raise his lid to the warming-pan, and the rocking-chair go backwards and forwards to the ticking of the grandfather clock.

Penny listened spellbound to all he had to say, but when she told her mother that the China Dog spoke to her, she was reproved for not telling the truth: things were bad enough as they were, said her mother, without Penny adding to their troubles.

It was true that things were still difficult at home. Even with the extra money from Penny's big brother, they often went to bed hungry, and their clothes were worn and darned beyond recognition.

One day, when she arrived home, Penny found her mother more anxious than usual. 'They're coming for the rent again tomorrow,' she was telling her big brother. 'There's nothing for it now, but to sell the furniture. When that's gone, I don't know what we shall do.'

Penny climbed into bed shivering and wretched. She hugged the China Dog even more tightly than usual, and recounted her troubles to him. His pale eyes were full of sympathy, and it was some time before he spoke.

'Listen, Penny, very carefully,' he said at last, in his strange, tinkling voice. 'Pay attention to what I say and all your troubles will come to an end. Penny, you must take me into the garden and break me. It won't hurt.'

'Oh no, no,' whispered Penny. 'Not that. You're the only friend I have.' The tears ran down her face and splashed on to his head. 'It's the only way,' he told her sadly. But she shook her head, and clutched him to her.

Next morning, when her mother called her, Penny placed the China Dog on the window-sill as usual. She was nearly dressed when her big brother came racing up the stairs and past the door. The China Dog shivered and fell to the ground, crashing into a thousand pieces.

And the morning sun lit up the fragments, and golden sovereigns rolled across the floor.

But Penny could not bear to look. She buried her face in her pillow and bit her lips to stop the tears from rising.

Yet there was to be a happy ending after all, for less than a week later, as Penny lay awake in bed, the door opened and a tiny face pushed round. It was a spaniel face, with big yellow eyes and golden hair. Penny sat up and gasped.

'He's all yours, Pen,' said her big brother. 'We're rich now, you know.' And he lifted the long-legged puppy on to the bed. He was warm and soft and wriggly. 'Like the China Dog come real!' cried Penny.

His long pink tongue shot out to lick her face.

THE WORLD'S FASTEST

by Hubert Redmill

Speed has long held a wonderful fascination for all of us, and a comparison between different creatures, including human beings, is very interesting. Unfortunately it is very difficult to time animals, birds, etc., in their wild state, and so there is some doubt as to which is really the quickest, especially amongst the insects. You will therefore realise that the figures given here are only approximate. A glance at the scale will show you how slow we human beings are when compared to the animal world, unless we use some mechanical means to carry us.

ANIMAL. Looking very much like its larger cousin, the Leopard, a Cheetah differs in that it has rather longer legs, and a smaller and more rounded head. It can easily be tamed and used for hunting.

BIRD. Swift, yes, the very name of this bird explains its chief characteristic, also it has great manœuvrability, necessary because it feeds upon insects whilst on the wing.

INSECT. Here we show a beautiful Hawk Moth which can fly at about 30 m.p.h. Some authorities believe that species of dragon-fly or horsefly have greater speed, but it is doubtful if the very high speeds sometimes claimed are correct.

FISH. The title 'The fastest of all fish' is well deserved by the beautifully streamlined Swordfish, which is much respected by deep sea fishermen for the game fight it puts up when taken on the line.

RUNNER. By running Man first experienced the thrill of speed, long before he learnt to ride horses or build cars and aeroplanes. The speed given in our scale is only achieved by the best of athletes.

SWIMMER. As Man is not in his natural element when swimming he cannot expect to put up a performance comparable with fish, so the speed of just over 4 m.p.h. is not so bad as it appears at first sight.

ompared with the universe, hbound speeds are low. The h itself is calculated to revolve 18½ miles per second. Light els very swiftly, at 186,325 s per second, but sound is h slower, and in fact some planes are now described as ersonic ' or faster than sound.

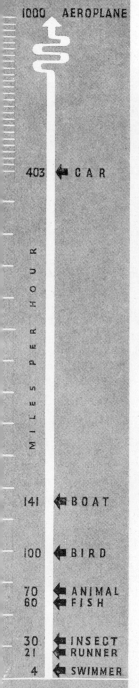

1000 AEROPLANE

403 ← CAR

MILES PER HOUR

141 ← BOAT

100 ← BIRD

70 ← ANIMAL
60 ← FISH

30 ← INSECT
21 ← RUNNER
4 ← SWIMMER

One of the most difficult and dangerous of tests is breaking the world's water speed record. Here we see the late Sir Malcolm Campbell in ' Bluebird II ' streaking across Lake Coniston at 141 m.p.h. This boat, which broke the record in 1939, has since been equipped with a de Havilland Goblin II jet engine which has further increased its speed.

John Cobb's ' Railton Mobil Special,' shown here breaking the high speed record on the salt flats at Utah, U.S.A., is one of the most beautifully streamlined of cars. It has enclosed wheels, cockpit and a body tapering to a fine point. Twin Napier-Lion aero engines of 1,250 h.p. have given it a speed of over 400 m.p.h., a very fine performance.

With the development of the jet engine the high speed record was successively broken by both British and American aircraft.

At the time of going to press, the official world's record is held by a standard North American F-86A flying at 671 m.p.h. This record has, however, been shattered several times unofficially by rocket propelled aeroplanes, and although the speeds reached are strictly hush-hush, we can safely assume that these are somewhere near 1000 m.p.h.

N

LOBSTERS AND CRABS

by ' Camera Talks '

Overnight the engine is made ready.

Bait is cut up and prepared.

Before dawn the fisherman sets out from shore.

Towards the end of October lobster fishers collect the willows they need for their baskets. They may need to make as many as fifty or more each season, for it is quite usual for many to be lost if the weather has been really bad and the lines broken. Care must be taken, for if you are able to put two fingers in the space between sticks, that is enough for a lobster to squeeze through and escape.

The fishing season begins in earnest in April. Each afternoon as much of the preparation as can be, is done for the next day. The tanks of the boat's engine must be filled with oil and petrol. Buckets of bait are prepared by cutting up dabs, plaice, gurnets, skate, dog fish, herrings and mackerel. Lobsters and crabs live on fish, and are lured through the necks of the lobster ' pots ' to reach the tempting morsel fixed on a piece of stick placed well in the middle of the basket. If it were placed near the side, the lobster would reach through the basket work and help itself to a succulent meal without danger.

Early bed is the fisherman's watch-word, for he must be up and off by 3.30 in the morning. It is still dark when he pushes off. Dawn breaks as he nears the stretch of sea where a line of bobbing corks mark his baskets.

Fishing grounds are open to all, but it takes experience and a watchful eye, to know where to lay your lines. If a ground has been fished over, it may be

He pushes the boat down the pebbly beach and sails away while it is still dark.

The lobster ground is seven miles out.   It is light by the time he reaches his line of floats.

The fisherman's livelihood.   He handles crabs and lobsters without concern, re-baits the basket and throws it overboard.

The position of the fishing ground is carefully checked and remembered.

Thirty fathoms of line to be pulled in for each heavy, wet basket.

His corks are specially marked so that none will interfere with his lines.

Beaching his craft on return. There is no harbour here.

'Fresh lobsters—caught this morning.' An average morning's catch is 20 lbs.

This winch is used to haul up the boat. In fine weather there are often extra helping hands.

nearly exhausted, and you must move off to a new stretch of water, until you strike lucky once more. The baskets are lowered on thirty fathom lines. A fathom measures six feet. Five are placed together, their position being marked by corks. Each fisherman has his own identification mark on his corks, and there is a strict code that no one else will tamper with them. Some boats drop off as many as seventy baskets, others between thirty and forty.

An average morning's catch will be about 20 lbs. of lobsters, for which the fisherman will probably be paid 3s. a lb. But there may be long stretches when he cannot go out to sea because of bad weather. Then he risks losing valuable baskets in rough seas, as well as having to go without his earnings until he can go out once more.

Then he will haul the baskets in and empty out his catch. Sometimes this includes whiting and conger eels, as well as crabs and lobsters. When each basket has been examined, re-baited

and the lines re-laid, he will bring his morning's catch in to shore, where it is weighed and sold.

After nine or ten hours' work (remember he started at 3.30 a.m.,) the fisherman's day is not yet done. He has his luncheon, and then returns to the beach, to repair damaged lines and baskets, check over his boat, and get the bait ready for the next morning's departure.

So it goes from April until the end of September. After that rough weather may make the risk of damage to his tackle greater than the possible value of a catch. Then is the time for trawling. With huge weighted nets, the sea bed is dragged, and fish scooped up. Nowadays it is quite common for bits from the wreckage of ships and planes to be hauled up too.

Summer time is the most profitable season for the lobster fisherman, as well as being the pleasantest. Although he may not make big profits, once having tasted the life, he would not exchange it for any other.

It is a good life, but a hard one. The fisherman sails out in all weathers. He has good days and bad. Here he shows his catch, and yarns with his mates. Today was a good day!

THE HOSTAGE

by Klaxon

Aloysius Knightshead put first things first. The bull terrier needed him more than did the tearful new boy, hiding under the railway seat. The Head Master might have thought otherwise, but two men in purple coats confused the issue.

THE LAST DAYS of the holidays were, like the last days of the previous term, spoiled for Lousy by the arrival of letters.

The first one, written by the Head Master to Colonel Knightshead suggested that the boy should not join the school train in London but should make the shorter cross-country journey in order to pick up a new boy whose parents were unable to take him to London.

'It seems,' wrote the Head, 'that the mother is delicate and the father is abroad. The boy (his name is Mackintosh) will be seen off at *Chorley Station* by the family lawyer, a Mr. Banks. He will be wearing the school cap. Aloysius, of course, will be wearing his, so there should be no trouble over recognition. Please tell him to put his head out of the window when the train reaches Chorley.

'I understand that Mackintosh, who is an only child, is reluctant to go to school, so it would be as well for Aloysius to help him to make the best of it, and not be more silent than he must.'

Lousy sighed as he returned the letter to his father. The London train reached the school station a good hour earlier than the other one. That meant that the best desks and lockers would be bagged by other people, and that there would be no chance of the corner bed by the big window that opened almost on to the Yew tree where Jackdaws nested Spring after Spring.

'Oh, Lou, darling, it shows how the Head Master relies on you, doesn't it?'

Lousy did not answer his mother. He knew there are some things no woman can understand.

The next day a letter came from Mrs. Mackintosh to Mrs. Knightshead. In it she explained that her Cecil was highly-strung and sensitive, that they were all in all to each other, and that he had 'a lovely nature'.

'Please,' she begged, 'please, please ask your little boy to be kind to my little boy. He is such a tiny little chap —small even for nine years old. We shall say our good-byes at home but I am afraid that Cecil, brave as he is, may be a little tearful in the train. Tell your little boy that there will be several clean handkerchiefs in his coat pocket.'

'Lumme!' said Lousy, awed not so much by the thought of the tears as by the thought of several clean pocket-handkerchiefs.

'I think he sounds bats,' remarked his sister Cordelia. 'Shall you hit him if he cries?'

'That's only in books.'

'Just jeer and sneer, I s'pose?' pursued Lousy's sister. The boy did not answer her. He was thinking that if this Cecil HAD to cry (not, of course, that Lousy would do anything to make him more miserable) it might be convenient, since his whimperings would drown any squeakings of the white rats with whom he proposed to travel. He

had discovered in the past that fellow-passengers were liable to be narrow-minded about live-stock.

The last day came. Lousy only just caught the train. This was because he had let one of the rats out for an airing and the creature had taken a fancy to the station. True the guard waited while the rat was stowed back into its travelling box, but there was no time to choose an empty carriage.

'In you get!' ordered his father, 'don't forget to look out at Chorley Station.'

'Be kind to the little boy, darling,' begged his mother.

'You needn't give Mr. Manders my love,' shrilled Cordelia, 'but you can if you think it'll make him kinder to you. Goodbye, Lou!'

'Goodbye!' shouted Lousy and then the movement of the train jerked him into a corner seat.

Two men sat opposite to him. They both wore purplish coloured coats with widely padded shoulders. Their hair was unpleasantly long and rather oily. One was dark, and the other was fairish. One was rather more spotty than the other but the skin of their faces reminded Lousy of the skin of some fungus that has been grown underground in a dank cellar. He did not like their flashy ties or restless eyes or anything about them. His own eyes, trained by bird-watching, took in all these details automatically. He did not want to look at them. He wanted to finish reading *Dead Man's Rock,* but something about them puzzled him, though he was not naturally inquisitive except about animal life.

'Very lower animal life!' thought Lousy, and decided to move into one of the corner seats. Yes, that was what was queer.

Usually when there are three people in a carriage there is only one spare corner seat. But these two men were sitting side by side, sharing a thick furry rug that covered all their knees and extended further along the seat where it was kept in place by an attaché case. Yet the heating was full on, and it was warm in the carriage—a good deal too warm for Lousy.

He took off his cap, tucked his mackintosh more closely over the rats' box and carried it to one of the corner seats on the corridor side of the train. He had just found his place in *Dead Man's Rock* when the darker of his two companions spoke.

'You don't want to catch 'flu, do you, old chap?'

'Yes!' said Lousy, speaking straight from his heart.

'Flu, or any other infectious disease caught during term-time meant peace in the sanatorium and plenty of time for reading.

'I don't quite get that,' said the man, and his companion added, 'I've just had a shocking bout of 'flu. Oughtn't to be out of bed really. I shouldn't like to pass it on to anybody else.'

'There's plenty of room in the other carriages,' announced the man who had spoken first.

'I never get 'flu or anything,' replied Lousy, and added, ' worse luck! '

He half-thought of moving back into the other seat so as to give any wandering germs a shorter way to travel but, though not fussy about things like caterpillars in handkerchiefs and over-ripe specimens for experiments in taxidermy, he decided he would rather make a home for germs from a rag-and-bone man than from the people on the opposite seat.

If he could find an empty carriage he could let the rats out for a run as soon as the ticket-collector had been round.

He opened the door leading to the corridor. Then, just for a moment he thought he was at home again, and that Raffles, the big white bull-terrier, who could not bear solitude, had found himself on the wrong side of a door, and was howling out his need of human company.

The reek of train-smoke, drifting in through an open window, reminded him where he was, but the howling of the dog continued.

It WAS a bull-terrier, and it was chained to a staple in the almost empty luggage-van that separated the dining compartment from the rest of the train. A muzzle, that might *just* have fitted a Pekingese, dangled from its collar. Lousy smiled approvingly; he knew that trick. According to railway regulations, a dog, travelling loose (not boxed) must be provided with a muzzle, but the size of this insult is not specified.

The boy sat down on a trunk, and opened his book. The dog (his howling had died on a whimper) began to read *his* book. That is to say his sniffings of Lousy's coat, trousers, socks and shoes told him the comforting tale of the sort of country home to which he was accustomed. A label, attached to his collar, flicked over the pages of *Dead Man's Rock* and came to rest there. On it was written an address and the name—*Garm*. Lousy, remembering the Kipling story, *Garm, A Hostage*, smiled again.

'S'all right! ' he said, 'It's all right, Garm! '

The great white head came to rest on his knee with a heavy nuzzling movement and a sigh of happiness.

'It's all right, Garm, we'll meet again. You're going to live with Colonel Travers near my school. I've got the run of his woods. He's all right with dogs. Good, Garm.'

A paw came up in search of further comfort and Lousy took it, felt the flexible pads curve in an attempt at hand-holding, and turned a page of his book as the dog closed his eyes. He did not open them again until a dining-car attendant hurried down the corridor with his cries of ' First Lunch! '

The attendant was followed by a ticket-collector who interrupted the reading of the last chapter. Then peace followed for dog and boy.

Presently Lousy closed his book, and spoke.

'It's all right, Garm, I'm only going back for my cap. Shan't be long. I'll look out at Chorley from here.'

A heart-broken whimpering followed him along the corridor.

Except for the rats in their box, the mackintosh and Lousy's case containing ' necessaries for the first night at school ' the carriage appeared to be empty. The other passengers had gone, and there was no sign of his cap. This was a nuisance.

Lousy looked out of the window just in time to see a station flash by and to read the words *Duncombe Halt* on a signal box.

But surely *Duncombe Halt* came *after* Chorley? Slow study of the map above the opposite seat told the boy that he was right. *Duncombe Halt* was three stations beyond

Chorley. And what of the new boy, Cecil Mackintosh?

Lousy glanced longingly at the communication cord. It was a thing that he (like each one of us) had longed to pull. Still, it wasn't worth the risk for, surely, the new boy must be somewhere on the train? If not, he was lucky. He'd have another day's holiday. It was Lousy who would not be so lucky when he reached school.

He wondered, as he had wondered so often before, why the words ' lacks concentration ' ran like a theme-song through his reports. If he had ' lacked concentration ' over reading, he wouldn't have been carried past *Chorley Station*.

He fumbled in his pocket for a piece of toffee, that might help thought, brought it out, with knife attached, dropped both, and went on to his hands and knees.

There was a small boy under the seat, and he was lying in a sort of glorified cricket-bag made of brown canvas. Beside him was a purple-and-white school cap, and beyond him was a rug that reminded Lousy dimly of something he had seen before at one time or other.

He hauled at the bag, and dragged it out into the day-light. Then he looked half-reverently at its content.

'Lumme! ' he said admiringly, 'they must have had a time of it! '

For the arms and legs of the boy (he was an absurdly small boy for a nine-year-old and he had a puffy petulant face, not at all improved by tear-stains and railway smuts) were bound by cords.

'School's not so bad as all that! ' remarked Lousy kindly as he hacked at the cords round the ankles. (The arms were tied behind the victim's back.)

The child looked at him plummily.

'S'all right! ' continued Lousy, repeating the words he had used to the dog, though he much preferred the latter, 'It'll be all right. You can get up now.'

Then remembering that the boy's ankles had been bound and that gone-to-sleep limbs are helpless, he dragged him into a corner seat.

'You're Mackintosh, aren't you? ' he asked.

There was no answer, but the corner of a handkerchief protruding from the lips of the child, told the reason why.

Lousy sat down, and considered things. He had never been one to over-estimate his own strength, and his school-masters had never over-estimated his ability. If the child on the opposite seat was so tough that he had to be gagged, and bound hand-and-foot by a family lawyer of full man-strength (presumably) how could he (Lousy) deal with such a demon, if the demon were set free? Besides, he had the dog on his hands. (One doesn't give a promise to a dog, and not fulfil it). The dog was safe enough to be unmuzzled: the child was gagged. That showed, didn't it?

The phrase—'Reluctant to go to school,' came into his mind.

'Comfortable? ' asked Lousy.

The boy looked at him balefully, and tears trickled through the railway smuts on his cheeks. There were smuts too on the golden curls but it was because of the latter rather than the former that Lousy picked up the school cap (it was a great deal too big but that was just as well since the curls were outsized and dangly) and crammed it on to the child's head.

'It'll be all right! ' repeated Lousy. He was unaffected by the tears. His sister, Cordelia, could cry from sheer rage and bear the resulting headache like a saint. He had not cried since he was six because he disliked a head-ache more than he enjoyed the luxury of tears.

'It'll be all right. We can go to school by a back-door, and you can have a hair-cut and a wash-down.'

He was doing his best to make a good job of this very bad job of a boy.

'You'd better start off right, though. You won't need this.'

He kicked at the canvas bag. 'We're only allowed a small attaché case for the first night.'

From along the corridor the howls of an abandoned dog interrupted the one-sided conversation.

Lousy crammed the thick travelling rug into the bag, which had a label on it. Hadn't his mother begged him to be tidy, and hadn't he promised to try? He fastened the zipper.

'Tell you what, Mackintosh,' he looked kindly at the boy on the seat opposite, 'I know the Station Master at Aston—it's the stop before the School Station. I found his ferret when it was lost. He'll ship this bag back to your people.'

By this time circulation had returned to the other boy's legs, and he was drumming them violently on the floor

I for IGUANA

The iguana is a lazy lizard.

His aim in life, as far as one can judge,

Is to be crammed with greens up to the gizzard,

And see to it that nothing makes him budge.

He lives in South America, it's hot there,

And though some people think the heat is wizard,

The iguana wishes he were not there,

And dreams, he *says,* of a refreshing blizzard.

He moons all day, his drowsy eye peers forth

From out a somewhat prehistoric vizard,

But nothing east or west or south or north

Can animate this lazy lounging lizard.

V.G.

of the compartment. Tears poured down his face. He ducked his head and made nuzzling movements against his own chest in an attempt to catch the end of the gagging handkerchief against a coat button.

'Listen,' said Lousy, 'if you hadn't been noisy you wouldn't've been gagged, and there's enough row in this train as it is.'

This was true, for the bull-terrier was continuing its theme-song of distress.

The child continued to make the ducking movements that would have been unnecessary if his hands had not been tied behind his back.

A sentence, from a letter he had read in the past, dodged into Lousy's mind—'clean handkerchiefs in his coat-pocket.'

He searched, found one, rubbed his companion's face to the improvement of neither it nor the piece of linen, and repeated, 'It'll be all right!' just as the train stopped.

There was still work to be done.

'You don't want 'em to see you had to be put in a bag!' said Lousy, 'besides we aren't allowed big luggage the first night.'

'Aston! Aston!' bawled a porter, 'Change for Clewbury!'

During the next minute-and-a-half several things happened. Lousy, after hauling the canvas bag from the carriage and leaving it near the only seat on Aston Station, noticed a basket labelled 'Carrier Pigeon' and chatted with the porter, who was a pigeon-fancier. That chat was fascinating. The porter, though nearly as slow (conversationally) as was Lousy, knew more about trains. The boy was tumbled into the luggage van just as two oily-haired young men in purplish coats (they had just noticed the canvas bag) dashed out of the restaurant car, and on to the platform. Lousy observed them with no particular interest as the train left the platform.

He was greeted by a bull-terrier whose almond-shaped eyes said 'You are my only friend,' and whose waving paw backed-up the statement.

'Don't leave me!' begged eyes and paw.

'I won't—not for long! but school's the next stop,' promised Lousy, and he hurried along the corridor.

The golden-haired child was sitting where he had been left. Since his hands were bound, he was not able to carry either rat-box or attaché case. However, once he had been jerked to his feet, he made a good enough coat-hanger. Lousy slung his mackintosh round the shrinking shoulders, fastened one button, said 'Come on. It'll be all right, but we've got to get back to the dog,' and strolled towards the luggage van. The little boy (possibly he recognised a master-mind) followed him.

Some ten minutes later the four of them (No, the five: there were two rats in the box, and now the bull-terrier was aware of them) made confusion on the platform of Littlecombe, the school station. The dog's lead was twisted round Lousy's right ankle. The dog's back feet rested on the skirts of the mackintosh worn by the strange boy. The rats were squeaking.

'Knightshead!' said a familiar voice.

Now Lousy, unaccustomed though he was to being met on railway stations by his Head Master, was not the sort of boy to be startled into bad manners. Politeness had to be delayed while he put down the rat-box, and jerked the dog clear of it. Then his hand searched for the cap that should have been on his head.

'Knightshead, we thought you had missed the train. Mrs. Mackintosh rang up to say that her son—' the Head Master broke off to bawl an order to the Guard, who was talking to a Policeman and two hefty-looking men.

'Guard! Hold the train!'

'Mackintosh, Sir? Yes, Sir. He's here, Sir. He can't take off his own cap because—' (Here Lousy uncovered the golden curls of his small companion.) 'Well, because—'

'So you are Mackintosh,' said the Head in the gentle voice he reserved for new boys during the first six hours of each term.

'Garm! Garm! Leave 'em!'

The dog, whose nose had been exploring the outskirts of the rat-box, leaped ecstatically not at Lousy, but at the smaller boy, snatched the handkerchief that protruded from between his lips, and shook it joyously.

The howling that followed did not come from Garm.

The Policeman, followed by the hefty-looking couple, sauntered into the Inferno.

'Would that,' he asked slowly, raising his voice as was necessary to the occasion, 'Would that be Master Almaric Dalrymple?'

'This *is*,' corrected the Head Master, 'this IS, I regret to say, a pupil of mine—Master Cecil Mackintosh.'

The Policeman turned to his companions—'Answers the description, don't it?' he said. 'Fair, curly 'air . . . blue eyes . . . highly neurotic manner . . . that's a very funny thing that is!'

Just then another funny thing happened. A small perky looking boy, wearing a purple-and-white striped cap, and carrying an attaché case joined the group and spoke to Lousy. 'Is it you that ought to have looked out for me at Chorley? I'm Mackintosh.' He nodded towards the other boy—'That your younger brother or something?' The only fact about which Lousy was clear beyond all possible doubt was that the howling child was not his brother.

He answered as patiently as possible, the questions of the plain clothes policemen (for these were the strangers who had been talking to the Constable and the Guard) who seemed strangely uninterested in the dog, and curiously inquisitive about the men who had shared Lousy's carriage during the first stage of the journey.

At the end of the interrogation he said slowly, 'I hope they got their rug all right : it was a good one.'

'Rug?' barked the tallest questioner, 'What rug?'

'Well, you see, I think it was *their* rug I put into *his* bag.' Lousy jerked his head in the direction of the golden-haired child. 'I've only just remembered they had it over their knees. And I gave the bag to the porter at Aston. They got out there too.'

'You say the two men got out at Aston?'

'Yes,' agreed Lousy, 'didn't I tell you? They got out of the restaurant carriage only just in time. I expect they were trying to finish their dinners—'

Somebody made a rush for the telephone box.

Later in the day, Lousy was summoned to the Head Master's study. He was told that he had been the means of rescuing a boy film-star from a couple of kidnappers, and that the men had been caught in Aston village.

'Kidnappers, Sir?' repeated Lousy, 'those two men in the carriage, the ones with purple coats?'

'I did not have the privilege of seeing their coats.'

'Kidnappers!' mused Lousy, 'and with a valuable dog like that in the luggage-van. Lucky I was able to keep an eye on him, Sir, wasn't it?'

The Head Master sighed, and went on to say that the child film-star's parents had offered a handsome reward, that Colonel Knightshead, who had been consulted by telephone, refused to allow his son to accept a large money-present from strangers.

'But,' added the Head, 'he has suggested that the boy's parents might like to give a new swimming-bath to the school. They have agreed and, for that, Knightshead, we are indebted to you.'

'Oh no, Sir,' said Lousy.

'What do you mean?'

'Well, Sir, if he hadn't licked my face, and held my hand—'

'What?' gasped the Head.

'I mean the bull-terrier in the luggage van. If it hadn't been for *him*—'

The Head's voice was dangerously patient.

'You suggest, then, that as the bull-terrier has merited the reward, the swimming-bath should be presented to IT?'

'Well, Sir . . . MERITED, yes, Sir, but *not* a swimming-bath. They get canker, sometimes, when water gets into their ears.'

for JERBOA

A jerboa, as you may observe, is a rat,
And a very peculiar one at that,
For his hands and feet or whatever you choose
To call them, are like a kangaroo's.

Should anyone cough, should anyone call,
He leaps in the air like a tennis ball,
Bounding and bouncing out of sight
Into the blackness of the night.

For only at night does he go abroad,
Stealing the corn for his secret hoard;
Wherever great sweeping plains are found
He's somewhere about there, jumping around,

Cutting the barley and nibbling away
Till the stars go out and the day dawns grey,
And then, with a last enormous leap
He pops into bed and goes fast asleep.

V.G.

You will take ten seconds to look through these photographs. The Viking Research Rocket took fifteen seconds to travel fifty miles, from the take-off until it looked like a puff of smoke vanishing through the sky.

Glenn L. Martin Co., Baltimore

SKY ROCKETING

by Harry Harper

IS SOME GREAT slow change now beginning in the world's climate? That is the vital question.

Our science of meteorology—the science of the weather—is still quite young. Really reliable records of what our weather has been doing do not go back even for a hundred years.

But in the years since they were first established, on a scientific basis, our weather services have been constantly expanded and improved. To-day we have our special weather-ships patrolling out in the Atlantic, which flash regular reports by wireless to the main meteorological receiving stations. Pilotless sounding balloons, with automatic recording instruments, go up daily to great heights to tell us what is happening in upper zones in such matters as temperature and wind-strength. Aeroplane pilots, too, go up in specially-equipped machines to

bring down similar reports. Such aerial observations, reinforced by reports from a chain of ground stations, are all built up to form the frequent daily weather reports we get over the wireless and in our newspapers. But when it comes to a question whether any great change is about to take place in our climate, this present system, well-planned though it now is, has one very serious drawback. None of the observations so far possible, either by aeroplane or balloon, reach high enough up into the sky. The highest point attained by an aeroplane is just on 60,000 feet. A pilotless sounding balloon, carrying recording instruments, has reached a height of 120,000 feet. High enough, one might think, but not high enough for the great research now in view.

What other machine is there that will climb to even greater heights? Well, it takes the form of a new giant wonder-

rocket designed and built solely for scientific research-work at immense heights above the Earth.

The whole root of the matter is a very remarkable theory which scientists have just been evolving. They believe that mysteries nobody has been able to explain hitherto, about the climate of our globe, can be solved only by a regular and systematic probing of what is going on in those hitherto unreached zones which lie from 100 to 200 miles above the surface of the Earth. What they believe is that there are tremendous 'air tides' rushing here and there at colossal speeds, and giving rise to conditions which, as their influence extends lower towards the Earth's surface, bring us rain, sleet, fog, or snow, to say nothing of gales of wind, or those fine spells which we all make the most of, and enjoy so much.

One might say, indeed, if this theory is true, that the weather we have to enjoy, or endure, down here in our daily lives, is, so to say, 'made' for us in vast weather 'factories' up there at heights so far unexplored.

A Hundred Miles High

The key to these great riddles lies, it is now believed, in the high-altitude rocket. Already what is called a 'two-step' rocket has climbed to a height as great as 250 miles. This rocket, launched not long ago by American scientists, consisted of a V2 rocket, as evolved by the Germans, and a smaller type of rocket designed and built by United States scientists. This smaller rocket was mounted on the top of the V2, and, after the latter had reached a certain pre-arranged height, this smaller rocket was launched from it automatically, and went on climbing higher still—higher and higher until it was actually out beyond the atmosphere of our Earth, and was for a time on the fringe of outer space.

Following this successful high-altitude test, what are now being designed and built are special high-climbing rockets which will be used solely for regular scientific researches in air zones 100 miles or more above the Earth.

One of the most interesting of these new projectiles is the streamlined, pencil-like 'Viking' you see illustrated here. This is the first American-designed research rocket for ascents to heights never reached before. It has been built for the United States Navy by the Glenn L. Martin Company, with its power-plant developed by Reaction Motors Inc.

Secret British researches, with large, long-range rockets of new designs, are now being carried out on a great 1,000-miles range which crosses uninhabited desert zone in Central Australia.

The American 'Viking' is 45 feet long, and has the most powerful rocket propelling plant yet developed in the United States. Liquid fuel, after being fed into a specially designed combustion chamber, is ignited, expanded, and ejected from the rear of the rocket in the form of gas, in an immensely powerful stream. It is the rocket's reaction to this constant rearward gas-stream, rushing downward with tremendous force, which thrusts it up at a speed as great as 2,250 miles an hour.

When launched from the White Sands proving-grounds, at Les Cruces, New Mexico, this first 'Viking' ascended at such a speed that within fifteen seconds of leaving the ground it was a mere speck in the sky, climbing until it had reached a height of more than fifty miles. In further tests, now to be made, it is expected that one of these 'Vikings' will be able to attain a maximum height of 200 miles, or even more.

The 'Viking' is balanced, and kept in an upward position as it climbs, by an automatic gyroscopic mechanism, while it is guided and controlled by wireless from the ground. Each of the rockets is fitted with an intricate form of automatic 'brain', the details of which are secret. The purpose of this apparatus, fitted in a compartment in the nose of the rocket, is to send down to ground receiving-stations a stream of short-wave wireless signals. All the time the rocket is climbing into the stratosphere these signals are telling experts on the ground just what they want to know about pressure, temperature, and other atmospheric conditions at great heights from which, so far, no accurate scientific information has been available.

Of course just one or two such ascents would not tell a sufficiently clear story. This new research must be carried out according to a carefully arranged system, over a wide area, and for some considerable time.

One of the theories on which these rocket ascents may throw light has been discussed for some time now, by men of science in many countries.

It concerns the effect of the Sun on the atmosphere and weather of our world. It is known that changes take place, from time to time, in the activity of the Sun. Big spots may appear on its surface, and these affect the rays it sends out across space. Other changes, too, take place which may have their influence on the heat reaching the surface of our globe from the Sun. Many experts who have been making a special study of this particular subject believe that for some time past the rays of the Sun have been radiating more heat than usual into the upper zones of our atmosphere, and that it is this vast warming-up process—which may have been going on for a good many years past—which is leading to the reports observers have been sending in lately from stations set up on the edges of Polar ice-fields. What they say they have been seeing, with their own eyes, is a steady shrinking, winter by winter, of great icy glaciers which have previously shown no signs of melting. Not only this, but each winter for some years now, there has been a rise in temperature as reported from a chain of weather-posts dotted just along the fringe of the great Polar ice-fields.

Melting Ice Cap

What all this adds up to, expert observers now believe, is that huge glaciers on the Polar zones are beginning to melt faster than they re-form again, and that as great ice-fields shrink back, breaking up and melting here and there, so vegetation begins to replace what was formerly just a barren, frozen waste.

Is what is going on up there along the grim Polar ice-cap just something temporary, or does it mean that this warming-up of the North may bring a gradual change in the whole of the climate of the world? Experts in geology who study the layers of soil which, at various depths, cover the surface of this globe, can tell us a fascinating story of how the climate of our globe has developed from the days—many, many millions of years ago—when the Earth first began to grow solid after being at first in a more or less gaseous state.

Each great spell of weather has left its own particular story in some layer of earth or rock. These great weather spells have been like the swing of some huge pendulum. From icy cold to tropic heat, and then back again to yet another Ice Age. And each of these great periods of weather has not been just a question of weeks, or months, or years, but of many centuries—even of thousands of years.

What is it that young folk of to-day have now to look forward to? Well, a great deal depends of course on what sort of information our scientists obtain from their work with high-flying rockets. And here I might add that apart from pilotless, instrument-carrying rockets to rush up to the limits of the Earth's atmosphere, plans are already being drawn up for manned research rockets in which technical observers will be able to ascend to heights never reached by human beings before, and make personal observations of conditions at these super-altitudes.

Fine Weather Ahead

What everything already seems to point to is that for quite a long time past we have been gradually leaving a cold climatic spell behind us, and that slowly year by year—almost perhaps without our noticing it—our winters have been growing less severe. Of course we still get—and shall continue to get—an occasional very cold snap, and this will be welcome to those of us who enjoy skating, tobogganing, and other sports that a really wintry spell brings with it. But if you talk about the weather with any old person, to-day, you will almost certainly hear them say that our winters, in recent years, have been nowhere near as cold as they used to be when they were young. And figures show that they are right.

What some experts believe is that the world may now be entering a spell of perhaps a hundred years of less severe winters, and of finer summers.

This belief is based on the theory that, if the ice of the North Polar zones continues to recede, as it is doing now, there may be a general shift northward of weather from big tropical belts lying around the Equator, with milder winds blowing over our British Isles, and with the sun shining more of his warming rays upon us. Some experts even go as far as to tell us that it may not be many years before we in England begin to have something like the delightful climate they now have down on the Riviera in the South of France. Which I think you will agree is something quite pleasant to look forward to. Far better for all of us, at any rate, than any drifting back into another grim, cold climatic spell.

Weather plays such a vital part in our lives. If it is beastly it can make us all feel irritable and out-of-sorts. It can slow us up in our work, and mar our leisure hours. But if it is fine it can send us cheerfully about our daily tasks, and make after-work sports and hobbies so much more enjoyable. So let us hope it will be news that will mean the dawn of a great fine-weather era that those big rockets will be bringing down to us from high in the sky.

MR. FORTIMO'S PRESENT

by Jean Simpson

Dear Mr. Fortimo,
Dapper Mr. Fortimo
Tiptoed down the bobbly pebbles
To the water's edge,
Dipped in a little toe,
Danced a fandangio,
The weeny waves all laughing-o
Beside the water's edge.

Now Mr. Fortimo
Has fetched a large and coloured towel
Has wrapped it round his shoulders-o,
Is walking on the shore;
He's peeping in a little pool
Inside a little hidden pool
Where big waves are forbidden, tell me,
What's he looking for?

Jill had an oldish great aunt who
Said, ' Sea water will never do
For one who sneezes quite like you!
We'll take a walk instead.'
They saw a policeman in the square
But not a single shell was there,
' In London, shells are very rare,'
Jill's oldish great aunt said.

Now jauntily on Sunday,
The yawny, shops a closing day,
The after dinner dozing day,
Mr. Fortimo
Goes walking, cane a-swinging,
With the chapel bells all ringing,
Mr. Fortimo is kinging it
Today.

He's coming almost past Jill's door!
Oh will he turn at last, before
He keeps on walking any more?
And perhaps he'd stay to tea—
He's stopping by the cedar tree,
And holding something up, all glee,
And shouting, ' Got it from the sea!
Right piping from the sea! '

And packed inside a black valise,
Inside a little screwed up piece
Of paper, wet and all a-crease
No bigger than a pill
There lay a little pinkish shell
A little glint-and-winkish shell
A palish, finger nailish shell,
For Jill.

BIGGLES—continued from page 182.)

haboob had passed, for although the cigarette end lay in the open it was clear of sand. He could assume that Biggles had survived the *haboob* and was now making an air reconnaissance of the area. At all events, he felt pretty certain that Biggles had not gone home, or he would have seen him.

Polishing his monocle mechanically Bertie considered the matter, not knowing what to do next. If, as he supposed, Biggles was making an air survey of the district, it was obvious that, at the end of it he would do one of two things—possibly both. He would either fly straight back to Aden or return to aerodrome 137. Even if he decided to return to Aden there seemed a possibility that he would look in at the old aerodrome on the way on the off chance of his being there. Reasoning thus, Bertie decided that the best thing he could do was stay where he was—for a little while, at any rate.

He had cause—or he thought he had cause—to congratulate himself on his reasoning, when, about twenty minutes later, he heard the drone of an aircraft approaching from the south. Naturally, at first it did not occur to him that it could be anyone but Biggles, and he was about to run into the open to greet him when, to his unbounded astonishment, he observed that the machine was a Moth. Taken aback, he remained where he was, watching; and as he watched the engine died, and the nose of the machine tilted down in a way that told him beyond any doubt that the pilot intended to land. What such a machine was doing in such a place and at such a time was beyond his comprehension, so it was with no small interest that he adjusted his eye-glass to await the solution. He noted that the aircraft carried neither civil registration letters nor military insignia.

The Moth landed, but instead of stopping in front of the hangars, the pilot taxied on beyond the end hangar and so out of sight. The engine stopped. A moment later there came a clang of metal. After that, silence.

Wondering not a little at this strange behaviour Bertie strolled along the line of hangars to see what was happening. Not for an instant did it occur to him that he might be in danger. Pilots of all nationalities are at heart a friendly brotherhood, and if he thought about the matter at all, he supposed that his appearance would be greeted with, if not open arms, fraternal pleasure.

When he came in sight of the Moth he saw that the pilot had left the cockpit and was busy at something on the far side of it. Drawing nearer he saw to his astonishment that he was working a hand pump; that he was, in fact, in the act of filling his tank from an underground supply, a small man-hole cover having been removed for the purpose. Actually, Bertie was not so much surprised that a quantity of fuel had apparently been left behind when the airfield was abandoned, as by the fact that this wandering pilot should know of its existence. Drawing still nearer he saw that the man—who still had not noticed him—was not a European. His skin, even allowing for sun-tan, was too dark. Not that this made any difference as far as he, Bertie, was concerned. To him a pilot was a pilot, whatever his colour or nationality. From a distance of perhaps a dozen paces he hailed the Moth pilot cheerfully. ' Hallo there! ' he greeted, from the opposite side of the aircraft.

The result was quite outside his calculations. The man started violently, as if caught in the act of committing a crime. With a quick intake of breath, he whipped out a revolver and fired it over the top of the fuselage.

(*Continued on page 220*)

JOHN SEBASTIAN BACH 1685—1750

by Helen Henschel

When you start learning the piano, your first 'piece' is more than likely to be a Minuet written by Bach. All musicians, orchestras, organists, singers and choirs can find masterpieces for every occasion among the wide range of 'Works' of this great composer.

Bach, after writing fugues all day,

With his dear children loved to play;

And when they went to bed at night,

To bath them was his chief delight.

Every piece of music Bach composed was written by hand clearly and neatly, and copied out by Anna Magdalena.

IT IS 200 YEARS since the death of John Sebastian Bach, one of the greatest composers who ever lived. He was a very different kind of person from Mozart, the subject of the last article I wrote for you. Mozart was in the public eye when hardly more than a baby, whereas comparatively little is known about Bach's childhood.

But there is one particularly interesting thing about the Bach family: they were nearly all musicians. From the time we first hear of them, in the early sixteenth century, we find music in some form or another passing from father to son—whatever other profession they may have followed as well; so much so that the name 'Bach' often came to mean the same thing as 'musician'.

It is sometimes thought that musicians and other artists must be very excitable and different from other people. J. S. B. was the most conclusive proof that this is not the case. His whole life was marked by the greatest simplicity and modesty; all he cared for was his art, and in its service he worked unceasingly from morning till night, without the least thought of public recognition or applause. He once said: 'The sole object of all music should be the glory of God and pleasant recreation', and he showed, all through his long life, how true this is.

His simplicity and lack of conceit are shown by another saying of his: 'Anybody could do what I have done if he worked as hard.' Of course we know this is not so, because after 200 years, music such as Bach's great 'Mass in B minor' or the 'St. Matthew Passion', remains the grandest and most sublime of its kind.

John Sebastian Bach was born in Eisenach, in the Thuringian Forest, in 1685. His father was Johann Ambrosius Bach (almost all the Bachs were called Johann along with their other names) who was the 'Court and Town Musician' of Eisenach.

I've said that we don't know much about Bach's very early years except that there was never any question of his being anything but a musician. He almost certainly learnt the viol and the violin from his father, and when he was about eight he started going to school. His parents both died when he was ten, so he was brought up by his eldest brother, Johann Christoph, who was organist at a place called Ohrdruf. It was here that a famous incident occurred that you will read of in every book about Bach, because it shows that even as a child, J. S. was not only entirely devoted to music, but was already possessed of the patience and capacity for work that made him one of the most industrious as well as the greatest of musicians.

His brother had begun to teach the little boy the harpsichord, but Bach soon mastered all he was given to study, and was impatient to learn a great deal more. Johann Christoph possessed a fine collection of manuscript music by various contemporary organists, which he kept in a closed bookcase, and which he had forbidden the child to touch. But Bach used to get up in the middle of the night and copy out the precious music by the light of the moon, having managed to get it out through the lattice-work doors of the bookcase. It took him six months. But when he began to practise from his hardly-won copies, his brother took them away from him. This sounds rather hard-hearted, but we must remember that, to his grown-up brother, Bach was just a little boy who had to be punished for disobedience and for sitting up all night when he ought to have been in bed!

Bach went to school in Ohrdruf and there, besides acquiring a good general education, including Greek and Latin, he joined the school choir. This corresponds pretty well to our church choirs; the boys sang in church every Sunday, and also at weddings and funerals. Bach soon became one of their principal singers.

When he was fifteen he left his brother's house and went to a place called Lüneburg, where he and his friend Georg Erdmann joined the choir of the Convent of St. Michael. Both boys were paid for their services and from now on Bach became entirely self-supporting. This was what he had wanted almost from his childhood, and it was just like him not to be satisfied until he reached that happy state. Bach soon had to leave the choir because his voice broke, but, with his mastery of both harpsichord and violin, he joined the town band and also acted as accompanist.

And he learnt to play the organ. His enthusiasm for that great instrument was so tremendous that he once *walked* 200 miles (incredible as this may seem), from Arnstadt, where he himself became organist in 1704, to Lübeck, to hear the great organist Buxtehude. Before many years Bach was elected organist and choirmaster at the church of St. Thomas in Leipzig, one of the most important positions a musician could occupy.

From now on, he worked harder than ever. Just as a business man to-day starts off for his office in the morning, so Bach would go to his study to write the music for next Sunday's services. As a result of this 'routine work' alone, the world is enriched by some of the greatest church music ever written, quite apart from all the keyboard music which we know so well.

Bach was twice married: first to his cousin, Maria Barbara, and after her death to Anna Magdalena Wilcken. She was a tremendous help to him in his work; being an excellent musician herself, she was able to act as copyist for him, and if you have ever tried copying music yourself you will realise what a tiresome and exacting job it is.

Bach had twenty children—a huge family, isn't it? But don't make the mistake I once heard from an over-enthusiastic little boy, who announced that Bach had forty-eight children and wrote twenty preludes and fugues. Of course, it was the other way round. The preludes and fugues the boy meant were those comprising the book called *The Well-Tempered Clavier*, generally referred to just as *The Forty-eight*.

Of Bach's sons, several grew up to be great musicians too. There isn't room in this short article to tell you about them, but you can read about the whole of the Bach family in a perfectly delightful and often amusing book called *John Sebastian Bach*, by Hendrick William Van Loon (Harrap, 6s.). There is also a volume on Bach in the *Great Musician Series*, by Opal Wheelers (Faber, 9s. 6d.), which has gay illustrations and prints a selection of music for readers to play.

Bach was a very affectionate and devoted father: when his children were babies he used often to help bath them—surely an unexpected occupation for a great composer! But after all, it's nice to find that great composers are just people like the rest of us, and we know that Bach had all the simple kindness that makes for a happy home life.

For Anna Magdalena he loved to write little songs and keyboard pieces, which are collected in a book called *The Little Clavier-Book of Anna Magdalena Bach*.

One of the most delightful things to remember about the Bachs is their devotion to each other. The many branches of the family were scattered about all over Germany, but they made a point of meeting all together once every year to enjoy each other's company and to make music together.

What lovely music it must have been!

Murder !

by M. A. J. Ward (14)

'THAT WAS A lovely meal,' said David, leaning back in his chair. 'I give Monsieur Rumeux full marks for it!'

It was in the south of France in a quiet little village called Lepages that my brother and I halted for a few days in our tour. We were using a new Vauxhall 'Velox', and Lepages seemed such a delightful place that we had booked a pair of rooms at the Hotel, which was very pretty and certainly lived up to its name by calling itself 'Le Jardin Fleuri.'

After coffee we decided to go and have a rest, since we had completed the long and tiring journey from Paris that day. We had been sharing the driving—that is, when there were no gendarmes about, for I was only fourteen! We went upstairs to sleep. About half an hour later I woke up and could not go to sleep again. Strolling across the room I went out on to the balcony which looked on to the Place du Soleil. This also lived up to its name, for the sun was beating down on the scorched square, and my eyes smarted with the glare.

All was still and quiet, and the only noise that came to disturb the peace was the gentle snoring of my brother on the bed behind me.

Little did I know it, but I was about to witness a sight that would have frozen the blood of any onlooker—a cowardly, cold-blooded murder in broad daylight! The square was completely deserted, but presently I saw from the far corner a dim figure come slouching along, scraping an old fiddle, and followed by a thin, wizened monkey on a length of string. The old man came out of the shade into the full glare of the sun, and I could now see his swarthy Italian complexion, and even recognise the slow serenade he was playing. Then, from the same corner of the square there came, creeping stealthily, a young man in waiter's attire. Step by step he followed the old man, and suddenly to my horror the sun showed me the glint of steel in his hand! When he was within striking distance, he raised his hand high in the air and buried the stiletto deep in the shoulders of the old man!! There was an agonising scream, and the old man crumpled in an ungainly heap before my eyes. I could see the blood spurting spasmodically from the gaping wound on to the scorched cobbles of the square. The old man gave a few convulsive wriggles, and then lay still and lifeless in the glaring sun...

Meanwhile, the assassin had taken to his heels down a nearby alley. I yelled to my brother and dashed down the stairs, with ghastly ideas flooding my brain. As I reached the hotel entrance to my utter horror and amazement, the body moved! More than that—it slowly got up and began to slouch away to the corner from which it had come! I stood rooted to the spot, and as I stared the explanation of such a monstrous event came upon me. Far away in the shadows in the corner of the square I could see a small group of figures. In the centre was a large, fat man, seated in a folding chair. He was wearing a wide panama hat and smoking a cigar. Beside him, mounted on a tripod, was a large studio camera. . . .

COMFORT IN CAMP

by Richard Graves

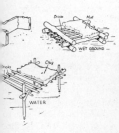

RAISED FIREPLACE

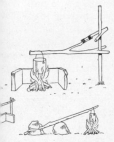

POT BOILING

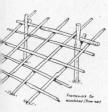

WOODSHED

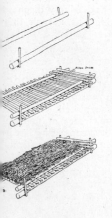

CAMP BED

IT'S ONLY the mug camper who is too lazy to make the few things necessary for comfort in camp. A fireplace is essential, but what is the use of a fireplace which is flooded with the first heavy shower, or one where the billy falls over because there is no proper place to hang it with safety? . . . or what sort of a camper is it who grabs the handle, and burns his fingers because he was either too lazy to cut a billy hook, or didn't know how to make a swinging gantry? Only a greenhorn does these things, your real backwoodsman camper neglects no chance to make his stay in camp comfortable.

Camp fireplace.—Select a site where the fire will not be flooded in heavy rain. If for any reason you have to camp in marsh or very wet ground build your fireplace well above ground level. Fire for the cooking of food, the drying of clothes and the warming of your body is an essential to comfort in the camp.

Above your fire you will need a place for your pots and pans. Two forked stakes driven into the ground on either side of the fireplace and a cross-bar, well above the flames is one method. Another is a swinging gantry, hanging from a single pole driven in the ground to one side of the fire. This has the advantage of being instantly adjusted for height and position over the flames.

For a simple fireplace, a stick, lying over a stone, and with the far end held down by another stone is quite effective. When trying to boil a billy in high wind, build your fire on the ground to windward of the billy, and then build fire all round the pot. If you try to hang the billy above the flames it will never boil.

Hook and Tongs

A billy hook will save you burnt fingers, and is quickly made from a hooked stick with a single nick cut at the end for the wire handle of the billy. A pair of fire tongs made from a forked stick, and a straight one will allow you to handle burning sticks with safety.

For comfort you want a place to sit. If you propose being in camp some time, then a camp chair is worth making. Two widely splayed forked poles are lashed together at the top, which in turn are rested in a shorter fork, so that one arm of each of the two forked poles lies horizontally, and about twelve inches above the ground. Sticks are lashed across the seat and up the two poles at the back, and you have your seat, movable and comfortable. If widely splayed forks cannot be found two hooked poles can be used.

A camp bed may either be made on the ground or, if required, above the ground. Two logs, six to eight inches thick and about seven feet long are cut.

Pegs are driven in the ground at either end of these logs and on what will be the outside of the bed. These pegs should be about six or seven inches above the top of the log. Across the two logs stout sticks an inch thick are laid. These sticks are about four inches apart. And above them are laid two more poles three or four inches thick. The space between the poles is piled with green branches up to an inch thick in the stalk. This pile, lying loosely can be twelve or fourteen inches thick. On top of this you make your bed, and it is the most comfortable bed you ever slept in.

If you have to make your camp bed well above the ground, follow the idea of a camp table, and pile the branches along the table top.

Dining Room Suite

A camp table and seats are essential in a large camp. The best style of camp table is made by driving two straight, strong forked stakes into the ground seven or eight feet apart, with the forks in line with the direction of the table. Into each of these forks, poles are laid at a flattish angle as shown in the sketch. Across these poles about twelve inches above the ground two strong poles are lashed, and the lashing may also be made to the forked pole. Heavy poles are laid along these cross-poles for the seats, and these are not lashed or fastened, but may be moved in or out at will. Twelve inches above the cross-poles two long poles are lashed, and across these the sticks which make the table top are laid and tied. If the soil is sandy and the table requires bracing, then braces may be put in from the fork of one end to the base of the forked pole at the other end.

Light in camp is often a problem, one of the most simple of all camp lights is the slush lamp, made from an old tin, three-quarters filled with dirt, and then any surplus fat is poured in on top of the dirt. A twig is stuck in the centre of the dirt, and a bit of cotton rag twisted round the twig. This is the wick. A slush lamp will smoke after it is blown out, and therefore it is advisable to remove it from the tent when not in use.

A careful camper will always make sure that his wood is dry, and he will always have a supply of timber ready to start the cooking fire in the morning. A woodshed, built close to your camp fire may take half an hour to erect but if you get bad weather that half hour's work may well save hours of time lighting your fire in rain.

The sketch shows the simple framework for a woodshed. The covering may be long grass, sods, branches laid lengthways, reeds or any other local material to make a watershed.

HOOK AND TONGS

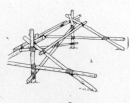

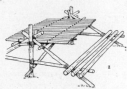

TABLE AND SEATS

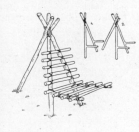

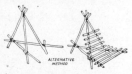

TWO CHAIRS

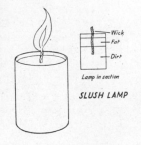

SLUSH LAMP

HIKE ON YOUR BIKE

IF YOU WANT TO GO away for a few days in the holidays, here are some suggestions which may be of some help.

Suppose you plan to set off on a bicycle with some friends. It is wisest of course, to choose a time when the weather is settled, but of that you can never be certain, so you must be prepared for anything.

Perhaps you will decide on your route before you start. In this way you can keep in touch with your home more easily, should anxious parents wish you to do so! They can always write poste restante to post offices, where you can collect the letters.

But whether you work out your routes beforehand or not, do procure a large scale map of the district you intend to explore. Many small lanes, leading perhaps from a main road to the sea shore, are not marked on many motoring maps, and so you miss them.

You should aim to be self supporting where food is concerned. It is risky to rely on getting a meal in a country village. But as you will be carrying everything on your back or your bike, you will only want to take the minimum amount of luggage with you. Therefore plan together which items each one of you will take, so that unnecessary things are not duplicated.

First of all, you will need a small tent. It will be most economical as far as space is concerned, if you procure one which will sleep two people. This can be strapped in its own canvas bag, with the poles rolled inside, along the bar of your bicycle.

You will need a ground sheet each, and the tent pegs can be rolled inside the ground sheets and tied securely. These can all be strapped along the bar of another bicycle. Take an extra ground sheet for every two people, which can be used as a cover for bicycles.

Even if it does not rain, dew can make everything very wet, and bicycles soon get rusty.

Your personal belongings can be packed into a haversack for your back. It is surprising how quite heavy weights can be carried easily in this way.

It is wise to take a spare pair of shoes, if only to change into should your feet get tired or blistered. Another pair of shoes does help on these occasions.

Bathing Suit for rainy weather

Pyjamas you must take, and a change of clothes if you have room, but what is really more practical, is an extra bathing suit. Then, if it rains, take off all your clothes and wear it. Otherwise, you may be landed with wet clothes and nowhere to dry them. No one ever caught cold from actually getting wet, (as long as you keep moving and warm) but, standing about in wet clothes, is a sure way of getting a chill. The result is, almost certainly, anxious parents, who may not let you do this sort of thing again!

Besides your toothbrush, washing things and a towel, try to fit a plate, mug, knife, fork, and spoon into your haversack.

If you have a proper sleeping bag, so much the better, but it is quite easy to make one out of old blankets yourself. Line this if you can, so that you have enough warmth both above and below without having to bother about extra blankets. It is a good idea to pad one end to make a pillow, or sew an odd piece of material in the right place, so that you can slip in your folded clothes when you take them off at night. This will both keep them dry and raise your head.

There is no need to bother about any kind of mattress, even if you are afraid the ground will be hard. Hollow out a small place for your hip, and you will be surprised how comfortable it is.

Your sleeping bag can be rolled up and strapped on to the carrier at the back of your bicycle. If it is not waterproof outside, cover it up with a spare ground sheet when travelling, or a sudden shower may land you with a wet bed. Do not pack your own mackintosh where you cannot find it in a hurry. It is such a nuisance to get soaked through.

You must see that your luggage is balanced properly on your bicycle. Otherwise you will find it extremely difficult to push up hills, with your front wheel wishing to rise up into the air!

A canvas bucket is most useful if you can procure one. It can be used as a basket when it is dry, water can be carried in it, and you can wash yourselves, and your dirty plates in it too. It is light, and takes up little room when not in use.

When you are travelling, this canvas bucket will be useful to carry several of your necessary articles. One of these is a small mallet or hammer, which you will need to knock in your tent pegs.

Take a trowel with you. Digging is more easily done with a spade, but a spade is rather clumsy to carry on a bicycle. You will want to bury your rubbish from day to day, and a trowel will suffice.

For a temporary camp, where you may only spend one night, and move on to a different place each day, it is not worth the bother of putting up a proper latrine. You can easily find a secluded place, but do be tidy about it. There again the trowel will come in handy.

If you can procure a billycan with a lid, this will be your best method for cooking.

A small tin kettle and a frying pan are your alternatives. Eggs can be boiled in the kettle after you have made your tea, but it is not so useful as a billycan.

You will find it best to take what food you must, in a tin box. Obviously you will not want to carry more than necessary. The advantages of a tin box are that it can be left outside without fear of the contents getting wet, and, earwigs, and other creatures which have a habit of congregating round foodstuffs in camp, cannot get in either.

Butter in a Jam Jar

Butter or any kind of fat is best packed in a jam jar with a screw top lid. Sugar, too, will keep clean and dry in a jam pot as well. Your easiest method for making tea, is to tie up spoonfuls in little muslin bags, before you leave home. These can be placed in your mug, and the boiling water poured straight on to them. This does away with the bother of taking a tea pot. A tin of dehydrated coffee is easy to make too.

You will have to buy milk as you go along. It can stay in the bottle until that is returned, but be sure to keep it covered up and in a cool place.

Take with you some greaseproof paper in which to wrap any food which may not be eaten directly it is bought, or anything which is left over from a meal.

The tin box of food, and the canvas bucket and its contents can be fixed either on the top of your sleeping bag, or in the front of your bicycle. But be sure that the brakes are free to work, and not jammed by heavy weights.

Take a torch and a box of matches to light your fire.

A small first aid outfit is not fussy, but essential. It should contain a small bottle of disinfectant for cuts, a tin of plaster with dressings attached, and some soda bicarbonate, which is invaluable for burns or stings. Wasps and mosquitos have a nasty habit of attacking campers, and if the results are not dealt with at once, they can spoil a holiday.

A great many places nowadays display notices saying that campers are allowed in certain fields, and there you would be able to pitch your tent for about a shilling a night. But if you have no idea where to go, it is always a safe and good plan to enquire at a Police Station.

Always ask permission before you unpack. It's not worth the risk of being turned off after you are settled for the night. Most farmers are kindly disposed to people if they look as though they will not leave a mess behind them.

One last word of warning. Take every possible precaution against fire spreading. Cut out neatly in strips and roll up the turf on the ground where you want your fire. This will give you an earth base, and the turf can be replaced when you leave, covering up all traces of the fire. If there is sand handy, keep a small heap near the fire, just in case of accidents. It will quickly extinguish the flames.

When you are packing up your bicycle, see that your pump and repair outfit are accessible, though it is to be hoped there will be no punctures!

Good luck!   MARIGOLD KEEBLE.

for KOALA BEAR

What can I say about these little bears,
having their portrait taken here together,
save that the one with t'other fairly shares
a nose composed of shiny patent leather.

Each ear, as soft as down, is like the other,
and interchangeable the button eyes,
and anybody, save their mother
who says they're easy to distinguish—lies!

These heavenly twins, whose days are all expended
in playing in the branches overhead
know, sure as fate, that when their play is ended
they'll always get a pick-a-back to bed.

Australia they come from, way down under,
(or way up top if you're already there)
and oh, I'd tear my very soul asunder
to have the left hand . . . no, the right hand bear!

V.G.

'Well,' said Nancy after a long uncomfortable pause, 'We've all pleaded "not guilty". Has no one anything else to say?'

A STICKY BUSINESS

by M. E. Atkinson

ILLUSTRATED BY VICTOR ROSS

IT COULD have been any one of us.'

Nancy swept the group with an unpleasantly searching eye. She might say 'any one', but it was clear that she did not include herself. We were—all five of us—sitting underneath the cedar tree in the centre of the lawn. There was shade here, and we needed it. Beyond the few square yards protected by the branches above us the sun went on scorching the parched turf.

'Who's got a guilty look?' teased Nancy. She laughed.

I knew myself to be flushing—an unfortunate habit and one that I have not yet outgrown, although more than a year has gone by since that hateful series of events I am now doing my best to set down. I was barely sixteen then. I remember hoping that my scarlet cheeks might be put down to the heat of the August day. If guilt were written upon any face, then surely mine must seem the most suspicious? The twins, Tony and Rosine, my young brother and sister, were then thirteen and only just back from their long years in Canada. Our people had sent them out of the country at the time when Britain stood alone against Hitler's Germany, and things were not looking too rosy. I, for various reasons—health among them—was kept at home. I now glanced furtively at Rosine. Her eyes were upon her shoes. Tony, on the other hand, was giving Nancy stare for stare. He looked brazen. That's because he's nervous, I thought. He's feeling just as bad as the rest of us, but he won't show it if he can help it. Hubert, Nancy's brother, was chewing a blade of grass. He appeared bored, or perhaps sleepy.

Nancy and Hubert Sanders and our three selves (the Hendersons) were spending the summer holidays with a Miss Lacey, our respective parents having gone abroad, both pairs to military stations. Miss Lacey liked to have children about, and often housed those temporarily homeless. We were not meeting the Sanders's for the first time. Our two families had been friendly for years. Nancy is more like a boy than a girl—at least, she likes the things I like, fishing and games and so on. So, up to the time of this affair I'm now writing about, we had done quite a lot together and always kept our friendship, though her teasing, I must admit, was sometimes more than you felt you could bear.

'Well,' said Nancy after a long uncomfortable pause, 'we've all pleaded "not guilty". Has no one anything else to say? We came out here specially to discuss the matter. *One* of us most probably could tell the whole story.' She looked at me. 'Go on, Stephen. Can't you speak up?'

'I've nothing to say,' I muttered.

'Not even if I accused *you*?'

'You'd have to prove it,' said Tony hotly.

'Yes,' put in Rosine, echoing, as always, her twin, 'you'd have to prove it.'

Nancy turned to her brother. 'That's just what we can't do, can we, Hubert?'

Hubert yawned. This infuriated the energetic Nancy. She seized him by his shoulders and shook him. Hubert spat out the piece of grass.

I thought:—'If Hubert's guilty, he's putting on a jolly good act.'

And then I felt awful at having let myself suspect him, though it was not half as bad as being even doubtful of my own brother and sister. The trouble was—I knew so little about this present day Tony and Rosine. The war had separated us for so long.

Nancy produced a piece of paper.

'I don't know exactly how detectives go about these things,' she said, 'but I've set out the facts. We all know them now, of course, but it's more professional to put them down.' She read aloud:—'Missing, from Miss Lacey's drawing-room, a painted glass jar full of toffee. Noticed to be missing by Marjorie, the house-parlourmaid, this morning when she first came into the room to dust, etc. Also noticed, by Marjorie, as having been there on the table in the window after we had all gone to bed last night. She was late in, having been to the pictures.'

Tony broke in:—'Had Mr. Dalton gone to bed?'

Nancy nodded. 'Marjorie said everyone. She was sure because she went round to see the windows were all shut and latched and the outer doors locked. Someone,' she went on, putting down the paper and mercifully fixing her gaze this time upon the branch over her head, 'someone stole out of his or her room last night and pinched that toffee, jar and all. It's pretty obvious Marjorie suspects one of us. She said:—"I haven't said anything to Miss Lacey—yet," just as if she were meaning to give us a chance to put the thing back.'

At the Cedars everyone except Tony and myself slept alone. I remembered having gone to sleep early the previous night. Tony, so he says, once asleep never wakes until he is called. I wished now, with all my heart, that I could be sure of his having been asleep before me. . . .

It was Tony who asked now:—'Why one of us? What about the maids?'

Nancy raised her eyebrows. 'Marjorie is really Miss Lacey's housekeeper. She's been with her for twenty years. I heard Miss Lacey saying so. And Bessie (Bessie was the cook) doesn't sleep in, and so wasn't in the house during the hours in which the jar disappeared. If you say it was Bessie, you might just as well accuse Miss Lacey herself.'

'Or Mr. Dalton?' suggested Hubert, through a yawn.

'Mr. Dalton is a writer of detective novels,' said Nancy loftily, telling us what we already knew. 'He's Miss Lacey's nephew *and* the father of a family. *Do* grown-ups steal toffee? I've never heard of it.'

'Grown-ups don't get any more sweets points than we do,' I put in defensively. But I really could not think of Mr. Dalton as a criminal.

'You can rule him out,' said Nancy. 'He gave me some of his sweets points. Doesn't like sweets. So—what?'

'Cleared,' said Hubert. 'And the jar itself wouldn't interest him. It was frightfully ordinary.'

'It had flowers painted on it,' I said. 'It was good enough for Marjorie to be afraid of breaking.'

'How d'you know?' asked Nancy. She added, 'You seem to know a lot about that jar, Stephen.'

'I know,' I said, nettled, 'because Marjorie asked me to move it for her yesterday afternoon when she was laying the tea. She—'

Nancy broke in impatiently:—'Oh, she'd be afraid of breaking anything. It's her sight. Can't you see how she peers? And Miss Lacey may be kind enough, but Marjorie's told me how she carries on if anything gets even chipped. She told me as a warning when I was helping with the washing up. Of course I know Miss Lacey's things are *good,* but Marjorie seemed scared stiff of anything happening to the china.'

'Well, you are a bit slap-dash,' said Hubert.

Nancy glared at her brother.

We were getting no further, only becoming personal. I thought it best to break up the meeting. It was time for elevenses, anyhow.

As we strolled back to the house the twins and Hubert were silent. Nancy went on talking. I was thinking, trying desperately to review the situation. If only I could solve the problem and clear our three selves!

'Of course I don't really suspect Marjorie, but one must be thorough. I shall certainly search her bedroom,' said Nancy, dropping her voice as we neared the house.

She saw how horrified I looked. She laughed.

'Why not? I happen to know it's her afternoon off.'

At home Mother never dreamed of going into the maids' rooms—not without asking them first. It was a thing you didn't do—any more than you opened and looked into another chap's desk at school. A hateful thought then came to me. The high-handed Nancy might not stop at Marjorie's room. She would be planning to come into ours, mine and Tony's—Rosine's also. And just suppose one of the twins happened to have left toffee papers about? We usually spent our sweets points on toffee. Nancy would pounce at once. I remembered the toffee in the jar being the wrapped kind.

With this fear before me I gulped down my lemonade and ran up to the room Tony and I shared. Then, remembering that Rosine was still only halfway through her drink, I stole along to her room. No one could be suspicious at finding me in my own quarters, but Rosine would most certainly wonder at my being in hers. Better to make my search there while I knew her to be occupied. I was lucky. No one caught me trespassing. Hastily I pulled open drawers, looked into the waste-paper basket, searched every likely spot. No toffee papers anywhere. Then I went back to Tony's and my room. Our clothes overflowed into one another's compartments. Were Tony to come in and find me poking about among his own particular possessions he would not be surprised. My search here could therefore be made more leisurely than the one rushed through among Rosine's belongings.

Although I feared most desperately what Nancy must conclude should she come upon even one toffee paper, yet I was not really expecting to find any, since Tony, I knew, had bought the whole of his month's ration in the first week, and we were now nearing the end of the period. Still, with Nancy on the war-path, one could not afford to take risks. It was maddening to have her setting herself up as a detective, yet if Marjorie were out to fasten the guilt upon one of us, you could hardly blame Nancy or anyone else for trying to find the real culprit. That at least, was how I reasoned it out at the time.

I was getting along famously in our room, finding no 'incriminating evidence' at all, when, opening a little drawer in the dressing-table, I saw them—a whole bunch— toffee papers! They even had 'toffee' written on them. My heart seemed to stand still. Then it began to pound away just as if there were a hammer in my chest. I

grabbed the lot, stuffed them into my pocket, slammed the drawer shut. Of course, I told myself, these must be from Tony's own sweets ration. Yet—*why* had he kept them? Why should I find them all together like this? When you eat toffee you take it out, piece by piece, from your pocket and then throw the sticky bit of paper away. Careful people might save it for paper salvage, but that would not be like Tony. No, it all looked black enough, hatefully black.

All sorts of wild ideas flew into my head. I would go to Nancy, produce the papers, say I had taken the toffee myself—anything to shield Tony. Then, when actually at the door, I remembered how Tony had flown out at Nancy when, half laughing, she had aimed one of her barbed shafts at me. 'You'd have to prove it!' he had cried. Was it likely, then, that Tony would allow me to shield him by taking the guilt upon myself?

Now, more than ever, was it necessary for the problem to be solved. I *must* get rid of this hateful suspicion— scotch it for ever. One moment and I was prepared to go bail for Tony's honesty—the next, and I could almost hear myself saying:— 'Oh, well, it was only a jar of toffee.'

Had Tony eaten in the night all the toffee once contained in those papers now in my pocket he must, I reasoned, be feeling pretty queer. Could he have shared it with Rosine? Between breakfast and the meeting under the cedar I had been to the village on an errand for Miss Lacey. It would have been possible for the two to have enjoyed an orgy in the bedroom while I was out. Neither twin would give the other away. They had been like that even when they were small. What used Nurse to say? As 'thick as thieves'. Thieves? I shuddered.

'No!' I said, and was surprised to hear myself speaking aloud. 'I would *not* suspect my own family.' Of course I could have got the twins together and asked for an explanation of the strange hoard, but to do so would have been to show them I was suspicious. We had been re-united for so short a time. *That* would be no way to bridge the gap the years of separation had made.

I ran over the remaining 'possibles'—Hubert, Mr Dalton, Marjorie and, yes, Nancy herself. Yet, were Nancy the culprit, would she have been so ready to pass on to us the news of the loss? And—Marjorie? If *she* were the thief, then why point out the disappearance of the jar to Nancy? Yet whoever had taken the toffee must have expected it to be missed. Perhaps, I reasoned, if you took something and then started talking about the disappearance, you yourself would be the last to attract suspicion. This was deep thinking. Was Marjorie capable of working things out thus far? Nancy? Oh, yes, her wits were quick enough. But—Nancy was my friend.

I turned to the remaining two. Mr. Dalton? Nancy's statement had as good as cleared him. You did not give sweets points away with one hand and steal toffee with the other. Mr. Dalton had left soon after breakfast, his visit at an end. Hubert? But I could not make myself go into his room and search there. I do not want to appear a prig, and I am pretty sure it was the fear of being caught in the act that held me back. My head was buzzing now. The thoughts were going round and round in it like a squirrel in a cage. Now I was considering Marjorie again. Suppose she *had* taken the toffee, what could have been her motive? Toffee has no wild attraction for grown-ups. Could Marjorie have fallen for the jar? It would be the sort of thing that might easily take her fancy. Yet she had been with Miss Lacey for twenty years. Suppose— and now my heart was thumping again—suppose Marjorie had accidently *broken* the jar— Her sight was bad. Both Nancy and I had produced evidence to prove Marjorie's tear of breakages. Why should she be afraid to own up? Was she—and now my heart was nearly jumping out of my chest—was she afraid of being sent away . . . afraid that Miss Lacey, having realised how bad her sight had become, might feel it too much of a menace to her precious china and glass?

'I won't go into Marjorie's room,' I told myself, 'but there's nothing against examining the dust bin. I'll do it this afternoon when she's out.'

If Marjorie were indeed the criminal, then it was pretty mean of her to be sheltering behind us. She must know we would be suspected. Toffee—and kids. It is almost as natural to say as Marshall & Snelgrove. Would Marjorie have told Miss Lacey of the loss? Miss Lacey had seemed ordinary enough at the breakfast table. In time, told or not, she must miss the jar. I wondered whether she would question us singly or wait until we were all together, at lunch for instance. Should I take the bull by the horns, go to Miss Lacey and ask what kind of toffee was in the jar? The sticky pieces of paper now in my pocket were marked with a maker's name. Yet—suppose that *was* the make? And again—was Miss Lacey likely to remember? It might be proved at the shop where the toffee had been bought, but the jar had the look of a bazaar product. In that case it would be a frightful job to trace the shop from which the toffee had come.

I found that I was pacing up and down the room. Useless to go on like this. I had done a stout bit of thinking. It would be best now to join the others. Forgetting I had the toffee papers still in my pocket I went downstairs.

What we did during the rest of that morning I cannot remember, but I do recall the heat. It was positively tropical. The two labradors were panting where they lay in the shade of the porch. Lunch-time came.

'Well,' said Miss Lacey, smiling upon us. 'I can remember few English summers to come up to this. What a pity there is nowhere for you all to bathe.' She laughed. 'And to think of the plans I had made for wet days! I remember last August it was so rainy we actually had to resort to sweet making. Just as if it were Christmas! I wasn't prepared then, but this time I've managed to save some sugar and treacle and fats. I don't care for toffee, but I expect you all do.'

It was as if a pebble had been flung into a pool. If any one of us had forgotten the affair of the toffee jar, we were conscious enough of it again now. I had dropped my eyes to my plate, but I could feel Nancy looking at me. I knew my cheeks were flaming.

'Of course we like toffee,' said Nancy brightly. 'I expect we would all have loved making it.' She added politely: 'It was very kind of you to plan it for us.'

I longed to look at Miss Lacey, but I did not dare. Were her remarks entirely innocent or had she thrown them at us so as to notice how we would react? Again I realised I must be appearing the guilty one. I took up my knife and fork and attacked the cold pie with such unnecessary vigour that a piece flew from my plate and landed on the floor.

'We used to make lots of toffee out in Canada,' Tony was saying. 'Rosine's got the what-d'you-call-it—the recipe somewhere. It was easier getting the stuff for it out there.'

Gradually the conversation returned to what might be called the normal. When the meal was over we all strolled out into the garden, everyone anxious to find a patch of shade. Miss Lacey installed herself in a deck chair in the porch and at once appeared engrossed in a letter. Nancy flung herself down beside me under the cedar. I had sought out this spot as a useful vantage point, and I guessed Nancy to have done the same. From here we could see the path to the kitchen door and would know when Marjorie left the house. I would have to wait for Bessie's departure as well. Nancy would make for Marjorie's bedroom, I for the dustbin. Her quarry was the jar—intact; mine the pieces of broken painted glass. We neither of us spoke of what was in our minds. I wondered whether she had visited *our* rooms as yet. I smiled grimly to myself. With the toffee papers secure in my pocket I felt reasonably safe. But I must get rid of them. With no fires going, this would not be so easy. I did not like to risk dropping them among the bushes. They could be buried, of course, but just now I needed to stay where I was so as to watch for Marjorie.

I did not mean to close my eyes, but the heat was making me sleepy. When I opened them Nancy was still beside me, but Miss Lacey had left her chair. I heard the telephone tinkle faintly and guessed her to be ringing up somebody. Later I was to connect this with the return of Mr. Dalton. When she came back she took up the letter again.

The back door opened and Marjorie came out. Bessie was with her. She always went home as soon as the luncheon washing up was over, coming back in time to cook the evening meal. Through half closed eyes I looked at Nancy. She was sitting up now. In less than a minute I was alone. I let her get inside the house, then strolled, in as casual a manner as I could affect, round to the back door. There, a quick look in all directions, including one at the windows above, and I flattered myself I was unobserved. In a flash I had the lid of the dustbin off and was rummaging as quietly as I could among the unpleasing contents. No luck. No evidence here. Standing beside the bin, the lid in my hand, I asked myself—what next?

'Hullo, sleuth!'

Looking up I saw the mocking eyes of Nancy gazing down at me from the window I realised, now, must belong to Marjorie's bedroom. My first reaction was one of relief. I had so nearly consigned the toffee papers to the bin. Only the thought of the kitchen fire (cremation being a safer method of disposal) had saved me. What an escape! I pulled myself together, managing to grin at her.

'Nothing here,' I said, replacing the lid.

'Nor here.' Nancy was remembering now to lower her voice. 'Half a jiffy,' she whispered. 'I'll join you in the kitchen.'

Gone, then, were my hopes of the kitchen fire. The toffee papers must remain with me until I could be certain of solitude. To be found poking something in among the glowing coals—that *would* be a give-away. I had only to stay downstairs, I told myself. Unless Nancy had already visited our bedrooms she would have that piece of sleuthing still upon her afternoon's programme.

'I tell you what,' said Nancy, as we stood together beside the kitchen table. 'I ought to have got into Marjorie's room before she went out. If she took the thing, she might have it with her. And she *was* carrying a biggish bag.'

I was silent for a minute, considering whether I should tell Nancy of what I half suspected—that Marjorie had broken the jar and was afraid (for reasons I had already worked out) to confess. That I decided against sharing my suspicions was due mainly to my fear of the way in which the headstrong Nancy might choose to act upon them. But I had also a strong desire to beat her at this game of sleuthing and to find things out without her interference. And, too, there was the hateful knowledge of what I had found in that drawer in our room. If Tony *were* the culprit, then it would be unfair to cast grave suspicion upon anyone else.

'Do you think Miss Lacey knows yet about the toffee

being pinched?' asked Nancy, for the second time. And again, just as when we were together under the cedar, she said:—'I thought it very fishy—her mentioning the toffee-making at lunch.'

Could that have been no more than a coincidence? What was there for me to say? Then Nancy started poking about the kitchen premises, opening drawers, peering behind the jars and canisters on the mantelshelf, even going into the larder.

'Complete blank,' she admitted finally.

I hoped she would go now and leave me alone with the kitchen fire. Instead she linked her arm in mine and drew me out of the room. It had been terribly hot in the kitchen, even with the window open, and now I jumped at Nancy's truly brilliant suggestion that we should get into bathing kit and turn the garden hose upon one another.

Miss Lacey said we could have the hose. I found the others, and sent Tony up to get our things. We were to change in the garden sheds. That was Miss Lacey's idea. I suppose she did not fancy the thought of dripping creatures returning up her stairs. As if the sun would not have dried us in two ticks! However, it did not matter to us—at least, I could not see then that it would matter—and we boys undressed in the potting shed while Nancy and Rosine enjoyed the greater comfort of the summer house. Trust girls for that!

It was grand, that hose—the icy spray, so terrifically in contrast with the stifling atmosphere, made us shriek. Even Hubert woke up. Rosine forgot her shyness. As for Tony, he was like a mad thing. In his scarlet bathing slip he raced about the lawn, darting into the stream of water and away, turning cartwheels, standing on his head. If Tony were our criminal—then his powers of forgetfulness were phenomenal.

Halfway through the performance I missed Nancy. It was only when we were dressing that I connected this with what I guessed to have been a visit to our discarded clothing.

The toffee papers were gone!

I had put my hand in my trouser pocket. The handkerchief I needed was there—but no papers.

Tony had been with us all the time. I was sure of that. *He* had not re-visited the potting shed. I couldn't remember about Hubert. It would not have entered Rosine's head to go there. Indeed, Nancy was the only one of us I had missed. How I blamed myself! But it was too late now. Well, there was one thing about it. She would accuse me, not Tony. And if I could prevent the accusation from coming to his ears. . . .

At tea I avoided Nancy's eye. I knew just what she must be thinking. It hurt—yet how could I clear myself without throwing suspicion upon Tony? I imagined Nancy saying to herself:—'Clever of Stephen to pretend to be looking in the dustbin for clues. I must have called out to him just when he was going to get rid of the toffee papers.'

Two emotions now warred within me—self pity and a queer pride that I should be suffering to save my brother. Heroics, if you like. In this silly morbid state of mind it was not likely that I should notice much about other people's troubles, and it was Nancy who told me afterwards how worried Miss Lacey was looking. Nancy had put this down to the toffee jar affair. She felt sure, now, that Marjorie must have spoken about it. I had begun to feel furious with Nancy. Why need she set herself up as a detective? It was going to put an end to our friendship. She would never want to go fishing with me again—not after having proved to her own satisfaction that I was a thief. And did *I* want the friendship of a girl who thought nothing of going through one's pockets as she had?

When tea was over Miss Lacey asked if we would mind washing up. 'My nephew is coming back this evening,' she said. Then, when we looked surprised, she added:— 'I need his advice over a rather difficult matter. You'll be careful with the china, won't you? Marjorie is out. I must get his room ready myself.'

That Mr. Dalton should be coming back, and to deal with 'a rather difficult matter,' was appalling. What could it mean but that Miss Lacey needed his advice in the matter of the stolen toffee jar? Mr. Dalton, a writer of detective novels. . . . Why, it was as good as to employ a detective.

In the face of this you might have expected a babble of excited chatter round the pantry sink. Hubert and Tony did begin to talk about Mr. Dalton's return, but Nancy shut them up. They gaped at her. Nancy, of all people, to have lost interest in the problem of the missing toffee jar!

'Miss Lacey might have asked us herself,' complained Hubert, 'before putting it in detective hands.'

'Oh, what's it matter!' snapped Nancy.

The younger ones soon drifted away, leaving me alone with Nancy. This was not at all to my liking, but there were still some knives and spoons to put away, and I could not very well rat on her. Nancy rinsed out the washing-up bowl without speaking. Then, careful not to be looking at me, she said very low:—'Don't worry. I know I teased you, Stephen, about the wretched toffee, but truly I'd never have said a word if I'd thought. . . .' She paused. I dropped the spoons noisily into the silver basket. 'Don't worry,' she said again, and then, even lower:—'I'm not going to split.'

I was angry, miserable—but under the circumstances what could I say? I said nothing. To be honest—well, I very nearly disgraced myself by bursting into tears. Our job was ended now. Ungraciously, still saying nothing, I left her.

By dinner-time Mr. Dalton was with us again. Miserably I waited to see the 'detecting' begin. I had no plans. Let what would be—be. That was now my attitude. Perhaps the heat had something to do with it. In spite of our afternoon's refresher we were all exhausted. Before the meal ended the first roll of thunder came.

'In for a storm,' said Mr. Dalton. He turned to us. 'I prophesy a deluge. You'll all be house-bound to-morrow.'

'Poor dears!' sympathised Miss Lacey. 'Never mind. It will be a chance to do the toffee-making we were talking about.'

'That'll be super!' cried Tony, excitedly. 'And I know I've got some wrapping papers somewhere.'

I held my breath. *Could* he have forgotten the cloud that hung over us? Must he give himself away like this? Nancy was beside me at the table. I could feel her stiffen. We shared the tension of the moment.

Tony went on, unconcernedly:—'In Canada we could get the stuff to make it with, but, where we were, there wasn't the right kind of paper for wrapping it up. So Rosine and I got in the habit of saving the bits off the toffee we bought.'

'Off the toffee we bought,' echoed Rosine. 'We always saved it.'

If Miss Lacey disliked the idea of using toffee papers that must have seen the doubtfully clean linings of Tony's pockets, she did not say so.

There came now a second roll of thunder. The air seemed charged with the electricity of the advancing storm. We were to provide our own electric shocks, however— one after the other.

(*Continued on page* 259)

What are you going to be? ANIMAL DOCTOR

Photographs by Pictorial Press

The ambulance calls to pick up a patient.

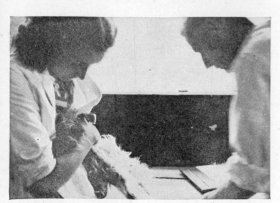

An assistant reassures a nervous dog while a dressing is applied

If you want to be a doctor, you must take a five-year training, whether your patient is a human being or a dog. The medical knowledge you need is much the same in either case. You have to study Chemistry, Physics, Biology, Anatomy, Pharmacy, and a host of other matters. To love animals and want to work with and for them is not enough. Animals need scientific care when bones are broken, diseases take hold, or accidents happen.

The People's Dispensary for Sick Animals has a network of dispensaries, and mobile units all over Britain, staffed by trained men and women. Anyone who cannot afford the services of a veterinary surgeon can take their dog, cat, monkey, horse, guinea pig, mouse or goldfish if it is suffering, and find help and treatment at a P.D.S.A. Dispensary. If the trouble is too serious or complicated, the animal will be taken to one of the P.D.S.A. Animal Hospitals, where it is admitted as a patient. It can be examined by X-ray, tests can be made in the laboratory, and the trouble will be diagnosed and dealt with. There is a ward for all small animals and there are stables for sick horses.

The Sanatorium at Ilford has students in training to become Technical Officers, where they receive their training from a Teaching Staff of veterinary surgeons, doctors, pharmacists and others.

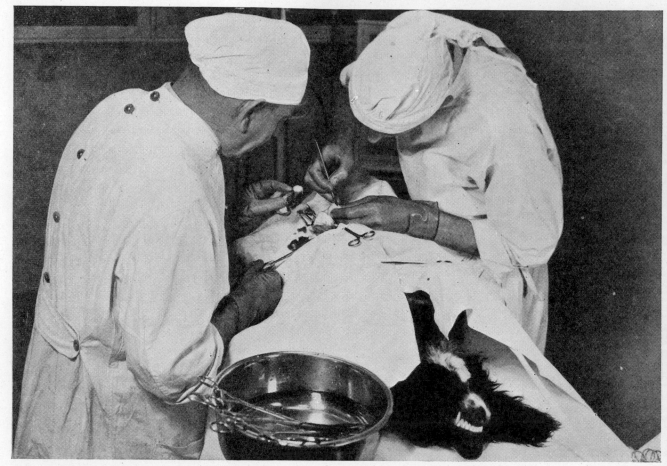

The operating theatre is equipped like any other.   This dog has been given an anæsthetic while the operation is in progress.

This protective hood stops the dog scratching his sore ear.

An injured swan has his leg bound. He is very strong and the assistant holds him firmly.

The work of technical officers is more difficult than ordinary medical work, for the patients can't describe their symptoms. They can't say 'thank you' either, but they have a way of looking, which is more expressive than words and this more than satisfies the staff who have helped them to recover.

To become one of the students who are taken for training, it is necessary to have reached the age of 21 years and have had at least a Secondary School Education, be willing to work away from home and to take up P.D.S.A. work as a career.

The P.D.S.A. is an organisation supported entirely by voluntary contributions from animal lovers. All treatment is free but boxes are placed in the dispensaries in which donations may be put.

All who want to become qualified surgeons, have to win the Diploma of Membership of the Royal College of Veterinary Surgeons. All the information about details of registering and being admitted to veterinary schools attached to Universities and Colleges, or affiliated schools, can be obtained from the Secretary, The Royal College of Veterinary Surgeons, 9, Red Lion Square, London, W.C.1.

The veterinary surgeon plays a big part in keeping farm animals healthy, in keeping horses well for the many different kinds of work they do, but there is also endless work to be done with pet animals of all shapes and sizes and kinds at home and throughout the Colonies and the Commonwealth.

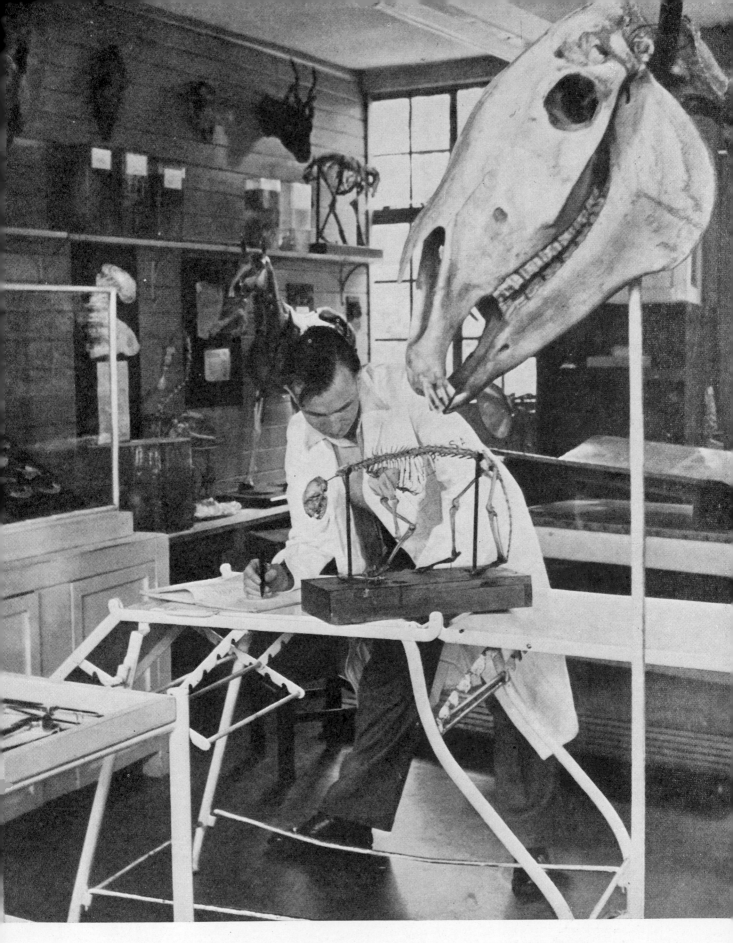

The lecture room at the P.D.S.A. Animal Hospital has specimens and equipment of all kinds. Students can study here and learn all that is necessary before they take up work in one of the dispensaries.

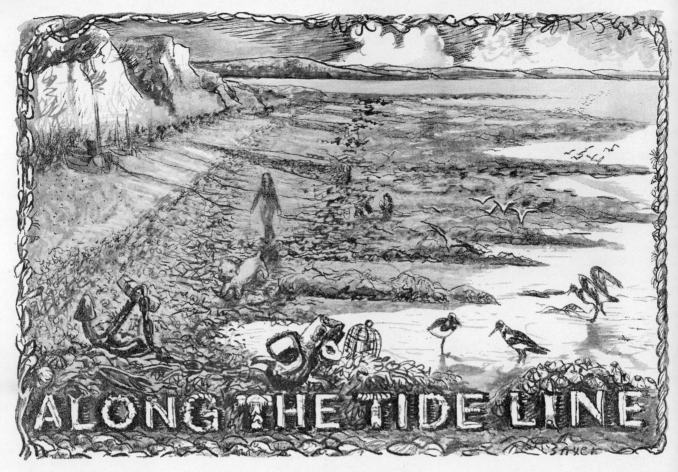

ALONG THE TIDE LINE

By Joan Heywood

ILLUSTRATED BY DERRICK SAYER

WE HAD BEEN down on the beach all the afternoon. After picnic tea, a laziness spread across the bay, and only Squib, the sealyham, had energy for any more games.

I got up and wandered slowly down the beach to where the green sea, now far out, was breaking idly in little waves. I picked up a pebble and rolled it in the palm of my hand. It was pink and grey, and as round and smooth as a marble. The waves seemed to have hardly enough strength to break, and drew back each time with a sigh, leaving a curling line, a lace pattern of scum and bubbles on the sand. I picked up another pebble, greeny-blue, with a hole right through the middle, big enough to put my little finger into, and make a ring. Mermaids' rings, my grandmother used to call them.

I walked along with one foot in the sea and the other on the wet sand, and the waves tossed up out of themselves, almost at my feet, a jelly fish, and left it lying wet and shining on the beach. It reflected all the colours of the rainbow, and was so transparent that I could see completely through it.

Just beyond it, on the sand, was an oval shape, white and salty looking. A large seashell, I thought, but when I got close, I saw it was a piece of cuttlefish— part of the body of a dead fish, bleached white and hard by the sea. If you find any of this, and have a canary, take a piece home, for he will love to peck at it. The live cuttlefish is a very curious

Sea Shells
(1) Wide Mouthed Whelk. (2) Spiny Cockle.
(3) Top Shells. (4) Glaucous Trough Shell.
(5) Piddock. (6) Mussel. (7) Razor Shell.
(8) Wentle Trap Shell. (9) Great Scallop.
(10) Grey Coat of Mail Shell.

creature, striped grey and brown with bulging eyes and eight octopus-like tentacles at his head. He swims backwards and forwards with equal ease, propelling himself along like a water rocket by squirting jets of water through a tubular siphon under his head. When he is alarmed he lets out an inky liquid, and makes a 'smoke screen' all round him, and escapes behind it.

Shells were lying scattered all over the sands. There were long, thin, empty razor shells, sometimes joined together in pairs, sometimes separate. Near them I found a live razor shell, half buried in the sand. It was not white like the empty ones, but covered with a polished olive green skin, marked with purple. As the tide goes down, razor shells, like many other shells, burrow into the sand for safety.

There were large, elongated piddock shells, too, white with pale purple and yellow and blue markings; and scallops of pink and cream, and dark red and brown; top shells, cone-shaped, like little tops, or turbans from the Arabian Nights, coloured red and yellow, and sometimes blue near the point; dark blue mussels; slender spiral wentle trap shells; and heart-shaped, prickly cockles, yellow-white with bands of rusty red. Cockles usually burrow into the soft sand like many other shells when the tide is

...ut, but when they are left on the sur-ace they sometimes behave in an amaz-ng way, hopping and skipping over the ands towards the incoming tide, as if hey were full of excitement to meet it.

If you hold a big shell, like a wide-nouthed whelk to your ear, even when ou are far inland, you will still be able o hear the sound of the sea breaking nside it.

A little way ahead, was a dead star ish, brittle and stiff, with hardly any olour left in its star. But live star fish an quite often be found, orange col-ured generally, in the water under over-anging rocks. Reach your hand down nder a ledge near the bottom of a tide ool, and you may find one.

I looked up and saw Ben, the beach-omber. Ever since most people can emember he has walked this beach, n all weathers to scavenge the flotsam nd jetsam left lying high and dry as the ide goes down. At the village by the eadland Ben has a ramshackle shop in n old stable behind the inn.

He lives at the shop with his brother, n old sailor with a white beard and a wooden leg. The sailor looks after the hop when Ben is out, and tinkers the roken pots and pans, and makes things rom the pieces of junk—beautiful models of sailing ships, animals and igures carved in wood, and ships in ottles—and he never uses any material hat has not been found on the beach. Sometimes the fishermen bring him sea urchins that have been caught in their lobster pots, round shell creatures, covered with dark, spiney prickles like a hedgehog. He cuts off the prickles, cleans the inside of the shell and polishes the surface until it becomes a coloured dome, sometimes beautifully patterned and sold as an ornament.

Today Ben carried a sack over his bent back and a very battered bird cage in one hand.

'Hallo,' I said, 'have you had a good day?'

'Not bad,' he said, 'not too good, but not too bad.' He opened the sack.

'Some tin pieces up near the point, a bottle or two, a bit of anchor chain, a kettle—'

'And the bird cage,' I said.

'A parrot's cage,' he said, 'I found it at the rocks. It once belonged to some sea captain as likely as not. They mostly keep a parrot.'

He said there were lucky days all the year round, but in general the summer was not such a good time, except for the things that picnickers left behind them. It was in the winter, after a storm, or during the spring tides in

Jelly Fish
Rhysastoma, Common, Chrysaora.

March and September, when the sea floods in higher and faster than at any other time of the year, that you found the most exciting things.

'Well, I must be getting along now,' he said, and tramped off towards the headland, his sea boots leaving heavy footprints in the wet sand. He collects flotsam and jetsam, others collect cockles and mussels and winkles, or dig sand eels and worms for bait, or cut sea-weed, or catch prawns and shrimps, and in winter every long-shore man is a wild fowler, for below the high-tide mark is free shooting and any man with a gun can try his luck with the wild duck and geese.

Near the rocks the beach became stony with sea weeds growing. I turned over some of the stones and underneath were hundreds of shore hoppers. When they were uncovered they squirmed helter-skelter, as quickly as they could back into another dark place.

I found some old dog-fish eggs, too. These are strange eggs, each enclosed in a shiny brown envelope, with tendrils at the end to attach them to a plant for safety until they are hatched. Sometimes you will find them still unhatched on the seaweeds, but generally it is the old cases, black and hard, that are seen lying about.

I came to the rocks, and wedged in a crevice I saw a cork float with a piece of tarred rope knotted through the hole at the centre. It was the sort of float used by the fishermen to mark the posi-tions of their lobster pots in the sea around the rocks.

I scrambled over the rocks, slipping and sliding on the seaweeds. They were all sorts of lovely shapes—wrack-covered with little bladders that popped when I trod on them or pinched them between my finger and thumb; long thong weeds, sometimes like a whip with handle and many lashes, sometimes like an ele-phant's tail; and thick, shiny strands of oar weed, about which there is the say-ing that if you hang a piece up in a room, it will foretell the weather, feeling wet when it is going to rain and dry when the sun is coming out, but I have never found it worked very well.

In among the rocks were pools of very clear water, left by the outgoing tide. I came to a big pool and looked in. Make yourself in your imagination as small as an inch high, smaller than Alice in Wonderland after she had drunk from the bottle down the rabbit hole, and when you look into the pool it will seem

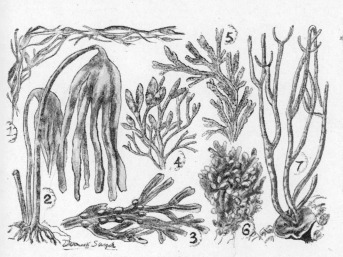

Sea Weeds
(1) Knotted Wrack. (2) Oar Weed. (3) Bladder Wrack. (4) Channelled Wrack. (5) Serrated Wrack. (6) Flat Wrack. (7) Thong Weed.

Cuttle Fish
(A) Cuttle Fish Bone.
(B) Living Cuttle Fish.

Sea Urchin
(A) Case or Shell.
(B) Living Sea Urchin.

like the deep sea itself, with a sea bottom of rocky mountains and valleys, more exciting than an aquarium and almost as full of creatures.

It was a fairy land, full of shimmering colours and strange shadows, pinks and greens, silver and dark blue-black. I saw shrimps of all sizes, almost without form, like ghosts moving in the water, and shoals of tiny fry swimming among the plants, always changing their minds about which way they were going, now dark, now silver as they turned, now disappearing altogether.

Clinging to the sides of the pool were sea anemones, each open like a flower-head, with a mass of gently waving feelers, long petals, round a mouth in the centre. They were pink and yellow, and blue-green, lovely to look at, but sinister—for beware the shrimp who swims too close. The feelers will move towards him, surround him, coil him nearer and nearer to the mouth, until he is sucked down altogether.

Under a ledge near the bottom of the pool, I discovered a greeny-yellow coat-of-mail shell, shaped like a woodlouse, and like a woodlouse, too, it will roll itself up in a ball if it is detached from its rock. I put a stick into the water, but before I reached the shell the silver sand on the floor of the pool moved. I looked again and saw it was not the sand, but the back of a flat fish, a little plaice. He was so well camouflaged, spotted and dappled like the shingle,

that until he moved I had not seen him.

There were other fish in the pool, too. I caught sight of their bright eyes looking out from black crevices or dark plant shadows. I saw them for a second at a time as they darted from their hiding places and back again—blennies, with high spikey back fins, shannies and gobies. Both blennies and gobies like to hide in old bottles. I once saw a blenny in a tide pool, looking out of an old Bovril bottle, filling up the entrance with

its body like a cork, and guarding the eggs it had laid inside.

I dropped a little piece of bread from my pocket into the water. At once there was great excitement. Fry and prawns and shrimps dashed from all corners towards it, moving the water in rings and swirls, and tried to nibble it as it floated down. Anemones reached towards it with their feelers. A goby darted from a rock, two blennies from the weeds. Then a crab rushed out of his crevice, scattering them all, and carried it away.

I left the rocks and walked back along the high-tide mark; a wavey line of debris—grasses, sticks and old seed pods—left on the shingle at the tide's limit. Beyond it, many yards higher up the beach where the grass now grew, was the spring tide's mark, a thicker line of rubbish, matted together, dried and white in the summer sun. Among it I saw an old teapot, part of it still enamelled blue. There were sticks and grass coming out of the top, and inside was a nest, empty now, but that had been full earlier.

The sun was dropping behind the cliffs. I ran between the tide marks and as I went I felt in my pockets and touched and counted with my fingers the things I had scavenged from the shore—a piece of cuttlefish, two razor shells, the marble pebble, three or four curious-shaped shells. Tied to my belt was the cork float, and on my finger a mermaid's ring. I felt quite a beachcomber.

VISITS TO THE ZOO

by Barbara Bower and Geoffrey Dearmer
FELLOWS OF THE ROYAL ZOOLOGICAL SOCIETY

Mainly About Food

*'Stone walls do not a prison make
Nor iron bars a cage'*

wrote Richard Lovelace, to which animals at the Zoo might reply, 'Perhaps not, but they make a jolly good imitation.' So it's up to visitors to repay the pleasure they get from staring at the happy captives. The great majority of them are quite obviously happy, and enjoy human company. If you don't believe this, notice the way that a tiger mother will bring her cubs right up to the front bars of the cage to be admired by visitors. Zoo authorities tell us that animals often resent being moved into bigger and better accommodation. All the same, the creatures' lives are monotonous, and you can help them by never going to the Gardens unless you take some food with you. This is as great a pleasure as it is a duty, and it adds to the happiness of your visit.

Fill a basket with whatever scraps can be spared—stale bread and cake, outside leaves and stalks of vegetables—a carrot or two will go a long way if cut in segments. Take any sort of fruit, but remember grapes are the best if you can get them because some of the smaller birds in the Bird House live on little or nothing else. Many of the larger birds like the toucans are surprisingly expert grape-catchers. Cherries, sultanas, indeed any fruit is welcome in the right quarters. But don't forget *the right quarters.* Whatever you do, don't feed the animals that may not be fed (among these are camels and certain monkeys) or offer unsuitable food to them.

Don't believe the people who tell you that animals will eat only what is good for them. A horse, for instance, may die from colic after eating too much wet grass, or be poisoned by yew-leaves. It cannot be sick, and so reject what disagrees with it. Many of the animals at the Zoo have fads about food, and if you want to experiment, ask a keeper first.

Some animals will eat almost anything, but, as a rule, carnivores will only eat flesh—though the little jennets (they belong to the cat family) have varied tastes.

The herbivores are so called because they eat herbs, *i.e.*, vegetable food, like the elephants and the hippos.

Get a supply of nuts if possible, not preferably monkey-nuts because animals get too many of them. Make friends, if you can, with a human herbivore (a vegetarian) for vegetarians are allowed a generous supply of nuts of all sorts instead of meat, and there is no more pleasant or portable food to take with you. Some of the larger birds, such as ravens and jackdaws, take them eagerly and gently, and the monkeys will swing down to you if you are nut-conscious, as indeed they are.

Ask your grocer for locust beans and, if he has any in stock, lay in a good supply. They look like bars of chocolate, taste sweet, last for ever and are very popular. If you approach the head keeper of the Giraffes he will probably let you feed the giraffes with locust beans or spring onions, and you will feel particularly privileged, for the public is not allowed to feed these animals.

Perhaps the same keeper will let you come with him into the enclosure of Peggy, the pigmy hippo. If she is in a good mood, she will lumber out of the warm, muddy water, and open her anything but pigmy jaws, for she, too, loves locust beans. The folds about her shoulders feel like very hard and warm indiarubber.

You can take raw meat for the larger predatory birds and the animals in the small cats' house. You can even take any but flat fish for the seals, but fish can be nasty stuff to handle. If you must take fish to the seals and otters, it is best to put sprats or herrings into a screw-topped jar.

Keepers at the reptile and bird houses will welcome you if you bring meal worms or any grubs and, of course, you will be doing a good turn to the home garden as well as the Gardens if you collect grubs, particularly the little grey grubs of the daddy-long-legs and almost all caterpillars. But don't sacrifice a rare caterpillar, take it to the Curator of the Insect House and ask him what it is if you can't find out for yourself.

Remember, when you are feeding animals, that they hate jerky movements and sudden noises. Mind your fingers. Visitors are warned not to feed certain animals and birds by hand. Some birds have strong beaks, and a mongoose can do a lot of damage very suddenly, though it may seem very friendly at first.

Zebras like sugar and apples but should be fed, like horses, from a flat palm. Better still, put your offering on the ledge of the stall.

On the whole, we recommend animals with damp noses, such as all the deer tribe, as being the most pleasant to feed. Gentleman is their middle name: their others, though important, matter less.

Bears like ices, but PLEASE, don't leave the cartons about.

By the way, a hooked walking stick is a most useful thing to take with you because it will help you to retrieve the scraps of food that fall outside arm's reach of you and the animals.

If you have the chance of going often to the Zoo, you will have far more amusement if you visit a few animals at a time, and these regularly. It can be more fun to give a few sultanas to the fruit-bats, and spend ten minutes or so in watching them sidling towards you and opening their tiny jaws, and in noticing the frail rustling silk of their umbrella-like wings, than in hurling a bun at a bear and then rushing off to fling a scrap to a monkey.

It is best, too, to give your food before the official feeding times, for then the tiny monkeys, instead of looking at you with mournful contempt, will stretch their small and tender hands through the bars, and all the creatures will welcome what you bring to them.

THE SECRET CARAVAN

by Jean Simpson

ILLUSTRATED BY SHIRLEY HUGHES

IN A LITTLE CLEARING in the wood where the trees seemed to have stood back on purpose, it was. It hadn't been there last week, Judith was sure of that. Yet it was as if it had always been there, so settled it looked; a long twist of blue smoke coming from the tall chimney peaceful as an old man's pipe smoked by a gate on a Sunday evening.

It was a caravan. A blue caravan. A very upright caravan on big, blue wheels. A caravan whose right to be in the wood one would no more have dreamed of questioning than the right of the brambles to tangle the grass so spikily, or the flowers to grow at all.

Judith didn't want to disturb the caravan, not being an intruding sort of person. So instead she gathered blackberries all round it, although the ones that grew there were rather pink and hard, and she didn't suppose Aunt Anna would care for them much. Then she began to sing very softly, because she did very much want to attract the caravan's attention.

'Time of day—eleven o'clock. Time of year—September. School bell clanging. Sticky buns and milk. Skipping and such. But no little girl! Why? Little girl picking blackberries. Very strange. Very singular.'

Judith looked at the caravan door. An old man looked at Judith. A plum-coloured velvet coat, a bucket of very grey water in one hand, a mop in the other, and really not a fierce face at all. Indeed, it was smiling.

'School doesn't start just yet,' she said. 'I see you're busy,' she added.

'Ah! You can't catch me off my guard. Spring cleaning, you know. Always do it in Autumn. No competition.'

'But you aren't always here,' said Judith.

'I'm always somewhere,' said the old man. 'So's dust. So's dirt. Take a train away from them—d'you suppose they wait on the platform? Not at all. Catch a slow train. Join you next day. Got to nab them while you can.' And with that he shook the mop vigorously, splashing the cat, who withdrew in a leisurely and dignified way.

'I didn't know men ever did housework,' said Judith, feeling quite surprised by it all.

'Caravan work. Spick! Span! Not a speck! Come in and see.'

My! it was clean and sparkling inside. There were brass pans hung up all in a row; there was a lovely curly rug with a dog lying on top just like the rug; there were blue tins with 'spice', 'rice', 'mice', 'dice', written on in pink; there was a statue of a tall lady which Judith thought most elegant, and a little flight of steps that didn't lead anywhere.

Down sat the old man in a creaky basket chair, and down sat Judith on a little stool, and they shared a tin of biscuits with cream in the middle.

'If you will excuse my asking,' Judith said, 'were you here yesterday? And will you be here to-morrow?'

'First question, no. Second question, yes. Come to stay, you know.'

'Oh good,' said Judith very definitely. The dog rolled over and went to sleep with all four paws in the air.

'Showing off,' said the old man.

What was so nice was that Judith didn't have to be a bit inquisitive after that. Because first of all the old man peeped about to make sure no one was picking any more blackberries, and then he peeped behind the door, and inside the cupboard—'They get everywhere, you know,' he said, and then when he was quite certain there wasn't anybody anywhere he told Judith the most exciting things imaginable. That he was a duke, and usually lived in a huge white house with thirty bedrooms, and cannon balls all along the drive, and a big green pond with ducks all over it in front, and a ghost that ate blancmange. The blancmange, said the Duke, simply shook with fright when the ghost appeared.

'Decent fellow, all the same,' said the Duke. 'Wouldn't hurt a fly. Likes oysters. Head chopped off poor fellow. Barbarous days.'

Judith found the Duke's way of talking most easy to follow. He only said the bits that really mattered, and missed out all those wretched prepositions and pronouns and things. Now her Uncle Cedric, if he simply wanted to say it was cold, took oh! so long. Once Judith had

'*Judith looked at the caravan door. An old man looked at Judith.*'

undone and done up her hair ribbon seven times while he told her about a friend of his who fell off a tram.

But the Duke told her so many thrilling things in just a few minutes! He had two butlers, and the two butlers had two butlers under them, and then there was another butler underneath. And the Duchess put on a long shiny dress to have supper every night. And it took a whole hour to walk round the house!

'Fellow who was lame took'n hour and thirty-nine minutes once,' the Duke said modestly. 'Timed him myself.'

'Fancy!' said Judith. And then because she was so excited she said, 'Why then, please sir, do you live in a caravan?'

'Ah!' said the Duke. Then he went to the door again to make sure nobody was picking blackberries, and he said, 'Hemmed in. Butlers everywhere. Earwigs. Tripping over the fellows. Couldn't do up my own coat. Escape! That's what I'll do, I said. Go away. Live alone. Own boss. Work. Secret of happiness.'

'Well!' said Judith most surprised. 'Fancy! All those lovely ducks! And the ghost! But of course,' she said, for she noticed that when she said ghost the Duke did look a little homesick, 'this is a very nice caravan.'

The Duke sat down again and ate several biscuits. He confided in Judith that what he missed most was Yorkshire pudding. Up at the Hall it was always Yorkshire pudding on Thursdays. And he couldn't make the stuff.

'Failure,' he said. 'Lumps. Bumps. Humps.'

'Why,' cried Judith, 'Aunt Anna makes it twice a week! I will bring you some! And I'll be butler and wait on you, and we'll have a stew, and cook it in a pot, and stir it with a huge spoon, and oh hooray! please shall we?'

'Stew and Yorkshire pud! The very thing! Never was allowed them before! Don't go, says my wife. Nonsense! Delicious!'

And so it was all arranged. Judith arrived home feeling so full of it all that it was difficult not to tell Aunt Anna. Except that she knew Aunt Anna would pooh pooh the whole thing. She had a way of brushing the excitement from the corners of your mind like she would dust from the corners of a room. She didn't mean to be unkind, but she was too hygienic. She hadn't time for secrets.

That very next Saturday afternoon Aunt Anna wanted Judith to try on the sleeves of a dress she was making for her. But Judith wasn't anywhere. Not upstairs, not down; not in the big linen cupboard, not in the garden. Aunt Anna shouted for her everywhere. At last she decided to go and look for her across the fields. She did want to get on with that dress.

After she had climbed over the second stile (that was the worst of the country, all those stiles) Aunt Anna noticed a smell. Not an ordinary smell, mind. It was a most excellent smell. A most delicious smell. A smell that fluctuated, growing first stronger, then weaker, as the breeze twisted it over the stubbly field. Once Aunt Anna lost it altogether (smells are easy to lose if you are sniffing very hard) and she was even so undignified as to go down on her hands and knees to try and track it down. When she found it, she decided that she really couldn't let it go again. The dress could wait. Whatever happened, she must immediately find the source of that most wonderful, mouth-watering smell.

It took her over a particularly squashy ditch (she nearly left both shoes behind in that ditch). It caused her to tear her dress on a bramble and get hit over the head by a large branch. Wherever she walked there was a scurrying and a rustling of little animals and birds. But the smell was growing stronger, no doubt of that. Appetising! She hadn't smelt a dinner like that in years.

*   *   *

Judith and the Duke were getting on very nicely. The Duke had lit an enormous fire, and the huge flames seemed to leap right up into the sky. In the middle of the fire was a pot, and from the pot came a low rumbly burbly noise, and, let it be admitted, that very smell that had won Aunt Anna's heart. The Duke kept leaping about, tugging at branches here, and dodging the flying red sparks as they swept past him there, and rubbing his hands and crying 'Hooray! Hooray!' Judith was toasting a piece of Yorkshire pudding on a long stick which so far hadn't caught fire, thank goodness. It was a queer thing for a butler to be doing, but then what's the good of a butler, she thought, who won't turn his hand to anything except butling? Her hand got very hot indeed, and her face was almost as red as the fire, but she did want the Duke to enjoy his pudding. And even though she felt so hot, she was having a lovely, oh a lovely afternoon.

Aunt Anna heard the crackling. Gipsies, she decided. She reached up and pulled down a stick from a stout branch. She always expected everybody to be very fierce.

There was the fire! And there was the smell, all right, cooking merrily away in a pot in the middle of the fire. And there was the most extraordinarily attired old gentleman, who appeared to be entirely done up in sacking like a tree when it travels by train (the Duke hadn't felt like singeing his plum-coloured velvet jacket) leaping about round the fire like a maniac. Aunt Anna dismissed him as mad. But who—who was this little person crouching so quietly by the hottest part of the fire? Well! Aunt Anna could hardly believe her eyes! It was Judith!

Aunt Anna hastily grasped a bit of coat that seemed furthest away from the blaze, dragged Judith away from the inferno, brushed a few pine needles and twigs off her coat, and discovered to her surprise that the child appeared to be holding a stick with a piece of burnt pudding on the end of it. (Judith laid the latter reverently in her handkerchief. She suspected quite strongly that Aunt Anna might throw it in the fire.)

'And who,' said Aunt Anna, having completed these preliminaries, 'who is this gentleman on our right? This strangely attired creature? I don't think I've had the pleasure.'

'Oh, Aunt Anna,' cried Judith, jumping up and down, horrified that Aunt Anna might say something really dreadful, 'It's the Duke! He's a Duke! He's got a huge white house, and ducks, and lots and lots of butlers, and a ghost and a duchess oh! and lots more things.'

'Foof oof oof,' said Aunt Anna, this being the version of a laugh which she reserved for anything that struck her as particularly ridiculous. 'A duke! Oh ho! Foof! And would it,' she said, turning to the Duke, 'be rude to ask you, sir, what you are doing?'

'Not rude—stupid! Silly woman,' said the Duke, mostly to himself. 'Cooking,' he said in a loud voice. 'Cooking. Can't you smell it?'

In her excitement at finding Judith, Aunt Anna had almost forgotten about the smell.

'Indeed,' she said, 'it is rather a good smell.'

'Aha!' said the Duke. 'A good smell. A stew. Delicious. Stay and have some.'

And what with him rushing up the steps into the caravan,

and laying a really quite clean cloth over an old wooden box, and busying about with knives and forks and spoons, and heaving the pot off the fire and ladling a large quantity of stew into three dishes, Aunt Anna found herself in no time seated on a monstrously uncomfortable and spiky old tree trunk and partaking of what was, she admitted, the most delicious stew she had ever tasted.

It was not until she and Judith were walking home, (leaving the Duke engaged in spelling out the word MICE in pine needles for Cat, who looked on with the very slight interest of an animal whose stomach is already full of food), that Aunt Anna remarked that she didn't know what Cedric would say about having that extraordinary old tramp in his wood.

'Oh no, Aunt Anna, no! He's a duke, really and truly, only it all has to be very secret.'

'Duke! Foof!' said Aunt Anna, but in quite a lenient way. She was feeling as pleasantly full as was Cat, and in no mood for any kind of a disturbance.

About a week afterwards it started to rain. The rain fell so noisily, so incessantly, that Judith, snug and warm indoors, felt she wanted to run out and comfort the sky. She wondered about the caravan in the dark, dripping wood. From the house, the trees were just a black mass against the sky. Day after day, still the rain fell, and indoors began to seem very small and uninteresting. One day Judith read the paper right through; a thing she never did. The horses' names on the back, and the advertisements, and the tiny bits about people falling out of windows and old ladies reaching a hundred years of age. Aunt Anna blotted out the rain with noisy sleep in an armchair.

Suddenly Judith started. She laid the paper on the floor and began to read very slowly a small paragraph at the bottom of page three. 'Missing Duke' it said in capital letters. 'Alarm in Ducal household' it said in smaller capital letters. And then, in very small letters, it told how the Duchess of Dashworthy was investigating the strange and sudden disappearance of her husband, the Duke of Dashworthy. It ended with a short description of the Duke, which tallied exactly, although Judith did not care for 'flimsy build', and even in her horror she found herself trying to think out a more accurate description.

She jumped up quickly and ran out of the room. She could always think better if there wasn't anyone in the same room, even if that anyone was asleep. The paper, she decided, must vanish immediately. And being the kind of person that thinks and does all in the same minute, she hastened into Uncle Cedric's room where there was a rather sleepy fire, and held the paper up in front of it, until, as the fire woke up, the paper blew into a great burst of flame and drifted down in little fragile black pieces.

Well, that's that, she thought.

Then she ran out into the pouring pouring rain, splashing and sticking in all the muddy places, feeling the water trickling right down inside her clothes, screwing up her eyes to keep it out as it trickled off her hair, until at last, very pink and wet and breathless, she was knocking at the door of the caravan.

'Duke!' she cried, 'Duke!'

The door opened, and there was the Duke, and there inside were Dog and Cat, both fast asleep; and they all looked so warm and cosy that Judith felt she could hardly bear to break her news.

'One very wet girl. No breath, not a mouthful. Won't do at all. Come in, come in! Cup of tea all round,' cried the Duke.

And in no time he had her warming herself by the little oil stove and drying her hair in a huge coloured towel. Cat shook herself delicately as a shower of drops fell from it, but Dog enjoyed the whole thing enormously, pulling hard at one end of the towel and showing off like anything.

Over the tea Judith told the Duke why she had come, and what she had read in the paper.

'Hm!' said the Duke. 'So they miss me. Must expect it, you know. Venerable figure around the place. Add tone.'

'You must flee!' cried Judith excitedly. She thought how calm the Duke was being, but that was probably because he had such beautiful manners.

'Uncle Cedric's got a spotted handkerchief,' Judith said, 'you could try and look like a gipsy. Only you don't very, you know,' she added thoughtfully.

'No privacy in life,' said the Duke sadly. 'No solitude. Why, they're even in the air. Zoom zoom. Under the sea too. Fish takes a nap hundreds and hundreds of miles down. What happens? Bubble bubble. Divers. Poking about everywhere. Prying. No peace. Human nature. Too much of it. Very sad.'

Judith had never heard the Duke say so much at a time before, and she guessed he must be very upset.

'I'll guard the wood!' she said. 'I'll keep people away! I don't know how quite, but I just will.' And Judith felt the whole small force of her battling triumphantly against duchesses and butlers and goodness knows what.

And so, between breakfast and lunch, between lunch and tea, between tea and supper, with that dogged determination of so many people between the ages of six and sixteen, Judith guarded the wood.

'Where does that child go?' said Aunt Anna to Uncle Cedric. But one of Aunt Anna's best qualities was that she didn't interfere. Not much, anyway. Not if there wasn't a rim round the bath or too much spinach left on the side of the plates.

Judith sat on a gate on one side of the wood, and now and again she would run through the wood, which wasn't very big, and sit on a gate on the other side of it. And then she would run sometimes and stand on the other two sides. Even that didn't seem enough. She never would have believed a wood could have so many sides.

Once an old lady came up to the wood. It took her a long time to walk, being so old, and Judith watching her decided it couldn't be a duchess, not in that crumply old coat. . . . All the same it might be a duchess's decoy. Or even a spy. So she said to her, in a very warning voice:

'I shouldn't go into this wood. There's a frightfully fierce cow inside.' And then, remembering it was usually bulls who were fierce, she added, 'a fierce cow is much worse than a fierce bull.'

The decoy thanked her very much and went all round by the twisty white road.

Then a man in a bowler hat who could easily have been a butler in fact it was difficult to imagine him being anything but a butler—came up to the gate. Judith thought very hard.

'Sir!' she said, 'please don't go through that gate! A friend of my uncle's who is a very bad shot is shooting inside it, and my uncle has posted me here to warn everybody.'

At that moment there came a loud bang from inside the wood, and both Judith and the butler leapt into the air. (Fancy me believing my own story, Judith thought afterwards crossly.) The butler then moved very fast towards the twisty white road with scarcely a backward glance.

And once a little boy came up to the gate. He really looked too small to be a spy, but Judith was trusting nobody, not after all those bits in the paper. So she said to him: 'Half way down that white road, there's a tree with lovely milky white nuts growing on it.' Which was quite true. The little boy thanked her very much and went round by the long white road.

*   *   *

It must have been about a week later that a large car drew up in front of Aunt Anna's house. A tiny little chauffeur was driving it, and inside was a large, large woman who seemed to fit in the back like a nut in a shell. The car stopped, the tiny chauffeur opened the back door, and after much fluttering of rugs and careful heaving, out she climbed, and walked up the little path where long wandering leaves tickled your ankles, and into the porch of Aunt Anna's house.

The bell rang.

'Well now,' said Aunt Anna, who had been peeping round the curtain to make sure who she was letting in, as she always did, 'we seem to have an important visitor.' And so busy was she staring at the enormous hatful of feathers that the important visitor wore, that the bell rang three times before she opened the door.

'I have rung,' said the Important Visitor, 'three times.'

'Four, wasn't it?' said Aunt Anna politely. Really, those feathers! The house being rather draughty, they were nodding like anything—and didn't they, Aunt Anna wondered, tickle her neck? Aunt Anna herself had once worn a hat rather like that to a wedding, and now she could never hear that lovely wedding march without feeling a tickly feeling under her collar. 'Tum tum te-tum tum tum tum' she sang to herself to make sure.

The Important Visitor—let us call her that no longer, it was, of course the Duchess herself, did not care for Aunt Anna's rendering of the Wedding March. Nor, come to that, did she care for Aunt Anna. However, duty must be done.

'I daresay you are wondering why I am here?' she said.

Aunt Anna was still much too interested in the hat to wonder about anything else, but she pulled herself together and said well yes, she was.

'I have lost the Duke of Dashworthy!'

Aunt Anna thought for a moment. Now why did that remind her of something?

'And I have reason to believe that he is hiding in your wood!' Of course, thought Aunt Anna, that was it! That crazy old man! Not so crazy after all. This must be the Duchess of Dashworthy. She could quite see why the poor old man needed an occasional holiday.

The Duchess was tapping her foot imperiously. Aunt Anna took another look at the hat. Why should she give away the Duke's hiding place? Why tell this feathery creature his secret? It hardly seemed fair.

'A duke! In our wood! What an idea,' she said. 'The only person I can think of in our wood is Mr. Monger, an old friend of my husband's from Wapping. He lives in a caravan there. He's retired, and studies squirrels.'

The way she said all this surprised even Aunt Anna

herself. My, what an imagination she had! No wonder she had once won the English composition prize at school.

Just at that very moment Judith, who had been sitting on one of the gates thinking about the sticky buns that the baker brought on Tuesdays, found that she just couldn't sit there and think about them any longer. So she had run very quickly to the kitchen to fetch one. Outside the gate she had seen what she knew at once was the Duchess's car. And the Duchess occupied in her mind a place larger than any sticky bun.

She came at once into the parlour, and there stood Aunt Anna, and there stood the Duchess. She tugged at the quickly snatched bun with her teeth, and thought she had never seen a more horrid looking person than the Duchess. Oh, how far, far nicer were Cat and Dog!

'Judith! Don't eat so noisily,' said Aunt Anna, suddenly noticing her. 'By the way,' she added, 'this lady has lost a duke. She had an idea,' she said, looking at Judith very hard, 'that he might be in our wood. Would you believe it? I explained to her that the only person in the wood was your uncle's old friend Mr. Monger.'

Oh well done, Aunt Anna, well done! Judith could have hugged her. Instead she said:

'Oh yes! Just Mr. Monger. I don't think Mr. Monger could be a duke. He can spit ten yards.' (Why Judith said this was simply because she did indeed know an old man who could spit ten yards, Mr. Roper, a sidesman at church. And she remembered him remarking, after one particularly successful performance, 'There now, that's further than any of your dukes could spit! Not, mark you, that dukes ever spit.' She felt that would clear Mr. Monger's name of being a duke for ever.)

It did. Waving aside any offers of further hospitality, the Duchess strode out of the room, down the path, and into her car. The tiny chauffeur woke with a start, fluttered the rug, slammed the door, and drove away. Aunt Anna and Judith never saw either of them again. (Judith was sorry about not seeing the chauffeur. He was like a dear little sparrow).

'I didn't like that bit about spitting much,' said Aunt Anna. Nevertheless, she gave Judith another bun. And as Judith ran down towards the gate, for she must immediately tell the Duke about it all, Aunt Anna called out:

'By the way, you might tell your friend Mr. Monger of Dashworthy that if he'd like to call in to supper one evening, while I don't cook as well as he does, I might be able to find him something he'd like.'

And Aunt Anna laughed to herself. Really, that hat! And those feathers! And a duke in the wood! What next?

That night when Judith was in bed, the curtains flapping restlessly because of the strong wind that blew, and the night itself black as coal, Judith thought about all that had happened. And although sometimes she felt scared of the darkness, tonight she thought how it held the wood, and the wood held the blue caravan, and the caravan held the Duke and Dog and Cat. She thought how nice it would be if Aunt Anna married the Duke. But then there was Uncle Cedric, who was very kind really, and besides, the Duke didn't seem to need to be married. Then she had a little dream, and in it she thought she saw the Duchess almost slip into the green green pond with the ducks in, but then the tiny chauffeur pulled her out, and Judith woke with that funny jolt that you sometimes do in bed, and she felt very guilty at having dreamed such a thing. 'I'm sorry, Duchess,' she said out loud. And in two, three, four minutes, she was asleep.

ILLUSTRATED BY WILLIAM STOBBS

BIGGLES in Arabia

by Captain W. E. Johns

PART FIVE

BERTIE WAS nearly caught napping, as the saying is; but not quite. The instant the revolver appeared above the fuselage he side-stepped smartly, with the result that the bullet came nowhere near him. His own automatic was out in a moment, although even now his purpose was defence rather than attack. For the same reason he backed away hurriedly. Thinking that the man must have mistaken him for someone else, he shouted: 'Hi! Hold hard there! What's the matter with you? I don't bite.'

The reply was another shot, fired under the fuselage.

Bertie continued to back away, keeping the machine between them and watching the man's feet which he could see below the fuselage. He was more irritated than angry, although anger was not far away. It was with relief, therefore, that he perceived that the belligerent pilot had apparently resolved to cease hostilities. The man swung up into his cockpit, switched on, and eased the throttle open with the obvious intention of taking off. This suited Bertie well enough; and had the fellow been content to leave it at that he would have saved himself a lot of trouble. But evidently he was not. As the Moth began to move he took another snap-shot at Bertie, holding the revolver in his left hand. This was going too far. The bullet, as might be supposed considering how it was fired, went wide; but it caused Bertie's simmering anger to boil over.

'You confounded cad!' he called shrilly. 'All right! Two can play at that game, yes, by Jove!' He then opened fire on the nearest wheel of the aircraft. He hit the tyre. There was a sharp hiss of escaping air. The machine slewed round and nearly tilted up on its nose before coming to an abrupt stop.

'Ha! ha! you blighter. How do you like that?' scoffed Bertie, and then stood, pistol at the ready, to see what the pilot would do next.

Apparently the man did not like it at all, for he evacuated his cockpit with alacrity. Naturally, he chose the side farthest from Bertie, so that for a few seconds it was not possible to see what he was doing. Bertie, not liking the idea of offering himself as a stationary target, dodged towards the tail unit; but by the time he had reached it the man was a hundred yards away, running in the direction from which he had come. In a moment or two he had disappeared over a slight rise.

'Silly ass!' muttered Bertie. He pocketed his pistol, and then, prompted by nothing more than idle curiosity, strolled on for a closer examination of the aircraft.

The only thing of interest that he found was a small sack tied in the back seat, a sack that looked as if it might be full of sawdust. He prodded it with a finger and ascertained that the contents were soft. Curious to know more about this unusual cargo, he took out his penknife and made a small incision. This disclosed a brown, earthy-looking substance. He extracted a little and rubbed it between his fingers. It had a smooth, oily, slightly sticky quality. He smelt it. A sickly, aromatic aroma gave him a clue to the truth. He had never seen hashish in his life, but it did not need much imagination to work out that here was a load of the prohibited drug on its way to Egypt.

Leaving the aircraft as it stood, for there was nothing he could do about it, he went back and examined the underground tank at which the Moth had been refuelled. There

Biggles nodded grimly. 'I see what you mean all right,' he muttered.

Bertie looked puzzled. 'What about the hangar?'

'I don't care two hoots about the hangar,' replied Biggles. 'I'm worried about what's underneath it.'

'What is underneath it?'

'My machine.'

Bertie whistled softly. 'Is it, by Jove! Blow me down! Too bad! I didn't know. I'm afraid it'll be more than somewhat bent.'

'Of course you weren't to know,' sighed Biggles wearily. 'When I was last here that shed was standing up. I put my machine in it.'

'I'm afraid you're going to have a beastly job trying to get it out,' murmured Bertie sadly.

'I'd already worked that out,' returned Biggles, with biting sarcasm.

He walked forward to the wreck. 'Sand,' he said, 'that's what did it. That infernal storm dropped more sand on the roof than it could carry and the whole thing caved in.'

'I'm afraid you're right old boy, absolutely right,' agreed Bertie sorrowfully. 'That's the trouble with this beastly place. There's too much sand—too much altogether. They ought to take some of it to the seaside for the kids to play with. They'd love it.'

'This is not the moment to be funny,' Biggles told him coldly.

Bertie looked hurt. 'It was just an idea—just an idea.'

'Where's your machine?' enquired Biggles.

'In the other hangar. It's a bit cock-eyed—the hangar, I mean—but it was the only one.'

'The one I chose looked better to me,' asserted Biggles. 'Unfortunately there weren't enough holes in the roof for the sand to fall through.' He pointed to the Moth, still standing where it had stopped. 'Who did that? It wasn't here last night.'

'I did it,' replied Bertie. 'I mean I helped the bloke who was flying it.'

'What do you mean—you helped?'

'Well, I shot a little hole in the tyre. That sort of—er —stopped it.'

'I see. Why shoot a hole in the bloke's tyre?'

'He shot at me.'

'So you've been having fun whilst my back was turned?'

'He started it,' declared Bertie. 'There's some petrol over there. He landed and started refuelling. I merely strolled over to say what cheer and he popped off his pistol at me. Naturally, I popped back at him.'

'And then what?'

Bertie gave an account of what had happened.

'Now I get it,' remarked Biggles, at the finish. 'It must have been your Moth pilot who had a crack at us as we were walking home. No doubt he was on his way back, on foot, to El Moab.'

'Which reminds me. What have you been up to?' asked Bertie. 'Where's Ginger?'

'Ginger,' answered Biggles, 'is wandering about somewhere in the desert. We've spent half the night looking for him. I was hoping he'd found his way back here.' He explained what had happened. 'I shall have to take your machine to look for him,' he concluded. He walked right up to the collapsed hangar and examined it closely. 'There's a chance that this may not be as bad as it looks,' he observed. 'Of course, if one of the metal roof supports has fallen across a wing, with the whole weight of sand on it, the machine's finished. But looking at it, from the way the framework has crumpled up, that may not have happened. But it's no use guessing. I'm going in

was not a lot of petrol left in it. He replaced the man-hole cover then walked back to the shade of the hangar to resume his vigil. He now felt pretty certain that Biggles had gone straight back to Aden, but as he was on the spot he decided that he might as well wait a little while longer in case he was wrong in this assumption.

Five minutes later he heard a shot in the distance. It was not easy to locate the direction from which the sound had come. Anyhow, as he was not involved he paid no attention to it, beyond keeping a watchful eye on the rise over which the Moth pilot had disappeared.

Shortly afterwards two figures came into sight. He recognised Biggles and Zahar, plodding like men who had travelled a long way. Ginger, he observed, was not with them, which worried him somewhat, for he feared that Biggles had been forced down in the desert and that Ginger had been hurt. Leaving the hangar he walked to meet them.

'What ho!' he hailed. 'Why the footwork so early in the morning?'

Biggles did not answer. He was staring past Bertie at one of the collapsed hangars.

Bertie did not like the expression on his face. 'Here, I say, old boy, what's wrong?' he asked anxiously.

Biggles continued to walk towards the hangar. At last he stopped. He looked at Bertie and then pointed to the hangar on which his interest had been focused. 'How long have you been here?' he asked.

'About an hour or so.'

'Was that hangar like that when you got here?'

'Absolutely. Why? Do you think I pushed the bally thing over—if you see what I mean?'

to have a look. Stand fast.'

So saying he climbed on the sagging fabric and with his knife cut a long slit in it. Through the aperture thus made he disappeared from sight in a river of sand.

While Biggles was under the sagging fabric the others could only guess from sounds what he was doing.

After some few minutes he reappeared, and climbed out shaking quantities of sand from his clothes. 'It isn't too bad,' he announced. 'At any rate, I don't think any serious damage has been done, but before the machine can be got out it'll be necessary to cut away at least two girders. They are all buckled up and are jammed one each side of the airscrew. The fabric offers no difficulty. It's rotten, and we can cut it away with our knives. To clear the metal work will require an acetylene cutter or a hack-

'He rubbed it between his fingers.'

saw. An acetylene cutter would soon do the job.'

He sat down and thought for a minute or two while the others remained silent. 'I'll tell you what, Bertie,' he said at last. 'I haven't time to tell you the whole story, but I've been to El Moab. The gurra is here. The place is twelve miles or so from here, in that direction.' He pointed. 'The problem is to know the best way of dealing with the plants. It would be a long and tedious job to pull them up by the roots. I don't think that would be practicable anyway. There's an easier way of wiping the whole stock out. Close to the place where it grows there's a big reservoir of water held up by a dam. If that dam was knocked down the rush of water would sweep the plantation out of the ground—the earth, as well as the plants, I reckon. To blow the dam all that's needed is a charge of explosive. A few sticks of dynamite would do the trick because, from what I could see, the thing is only a home-made affair. I want you to go back to Aden. See the senior Engineer Officer. Tell him what we aim to do and ask him to let you have what is necessary. If he jibs, make a signal to Raymond and ask him to radio the necessary authority. That's one thing. Next, ask the Station Commander to lend you an acetylene welder or a good fitter who knows his job. Explain what's happened here. Fly him out and we'll get him working on this hangar. While you're in Aden you might also try to pick up a spare wheel, or tyre, for that Moth. There should be one about. The idea, if we can get one, is to fly the Moth out, complete with its load of dope and hand it over to the proper authority. Is that clear?'

'Absolutely, old boy. Three things. Dynamite, an acetylene cutter and a spare tyre.'

'That's it.'

'What are you going to do?'

'I shall have to wait here,' answered Biggles.

'What about Ginger?'

Biggles hesitated. 'I hadn't forgotten him. He's the snag in my scheme. Your machine can't do two jobs at once. If I keep it here, you can't go home. If you go home, I can't use it. I want those things from Aden right away. That Moth pilot is now going hot-foot to El Moab, and when he gets there, the tale he'll have to tell will bring the enemy along in force to mop us up. The Sultan's manager will also be anxious to save the hashish in the Moth. So there's no time to waste.'

'Couldn't I have a look round for Ginger first?'

'If you did, it would probably put the lid on the whole show. That dam has got to go up, and the job will have to be done tonight or we may never get another chance. If anything happens to me, you carry on with it. Ginger shouldn't take any harm for an hour or two. Zahar says he'll fall asleep, and when he wakes up most of the effect of the drug will have worn off. There's just a chance that in daylight he may be able to find his way back here on foot. He's seen the country from the air, so he must know the general direction. If he doesn't turn up, I'll go and look for him as soon as you get back. Tonight we'll tackle El Moab and clean the place up.'

'Okay, old boy, as you say,' agreed Bertie. 'I'll push along and I won't linger on the way.' With a wave he turned to the hangar in which he had parked his machine.

Biggles and Zahar watched him take off, after which Biggles returned to the hangar under the ruins of which his machine had been buried, feeling not a little annoyed that, having survived the storms of years, the structure should choose this particular moment to collapse. Rather than waste time doing nothing he enlarged the hole in the fabric and went inside again, firstly to get some food and water from the lock-up, and, secondly, to decide on the exact place to start work when the cutting equipment arrived. Zahar followed him in, slashing holes in the canvas with his dagger to let in more light and air.

Having satisfied his appetite Biggles spent some time, again with Zahar's assistance, cutting away such fabric as might impede the work of salvage when the metal-cutting appliances were available. It was warm work as the sun increased in power, and from time to time he went outside for a breath of air which, while hot, was at least fresh. Zahar, to whom heat meant nothing, went on working.

It was during one such interval that a shout brought Biggles round to face the direction of El Moab. A small group of native horsemen had appeared suddenly from somewhere and were galloping towards him. It was obvious that they had seen him so there was no point in trying to hide; but he spoke swiftly to Zahar who, fortunately, was still out of sight. 'Some horsemen are upon us,' he said tersely. 'Stay where you are, keeping still, and they will not know you are here. They have guns so we cannot fight them all. If they take me away with them, remain here, so that you will be able to tell my friend, when he comes, what has happened. You understand?'

'There is no God but God,' came in a muffled voice from under the canvas.

'Tell my friend, when he comes, that I rely on him to destroy the wall that holds the water at El Moab.'

'God sparing me it shall be as you say, Sahib,' answered Zahar, without exposing himself.

There was no time for further conversation, so Biggles turned to face the horsemen, a wild-looking lot who, leading spare horses, did not steady their break-neck pace until the last moment, when they pulled their mounts to their haunches.

'*Salaam aleikum!*' greeted one—somewhat to Biggles's surprise, for the words mean 'Peace be unto you!'

'*Aluikum salaam!*' responded Biggles.

The man who had spoken urged his animal forward. 'Have you lost a man of your tribe, O Nasara?' he cried in a hoarse, guttural voice.

'I have,' acknowledged Biggles.

'Stricken with sickness he rests in our *menzil*,' announced the man.

'Where is your menzil?' asked Biggles.

The man made a vague sign towards the desert.

'At what distance?' asked Biggles, although, really, he knew the futility of the question. The desert Arab has little idea of time or distance in European terms.

'A short march,' was the answer, which Biggles knew could mean anything. 'Will you go to him?'

'I will go,' replied Biggles, without hesitation. 'Will you show me the way and lend me a horse?'

'One was brought for the purpose,' declared the man.

There was nothing more to be said. Biggles stepped forward and swung up on the back of the animal offered. The party at once moved off at a gallop.

The whole thing had happened so quickly that Biggles had had little time to consider the step he was taking. Not—as he afterwards brooded—that it would have made much difference. The natives had really been in control of the situation from the moment they had seen him. At first he had felt quite sure that he was about to be attacked. The friendly greeting had disarmed him, so to speak, and by the time he had mounted he felt satisfied that the motive of the men in coming to see him, was genuine. That Ginger was in their camp he did not doubt, for had they not found him they would have been unaware of his existence. In those circumstances he was bound to go to Ginger's assistance, so it came to the same thing in the end. The one weak point, the one thing that should have warned him to be prepared for treachery, he thought afterwards, was the curious fact of the leader of the party being able to speak English. That could hardly be coincidence. Obviously, he had been chosen for the job for that very reason. A man, having no contact with Europeans, could hardly be expected to understand English, much less speak it.

He observed with some misgivings that the direction they had taken, if maintained, would bring them to El Moab; but still, as Ginger had been lost in that area, this was perhaps only to be expected. After riding for a time he asked the man who spoke English, for the man had kept close to him, if they were going near El Moab. The man did not answer, which, thought Biggles, looked bad. He could only console himself with the thought that if treachery was intended, Zahar would be able to tell Bertie, when he returned, what had happened. Not that Bertie would be able to do much about it beyond blasting the dam, which he could be relied upon to do.

Another hour and there was no longer any doubt in Biggles's mind as to their destination. They were riding straight for El Moab. He recognised some of the ground over which he had walked during the past few hours. However, nothing could be done about it. There was just a chance that the Sultan's men at El Moab did not know who he was, who Ginger was, or what they were doing.

It fell out as he expected. They rode straight into the encampment. A number of men who were standing about stared curiously as they galloped up. What had happened was now plain enough to see. Ginger had been captured. The pilot of the Moth had made his way back on foot to his starting point. He had reported the presence of a

white man at aerodrome 137, and a party of natives had been sent out to bring him in. He wondered if the pilot had been close enough to Bertie to recognise him; or rather, close enough to realise that the white man whom the natives had fetched from the airfield was not the man he had seen there. On that occasion he had, of course, seen Bertie, not Biggles.

There was little time for conjecture. A man obviously of some authority appeared—an Egyptian, Biggles thought, judging from his features and the fez he wore on his head. He made a sign to the natives who closed in suddenly and laid hands on Biggles's person. Biggles did not resist, perceiving that resistance would be futile.

The man in the fez went through his pockets, removed his automatic, and with a smug smile put it in his own.

'Come with me; my master wishes to speak with you,' he ordered, and walked towards the door of the bungalow which Biggles had noticed during his reconnaissance.

Biggles followed the man in. He was in no case to argue,

'*The man in the fez went through his pockets.*'

so he did not waste breath on questions or objections. Moreover, he was very anxious to know if Ginger was really there, for if he was not, if he was still out in the wilderness, he would by this time be in a bad way.

Having entered the house his guide turned into a room that led off from a small, bare hall. A man was standing there waiting, legs apart, his hands clasped behind his back. It was Nicolo Ambrimos, otherwise known as the Sultan.

This really did surprise Biggles. Such a possibility had not occurred to him. Knowing the type of man he was, he had assumed—without giving the matter any serious thought—that he rarely left his comfortable villa in Aden. Only in dire emergency would such a man face the austere conditions of the desert. This, presumably, was such an occasion. Besides, there was the time factor. How had he got there in such a short while? The Sultan had not only moved, but had moved fast.

Said Ambrimos, with a curious smile, rocking himself gently on his toes: 'Well, major, so we meet again?'

'You must have been fascinated by my personality to

arrange another meeting so soon,' returned Biggles, sarcasm in his voice.

The Sultan's smile broadened; but there was no humour in it. 'I was so anxious to see you that I risked my life in a flying machine to bring us face to face,' he purred.

'Permit me to congratulate you on your courage,' answered Biggles coldly. 'But what to me is more important is the whereabouts of a young friend of mine who, last night, had the misfortune to fall sick and wander away from my camp. I was told he was here. I trust I was not misinformed?'

'What you were told was perfectly true,' replied the Sultan. 'He is here, looking rather sorry for himself. But please sit down. You must be tired after all your exertions.' There was a sneer in the last sentence.

Biggles accepted the invitation, for he was, in fact, tired. 'Where is this young man of mine?' he enquired.

'No doubt you would like to see him,' was the answer. The Sultan said something, in a language unknown to Biggles, to the man who had brought him in. The man at once left the room. To Biggles, Ambrimos went on: 'You see what comes of interfering with matters that are not your business, matters that you do not understand. Do you know what happened to this young fellow of yours?'

'I've a pretty good idea.'

'He drank water without first informing himself of its quality—always a dangerous thing to do in the desert. In this case it happened to be somewhat polluted by certain industrial operations which I have undertaken. Naturally, he was sick.'

'In plain English he was nearly poisoned to death by an overdose of hashish which you, regardless of the consequences to anyone else, had thrown into the wadi,' said Biggles icily.

The Sultan shrugged. 'That is a crude way of putting it, if you prefer it that way. But allow me to remind you that no one invited you to come here and drink the water.'

'I must also remind you that water in the desert is the common property of all travellers, and only a man with the mentality of a diseased weasel would foul it,' asserted Biggles caustically.

Ambrimos flushed. 'In this case it happened to turn out to my advantage,' he sneered, a rising inflection in his voice.

'It may look that way to you at the moment,' admitted Biggles.

At this juncture, Ginger, still looking pale and shaky, was brought in. He smiled wanly when he saw Biggles. 'Sorry I've dragged you into this,' he said apologetically.

'It may not be as bad as it appears,' answered Biggles. 'How are you feeling?'

'Pretty cheap.'

'By the way,' put in the Sultan, speaking to Biggles. 'In case you have jumped to a conclusion, may I point out that this young man was in no way coerced into coming here. He came entirely of his own free will.'

'Perfectly true,' agreed Ginger. 'But I think you should make it clear that at the time I was more than slightly doped, through no fault of my own, and cannot therefore be held entirely responsible for my actions. If you hadn't doped the water supply I shouldn't be here.'

'A mere detail,' purred Ambrimos. 'The fact remains you came, and being delighted to see you we made you welcome. But let us not go into that. Sit down and let us get to business. We have some serious matters to discuss—serious for me, I own, but more serious for you.'

'I have nothing to discuss with you,' said Biggles shortly.

The Sultan sighed. 'Always so belligerent, you British. Never mind. Let us say I have things to discuss with you, and you would be well-advised to listen. And in case you should attempt to break off the conversation with the object of leaving El Moab, I must remind you that my men are outside awaiting the outcome of our talk. They do not like infidels at the best of times, and the knowledge that you have come here with the object of depriving them of their livelihood, has, quite naturally, done nothing to make them well-disposed towards you.'

Biggles lit a cigarette. 'Go ahead,' he invited. 'I'm listening.'

(Continued on page 253)

WHAT ABOUT THE WEATHER

By Vere Shepstone

As THE WEATHER is in November, so, the weather-wise say, will it be in the following March.

If one gets any skating this month, there won't be much to be had later on, because:

'If there's ice in November that will bear a duck,
There'll be nothing after but sludge and muck.'

November 11th, St. Martin's Day, is an important one in weather prophecy:

'If the wind is in the south-west at Martinmas,
it remains there till after Candlemas.'

Some people hang up a piece of dried seaweed to act as a barometer. Any sign of dampness will be a warning of rain.

Indoors, too, if chairs and tables creak, it means that rain is not far off, and the sufferer from rheumatism will feel his joints more than usually painful when it is going to be wet.

November is the month of fogs.

'If there be a damp fog or mist, accompanied by wind, expect rain.'

When bad weather is on the way, pigs are often seen carrying straw to their sties—presumably with an eye to greater comfort indoors until things outside are more inviting!

Weather prophets can learn a lot from looking at the stars. In Lancashire they say:

'One star ahead of the moon, towing her, and another astern, chasing her, is a sure sign of a storm.'

If the stars seem to be twinkling more than usual, it indicates heavy dews, rain and snow, or stormy weather in the near future. And when the sky is very full of stars, then you should expect rain, or, in winter, frost.

Drawing for Those Who Cannot Draw

by Joseph Natanson

'**H**OW LUCKY YOU ARE to be able to draw and paint! I can't even trace a straight line.'

I have heard this nonsense many times in my life, and yet it still makes me angry. What has tracing straight lines got to do with drawing—artistic drawing, I mean?

For straight lines you use a ruler, for drawing you use only your brain. If you can write a letter to a friend in a more or less legible hand, you already have enough ability in your hand to draw as well as Raphael. If you fail to do so, it is only because your brain is *slightly* inferior, but that does not mean you can't draw at all.

Thus, having agreed that your hand is the hand of a great master, but that your brain is different, it is best to make a firm decision once and for all: you have no intention (and no possibility!) of drawing like Raphael, Leonardo or your favourite illustrator of *Collins*. If you have to draw, you must find your own way, and if it pleases only you—well, you will be quite satisfied.

Imagine that you are a cave man, one of those who drew animals 20,000 years ago. You have never seen a drawing before but you believe that once you have represented a bison on a wall, the bison will be in your power and to-morrow with your ridiculous bow and arrow, or whatever you use for hunting, you will shoot it dead at the first go, and have roast bison for yourself and the family every day for the next four weeks.

A bison is a big thing, bulky, covered with curly hair of different shades, and moving all the time. You have only a kind of chalk made from soft reddish stone and the flat wall of the cave to draw on. The main problem is how, with one, or at most, two colours and a flat surface, you can represent many different colours, shapes and details.

Some people believe that the first drawings were made by outlining with coloured earth the accidental cracks and irregularities on the wall, which resembled the shape of an animal. That is quite possible, as surely you have noticed when looking at clouds, leaves, a cracked and damp wall, or a glowing fire, that after a while you begin to see figures. Some people look but never see anything. They are out; they will never draw.

You must have a lot of imagination to be able to translate into lines what in life has many curves and surfaces. When people had tried and eventually succeeded in doing that for many centuries, they established for most usual objects an easy way of describing them in lines which are now understood by anybody. Thus a straight horizontal line is enough to represent sometimes the sea, or the top of a table, or a footpath in the street. A child will represent a face by a circle with four dots for the eyes, nose and mouth, with a few squiggles on top for the hair. The illustrator of a comic does very little more than that, and yet you see all these lines, dots and dashes as people and animals very much alive and active. A few lines make a house, a car, they make you know that the story happens in a house, in the country or on a boat. You are not tempted to cut out one of the pictures from a comic and hang it on the wall for the pleasure of looking at it. Even if you tried to do so, very soon it would not amuse you any longer. You would be bored to look at lines which, by themselves, if you forget what they are trying to represent, do not give any pleasure to your eye.

FIRST RULE: **A drawing is a composition of lines and shadows forming a pattern which should be pleasant to look at, regardless of what it is supposed to represent in real life**

If you wish to give yourself satisfaction with your drawings and perhaps give pleasure to other people in

A drawing done with a brush, diluted Indian ink and white poster paint.

Pencil only makes quite a different effect, though the subject is the same.

The camera saw and recorded all the details in the foreground and at the back.

the future, you must not only avoid, for the reasons stated, the imitation of great masters, but also you must leave contemptuously behind you the cheap tricks of the comics.

All that is good, sound theory. Now we must get down to practice. To make things easier, let's divide drawing into two categories: drawing from nature, and drawing from imagination. That is, of course, simplifying things, as I believe that both are the same thing really and one requires as much imagination as the other.

1. Drawing from Nature

When I started writing this, I saw in the corner of my studio several objects accidentally assembled as you see in the photograph. The camera has recorded more or less faithfully whatever was in front of it, including a lamp and a typewriter in the background, which I did not even notice when I started drawing the group.

SECOND RULE: **Drawing is a problem of selection; you draw only what you wish to draw to give (a) a pleasant pattern to the drawing, (b) to give proper expression to each object, and (c) to give unity to the whole subject.**

The glass vase is hard, smooth, transparent and very definite in shape. The branches are flexible, rough and covered with untidily growing leaves here and there. The apples are round and shiny. The books are angular and of dull texture. The gloves are soft but they keep the shape of the hands which wore them. The scarf is also soft, but it drapes itself in accidental folds.

Try, when drawing, not to copy thoughtlessly whatever you see but to draw the character of each object. If it helps you, talk to yourself all the time; ' Now I am drawing a scarf. It is made of soft, shiny material. Folds are very difficult to draw—but they have continuity, they start here and finish there. Some of them are important to show how the material lies; others not.'

A fine, more detailed impression is obtained when a mapping pen is used.

A fountain pen sketched in the main points, leaving out many details but translating the pattern into a design.

You do not draw the 'not', and the others come out beautifully in your drawing, fluent and expressive.

As you see, I made several drawings. One with a brush, Indian ink (diluted with water which I kept in a saucer) and some poster white. The second with pencil. A third with a mapping pen. The last with my fountain pen. You can see at a glance that the subject in each one is the same as in the photograph, but each drawing is different. I tried to be as impersonal as possible and to follow simply what each different technique dictated that I should choose from reality, to give character to the objects and unity to the composition.

You can see for yourself the difference in the details and the general approach. In the last drawing, for instance, the character of each object is underlined, but the unity and the atmosphere of reality of the first one are gone.

THIRD RULE: **You must find your proper technique when drawing—the one that suits your own temperament and the way you look at things.**

If you cannot draw with a pencil, try a very finely pointed sable brush. If you see the world in fine lines without any shadows, wholly composed of linear patterns, use a pen and Indian ink. But if on the contrary everything for you is light and shadow, use a soft crayon and blacken your paper energetically.

There are thousands of ways to draw, but the only good one is—your own.

2. Drawing from Imagination

It is quite obvious that all the rules we have established for drawing from nature apply equally to drawing from imagination. I believe that everyone can be taught to draw from nature, but any child without any teaching can draw from imagination. A child who cannot draw is either too shy, or too self-critical, or discouraged by more gifted fellows. You won't tell me that there are children without imagination. I shudder at even the thought of such a thing.

When I was a child I had two friends of my own age who drew and painted all the time. I was in despair because nothing that I did ever looked like their drawings. Everybody admired their work, everyone laughed at mine.

One of my pals became a lawyer, and I suppose the only drawing he does is doodling on the blotting paper. The other is an industrial designer who never draws anything without a set square, ruler and compass. I am an artist, and very pleased to be one.

By the way, I would be very interested now to see those drawings of my playmates and myself. Perhaps we simply had the wrong public. I rather suspect that, while I was naïvely digging in my own imagination, they were helping themselves, not exactly by copying, but at least by imitating the style of magazine illustrators.

FOURTH RULE: **When you draw from imagination, draw from your own imagination.**

When you imagine things they are much more beautiful than anything you really see. Perhaps you will find it difficult at first, but very soon you will agree that it is even easier to draw a fantastic type of tree of your own than an ordinary tree, and in a similar way, a house of unknown architecture, animals which never existed, people with strange faces and dresses of a fashion entirely invented by you, landscapes of countries which are not to be found on any map. And you can draw portraits of imaginary families, to find out which child resembles the father and which the mother.

Once you have discovered how prompt your imagination is in giving you at a moment's notice all that you require for your drawing, it will be child's play to draw a bus with thirty passengers on the upper and twenty-six on the lower deck (and only five standing), Piccadilly Circus with all its traffic, a football match, your sister combing her hair, your own face in the mirror or even the back view of an elephant.

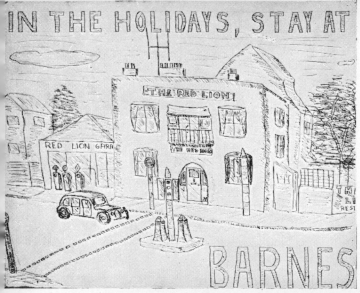

IN THE HOLIDAYS, STAY AT
THE RED LION
RED LION GARA
BARNES

MY IDEAL HOLIDAY

A magic carpet and a wish, and you can whisk into whichever holiday you choose. In Manchuria, on a sailing boat with Arthur Ransome, among sea lions, or in a ring of machine-gun fire! Happy landings!

A No, I don't want to go to the South Seas. Kipling, Conrad and now the splendid Kon-Tiki can take me there far more excitingly than I could myself. I don't want a magic carpet, not even the glorious E. Nesbit's. I want an idea and the ability to develop it so that the whole design falls into place with the ease and certainty of a diagram in a documentary film. My story would rise to a climax and topple over, not into fragments, but into a gleaming spread of revelation like a wave. Then you, dear reader, would say, ' Oh, I am sorry that story is over.'
—GEOFFREY DEARMER.

In my boat, well out of earshot of other people's wireless and of half-wits who go about whistling. Plenty of nice new rope and tarred twine to keep my fingers busy. A sunny day and a pleasant ripple. A dinghy, with some of you in it, rowing off from the shore and coming alongside without a bump. Hoist sail, up anchor and away, with one or other of you at the tiller, steering, earnest-eyed, and hoping nobody has noticed the horrible wiggle you have put into our wake drawn out on the water astern. Perhaps, sometimes, there wouldn't be a wiggle. We would sail on all day and anchor at evening within reach of an island or a sheltered bay. Sitting on the cabin-top in the dusk, I'd see a glimpse of white tents among the trees and the glow of your camp fire. Next day, the same again. With a little exploring and a touch of piracy anything might happen, but it wouldn't matter a bit if nothing happened at all.
—ARTHUR RANSOME.

My ideal holiday would be devoted to shooting duck, snipe and geese (and probably a few pheasants and blackgame) in Manchuria. My headquarters would be on a houseboat on one of the rivers—perhaps the Sungari—and the houseboat would be towed by a small, fast launch which would, of course, operate independently of the house-boat during the day. I should also have a little amphibian aircraft (on the lines of the ' Sea Bee ' which the U.S. Navy had in the war) so that I could go as far afield, within reason, as I wanted to. I should have one personal servant, one mechanic, two boatmen, a dog-coolie, and a very good cook. They would all be Chinese.
—PETER FLEMING.

COME TO THE FAIR ON BLACKHEATH

I will voyage to some tropic country I had never visited, on a slow ship. There will be an entire circus travelling with me, and all the animals working in the circus will be tame enough to walk about the ship and let me get to know them. As well, there will be a ballet company on board who practise every day where I can see them. I am taking with me a niece and a nephew aged twelve who will enjoy themselves in their own way without interference from me.
—NOEL STREATFEILD.

I have been playing either cricket or football all the year round, ever since I was a boy and I don't believe I have ever had a holiday in the accepted sense of the word. If such a chance were offered to me, I'd like to go somewhere like the South of France, and lie in the sun, swim and eat ice-cream, without having to worry about my weight.
—DENIS COMPTON.

I am an isolated lighthouse keeper, and this is what I would like my holiday to be, if and when it becomes possible.
A holiday in Denmark would, in my opinion, be the ideal place. I should like to travel about visiting places of interest, and the beauty spots, and above all, live for a while with a typical Danish family. In my imagination Denmark and the other Scandinavian countries always stand out as places of beauty and peace, and I think after eight months of the year listening to the thumping of the sea and blowing of the fog signal this would be a complete change and a first-class holiday.
—WILLIAM RALPH.

PICNICS IN THE FOREST

RIDING?

WHY NOT COME TO WOODFORD

C

Give me a butterfly net, my camera, a bike, and a fine week in July. I shall make for the New Forest, where in the open glades and sunny ridings I know I shall see Fritillary butterflies and the lovely White Admiral. I'll spend my time trying to photograph these two kinds together on one picture, and won't it be a difficult job ? I'll catch one or two females, boxing them alive. When I get back to my Butterfly Farm I'll turn the butterflies loose in a cage already planted with their food-plant. They will lay lots of eggs, and that means more butterflies again next season to look forward to.
—L. HUGH NEWMAN, F.R.E.S.

My perfect August holiday would be to drive very slowly through France or Italy, doing a lot of sightseeing to begin with and ending up somewhere where I could lie in the sun with practically no clothes on. I would eat enormous meals all the time, sleep on downy beds, not have to worry about money, and never meet anybody I knew.
—VIRGINIA GRAHAM.

I'd like to go by boat to Australia. There I should spend my time at the seaside right away from animals. I don't think kangaroos would bother me while I was near the sea, and as I don't understand sealions, it wouldn't worry me if there were any of them about. I'd have a really lazy time without having lions and people round me all the day long.
—C. HITCHCOCK, Zoo Keeper.

THE GARDEN OF ENGLAND

KENT

D

228

Edinburgh Festival

OTTINGHAM.

hatever holiday plans we make, according to our
...es and purse, we should be elastic in carrying them
 If you are staying in England, prepare for arctic
...ropical conditions, as you may have either, or both,
... also, it is very refreshing to change one's mind
...ut the kind of holiday it is going to be. Plan, for
...ance, to do a lot of reading and take masses of
...ks, then, when the time comes, spend every
...ute building sand-castles. Incidentally, if sand-
...les are the order of the day, I strongly recommend
...ves. I once started a concert season with so many
...ken nails that I could hardly look the keyboard in
... face. But, whatever we do for our holiday, we
... hope that it will come somewhere near the perfect
... it was, in our anticipation.
—DAME MYRA HESS.

E

The ideal holiday would be definitely abroad, with my
wife and two of our best friends who enjoy the same things
as we. We should like to walk each day, and just put up
where we thought fit, seeking out the seaside places when
we felt like bathing, moving to the country when we felt
like walking. I should hate to have anything organised
on my holiday, and to add to the fun I should prefer a
country where I cannot speak the language !
—WILFRED PICKLES.

SPEND your HOLIDAYS IN HIGHGATE

F

6.45 p.m. The seaside. Snowey, Jock and I
on holiday. We are on the beach and bored.
6.46 p.m. Rat-tat-tat-tat. Machine-gun fire
from a motor-boat off-shore. A man falls
dead, a woman screams, I shout ' Action,
chaps ! '
6.47 to 6.58 p.m. Action, Action, ACTION !
until :
6.59 p.m. Snowey is at sea, bound and gagged
in a rowboat with a hole in it, gradually sinking. . . .
Jock is in a deserted barn, bound and gagged,
on a sawbench, with the circular saw blade
spinning nearer and nearer. . . .
I am in a lonely house, bound and gagged,
locked in a hermetically sealed cellar, with
poison gas being pumped in through a
valve. . . .
7.0 p.m. Can we escape ? Listen to the
next. . .

Sorry ! I was forgetting. This never happened, did it ? But you must admit it would
have been the start of an ideal holiday if it had.
—DICK BARTON.

G

Cornwall : coast of great Atlantic rollers and surf boards,
though I am unable now to use one myself. Long days at sea
with the crabbers from some of the smaller coves and fishing
villages. Long days, hauling the nets and the lobster and the
crab pots.
 Deep pools in the rock of sheer serpentine ; pools with
darting, transparent shrimps, minute crabs, prettily-coloured
weeds and delicate, alive, sea anemones. The endless cries
of the gulls echoing about the cliffs ; mocking cries, mournful
and haunting cries, clamorous cries ! An unforgettable
chorus of sound.
 Up on the moors, the hot sunshine, scent of wild thyme, and
fresh ferns. Tall, spotted foxgloves, dog-rose, honeysuckle,
early blackberries, frisking rabbits and an occasional fox or
badger.
 Nor must I forget—how could I ?—the people of Cornwall,
so many of whom I count among my real friends.
 My holiday is repetitive—always the same, yet invariably
different.—DEREK McCULLOCH (Uncle Mac of Children's
Hour.)

 My ideal holiday is a holiday without a timetable—a motor-
trip through the sunshine of France or Italy, with no fixed
destination nor time of arrival.
 I travel with my wife and we take a small tent and a cooking
stove. We dawdle in pleasant places, often spending several
days to cover several miles.
 We make camp by a stream where we can swim and wash
off the dust of the road ; and in the evening we walk to the
nearest village or sit long over a simple meal, enjoying the
strangeness of the foreign scene. —ERIC WILLIAMS.

VISIT SARUM

COME TO BLAGDON
...TUATED ON A FARM, IN A VALLEY
...ROUNDED BY BEAUTIFUL DORSET DOWNS

PONYS TO RIDE AND ABOVE ALL
A SMALL BUT PERFECT
SWIMMING-POOL!

H

...r chosen place will always be
...ar brook or river, lake or sea.
... must, of course, be nice and
...quiet,
...eam, eggs, and fruit my staple
...diet.
... take one friend who likes to
...walk,
...ho can, but doesn't always, talk.
...o not want to hear the news,
...o not want to stand in queues ;
... symphonies I want to hear,
... only bird-song, loud and clear.
... fortnight of such happy leisure,
...d I'll return to work with
...pleasure.—HELEN HENSCHEL.

SEE THE BEAUTIES OF NORTH WALES

POSTER ARTISTS
A Colin Seymour-Ure (11)
B Margaret Shillan (15)
C Jane Hensler (13)
D Thirza Farnham (13)
E Catherine Richards (12)
F Susan Fraser (10)
G Keith Albarn (11)
H Brigid Hays (16)
I Margaret Miller (14)
J Louisa Nicholson (13)

I

 I am a stick-in-the-mud about holidays. While the children are
young I like to go to the same place year after year. And I know of
no more delightful place in Britain for a family than Tenby, in South
Pembrokeshire.
 The essence of a good holiday is to do what you like. Being a
lazy fellow, this means, for me, doing precious little ! The day
passes with a bathe, a book and a boat. I like meeting new faces
and making new friends. Occasionally I indulge in a burst of
exercise and tramp over the Prescelly hills. Oddly enough, I like
to do an hour or two's writing each day on the principle of the man
who went on whacking his hand because it was nice when he left
off !
—Dr. CHARLES, HILL, M.P.

229

HALF-HOLIDAY WITH CROOKS

by Dudley Jarrett

ILLUSTRATED BY MARCIA LANE-FOSTER

TOM MARLOWE lived at number 9 Wildgrove Way, in the Hampstead Garden Suburb. It was a pleasant neighbourhood, but not the sort of place where you would expect to meet with exciting adventures for the only wild thing about it was its name.

There were times when Tom could not help envying his friend Martin Penrose whose home was a ranch in Alberta.

But as Mr. Marlowe had pointed out to his twelve-year-old son more than once, it would be very difficult for a gem engraver to earn any money on a ranch in Alberta. Tom's father was an engraver of gems.

Built on to the side of his house was a studio-workshop. This contained a small safe in which Mr. Marlowe kept any precious stone that might be in his possession, unless he was actually at work on it.

At eleven o'clock on a November morning, when Tom was at school and his mother out shopping, Mr. Marlowe was in his studio engraving a valuable emerald. Magnifying glass in eye, he bent low over the lovely stone as he cut a delicate design on its hard, smooth surface. Suitably set in gold and platinum the emerald was to become the special private and personal seal of the Indian prince to whom it belonged.

Having completed a particularly tricky piece of engraving, Mr. Marlowe tried to straighten his back. It was at that moment the lumbago caught him. The pains were sharp and stabbing. For a while he felt unable to move. He gave a little grunt as he tried unsuccessfully to stand upright.

Then, slowly and painfully he wrapped the precious emerald in cotton wool, pushed it into a little wash-leather bag and popped it into his waistcoat pocket. This was the best he could manage in the circumstances.

Still bent with pain, Mr. Marlowe found the easiest way to get upstairs was on all fours. He felt and looked very ridiculous and was glad he had reached the top before he met Mrs. Chapman, the new daily help.

Nobody, however, could have been more sympathetic. When Mr. Marlowe told her of the pain he was in and that he would be in bed for two or three days, Mrs. Chapman said all the nasty things she could think of about lumbago. Then she hurried downstairs to fill a hot-water bottle and make Mr. Marlowe a nice cup of tea. She also removed a spare latch-key from a drawer in the hall table.

Tom's father undressed painfully and got into bed. That is where Tom's mother found him when she returned home just before Mrs. Chapman left at midday.

'Oh dear,' sighed Mrs. Marlowe, who had not been very successful with her shopping. 'I wonder what will go wrong next.'

Mrs. Sarah Chapman did not wonder: she knew.

Sarah was not due at her next place until one o'clock. She had plenty of time to join her burglar friend Jerry the Gent for a bite of lunch at 'The Spotted Pig'.

'Well, how goes it?' said Jerry when they were settled in a quiet corner.

'Fine,' answered Sarah, 'when 'e aint workin' on it its kep' in a saife in 'is stoodio. And 'e aint workin' on it nah 'cos 'e's in bed wiv lumbager.'

'So what?' asked Jerry.

'So I brought the front door key away wiv me, ducky,' replied Sarah. 'Th' brat's at school, yer phones the old woman an' Bob's yer uncle.'

During the meal Mrs. Chapman gave Jerry a detailed description of the inside of Mr. Marlowe's house. Finally, the latch-key and a five pound note stolen by Jerry from a local pawnbroker a few weeks previously, changed hands.

It was about quarter past one when Mrs. Marlowe received the telephone call. She was informed that her sister Ruth, who lived at Godalming, had been taken to hospital suffering from acute appendicitis. Mrs. Marlowe was asked to come at once. It never entered that lady's head to doubt the call was genuine. Why, she had distinctly heard a voice say 'You're through Godalming, speak up, please,' as she lifted her receiver.

Jerry the Gent was quite an artist in his own line but he was no good at opening safes. That was where Conk Craddock came in; safe-breaking was Conk's speciality.

It was a bad day for the Marlowes at home, but with Tom and his friend at school, everything was going splendidly. News that Martin Penrose had won a scholarship had been received by the morning post and the Head had announced a half-holiday to celebrate the event.

Martin, of course, was a boarder. Tom, like most other day boys, had dinner at school. After the meal there was the usual scrum round the cloakroom lockers and some rather assinine cap-throwing, which resulted in Tom and Martin unknowingly wearing each other's caps. A small matter, but one which was to have unpleasant consequences.

It was a fine afternoon. Martin had no difficulty in getting permission to walk home with Tom across the Heath and stay to tea. It would be dark when he returned at six o'clock, but he could take a bus to the school door.

'"So I brought the front door key away wiv me, ducky."'

Parts of Hampstead Heath are sandy and violently uneven. There are tiny woods of silver birches and irregular lines of massive oaks. Gorse, blackberry and bracken grow everywhere, and here and there a reedy pond offers a home to mallards and moorhens. In short, parts of the Heath are ideal for tracking and trailing.

As the boys slithered quietly through some dead bracken they saw a man standing beside an oak tree with his back towards them. He was about thirty yards away. It seemed only natural to attempt a stealthy and unobserved approach.

In a very short time Tom and Martin were crouching behind a gorse bush within a yard of their quarry. Little of the man's face was visible to them but that little they disliked. He looked a thoroughly tough customer and there was something so furtive about his manner that the boys knew instinctively he would accuse them of deliberate spying if they made their presence known.

They were about to slip away as quietly as they had come, when a second man appeared facing directly towards them. For the moment retreat was impossible. Scarcely daring to breathe, the boys overheard the conversation which followed.

'So you got my message, Conk,' said the new arrival.

'Sure, guv. What's on?'

'The 9 Wildgrove Way job.'

'When?'

'Now. Got your tools?'

'Sure.'

'Anyone about?'

'Ain't seen no one since I got 'ere.'

'Then listen and I'll give you the low-down. Marlowe is ill in bed. His old woman has gone off to Godalming. I've just seen her start. The kid's at school and I've got the latch-key.'

'Nice work, guv,' said Conk.

Jerry the Gent grinned. Then he continued:

'We'll drive up to the front door all straight forward and above board. No need to worry about Marlowe hearing us, his bedroom is at the back of the house. Just in case any busy-body is watching, keep a bit behind and mask me as I put the key in the front door. It won't look much different from ringing the bell anyway. After a second or two I'll push the door open and pretend to have a word with someone inside. Then, in we both go. The safe is in the studio and the emerald is in the safe. Now we'd best get cracking.'

'Where's the car, guv?' asked Conk as the two men moved away.

'On the corner of the road with a faked number plate,' replied Jerry. The two men passed out of earshot.

Both boys were trembling with excitement. They had not dared to speak and now there was no time to make plans.

Tom's one idea was to get to his father.

He said: 'Come on, I know a short cut to the car,' and plunged into the undergrowth. Martin followed.

Only about ten yards of open ground separated Tom from a fair-sized saloon car when, a minute later he burst out of some bracken at a point overlooking the corner of the road. The men were not yet in sight. Without hesitation Tom opened the near rear door and threw himself on the floor of the car. He was closing the door when Martin arrived.

'Buzz off and telephone the police,' hissed Tom.

The door shut. Martin turned to dodge away, but it was too late.

There was an angry shout just behind him and he found himself struggling in the grip of Conk's ape-like arms.

'"*Buzz off and telephone the police*," hissed Tom.'

'And what would a nice little boy be doing at the door of my car when he ought to be at school learning his lessons?' enquired the gentlemanly voice of Jerry.

'It's a special half-holiday,' spluttered Martin replying to the second part of the question because he had no answer to the first.

But Jerry did not press his enquiry. He was staring at the cap which had fallen from Martin's head in his efforts to break away from Conk. It was Tom's cap, with his name clearly marked on the lining.

A horrid grin spread over the face of Jerry the Gent.

'Well it's not going to be much of a half-holiday for you Master T. Marlowe,' he said as he hit Martin squarely on the jaw.

'Strewth, guv,' said Conk, as the boy suddenly became limp in his grasp, ''Ave yer killed 'im?'

'Of course not,' snapped Jerry. 'Don't stand there like a fool. Shove the kid out of sight in the bracken whilst I start up the car.'

The horrified drumming of Tom's heart seemed to fill his ears.

Jerry walked round the front of the car and let himself into the driving seat. He started the engine. Then he lent across and opened the opposite door so that Conk might occupy the seat beside him.

'Hurry, man, we've wasted too much time already.'

The car was moving even before Conk sprang in.

Tom pressed himself closely against the back of the men's seats, the position in which he was best screened from view. Desperately he tried to make a plan.

There was no particular reason why he should be spotted unless either of the crooks opened a rear door, in which case discovery would be inevitable. What might happen then, he dared not think. He hardly dared to think of Martin, either. It was a rotten journey.

Tom knew the front door of his home locked automatically when closed. It was unlikely the crooks would leave it open to attract the attention of passers-by. How then could he reach his father?

There seemed one hope of entry. The hall cloakroom was on the opposite side of the house to the studio. Only

'" Hands up!" he cried, in a voice which cracked shrilly with excitement.'

the top part of the window opened but this was seldom closed except at night. Though the opening was too small for a man to pass through, less than a month ago, Tom had got into a row for squeezing in to win a bet from Martin.

The car slowed to a standstill. Tom was outside his home at last. With pounding heart he waited for discovery; but discovery never came.

The front doors on either side of the car opened and Jerry and Conk stepped out. The doors closed. He heard Jerry mutter 'Behind me. Quietly, and don't hurry it.' Then came the click of the front gate and the sound of footsteps on the flagged garden path.

Tom sat up on the floor of the car and waited. After what seemed a lifetime but was really little more than a minute, he peeped through the window. The doorstep was empty and the front door shut.

Tom guessed that the crooks would go straight to the studio which was lit only by skylights. There was no risk of his being seen as he slipped out of the car and round to the cloakroom window.

In the studio, Conk was at work on the safe. Jerry stood by him watching and listening. Upstairs Mr. Marlowe lay thinking thankfully that it would be another two hours before he need drag himself out of bed to drop the back door key out of the window to Tom on his return from school.

Tom found the top of the cloakrom window open. He removed his blazer and kicked off his shoes. He knew from experience that the window would be a tight fit and he knew, too, that he must make no noise when he dropped on to the tiled floor of the cloakroom.

After much squeezing and wriggling he was inside and a moment later he was padding softly upstairs to his father's bedroom. Quietly opening the door, Tom entered.

'It's burglars,' he hissed. 'I mean it.' He held up a warning hand.

'Eh? Burglars? Where?' gasped his astonished father. 'At your safe,' answered Tom. In breathless undertones he started to explain.

'But the prince's emerald isn't in the safe,' said Mr. Marlowe.

It was Tom's turn to be astonished but before he could ask any questions, there came the sound of footsteps outside the door.

Tom dived under the bed as the crooks burst into the room.

There could be no doubt that Jerry and Conk were in an ugly mood. They were taking big risks and the contents of Mr. Marlowe's safe had proved of little more value than the fiver Jerry had given Mrs. Chapman.

Now they stood on either side of Mr. Marlowe's bed. Conk produced a short length of rubber tubing loaded with lead, which he brandished menacingly in Mr. Marlowe's face. The muzzle of Jerry's automatic was pressing through the bedclothes against Mr. Marlowe's stomach.

'If you don't want to die a very messy death,' said Jerry the Gent, 'you'd better say where the emerald is, quick.'

Conk said much the same thing, but he put it even less politely.

A middle-aged man, lying in bed temporarily crippled by lumbago, can offer little resistance under such circumstances.

All the fun of the fair—cover design by John Verney

Tom's father thought it wise to end this unpleasant interview without delay.

'The emerald is in a wash-leather bag in my waistcoat pocket, and my waistcoat is hanging on a chair in my dressing room,' he said. He nodded his head in the direction of a door leading to a small room adjoining the bedroom.

'Garn. He's kiddin',' said Conk, 'but I'd better go and 'ave a look, guv.'

'No you don't,' said Jerry, 'we'll go together.'

'What! An' leave 'im 'ere?' questioned Conk.

'When you've roped and gagged him,' replied Jerry.

'But I've got lumbago and can hardly move,' protested the unfortunate gem engraver.

'Lumbager won't stop yer from 'ollerin',' said Conk.

In an astonishingly short time Mr. Marlowe's wrists were securely bound with his pyjama girdle. His handkerchief was stuffed into his mouth and his head wrapped in a bath towel.

'Come on,' said Jerry as Conk tied the towel in place with the cord of Mr. Marlowe's dressing gown.

The crooks disappeared into the dressing room.

On the bedroom side of the door there was a key and a brass bolt. Tom knew this.

In a flash he rolled from under the bed. His stockinged feet made no sound as he crossed the linoleum-covered floor. He had a momentary glimpse of the two men's backs bending over his father's clothes, as he slammed the door and shot the bolt. Then he turned the key and tore it from the keyhole.

There was a furious roar from Conk, followed by a heavy thud as he hurled himself against the door. Then came a crash as Jerry, having pocketed the emerald, joined in the attack.

The door held but a panel smashed. Through the gap a hand groped for the bolt and key.

A ship model in a glass bottle adorned the centre of Mr. Marlowe's mantelpiece. Tom seized the bottle and brought it down with all his strength on the groping fingers. There was a howl, as the bottle splintered into fragments, and the hand withdrew.

He heard Jerry's voice shout, 'Out of the way, fool.' Three shots from the Gent's automatic followed in quick succession.

Tom threw himself flat on the floor. A second hand appeared, successfully withdrew the bolt and paused for a moment over the empty keyhole.

Only the frail lock remained.

The crooks returned to their battering-ram tactics.

The door burst open and Jerry and Conk landed in a sprawling heap on the bedroom floor. As they fell something spun towards Tom across the polished linoleum.

It was Jerry's automatic. Before the crooks could regain their feet, Tom had them covered.

'Hands up!' he cried in a voice which cracked shrilly with excitement.

A crash of broken glass sounded from the hall below. Then came the sound of heavy boots pounding up the staircase. The next moment a police inspector and three constables blocked the bedroom doorway.

On recovering consciousness, Martin, too, had done his stuff.

Sitting on the floor with their hands above their heads, Jerry and Conk looked remarkably foolish.

There was the trace of a smile on the Inspector's face as he spoke quietly to Tom.

'Careful with that gun, son.'

After that things happened quickly. The crooks were safely handcuffed and the prince's emerald found in Jerry's pocket. Mr. Marlowe was unbound and the things he

said about the crooks were even nastier than those Mrs. Chapman had said about lumbago.

That evening after Mrs. Marlowe had returned from Godalming, furious at having been hoaxed but much relieved to find her sister in the best of health, Tom heard two pieces of good news.

The first was about Martin. He had lost a couple of front teeth and his jaw was still several sizes too big, but the swelling was subsiding and he was otherwise unhurt.

The second concerned Mrs. Sarah Chapman. That slippery lady had taken her five pound note to a pawnbroker to redeem a few odds and ends she had in pawn. He was the pawnbroker whom Jerry had burgled and he recognised the number of the note. Now Mrs. Chapman, too, was under arrest.

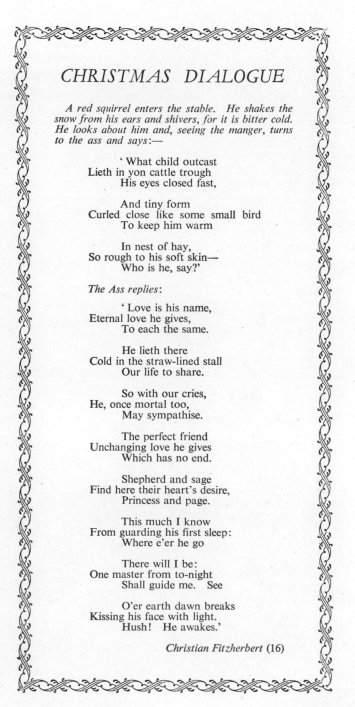

CHRISTMAS DIALOGUE

A red squirrel enters the stable. He shakes the snow from his ears and shivers, for it is bitter cold. He looks about him and, seeing the manger, turns to the ass and says:—

'What child outcast
Lieth in yon cattle trough
His eyes closed fast,

And tiny form
Curled close like some small bird
To keep him warm

In nest of hay,
So rough to his soft skin—
Who is he, say?'

The Ass replies:

'Love is his name,
Eternal love he gives,
To each the same.

He lieth there
Cold in the straw-lined stall
Our life to share.

So with our cries,
He, once mortal too,
May sympathise.

The perfect friend
Unchanging love he gives
Which has no end.

Shepherd and sage
Find here their heart's desire,
Princess and page.

This much I know
From guarding his first sleep:
Where e'er he go

There will I be:
One master from to-night
Shall guide me. See

O'er earth dawn breaks
Kissing his face with light.
Hush! He awakes.'

Christian Fitzherbert (16)

Q

SEA SCOUTS GO SAILING

Photographs by Camera Talks

The Yacht 'Schmoo'. Skipper: Lt.-Cmdr. G. Lennox Cotton. Mate: Jimmy Magee. Crew: Willis Williamson, Sam McCanstand, Wilson Clarke, Billy Foster.

Extracts from Log.

First Day. Boarded ship. Obtained stores. Hoisted sail. Moored in Fleet Dyke. Evening meal. Bathe. Turned in at 10.15 p.m.

Second Day. Breakfast. Sailed for Horning Light following breeze. Quanted* most of the way. Sailed with a cross-wind, gybing frequently, through Salhouse Broad to Wroxham Broad. After evening meal (stew) the dinghy sailed in a light breeze.

Third Day. Hoveton St. John. *First race*. We finished second. *Second race*. We won. Winning skippers given 5s. prize money. Sailed with a stiff breeze on our port beam to Horning where prize money was spent on cordials.

Fourth Day. Sailed for Malthouse Broad. Fed sandwiches to the very tame wild fowl, mallard and coots. Afternoon dinghy regatta.

Fifth Day. Sailed with a wind on the starboard quarter. Difficulty tacking down river, so Jimmy and Billy went ashore as a towing party. Sailed close—hauled along

Quanting is punting with a special pole with a disc on the bottom to prevent it sinking too deep into the mud.

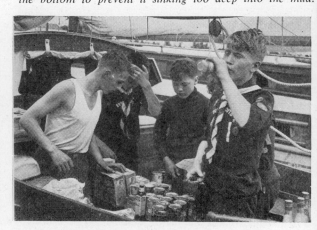

Sea Scouts from Ulster arrive and board the yacht 'The Shmoo'.

Stowing away (and testing) the stores for the voyage.

Towing party go ashore in the dinghy

Insubordination is dealt with promptly.

Flat Dyke to Upton Dyke. Grounded badly at entrance. It began to rain but we got off, and moored for the night downstream.

Sixth Day. Acle Bridge. Lowered mast. Quanted through bridge. Raised mast, hoisted sails. Sailed downstream close hauled with ebbing tide. Went hard aground on a shoal. Lowered sails and quanted off. Moored in Yarmouth Yacht Station. Donned full dress uniform and visited Yarmouth.

Seventh Day. Sailed upstream. St. Olave's and Sumerleyton swing bridges opened for us.

Eighth Day. Day's run: 15 miles.

Ninth Day. Off St. Olave's Bridge. Marched to St. Edmund's Church, Fritton, for Morning Service, and back. Quanted through bridge, Willis fell in.

Tenth Day. Day's run: 23½ miles.

Eleventh Day. Sailed to Barton Broad. Races round Pleasure Hill Island. Sailed to Womack Water. Willis fell in.

Twelfth Day. Collected stores at Potter Heigham. On to Hickling Broad. Tests for Oarsman's Badges.

Thirteenth Day. Cross country run. After dinner held a camp fire. Returned late to our ship.

Fourteenth Day. More races. Sailed for Potter Heigham. Jimmy, throwing bucket of water at Willis, missed him and splashed the Commodore, who pushed him overboard. After evening meal, packed gear.

Total distance travelled: 136 miles.
Average day's run: 9½ miles.

Part of a frieze showing Greeks fighting Amazons, carved out of marble, probably by Scopas in 350 B.C.—

LIGHT AND SHADE

by Joseph Natanson

Even those of you who are not interested in painting or sculpture, must have noticed how the most ordinary scene changes when the sun comes out. What was flat, is suddenly full of life. In this article Joseph Natanson shows how great artists used the qualities of light and shade to give their figures a greatness far beyond their usual human form.

A detail from 'The Madonna and Child, St. John and Angels' by Michelangelo, painted in 1494 and now in the National Gallery.

SCULPTURE is a composition entirely in light and shade. A sculptor has no pencil with which to draw the outline of his figures, nor colour to enliven its surface. He uses marble, stone, bronze, clay or plaster to catch the light and cast shadows. The real medium of a sculptor is light.

Very often you are disappointed by a snapshot of what seemed to you a perfect subject for photography. It looks flat, grey and with many unnecessary details which came, nobody knows how, to muddle up a well planned composition. Professional photographers use strong lamps to create contrasts and pick up the important features, choosing between essential and non-essential things, which a camera, brainless artist, could never do in making the picture. Thus, by a clever arrangement of lights, a silly little face becomes the great beauty who uses a well-known toothpaste and smiles at us from an advertisement. Film studios are still more extravagant and have to use

whole batteries of artificial suns to give life to a group of actors, who would otherwise become as expressionless as a monument to a famous man, standing in a square, made not too long ago, and which you could pass every day of your life without caring who he was or who made him.

There is nothing wrong with the monument. Every detail is right and yet it is as dead as your unsuccessful snapshot. Light picks up irrelevant details and slips over important features which would give character to the sculpture. Is it the fault of the light?

The admirable sculpture of Scopas was not carved to stand in the gloomy, grey light of our museums. It was made for the glorious brilliance of the sun under the almost continuously clear sky of Greece. Yet it has not lost a fraction of its wonderful power.

Even in a photographic reproduction it is very moving. The rhythm of the composition, the dramatic expression of each figure, but above all, the greatness, impossible to describe, of each movement, makes you move from figure to figure with intense interest watching the mysterious unity so strongly linking them together. Your imagination will soon

supply the missing parts of the cruelly mutilated relief, and once the perfection is restored, your eyes will move along the frieze, up and down, following a rhythm composed by Scopas the musician (one would like to say), over all the marvellous details carved by Scopas the sculptor. Your eyes will move from a naked figure of a Greek hero to a draped figure of an Amazon or the body of a horse. They all have a very natural human or animal character, unless you suddenly discover that they are somehow different.

In a crowd of living people you can always find your preference—some person you would call handsome, very rarely beautiful. Here, you are at a loss; each figure you look at is the most harmonious, the most perfect creature.

I wonder sometimes if the Greek artists were inspired, as we have to believe, by the stories of Greek mythology, or was it not rather that they had to invent all those gods, heroes and superhuman beings in order to excuse the unbelievable beauty of the figures they created.

Your eyes, fascinated by the great variety of forms and the different character of each figure, are still wandering

—Brought from Greece by Lord Elgin, it is now in the British Museum where you can see it, and many others, for yourself.

over the springing harmony of lean muscles, pausing for a time on the detail of a head, arm or leg, or at the modelling of a torso, round the curve of a shield, following the delicate folds of a drapery, or alarmed by the drama of a raised hand. Sometimes your eyes cover a long distance with a glance, sometimes you scrutinise a small area intensely. Have you realised already that you are all the time following the play of light and shade?

Once having made this discovery, you are on the way to make others, more and more amazing.

The shadows and their intensity are spread very evenly over the whole surface of the frieze (remember the missing parts) and their alternation with the lighted parts make the rhythmical pattern you were following all the time with your eyes. It almost looks as if Scopas designed this pattern before starting to cut his figures. And yet there is no movement which would have a purely decorative character.

The action of each figure is perfectly simple and logical, the intention of each movement (a very deadly one, I am afraid) is perfectly clear and every part of each body plays its natural part in the action. On the other hand, there is not one shadow in the whole frieze cast accidentally, and not one more nor one less is needed to give a precise definition to each form.

I am sure that you have never before thought about light and shade in connection with sculpture. It is so obvious!

Nevertheless, as you see, it is quite a problem, and it becomes still more complicated if you think about sculpture in the round where the play of light and shade must be perfect from whichever side it pleases you to look at it.

The idea of light and shade makes everybody think at first of those painters who made so much use of it, and of the most famous of them all, Rembrandt. He

'The Angel leaving Tobias and his family', painted by Rembrandt in 1637, and now in the Louvre, Paris. The artist's family (and dog) were used as models for this picture. (There are many famous examples of Rembrandt's work in the National Gallery.)

237

The Annunciation, painted by Duccio about 1311 *and now in the National Gallery.*

used it perhaps in the most impressive way, but certainly he was not the first to discover its importance.

You cannot imagine a painting without the problem of light and shade. Just as the sculptor is building a form on which light and shadows make the pattern of the composition, so the painter, on a flat surface, has to paint light and shadows to create an abstraction which suggests a three-dimensional form to us. To illustrate what I want to say, we are going to leave the incredible perfection of Greek art and have a look at a painting by one of the so-called primitive Italian masters. Needless to say, you will not find anything primitive about the painting. Only people in the nineteenth century could call ' primitive ' an art so refined in its noble simplicity. But, of course, for someone who likes photographic accuracy and theatrical affectation, Duccio is not only a primitive but almost a ' modern,' which still to many people is the greatest insult in art.

If you have the opportunity to look at this painting in the National Gallery, you will see all the beauty of its colouring and also of the gold which is profusely used. Duccio wanted to make the painting as decorative and pleasant to the eye as possible. He is not trying to create a representation of a real room in which the Virgin would receive the divine messenger, any more than Scopas thought about carving a landscape at the back of his figures. The simple architectural

forms are used to indicate space, to balance the figures and to give rhythm to the whole painting. Try once more to notice how your eye moves along the arcade from figure to figure, going from light to shade and from shade to light— or, as I would rather say, from colour to colour, because Duccio translated light and shade, as every great painter does, into a harmony of colour.

Thus the play of light and shade is used by Duccio to give body to shapes and to enrich the play of colour. It is a diffused, gentle light which does not want to intrude dramatically into a peaceful subject.

To give another example of light used chiefly to give relief to form, I have chosen a painting made by an artist who was above all a sculptor. For a reason which we do not know, Michelangelo left the painting unfinished. That explains the light patch over the head and a kind of halo to the left which is a part of two whole figures, outside the fragment here reproduced, which are only roughly sketched. But, as you see, some parts of the painting have already achieved perfection. Here also the light is diffused, softly modelling graceful, beautifully rounded forms. The gradation is extremely gentle. One side of the face is lit by direct light, the other by a reflection. Look at the detail of the eyes, or the mouth disappearing into the shadow. Each form has been simplified to almost geometrical purity, achieving

in this simplicity a great expression of serenity and grace.

Now look at the Rembrandt. Here the lights and the shadows make a very strong contrast; they are no longer used only to give body to forms, they are a part, perhaps the most important part, of the composition. The light is no longer still and diffused. It is violent and sharp as lightning in a dark night.

In a flash of sudden illumination we see the angel taking the air with great energy; we almost hear the slap of his feet kicking off the ground and the rustle of his wings, and we see below the family assembled at the porch of the house, each figure expressing in a different way their emotion. But all that would last only a second. Very soon it would be dark again, the angel would be gone, the silence of the night very close, and one by one the members of the family would walk silently inside the house and shut the door.

In spite of a very imaginative subject, Rembrandt tries to take all the details very much from everyday life. The people, including even the angel, have no pretention to beauty. We are far away from classical perfection. Look at the prostrate old man and the other in darkness. Look at the two women, and the poor old dog, terrified. Look at the angel, superhuman being, how very realistic he looks with his wings and those very human legs moving in the air.

You cannot help looking at those legs because one of them is exactly in the centre of the picture and is also its brightest spot. This leg gives you the idea of the flash of light between Tobias, kneeling below, and the supernatural light in the sky where the angel is going. Everything else is only a reflection of this light, just enough to give character to each form appearing from darkness. It seems that in his vision, lasting only a fraction of a second, Rembrandt has no time to give a complete explanation of every form. He uses a kind of shorthand, his brush applying colour which is almost pure light. It only touches a face, a hand, part of a dress, yet immediately, not only does everything become alive, but also it achieves a greatness far beyond its usual human form.

And thus the touch of his brush, and his vision of a supernatural light breaking through the darkness of our understanding, gave to the simple people who lived in Holland at the time of Rembrandt a greatness sometimes even more moving, because more unexpected, than the perfection of Greek heroes.

The frieze is reproduced by kind permission of the British Museum, the painting by Duccio, and the detail of the Michelangelo, by kind permission of the National Gallery, London. The reproduction of Tobias and the Angel, is by courtesy of the Louvre, Paris.

THE MARE'S NEST

by Klaxon

There was no possible hope of the bathing pool being finished, when Lousy was taken, unwillingly, to the sea. A few spilt crumbs and bits of broken china caused quite a change in the situation by the time he came back

IT WAS THE FIRST day of the summer holidays, and it was seven o'clock in the morning. Cordelia, Lousy's sister had awakened with the feeling that something tremendously exciting had happened. She stretched herself and then remembered two things. The first was that Miss Potter, the daily governess, would not come pedalling down the drive for another six weeks. The second was that her brother was home again.

Her bedroom door was open as well as the window.

'Lou!' she called, 'Lou, wake up!'

There was no answer so she ran across the passage and into the room that had once been the old night-nursery. The bed had been slept in, but not very lately. Cordelia, newly-steeped in detective stories, discovered that by feeling the pillow and the hollow in the middle of the bed. She went to the open window, and leaned out. There on the lawn, and leading from gravel to shrubbery was a trail of footprints, showing dark green in the silver dew. Five minutes later she was dressed. Two minutes after that she had followed the footprints and caught up with her brother. He was standing by the big gates and listening to Lily, the paper-girl, who bicycled from the station every morning, and carried more news than was to be found, as a rule, in the daily papers.

'They say it's a lovely skeleton—girl of about sixteen . . . Oh, yes, Mr. Lou, it's a new one all right. There's a brooch and a hair-grip and everything.'

'Skeleton?' asked Cordelia joyously, 'Where?'

'On Dewbury Hill. They dug it up yesterday.'

'Who did?' asked Cordelia.

'Some strange gentlemen and a lady—one of those plain-clothes women policemen I shouldn't wonder. It makes you shudder to think it might be anyone of us that was murdered in our beds. I did hear they'd found the implements, too.'

Cordelia did not shudder though she gave two or three little hops of annoyance at her brother's answer.

'Not in our beds—not sort of murdered in our beds, I mean if they found the implements on Dewbury Hill. They must have murdered her there if they left the implements by her.'

'But they'll do anything to put you off the scent!' objected Cordelia.

'And anyway,' pursued Lousy, 'anyway, not a skeleton after a *new* murder. You've sort of got to wait for skeletons. I know because of a mouse I had to wait for, and that had been dead for ages.'

'Don't be REVOLTING.'

'I told you it had *been* dead,' Lousy's voice was still patient, 'I'm not a cat or a mouse-trap, and it was you that got excited over murder.'

'Mice are different. Nice mice, mice like—' and here Cordelia's eyes filled with tears of the tenderest compassion —'mice like that pet mouse in the spare-room that Aunt Amy's so horrid about.'

Lily put foot to the pedal of her bicycle. She was looking forward to telling Mrs. Briggs at the village shop all about the skeleton.

'Well, I must be off. Here's the papers. If you want to know more about murders, Miss Cordelia, you ought to get your Dad to have some penny papers instead of that old *Times*.'

'Wait a sec!' said Lousy, 'Just where did they dig up the skeleton?'

'Nearly on top of the hill.' Lily's voice sounded more faintly as she whizzed down the slope. 'On the edge of the spinney . . . looking towards Paston.'

'Hope they haven't disturbed the badgers,' was Lousy's comment.

Breakfast was a rather argumentative meal. Cordelia, bursting in with the news of the murder, was told to 'sit down quietly, dear.'

Later, her comments on the methods of murderers in general were answered rather crushingly.

'Darling, I don't think it's very nice for little girls to wallow in details of crime. It isn't awfully pretty. You'll only give yourself nasty dreams. Lou isn't nearly so blood-thirsty.'

'More coffee, please,' said Colonel Knightshead, 'there's nothing in the paper this morning.'

'Lily,' Cordelia smiled a milky smile, 'Lily said if you'd take penny papers instead of that old *Times*.'

'Do use your table-napkin!' said her father. He added, 'There's a Leader here about the excavations on Dewbury Hill. It seems they've found a Saxon burial-ground. . . . Several skeletons. There's one of a girl—sixteen or seventeen years old, they think—in a remarkable state of preservation.'

'Fancy!' said Mrs. Knightshead.

'Bone brooch, and some sort of pin as well,' pursued the Colonel.

'Saxon!' cried Cordelia, 'Saxon—all woad! Just history.' She dropped her piece of toast (marmalade side down on to the carpet to be disdained by a bull-terrier, who did not care for the flavour of oranges). 'History at the beginning of the holidays, and not a nice juicy murder. Mummy's quite right about village gossip!'

'Cordelia!'

'Well, I *had* looked forward to bagging a murderer.'

'I wish they'd leave the poor things alone,' said Mrs. Knightshead (she was referring to the Saxon remains). 'Surely one skeleton is very like another.'

'Not a bit,' said Colonel Knightshead, 'there's the Piltdown skull and the Neanderthal skull—very different types, and those in comparison with the skull of Dean Swift—'

Lousy continued to think about badgers, and to hope that the excavations had not disturbed them. It was easy to turn from one sort of digging to another.

239

and he asked his father how the new bathing-pool was getting on.

'It isn't,' said Colonel Knightshead, 'we got down to the clay and then Bruce' (he was the handy-man) 'Bruce went down with a gammy leg. There's no hope of its being finished this summer. By the way, I wonder if those fellows—the ones who're excavating Dewbury Hill—would be interested to see the bits of pottery we found when we were digging out the pool. Norman, I think they are—early Norman. Come and have a look at them, Lou.'

In his father's study, Lousy looked, with as much interest as he could at a number of chunks of thick grey pottery. Some, by their curving, gave evidence that they had been bowls or pitchers. On the edges of some were thickened rims that might have been made by pressure of fingers or of twisted rope.

'Like rough pie-crust when cook's in a hurry!' remarked Cordelia.

'It's a pity there are only fragments,' said Colonel Knightshead. 'I thought they were Saxon. I showed 'em to one archæological chap who was staying at the Vicarage, but he said they were Norman. His theory was that there might have been a rubbish dump down by the stream, and that the pottery was broken before it was chucked there. Anyway, the fellows on Dewbury Hill may be interested. You might take the bits along to them, Lou, I don't want 'em.'

Lousy clattered the pottery into an old rucksack, and went into the kitchen to collect some snacks for elevenses in case he should feel empty before lunch. Judy, the bull-terrier followed him into the hall where his mother was tidying an oak-chest that held the usual conglomeration of rugs, bee-veils, gardening-gloves and cardboard boxes full of junk. She was peering into one of the boxes.

'I wonder—' she murmured.

Then she too held out some fragments of pottery. These were almost black, and were finer and shinier than the pieces in the rucksack. A few of the tiny pieces showed traces of a raised design.

'Yes,' said Mrs. Knightshead, 'These might just as well go. I'm sure Uncle Charles will have forgotten all about them now. He collected so many things. Really we can't house them all and it may be ages before he comes back to England. Lou, darling, if you're going to look at the excavations, you might give these bits to the men who are doing the digging.'

Lousy took the bits of pottery, and jumbled them into the rucksack with the other pieces and the sandwiches and the hunk of cake.

He was thinking about his Uncle Charles and the curious tale he had told about a snake-charmer—a story remembered by Lousy from five, six, or was it seven years ago. Now, he was remembering it again, and he scarcely heard what his mother was saying.

'Tell the men I had meant to mend it with Seccotine, but I couldn't find all the bits. . . . It was broken that winter when you and Cordelia and the Lambton cousins played the " Mistletoe Bough " and Cordelia was shut in the chest and sat on the box. . . . She was much plumper then.'

'Who was plumper? When?' demanded Cordelia, who had just reached the hall by way of the banisters.

'When you played the " Mistletoe Bough," that Christmas with the Lambtons.'

'Not plump!' said Cordelia, 'Well-coupled up and muscled. Muscles weigh more than fat. I remember that " Mistletoe Bough ". Daddy gave me sixpence because my tooth came out in the chest, and another sixpence for not crying when I was shut up in it.'

'Yes darling', said Mrs. Knightshead. 'Lou, tell the men I don't like to throw away anything that might be useful to anybody, but I don't like *harbouring* things that might be interesting to somebody. And tell them about Uncle Charles and that he *was* a great expert.'

'Yes,' replied Lousy. He was thinking what fun it would be (if his mother were a boy) to have her in Form IV-B under Mr. Manders. *She'd* baffle him. She'd never stop making what the schoolmaster called 'irrelevant remarks'.

'I remember quite well,' put in Cordelia, 'and then I went down near the stream and hurled my tooth into it because there was a water rat with a hooky one, and one never KNOWS. Oh, Lou I've got the most marvellous idea—'

'Well, go and have your marvellous ideas somewhere else!'

By this time Colonel Knightshead had come into the Hall.

'Have them in another place and at another time or Mummy will never be ready. I've got to drive into Pollingford in exactly ten minutes.'

Mrs. Knightshead hurried up the stairs, and Colonel Knightshead turned to his son.

'Tell those fellers on Dewbury Hill (they'll want to know this) and that all the pottery was found at a depth of six foot. Give them my compliments and say I'll be delighted if they want to carry out any further investigations. Tell them the place is theirs. Can you remember that?'

'Six foot,' repeated Lousy, 'and they can sort of come along here and do what they like in the bathing pool—I mean what isn't quite a bathing-pool yet.'

'Oh, come ON!' urged Cordelia, 'I've got sandwiches, too, AND the most marvellous idea.'

After they had left the dull part of the village, Lousy and his sister saw Dewbury Hill rising before them through the dizzying haze of hot July. From its flat crown, a scar that looked like a painters' druggeting, ran from lynchett to lynchett until it ended in the grass below the hill. Turf had been lifted from the white bone of the Downs so that the men who came after might discover how the men before them had lived. Had the green terraces round the hill been cut for purposes of defence or agriculture?

Cordelia was not thinking about history. She babbled breathlessly, and gasped like a puppy, as she trod the close turf of the hill.

'Listen, Lou—that murder, the skeleton murder—don't you see . . ? Oh, Lou, you might listen.'

Larks rose all around them, and twittered new songs above the ancient hill.

Presently they passed a few bivouac tents on a plateau, and mounted to where the excavators were at work only a few hundred yards from the spinney and the badgers' holt.

Two or three men in shorts and shirts and a woman were standing in a trench, and peering into a sort of cupboard cut in the chalk. In it, whitish grey and dusty as its surroundings, stood something that looked like a drawn-up bowl.

'Sir,' as Lousy set foot to the edge of turf above the trench he spoke to the eldest of the men, 'Sir, my father sends compliments and these all came out of our bathing pool—six foot down, and he says—'

'Go away! Go away!' The woman waved her arms violently. 'The slightest vibration may crack the vase.'

Lousy backed politely, emptied the rucksack on the turf and picked up the sandwiches and cake from the jumble of pottery.

At this moment, Judy who had been ranging round the outskirts of the spinney, put nose to ground, and streaked after a rabbit, which tore towards the newly-dug turf, jinked round in bafflement, and headed back towards the trees.

'Traps!' said Lousy as a white scut disappeared into the brambles. 'That spinney's preserved, and it's a new Keeper.' He raced up the hillside, and Cordelia followed.

Sometime later she returned by way of a trail of scattered sandwiches, and Lousy, having made a lead from a handkerchief and a piece of string, meandered back with Judy.

The three excavators were on their knees and turning over the pottery and biscuit crumbs that Lousy had tumbled out of the rucksack. One of them asked, 'Where did you say these were found?'

'In our bathing-pool, Sir, the bathing-pool we were beginning to make.'

And now questions were asked as rapidly as though Mr. Manders, the Headmaster and Matron were all holding a Geography test in Form IV-B, and all the queries were being directed to Lousy, who answered in a dazed way—

'Yes, my father said to tell you that all the pottery was found six foot down. . . . No, I wasn't there, I was at school. . . . Yes, Sir, I can show you the place. . . . No, I'm afraid my father's out, but he sent his compliments. . . .'

Now the excavators began to argue among themselves.

'The red is much more common. . . . Surely this particular kind was made from local clay near Castor in Northamptonshire. . . . Hardly likely they would have brought clay from so far. . . . The traces of relief work are most interesting. . . . Remarkable glaze. . . . Might be of the greatest importance. . . .'

A chalk-hill butterfly fluttered across the turf. Lousy looked down from the hill, and imagined an invading band advancing. He was not interested in pottery.

'If you could,' the tall man was speaking, 'if you could show us where the pottery was found, we should be very grateful.'

A procession went down the hill.

Cordelia, tagging sadly behind, made moan to Lousy.

'They won't believe me about the murder; they're so wrapped up in the silly *old* bones . . . I almost wish we weren't going to the sea tomorrow. I'd rather find a murderer. . . . If only our bathing-pool was finished we needn't go to the sea. . . . O Lou, there's the skeleton of the dearest little Saxon puppy in one of those old graves. . . . They're going to send it to a stuffy old museum. It does seem a shame. . . . Just think, Lou, a dear little Saxon puppy galloping about the hill hundreds and hundreds of years, and now dead. Listen Lou, fancy being dead on a day like this.'

The successor of larks, once disturbed by a Saxon puppy, circled up into the dizzying blue.

'Bull-terrier, probably,' said Lousy, 'Daddy says that Caesar's hunting dogs must've been very like bull-terriers.

'A *dead* bull-terrier puppy!' mourned Cordelia, and flung consoling arms round the neck of Judy.

That evening Colonel Knightshead made announcement. 'I've told those fellows they can dig in the bathing-pool as much as they like, drain it and do what they like while we're in the Isle of Wight. It's odd how excited they seem. That other archæological chap—the one who looked at the pottery last month—can't have known his job.'

'Sea,' mused Cordelia, 'sea and pools, and putting your fingers inside anemones—they don't mind. They cling and like it. Anemones are much more loving than people know.'

'Finish your soup, darling,' said Mrs. Knightshead.

A fortnight later, the Knightshead family returned from the seaside. There was sand in the suitcases, and Cordelia's sponge-bag was stuffed with sea-weed.

The dust of the village station platform was gritty beneath their feet as they waited for the luggage to be piled into the ancient car.

'O, Lou, don't you wish we could have stayed there for ever?'

'No,' said Lousy. 'But I would sort've liked to move the bathing.'

He sniffed at the dry air.

The truth was that he preferred streams, woods and the tang of never very dry beechmast to all the smell of harbours and tar, rope-soled sandals and the fishy saltiness that destroyed all other scents, just as he preferred fresh-water bathing. But it was hot and he longed to get into cool water—silky, chilling *fresh* cold.

'I hope the refrigerator's working,' said Mrs. Knightshead.

At the front door they were met by a rush of archæologists. Lousy escaped them to go in search of Judy. Cordelia, with crumbs went to entertain the spare-room mouse.

The family did not meet again until tea-time when Colonel Knightshead unfolded some fragments of black pottery from their covering of cotton-wool.

'Anybody seen these before?' he asked.

Mrs. Knightshead wrinkled her forehead. 'Surely,' she said, 'surely, those are bits of the bowl that Uncle Charles brought home. It got broken, you remember? Oh yes, of course! I was tidying out the oak chest the day before we went away. I gave the bits to Lou because I thought the archæologists might be interested.'

'They *were!*' said her husband. 'They were so interested that they've been digging in the bathing-pool for the last fortnight. They've dredged every ounce of mud, and cleared it away. Lou, when you took the pottery up to Dewbury Hill, what did you tell them?'

Lousy chewed several times because it helped his memory. Then he emptied his mouth, and spoke.

'I sort of gave them your compliments, and sort of said they could do what they liked here—you'd said they could, and—'

'Did you tell them where the pottery was found—all of it?'

'Yes, I remember that, I told them what you said that it came from the bathing-pool—six feet down. Then Judy buzzed off after a rabbit and I had to follow.'

'Oh, Lou,' said Mrs. Knightshead. 'You should have told them that the black shiny bits came from the oak chest in the hall. You should have told them about Uncle Charles too—they'd have been interested.'

'They were,' said Colonel Knightshead. 'It seems that the shiny black bits are Samian pottery—a most unexpected treasure to be found in this locality.'

'Castor in Northamptonshire!' put in Lousy. 'Made from local clay.'

His father looked at him sharply.

'Come and look at the bathing-pool!' he said.

As Lousy and Cordelia followed their parents across the lawn, through the orchard and towards the stream, they heard snatches of conversation.

'Beats me how they could be bothered to dig so hard in this weather,' said Colonel Knightshead. 'The tall chap told me they'd have suspected the two lots of pottery (by the way the Norman stuff didn't interest 'em a bit) didn't come from the same place, if it hadn't been for one thing—'

'What was that?'

Photographic Study by Hans Kaden, F.P.S.A., F.R.P.

A curving arch of lucent green,
Lac'd o'er with milky foam,
Shot, like fine silk, with glistening sheen.
Poised like an em'rald dome.

Then, with a roar like falling trees
It falls, in seething white,
Like blossom, tossed by the breeze
Falls, from its crescent height.

Then spreads, in ripples o'er the sands
And silvers, glistens, where plump terns
And herring gulls, in little bands
Wade, with their crests like feather'd ferns.
JANET MARSHALL (12)

'Bit of a mystery. They found two more scraps of that black Samian pottery in the clay near the bathing-pool, and they *fitted* the other bits.'

'Well,' Mrs. Knightshead looked puzzled. 'But the bowl was perfect when Charles brought it back with him. I wish I'd mended it straight away.'

'Mummy!' broke in Cordelia.

'Hush darling, Daddy and I are talking.'

After that nobody spoke for a few moments because the water of the bathing pool lay below them. It was not very deep yet but its feeding-stream had been unblocked, and the sound of water trickling into it made the perfect tune for a summer afternoon.

The chalky bottom was scraped clear of mud, and the reflection of a cloud was broken by the scattering water.

'Bathe before breakfast,' thought Lousy.

'Mummy,' persisted Cordelia, after she too had taken in the glory. 'Don't you remember when my tooth had come out in the Mistletoe Bough chest, I brought it down here in case it should be handy for the poor rat with the hooky tooth. There were some bits of Uncle Charles' bowl in my hand too—bits of the bowl I'd sat on.'

'Heavens!' said Colonel Knightshead, 'And those chaps have written a frightfully learned paper for some Anthropological Society. If only Lou hadn't told them that all the pottery came from the same place.'

'It's what you told him to say, Daddy.' Already Cordelia had one shuddering toe in the icy water. 'I heard you, and he said just what you said!'

'We shall have to tell them,' said Mrs. Knightshead.

'After a fortnight's hard digging in this weather?' pondered the Colonel. 'Question is, do they want to be told they've been hunting for a mare's nest? I wonder. Let's sleep on it.'

'A mare's nest,' shrilled Cordelia. 'Wouldn't it be *sweet* if mares did build nests in paddocks, and had nine or ten foals at a time like wrens? Wouldn't it be lovely, Lou?'

Lousy did not answer, and this was not because he hadn't heard but because he was trying to reckon how many bathes he could fit in during the rest of the summer holidays.

His mother, misunderstanding the silence, put a hand on his shoulder.

'Don't worry, Lou, it wasn't your fault about the pottery.'

How blessedly unlike school home was—especially in the long summer holidays.

My Introduction To Riding

by Hilary Keeble (14)

WHEN I WAS about three I used to ride in a basket chair on a donkey which I cannot really remember, but I do know that it was a very stubborn donkey, and we have photos of the whole household trying to make it go.

The person who used to take me out on the donkey had a nickname, Scotty.

Scotty is really our groom. He spends a lot of time telling me about my Grandfather's horses that used to win at all the shows. He stands by Silver's (who is my present pony) loose-box and pushes his cap to the back of his head and says in his Suffolk way of speaking: ' I remember when I took Lillyleagh to Bury,' or ' when Grandpa went hunting on pore old Spring' and so on for ages. It is very interesting, and he has told me a lot of peculiar remedies for horse maladies.

After the donkey, I used to ride a black pony, called Merryleggs, and then a fat little pony of a brownish, blackish, whiteish colour.

Then, on my seventh birthday, my Grandfather gave me Silver.

Silver is the pony I have got now, and she is a grey about 13 hands high, and jumps very well.

When I first saw her it was the morning of my birthday, and I had measles. She was lead on to the lawn so that I could see her out of my bedroom window. Of course, I was frightfully pleased, though I still had to go on the leading rein.

Gradually, however, I got on better and the leading-rein got left off for some time nearly every day until I did not use it at all.

I used to ride a lot with Scotty, he would ride my Grandfather's horse, Playmate, and I Silver. Sometimes Grandpa came with us riding his mare Blue Bird and we went for very long rides indeed.

Grandpa was a very good horseman and judge of horses, both of riding and cart horses.

Grandpa enjoyed seeing how well people rode, or else seeing them come off. One day, we were all out on a long ride. I was just in front of Grandpa when suddenly he lifted his walking-stick (strange though it may sound, Grandpa always carried one with him when riding) high in the air and brought it down on the plump rear-end of Silver who shot forward at the same time depositing me in some deep grass. She did not go far away from the scene of the crime. That is one very good thing about Silver, when she gets rid of you, she always has the decency to stop and wait for you and not go tearing off home.

When I was eleven, I went to a proper riding school for the first time. There I learnt more finished and effective riding. I learnt how to hold the reins properly (in spite of others having tried in vain to teach me for years), the proper way to get your horse out of its stable, take off its rug and test the girths. Later, at the same place I learnt how to saddle and bridle and unsaddle and unbridle, correctly.

Many small but important points my riding master gave me explaining that if one thing was done properly, the rest would fall into place. For instance, if you keep your heels down, your knees and thighs should automatically go into the correct position.

I was also reminded always to look before going over a railway bridge at the signals and line to make sure that nothing was coming which would be likely to frighten a horse.

I was also told to be sure and water my pony before feeding her to prevent indigestion.

Another point was that when riding with a companion it is always a good idea to keep in the same order (side by side) as when you started out—otherwise if you start changing places, you may get tangled up.

It was while I was here that I regained some of the confidence I had lost, when some time before this Silver and I had an accident. A car which was coming along the road at great speed frightened Silver. At that moment she saw something in the hedge, and the handle on the door of the car caught her on the point of her shoulder. After this, naturally she did not like traffic at all, nor did I.

But with my riding master, on his perfectly quiet horses, I regained a lot of my lost confidence, and managed to pass some of it on to Silver.

My riding lessons here were very useful and at the end the chief thing I noticed was great improvement in my control.

When I was twelve, lovely things happened. I went to four gymkhanas—two cub hunts and one meet.

My first job when I came home for the summer holidays in preparation for my first gymkhana was to build a flight of jumps to practise over.

I had four jumps—a bar, a bush, a wall and a hurdle—and four stakes are required for each.

The bar was quite easy. I drove four stakes into the ground like this:

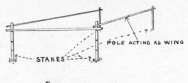

with the bar and some nails as shown. The bar could be raised or lowered on the nails as required. It was, of course, placed on the off side of the jump so that it would fall when knocked.

The bush was made like this:

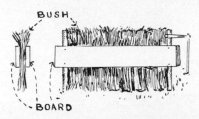

The four stakes were driven into the ground and a board was nailed each side of the stakes which were acting as support. Broom or gorse was then placed between the boards.

Perhaps it is just as well in some ways to have peculiar jumps over which to practise for gymkhanas, as frequently one comes across odd-looking jumps which one's pony doesn't like.

My wall was bad, and I am sure you could make a better one, but for interest's sake this is what I did.

I fixed my four stakes and then rested several boards on nails which came off at the slightest touch (wind included!). I'm afraid there were gaps in between these boards! I painted the fronts of the boards red—hoping Silver would think it looked like a brick wall. I didn't!

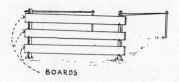

It is essential that the boards should be the farther side of the stakes from where you are jumping, so that they can come off when knocked.

The hurdle was leant up against the supporting stakes. It was upside down to make it lower—again placed so that it would fall when knocked.

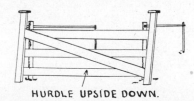

HURDLE UPSIDE DOWN.

The next thing is to practise, but don't overdo this. If you practise for a short time every day, you will soon be able to tell when your pony has had enough. This does not mean that he should be allowed to stop work after a bad performance.

Bending poles for practising should be placed six good paces apart.

I regret to say that my first summer of gymkhanas I neglected to practise bending and potato racing as I should have done. I intend to mend my ways!

Silver, being a grey, had a bath the day before the first gymkhana!

Scotty attended to this, and I watched, anxious to learn. He had some blue bag in water which brought up the white.

After he had washed her, Scotty rubbed Silver down until she was more or less dry. He would not have done this in the winter, or she would have caught a cold.

The night before she had a feed of oats, and in the morning before we started, her hooves were oiled. Her harness had of course, been thoroughly cleaned and polished.

The gymkhana was held in the village, so I didn't have far to go.

The events were much the same as those for which I had practised, with the exception of the races I have already mentioned.

All I did was to get a second Consolation award in the race for those of us who hadn't won anything before. We were lined up and at the word go—had to gallop up to a sack, get into the sack, and leading our ponies, run back to the starting place as quickly as possible.

When we got home, Silver had another feed and settled for the night.

After that, I went to other gymkhanas and collected several rosettes.

* * *

My first cub hunt was great fun. The meet was at 6.45 at the local railway station. I got up at 6 a.m. and collected my sandwiches which were in a special tin that had belonged to Grandpa. There was a little flask for drink too. They both fitted into a leather case which could be fastened to the saddle.

Daddy drove me to the meet where Scotty and Silver were waiting for me.

We set off and moved from cover, jumping ditches on the way. When at last we came to a place where there were some cubs, we stayed a long time.

Then the Master's wife came to me and said the Master wanted to blood me. She held Silver (who had been very good all this time) and I went to the Master who was standing in the middle of his hounds holding a small piece of cub. He wiped some blood on my forehead, chin, cheeks and nose and told me not to wash until it had worn off! He then presented me with the brush!

I was very proud.

I was so excited that I do not now remember much about my first hunt although it was quite recent.

We went round from 11 to 2 looking for foxes. It was very wet, but cleared up in the afternoon. I remember seeing the fox go away and the difficulties of getting the most out of my tired pony without over-taxing her. Fortunately, there was a check which gave her time to recover. The fox went to earth. We came home. I delivered Silver to Scotty who rubbed her down until she was dry and gave her a very large feed of hot bran mash, which she richly deserved.

The next day I let her rest. It is most important if a pony has worked hard, to see that it has adequate food and rest.

If a pony is sweating, it must be dried with a wisp of hay, and plenty of elbow grease.

The Space Ship

READERS of the April issue of *Collins Magazine* will know of the exclusive story secured by Jules Verney of *The Space Ship*.

Barton, having thrown the scheming Professor Sozzlefink overboard, into the mouth of a lurking Blobberwolly, was faced with a row of controls, knobs, pedals and a joystick. . . . He noticed a handle painted red and under it a little label which read, ' Penalty for improper use £5.'

' Better just try that one, thought Barton. Reaching up he pulled the handle. The ship gave a sickening shudder, there was a ghastly rending sound. . . . '

Sarah Halstead Thompson (aged 11) reports . . . . and the children were shot violently into the air and the ship crashed beneath them in fragments. The children whizzed along for a time narrowly missing shooting stars. Barton just caught a glimpse of the moon. It was a cold, waterless, airless land of mountains and craters, and he was glad they had not landed there. Gradually, they all became unconscious and when at last they awoke they found it was evening. They were in a hut in a strange land surrounded by people like eskimos. Outside were mountains, plains, and forests of fir and pine. It was a cold

THE DEPARTURE OF THE JABBERWOCK

but beautiful land lit by two moons. Barton, who knew some astronomy, realised they were on Mars. The Martians, who were very kind people, gave the children all sorts of fruit and cakes to eat. They made the children sleep for twelve hours.

Next day, the Martians showed Barton and the others the wonders of Mars. There were red polar bears, reindeer striped pink and green, purple cows and sweet little black ponies with specially thick coats to keep them warm. The animals were fearless because the Martians were vegetarians and never bullied or ill-treated them. The animals lived in dark forests or in meadows in which grew lovely alpine flowers with icy streams flowing through the meadows. The Martians soon showed how clever they were, for by looking into the children's eyes they were able to get a clear picture of life on the Earth and they were horrified to learn how cruel and

greedy the Earth people were, for Mars was a place of peace and kindness. They asked the children if they would like to live on Mars, but the children thought they would miss their parents. The Martians then took them to a balloon on which they were planning to visit Earth. They said the children could have it as the Martians would never, having heard about Earth and what it was like, want to visit it after all. They asked Barton to press a button on the balloon to destroy it as soon as they reached Earth.

The children and the Martians said good-bye very sorrowfully. The balloon was only just big enough to fit them all in, but they managed to squeeze in a baby black pony.

They whizzed back to Earth and landed in a lonely Somerset field near their homes. Barton then pressed the button and the balloon blew into tiny fragments that no one could see.

The Professor had landed safely and promised never to think of doing such a thing again, and to make up he gave them each a year's subscription to *Collins*.

They called the little pony Starlight, and it lived very happily, although it sometimes used to look up at the sky at night and neigh rather sadly at the red star that twinkled above.

Patrick S. McKay (aged 12) . . . . . the Space Ship, ' Lizzie ' (as Barton had nick-named her) lurched suddenly backward, with a sharp jar, turned one or two somersaults and began to get bigger and bigger: in other words, she began to expand violently. Even sinister Prof. Sozzlefink's patent ' Sozzla ' windows expanded.

How did it happen? Don't ask me—I don't know, neither does anyone else (including Mr. Verney), and don't suppose we ever will.

However, to resume, Barton was terrified. ' By the Lord Harry!' he exclaimed (this was his favourite expression). And to add to his horrors at that moment, he spied two sworduntias jabbing their sword-like snouts into the barrage balloon.

My Word! What a BANG there was! what shrieking and screaming followed (both from the children and the Upper Air fauna); what clamour; what general chaos, and oaths issued from the innocent wreck of ' Lizzie,' which was now just meandering aimlessly about in space.

All the scorpires, vampions, pteopotami, hippodactyls, saxaphonies, sworduntias, Blobberwollies, girasaus and dinaraffes and all the other tenants of the mysterious, dim Upper Air fled when they heard, saw or felt the BANG!

Barton realised that he had done a very foolish thing, but all the same he was not going to pay the £5 fine for pulling the little red handle; after all, he argued, there was no one to pay it to.

Climbing out of the stuffy cabin he shouted to the other twenty-three children to jump off the ' Lizzie ' when they were passing by Venupiter—an unknown planet—and to use their arms as wings. Did I say twenty-three other children? That's wrong, because J. H. A. Brown (short for Joshua Heliotrope Alexander Brown) had been snatched off the flimsy undercarriage (which was formerly part of the swing-boats of Oatlin's fun-fair), and digested by a boacobcereus, a snake-like dragon. The idea of getting back to earth had been long abandoned, and no wonder, for they were now 2,999,999,999,999 miles away from her and steadily drifting further.

Soon, however, they reached Venupiter (the unknown planet), and the crew hastily gathered their belongings, which consisted of cap, torch, umbrella, hockey stick and all the other odds-and-ends, needed and invaluable to a lunar expedition, and leapt into space.

Very shortly, after using their arms as substitutes for wings, they reached Venupiter.

A surprise awaited them on the queerest of queer planets, for when they landed on the soil (as they thought) it gave way beneath them, but it was easy to get out, for the spongy mass came only to their knees.

One small boy somehow managed to get some in his mouth, and pronounced, in a very high-pitched voice of delight, that it was 'super.' At once everyone started to munch and grub about in the soft, spongy mass. The taste was exquisite, a cross between milk chocolate, sweet and juicy grapes and ginger pop.

Soon, everyone was full, and not very strange to say, they all fell fast asleep. So much of the food had they eaten that they all put on at least a stone in weight. And, because of this, one by one they disappeared from view—sinking, sinking into the sweet, sticky substance.'

George Gardiner (aged 15). . . . After a few seconds the space ship lurched again, and this time so violently that it threw Barton over. He was saved from falling into space, however, by the stream of passengers coming outside the ship.

' What's happened? '

' Is something wrong? '

' Why . . .'

' It will be all right in a minute,' shouted Barton coolly, ' I'm going to see what's the matter.'

When he inspected the rear he discovered that the Screw was missing, and after further examination he found that by pulling the lever down, the air passage through the ship could be blocked at will. However, the machinery was rather faulty, and when Barton had pulled the lever a shaft had knocked the Screw away. The position was dangerous. They had stopped travelling forward, and were losing height rapidly.

' Make the ship lighter,' Barton yelled. ' Throw overboard all we don't really need. No, you ass, NOT the spare cylinders of Sozgene! '

But it was too late. Hopthornson had already rolled three cylinders over the side. One of them hit the undercarriage and the cork flew out, letting off all the gas.

' Sorry and all that,' mumbled Hopthornson.

But what was happening to the scorpires, vampions, pteopotami, hippodactyls, saxaphonies, blobberwollies, and the like? They were all tumbling about as if they were drunk. Barton's supersonic mind got to work.

' It's the Sozgene! It's doping them! I say, go and fetch another cylinder and pull the cork out! '

After a boy called Bing had done this, Barton ordered everybody to catch as many of the space creatures as possible while they were still doped.

The scheme worked wonderfully. Swinging from ropes, chains, and parts of the space ship, everybody grabbed as many creatures as they could and locked them in the hold, much to Hopthornson's consternation, as he was locked in with them. At the end of the operation when the Sozgene effects were starting to wear off, Barton and his comrades had three purple saxaphonies, two cerise hippodactyls, two plush vampions, and one gigantic pea-green blobberwolly!

Next, all the straps and bits of chain were gathered together and made into harnesses for these eight queer creatures. Barton's idea was to harness them in front of the space ship and make them pull it

THE JABBERWOCKIN THE UNDERCARRIAGE

as near the moon as possible, and then to float down with the balloon full of the remaining Sozgene. The plan worked, and all landed safely on the moon.

When they alighted, they could not find any silver, but Jameson, known at school as the ' stinks swot,' discovered uranium. They filled the hold with this, and then started worrying over how to get back.

However, they soon met some men from Mars on their way to Earth, who, in their supersonic jet rocket, took the space ship in tow. In this way, Barton and his companions handed valuable uranium to the British Government, and accompanied the Marsmen to Earth! '

Colin Jones (11.7). . . . ' Better just try that one,' thought Barton. Reaching up he pulled the handle. The ship gave a sickening shudder, there was a ghastly

rending sound as the rudder was torn from the space ship, and a green batodillo which was cruising around gobbled it up. Now that the rudder was gone, Barton had no control over the ship at all and it went twisting and twirling on upwards.

In the sky a large and unsuspecting Sapajougalago happened to open its mouth to yawn when a grey streak twisted into it, down into its stomach and rushed along its tail. Suddenly a loud report filled the sky and the Sapajougalago's tail was seen to burst open and emit the now dilapidated space ship. There was a gaping hole in the left side of it and, as the foul air was pouring in, Barton had to think fast.

Seeing a Zuglodona monster which instead of a nose possessed a long, straight, spirally pointed tusk, flying by, Barton grabbed a knife and hacked the tusk off. Turning round, he saw the cobweb of the hairy Tarrantula spider. Grabbing this he threaded it through the eye which he had cut in the tusk and proceeded to mend the hole.

Suddenly Barton realised that they had gone past the moon, so he ordered all the boys to climb down the ladder into the old horse of the fairground. When the horse was filled, they cut it adrift from the balloon and gradually spun down towards the moon.

Suddenly there was a terrific bump. They were on the moon, but not for long, for they had landed on a volcano which unfortunately was erupting. Tossed up in the air again, they soon came down, landing safely in a gooseberry tree. They scrambled down and stood on the moon, but suddenly they began to float upwards. Barton, who was in the space ship, saw their plight and threw some lead weights which they tied on to their feet and got back to the moon.

Meanwhile, Professor Sozzlefink had hacked his way out of the Blobberwolly. Floating about in the murky darkness, he had blundered into the balloon and had scrambled on board and because he had devised the controls of the balloon he knew exactly how to operate them. Flying towards the moon he saw the children with the horse. Landing during the night, he grabbed the horse and started on his journey back to earth. But, however, the controls were so badly damaged that he crashed on the planet Mars, where the ship burst into flames and put an end to Sozzlefink's sinister career.

The children on the moon, having returned from a fruitless search for silver, found the old inhabitant of the merrygo-round had disappeared. The children, finding some wood, set to work to form a makeshift ship. Barton took off towards the earth, but all of a sudden the ship began to disintegrate. Barton felt himself falling, and, on opening his eyes, found himself on the floor with his bed clothes on top of him.

It had all been a wonderful dream.

The illustrations are by Jean Dixon— (14).

SMILEY STRIKES GOLD

by MOORE RAYMOND

ILLUSTRATED BY JOHN ROBINSON

SQUATTING ON THE LOG that ran from the bank of the dam into the muddy water, Smiley tested his crayfish line.

'Anythin' on?' whispered his companion from another log not far away.

'Nothin',' Smiley whispered back.

The two twelve-year-old boys relapsed into silence. It was a scorching afternoon in late summer, and neither was in the mood for conversation.

The afternoon was quiet. They could hear some white cockatoos screaming over by the Warrego River. Occasionally the faint barking of a dog came down the wind from the little Western Queensland settlement of Murrumbilla.

The wind, soft and steady, had sprung up during the morning. Drifting in from the arid, semi-desert areas further west, it was so dry and hot that it parched the boys' lips.

Smiley tested his line again.

'A-a-ah!' he hissed as he felt the heavy pull of the crayfish that was clinging to the lump of meat at the end of the string.

'Got a bite?' whispered Blue—so called in those parts because of his red hair.

'Yairs,' murmured his mate with the wide grin that earned him the nickname of Smiley. As he hauled in the string inch by inch he could feel it was a whopper, and he imagined how sweet it would taste when it was cooked and cold.

Ignoring his own line, Blue watched breathlessly. At last Smiley could see the faint dark outline of the big crayfish. Another inch . . . and a curled whisker broke the surface of the water . . . the big black whisker of an old-man crayfish that would make a wonderful feast. Smiley slowly reached out his hand to make the catch.

'Rolypoly! Rolypoly!'

Both boys started at the shout. The crayfish flipped itself backward and downwards into the depths.

'Stone the crows!' cried Smiley, scowling at the noisy newcomer. 'You've gawn and scared the bonzerest crayfish I ever—'

'Rolypoly!' repeated frizzy-haired Jacky the aboriginal boy. Wearing only a tattered shirt and frayed trousers, he stood panting on the bank of the dam, showing white teeth in a huge smile.

'Where?' asked the excited boys in unison, their crayfishing now forgotten.

'Longa Wirrawirra,' replied Jacky, pointing in the direction of the big sheep station across the river.

'Come on, cobber,' cried Smiley to Blue as he ran up the bank of the dam.

Heedless of the ruts and prickly bindyeyes, the three barefooted boys raced across the sun-cracked river flat and plunged down into the sandy bed of the Warrego—now only a thin trickle they could leap across with ease.

Skirting the aborigines' camp, they came at last to the Wirrawirra boundary.

'Rolypolies! Rolypolies!' they cried—for at last the rolypoly season had begun.

Blown by the wind, three of the big dead bushes—dry and light and round as balls—went tumbling over the plain. All the summer they had grown in the baked earth, until, burned by the scorching sun, they died and turned brown on their short, brittle stalks. Now the wind was snapping them off in ones and twos, and trundling them across the paddock.

The boys scrambled up the tall netting fence and dropped down on the other side.

A huge rolypoly, as tall as any of the boys, came rolling towards them.

'Gee, what a big 'un!' shouted Smiley, leaping in front of it and blocking it with outstretched hands. He grabbed the stump of stalk and hoisted the bush above his head. Remembering what he had learned at school about ancient mythology, he called: 'Look, mates! I'm Atlas 'oldin' up the world!'

They all laughed—and laughed still more when the wind dragged the rolypoly and pulled it out of the boy's hands.

'I reckon we oughter 'ave races,' suggested Blue.

'Too right,' agreed his mate eagerly.

Little Jacky the aborigine was not interested. 'This pfella go longa home,' he told them—and he made for the camp.

The two boys went on playing with their new toys. They ran around snapping the stems and sending the plants rolling till nearly a score were bounding over the plain at the same time. Then each chose a rolypoly, and they held races over agreed distances, each boy panting after his own 'horse' and urging it on with a stick when it got caught in a bit of stunted saltbush or a tuft of dried-up grass.

At last they were tired, and they made for the shade of the nearby mulga scrub.

'Coo-ee!' It was black Jacky again. The boys were surprised to see him returning with all speed.

'K-k-king Billy!' he puffed. 'He say you go longa camp.'

'What for?' asked Smiley suspiciously.

The Murrumbilla boys, though not actually prohibited from visiting the aborigines' camp, were discouraged from going there because it was a rather primitive and smelly place. Their parents did not want impressionable children to come too much under the influence of the somewhat lazy and only half-civilised occupants.

'King Billy say you pfella chuckem boomerang,' said Jacky.

'Boomerang?' echoed the boys.

Jacky explained in his own kind of aboriginal English. The boys learned that a number of Myalls had arrived at the camp. These were wild black fellows who usually lived away up in the hills and rarely came anywhere near a white settlement. However, they were now the guests of King Billy, the corpulent boss of the black community of Murrumbilla.

King Billy, using little Jacky as messenger, had invited Smiley and Blue to come to the camp and meet the myalls —who would teach them how to throw a boomerang.

Smiley and Blue hesitated. In the past, none of the Murrumbilla blacks could teach them how to throw the curved stick that magically returned to the thrower. As most of these men and women earned their living by working in the township or on the neighbouring sheep stations, they had no more need to hunt in the bush for food. So the art of throwing the boomerang had died out as far as the inhabitants of the river camp were concerned. But these myalls were experts.

In a few seconds, Smiley and Blue were pattering alongside the dark boy.

At the camp—a ramshackle collection of bark huts called 'humpies'—Jacky went into the biggest humpy and told King Billy his guests had arrived.

This big man, wearing only a grubby singlet and faded trousers, came out and greeted the boys. Then he turned and called something in his own language.

'Myalls!' whispered Smiley, staring at the dozen aborigines who emerged. Clad in nothing but loincloths, they were a skinny, savage-looking lot with their spears, woomeras (throwing sticks), nulla-nullas (clubs), and boomerangs.

'This pfella Mungoongarlie,' said King Billy, pointing to the leader. 'Chuckem boomerang budgeree.'

'Boomerang!' cried Mungoongarlie. He lifted his arm and hurled the curved and polished piece of mulga wood. It sailed away out over the gunyahs, spinning as it flew. Then, as the rotary movement slowed down, the boomerang swung to the left in a wide arc and began its curious, curved flight. The delighted boys watched it circle over the tops of the huts and gradually turn on the homeward journey. The boomerang ended its flight by dropping at the feet of the thrower.

The black man took up the weapon and made as if to throw it again. As he swung back his arm, his knees gave way and he sprawled on the ground.

'Tucker!' he moaned. 'Gibbit tucker!'

'Tucker!' chorused the other myalls, rubbing their stomachs. 'Gibbit tucker!' Several men dropped in the dust.

Smiley and Blue were astounded by these cries for food. King Billy explained in his own way that the myalls had come to the camp because the prolonged drought had caused a scarcity of both food and water up in the hills.

'Gibbit tucker!' interrupted Mungoongarlie hoarsely. He crawled into the gunyah, followed by the other myalls.

King Billy went on to explain that the rest of the aborigines in the camp had shared what food they had with the visitors, but there was not enough to feed everybody properly.

'See tucker,' he invited, leading the way to the open fire where several women were standing round a huge pot hung over the flames.

'Snake longa this,' said one of them, poking a stick into the pot.

'Ugh!' cried the boys simultaneously. They stared with mingled horror and disgust as the aborigine lifted out an unmistakable piece of carpet snake—head and all.

King Billy, stirring the snake stew, told the boys that the arrival of the starving myalls had meant a swift clean-out of all the ordinary food in the camp. Now they had to fall back on the horrible mess in the pot.

'I reckon,' surmised Smiley, 'that old Mungoon— Mungoonwhatshisname would show me 'ow to chuck a boomerang if I brought 'im some real bonzer tucker.'

'I can git some too,' added Blue hurriedly.

'Budgeree!' cried King Billy delightedly.

'Too right we will.'

The two boys hurried homeward, each determined to get food for the poor abos. Meanwhile these same abos sat in King Billy's gunyah and chuckled gleefully among themselves.

When Blue told his story to his parents, his father, the blacksmith, laughed his disbelief. His mother said: 'Don't be silly. Come and eat your tea.'

Smiley, on reaching his tumbledown home that crouched beneath a huge pepperina tree, excitedly poured out his tale to his mother. There was no father to tell it to, because he was a sheep drover and away up in North Queensland.

Smiley's mother listened sympathetically, then commented: 'Well, it's no good you two boys thinking you can collect enough tucker to feed a mob of starving abos. You'd better tell the sergeant and see what he's got to say.'

'Aw, gee, mum,' wailed the boy in plaintive protest.

Smiley and Sergeant Flaxman, head policeman of Murrumbilla, were always clashing over matters of boyish behaviour which the sergeant regarded as reprehensible.

'I reckon the ole sergeant is me deadly enemy,' he grumbled to his mother, who laughed and went out to the kitchen to cook the steak and eggs for tea.

It happened that Sergeant Flaxman came riding that way after tea, and he dropped in for a chat. Prompted by his mother, Smiley told what had happened at the camp.

'King Billy is an old scoundrel,' said the sergeant. 'He's never done a stroke of work in his life. The others go out and work—but not King Billy. He loafs about and lives on the tucker the others give him just because he's the boss. You can bet your sweet life that King Billy will never starve.'

'But they 'ad snake stew,' began Smiley, 'and—'

'But,' cut in the sergeant, 'I'll go over and see what it's all about. I've never known a drought so bad that it'll drive the myalls down from the hills.'

Next day a message arrived at the school to say that the two boys were to report to the sergeant as soon as lessons were over.

'King Billy and his myalls were kidding you,' Sergeant Flaxman told them bluntly. 'They're not starving.'

'Aw,' began Smiley, 'I reckon —'

'King Billy is lazy. It's in the family. The Mungoongarlie cove is a relation of his, and he's lazy too. He brought the other myalls to King Billy's camp to see if they could get some tucker for nothing. Of course, King Billy can't feed his hungry visitors with the bit he gets from his subjects. So he and Mungoongarlie got the bright idea that if Murrumbilla heard they were starving, the camp would soon be overflowing with things to eat. That's why they got you to go and see their performance—and all that falling down and crying out from hunger.'

'Was it all really kidstakes?' wailed Smiley.

'All of it. Abos might have simple minds, but they're very good natural actors. And that horrible snake stew was cooked up for your benefit. Nobody ate any of it, of course.'

The boys shuddered to think of such a thing.

'Well, I told Mungoongarlie and his pals that I'd see they got well fed if they liked to do some work around town or on any of the sheep stations in these parts. But they just sulked and refused to earn their tucker. So I told them they'd better go back to the hills.'

'Aw, gee!' cried the disappointed boys.

'You keep away from the camp,' ordered the sergeant sternly. 'Now mizzle off.'

* * *

The boys thought the adventure with the myalls was over. But it had only just begun.

Next afternoon they went crayfishing again. And again young Jacky the abo found them there.

'You pfella go catchem wallaby?' he grinned.

'A savage-looking lot, with spears, nulla-nullas and boomerangs.'

'Go 'ome and tell yore mother she wants you,' retorted Smiley in a tone of dismissal.

Little Jacky grinned and went on to explain that the myalls were going wallaby hunting with spears and nulla-nullas and boomerangs. Smiley and Blue could join in if they liked.

So once again Jacky enticed them away from crayfishing, this time to hunt the small kangaroo-like creatures that made such good stew—especially the tails.

'Mungoongarlie longa kurrajong,' said Jacky, leading the way.

Blue reminded Smiley of the sergeant's warning. Smiley replied that the policeman had told them not to go to the camp. This was different. After all, who was to know that they didn't just happen to run across the myalls near the kurrajong?

Blue was only too happy to be persuaded.

Half a mile up the river they came to the enormous kurrajong tree that was a landmark in those parts. The half-dozen myalls beneath the tree were squatting or standing in dejected attitudes listlessly holding their weapons of the hunt.

But as soon as Mungoongarlie gave an order in his native tongue, the other five sprang up and ran off into the scrub in various directions.

'Mungoongarlie stay longa you,' said Jacky, explaining that the boys were to accompany the head man.

'We couldn't git you no tucker,' apologised Smiley.

The abo shrugged and pointed into the boree scrub. 'Wallaby budgeree tucker,' he said—and started off.

With the boys panting on his heels, he doubled and twisted through the bush till the youngsters had lost all sense of direction. But wherever they went they saw no sign of wallabies—or of the other abos.

The myall stopped, turned to Jacky, and spoke in his own language.

Jacky turned to the other two boys: 'This pfella say you wantem gold?'

'Gold?' they echoed incredulously.

The little abo explained that Mungoongarlie knew where to find gold. Though it was of no use to him, apparently white people wanted it. If they liked, he could show them where to find some.

'That's a bit 'o kidstakes,' grinned Smiley.

'Too right it is,' snorted Blue.

The myall shrugged and went on, leading them up a rocky gully, the dry bed of which was strewn with white quartz boulders. The boys frequently and painfully stubbed their toes. Mungoongarlie stopped and pointed. The others panted up to see the reason.

'Gold!' yelled Smiley, staring in wonder. 'Jist like in the specimen at school!'

Blue, too, recalled the geology lesson and the specimen showing the precious vein in the white rock. But this was no tiny bit of quartz with a thin yellow streak like the one in school. This was a big piece of rock with a thick, shining vein running through it.

'There's more!' yelled Smiley, pointing to another piece on the bed of the gully.

'There's another one!' shouted Blue.

''Nother pfella!' cried Jacky, infected by the excitement.

Meanwhile, Mungoongarlie stood by, watching the boys with a cunning look they were too excited to notice.

'Budgeree—gold budgeree,' said Smiley to the abo, trying to tell him its value. 'Gold fetchem plenty tucker.'

But apparently the myall's primitive mind could not grasp that fact. He spoke to Jacky in his own tongue.

After a brief conversation, Jacky translated: 'Mungoongarlie say you wantem this pfella gibber.' He pointed to the quartz boulders. 'Mungoongarlie no wantem. That pfella wantem bell.'

'What sort o' bell?' asked puzzled Smiley.

'Bell longa big goat.'

After much cross-talk, it gradually became clear. In exchange for showing them the gold, Mungoongarlie wanted the bell that was worn by Cantankerous, the leader of the Murrumbilla mob of goats. It was an extraordinary request, but all the explanation they could get was that the myall liked the noise it made.

'I reckon,' surmised Blue, ''e'll wear it round 'is neck to scare away the bunyips and evil spirits.'

The boys readily agreed to produce the bell in exchange for the gold.

'I reckon we'll stake our claim now,' asserted Smiley.

But the myall had other ideas. They must get the bell first. As they were plainly bushed, he would show them the way back to the kurrajong tree. Then he would take them to the gold again, marking the trail so that they could easily find their way back this time.

Smiley and Blue discussed these proposals. Of course, if they wished to avoid the crime of stealing the bell, they could go straight to the sergeant, tell him what had happened, and claim the gold as theirs. But would they ever find it again? How long would the secret be kept, especially as chatty little Jacky knew it as well? Others might come looking for it and find it and stake a claim before the boys did. Besides, if they broke their promise to the myall they might be in danger of revenge by nulla-nulla and spear.

'I reckon we gotter do what 'e says,' concluded Blue. 'It won't matter if we pinch the ole bell, because we'll buy 'im a thousand bells with our gold.'

'A million bells,' said Smiley.

So, by a devious route, they all went back to the kurrajong. Jacky wanted to accompany Smiley and Blue on their further adventures, but they insisted that he should stay with Mungoongarlie.

Murrumbilla, like every other township in those areas, possessed a mob of 50 or 60 goats. They grazed around the outskirts—on the sandhill by the school, up behind the hospital, away out along the Morven road, or down by the dam when they were thirsty.

The goats had a huge, curly-horned irascible leader called Cantankerous. He wore a bell that tonk-tonked a harsh note that could be heard a long way off. Half the families in Murrumbilla owned a goat each. Some were for milking if the cow went dry. Some were pets for the boys to ride. And, of course, the kids made good eating during the drought when beef and mutton were scarce.

Smiley and Blue, suppressing their violent urge to dash home with the news about the gold strike, hastily searched for the goats. They hurried here and there for nearly an hour before they heard the tonk-tonk of the leader's bell. The mob was grazing near the Morven road.

The boys sneaked up on Cantankerous from behind. While Blue clung to the tossing horns, Smiley swiftly unbuckled the strap. Holding the tongue of the bell to keep it quiet, he set off with Blue for the kurrajong.

'Th-th-there y'are!' puffed Smiley on reaching the big tree.

Mungoongarlie grabbed the bell and swung it gently, listening to the tonk-tonk-tonk. Satisfied it was the leader's bell, he turned and started off into the bush.

This time he marked the trail by scoring streaks on the bark of a tree with a sharp stone, breaking the branch of a shrub, scratching a mark on a bare patch of earth.

'King Billy came out and greeted the boys.'

They came to a gully. Through Jacky the interpreter, the myall said that if they followed it up they would come to their gold. He and Jacky abruptly ran off.

'It's gittin' near sundown,' panted Blue as they stumbled over the boulders. 'I reckon we gotter be quick stakin' our claim.'

After a time the boys began to have misgivings. Had the myall deceived them? After the affair at the abos' camp it would not be unlikely.

'Gold!' cried Smiley suddenly.

Sure enough, in the bright light of the late afternoon, the yellow veins gleamed in the white quartz boulders.

The boys had only a vague idea of how to stake a claim. Eventually, they agreed to scratch on the bark of nearby trees: 'This is our claim.' They added their initials.

'We gotter take a sample back to the sergeant to register with,' declared Smiley, pretending he knew the correct procedure.

'But we can't carry one o' them gibbers,' protested Blue, pointing at the boulders.

They fossicked about for a while before Smiley found what they wanted—a fragment of quartz with a thick vein of the metal running through it. Hugging it to his chest, Smiley made for Murrumbilla with Blue puffing alongside through the hot and windy dusk.

Sergeant Flaxman and his wife were having tea on the back veranda when the boys dashed up the steps.

'We've struck gold!' cried Smiley.

The sergeant grabbed the piece of bright-veined quartz and stared with wondering eyes. He turned it in the lamplight, peered at it, tested it with his nail.

'We're millionaires!' gasped Smiley.

'Trillionaires!' declared Blue.

'Ha-ha-ha!' roared the sergeant. 'It's newchum gold!'

The boys stared in astonishment.

'Copper pyrites!' laughed Flaxman. 'It looks like gold all right, but it's not worth a farthing!'

*　*　*

Next morning they were still recovering from the shock. Moreover, the news of their discovery of newchum gold had got around town, and they had to submit to some good-natured chiacking wherever they went.

Of course, they laughed to show they could take a joke, but privately they ground their teeth and muttered imprecations against Mungoongarlie and all his tribe.

It was not until the afternoon that they heard about the missing goats.

Several youngsters had gone looking for their animals

and had failed to find them. No sight of a goat—no sound of the leader's bell.

Thinking that the mob might have strayed too far, several men rode out to look for them. Still there was neither sight nor sound of the animals. The news soon went round the town, and all Murrumbilla was mystified.

Little Jacky the abo sought out Smiley and Blue. 'You pfella dinkum cobber,' he said, emphasizing their close friendship. Because of this, he whispered his secret before racing back to the myalls' camp.

'Stone the crows!' gasped Smiley.

'Stiffen the lizards!' snorted Blue.

Now it was all clear. Mungoongarlie wanted the leader's bell to make sure the goats would graze in silence—and just as silently be driven by the myalls across the river and up towards the hills.

With the setting sun in their eyes and the hot wind parching their lips, the boys set off to find the goats.

'Gee, ain't the wind gittin' strong?' commented Smiley, blinking hard as the dust from the western plain was blown into his face.

'Too right,' agreed the redhead mournfully. He was hungry and thirsty, and his teeth were gritty. After a while he slowed down and said: 'It's gittin' late, and I reckon me father and mother 'll be 'avin' tea soon, and I reckon I'd better mizzle orf 'ome.'

'Not on yore sweet life,' replied his mate firmly. 'We gotter git them ole goats back ourselves. We can't go tellin' the sergeant or anybody, because they'll go and git the goats from the myalls. And then they'll start askin' questions about 'ow the bell came to be missin' and all sortser things like that. Then the myalls 'll tell on us, then we'll git belted and—'

Smiley stopped suddenly and sniffed the wind. Though no smoke could be seen, he could smell it in the air, and he knew the blacks were near at hand.

As cautiously and craftily as a couple of dingoes, the boys made their way through the scrub. By a circuitous route they reached the spot that Jacky had indicated.

It was a small clearing on the edge of the plain just where the ground began to slope up to the hills. The myalls had driven the goats there during the night, kept them hidden there all day, and planned to drive them into the hills as soon as darkness came.

The scrub ended at the foot of the slope. To observe the myalls, the boys emerged from the trees. In the soft purple dusk, they crept silently up to higher ground, concealing themselves behind huge rolypolies.

Now and again the strong wind snapped some off and bowled them downhill till they came to rest against the curved brake of branches the myalls had built to keep the goats in check.

A few intermittent bleats came from the hidden mob.

Smiley suddenly clutched Blue by the arm and hissed: 'Stampede!'

'Eh?'

'That's what the cowboys did in a book I read,' he went on breathlessly. 'The deadly rustlers stole the cattle and took 'em up a gulch. It was night, and the cowboys snook up and stampeded the cattle and they all went gallopin' 'ome to the ranch.'

'But 'ow can us couple o' coves stampede them goats?'

'Rolypolies!' hissed Smiley, and he went on to explain his scheme.

Down in the clearing they could see black figures flitting here and there, doubtless getting ready for the night journey with the goats. Over in Murrumbilla everybody was sitting down to the evening meal—everybody but the impatient parents of the two boys who crouched in the dusk . . . waiting for the dark . . .

Soon the stars were brilliant overhead, giving just enough light for the boys to see by. Smiley decided it was time to start the stampede.

Fumbling in his shirt pocket, he extracted several wax matches. Meanwhile, Blue snapped off a big rolypoly and held it steady so that the wind would not blow it away.

Smiley struck a match on a stone and plunged the flame into the middle of the dry and highly inflammable rolypoly. It caught fire immediately, snapping and crackling. Blue let it go.

The wind hurled it down the hill towards the clearing, and as it tumbled it burned more and more fiercely till it became a ball of fire.

It was soon followed by another—and another—and yet another leaping, menacing globe of flame.

A dozen were on their way before the myalls saw them. Then came cries of alarm and yells of bewilderment.

The noise excited the goats, and they all began to bleat loudly.

The first two flaming rolypolies ran into the dead ones that the wind had piled against the brake. Soon they were all ablaze.

The abos yelled more loudly, and the goats became a swirling, terrified mob.

More and more of the balls of fire came rolling down. Now the myalls were nearly as frightened as the goats.

The climax came when several of the biggest rolypolies rose—like the hot-air balloons of the early aeronauts—and floated towards the myalls like flying furnaces. Never before had they seen such a terrifying spectacle. They were convinced that bunyips or some such demoniacal creatures were at work.

'Ah-ah-a-a-a-a-h!' wailed Mungoongarlie—and he bolted for the hills.

'A-a-a-a-h!' howled the rest of the abos, as they followed their leader.

The goats burst out of the brake and raced madly for home.

The stampede of both animals and myalls was clearly illuminated by the blazing brake, which had burnt itself out by the time Smiley and Blue reached the spot. Unaware of how close they had been to starting a disastrous bush fire, the triumphant pair set out in pursuit of the galloping goats.

They were heroes in Murrumbilla that night—both for bringing home the goats and for getting rid of the troublesome myalls. At the usual weekly dance in Hawkin's Hall somebody took up a copper collection for them. The total was 4s. 8d.

The boys were on their way to the nearest lollyshop when the sergeant overtook them. 'A bob each, please,' he demanded severely, 'for a new bell.'

'Bell?' they echoed in tones of feigned innocence.

'For Cantankerous. I know you pinched his bell and gave it to the myalls. Come on now—a deener each and I won't tell anybody you got that money under false pretences.'

They hurriedly handed over the money. The sergeant strode off.

'Gibbit sisspence?' said a voice. It was Jacky the abo.

'What!' they cried in angry unison, for they realised that only this little chatterbox could have told the sergeant.

But the sight of the gleaming grin, combined with the revelation of such colossal though innocent cheek, made Smiley and Blue burst into laughter. Each grabbed Jacky by the arm and hauled him off in search of the best lollies that two-and-eightpence could buy.

OLD CUSTOMS IN A NEW BUILDING

by Colonel Charles Ponsonby (M.P. from 1935–1950)

ON MAY 10TH, 1941, an incendiary bomb fell in the House of Commons. It burnt about half of it.

It was decided to build a new House of Commons. Some M.P.s wanted to follow the practice in most other countries of a semi-circular chamber, if possible with seats and desks—so that each Member had his own permanent seat, where he could keep his papers and even write his letters when the speeches were too dull. (In some countries M.P.s applaud by rattling the tops of their desks.) But we did not adopt this plan for several reasons. To start with, only very seldom do all Members attend at the same time, and to find permanent seats for 625 Members would make too big a Chamber.

Apart from the great days of great speeches, which happen perhaps once in every three years, so much of the work of Parliament is simple and intimate. There may be quite an important Bill, but only 40 or 50 watching it and only 10 or 15 are taking an active part.

The designers, therefore, were right to follow the old lines, and to keep the size of the Chamber to what has proved to be right through the last 100 years.

Then, and this was Mr. Churchill's point, there is something to be said for not having seats in a semi-circle. For some reason or other it makes for several political parties, as you have in France or Greece—and if the seats are in a semi-circle it is not difficult for a Member to glide from one little party to another.

The greatness of this country has been built up on the two-party system. There were Whigs and Tories, Liberals and Conservatives, Conservatives and Labour. In the 1920s there may have been a few Labour and in the 1940s a few Liberals, and a very few Independents—but, by and large, there have always been two main parties. Now, if they face each other, it is an act of great courage for a Member to change from one side to the other.

I saw this happen in the last Parliament. Two Socialists who became Conservatives were always under the glare of the eyes of their late comrades—and it took some doing.

Anyhow, this idea, put forward very eloquently by Mr. Churchill, won the day, and the new Chamber of the House of Commons, designed by Sir Gilbert Scott, R.A., is very much like the old, only a bit larger. It has seating accommodation on the floor of the House for only 350, and about 100 in the Galleries, but there is much more room for visitors and the Press upstairs, and the heating is much better. Before, they said that Members had hot heads and cold feet, and this was certainly true.

In the old House, though the acoustics were not too good, we had no microphones. The new House has special 'mikes' on the seats and in the Galleries.

Some people might have said if we are going to have a new House of Commons, why not be more businesslike? —why follow the old precedents and customs? The answer is that we prefer it this way. The precedents for Procedure are all enshrined in a big volume called, after the author, "Erskine May".

The customs have just grown up. So when the House of Commons sits in its new Chamber, everything will go on as before. The Speaker will enter the Chamber with his procession exactly at 2.30. The Sergeant-at-Arms will lay the Mace on the Table. Prayers will be said. Ministers will answer questions for the first House, and then the day's work,

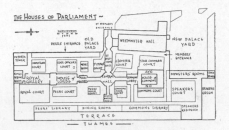

Plan of the New Palace of Westminster.
—From "The Houses of Parliament" (Batsford)

Ministry of Works

The Bar of the House and Strangers Gallery. The model shows a barrier, but in fact the 'Bar' is a line on the floor.

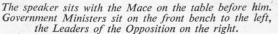

Ministry of Works

The speaker sits with the Mace on the table before him. Government Ministers sit on the front bench to the left, the Leaders of the Opposition on the right.

Central Press

A true-to-scale model of the New Chamber of the House of Commons designed by Sir Giles Gilbert Scott. The photographs above and to the left are models too.

The new Speaker's Chair, a gift from Australia and Canada, in the making.

L.E.A.

The old Speaker's Chair which was destroyed in the fire of 1941.

Topical

whether it is the consideration of a Motion or of a Bill, will go on without a stop till 10.30 p.m. (unless there is a special Motion to extend the time). At 10.30 the Speaker will leave the chair—bow to the Mace, and go home, and the Messengers all over the building will cry 'Who goes Home.' About 120 years ago, things were not so peaceful, and the police not so numerous as they are now. So it was the habit of Members going home to keep together to avoid foot-pads, thieves, and other importunates. Here is quite an obvious explanation of an old custom.

Now let us take another custom mixed up with procedure. On each side of the Chamber is a Division Lobby. Those who are going to vote 'Aye' or 'Yes' go into one Lobby and those who are going to vote 'No' into the other. At the end of the Lobby passage is a desk with room to pass on each side (letters A-K on one side, L-Z on the other). You jostle along the passage; you give your name to the clerk, who sits at the desk, and he marks you on the list. Then you pass through a door which only holds one at a time (like sheep going into a dip), and bow to the Tellers.

There are two Whips, one representing each party. One of them counts the Members as they pass; the other watches to see that everything is all correct. But here is another odd custom. As you pass the Tellers, you have to drop your hands. The origin (about 120 years old) of this is not too creditable. In those days, regulations about strangers were not so strict and Members not so punctilious as they are now. Sometimes they sent their servants to impersonate them at a Division. The servant concealed his identity by holding his top hat in front of his face as he bowed to the Tellers. This was found out and the rule went forth that Members must drop their hands when passing the Tellers! The funny thing about these old

customs is that even the most business-like or anti-the-old-régime people get used to them, and in the end become their strongest supporters. Every now and then a Royal Commission (representing the King) sits in the House of Lords to give the King's Assent to Bills which have been passed. Black Rod, a gentleman in the House of Lords (who corresponds to the Sergeant-at-Arms in the House of Commons), is sent to 'the other place' (in other words the House of Commons) to summon the faithful Commons to hear the Royal Assent given. And so, sometimes in the middle of someone's speech, three loud knocks, with the hilt of the sword, are given on the door, which divides the two Houses.

A Messenger of the House of Commons with a gold ornament across his stomach, advances to the Bar of the House and says in sepulchral tones, 'Black Rod'. Then Black Rod comes in and bows at the Bar, advances seven paces and bows again; and finally reaches the table, on which lies the Mace. He bows and then recites by heart (no one has ever dared bring a crib with him) the Messages from the House of Lords to the House of Commons. Then the Speaker, walking with Black Rod and followed by the Sergeant-at-Arms and representatives of both political parties in pairs, goes off to the House of Lords and stands at the Bar there to hear the Royal Commission read.

The Bar of the House just referred to may at one time have been a wooden structure—like any other bar—but is now represented by a yellow line on the floor. No one who is not a Member can cross it, and no Member can speak on the wrong side of it.

When you become a Member, you stand at the Bar of the House with a supporter on each side. It is rather nerve-racking. Suddenly, you hear the Speaker's voice—seemingly miles away, 'Members desiring to take their seats, will please come to the Table.' You

and your supporters bow low; advance seven steps; bow again; advance another seven steps and you arrive at the Table. Here you are left all alone and the clerk, in a wig, comes forward with a Bible and the oath of allegiance, by which you swear that you will ' bear true allegiance to His Majesty the King, his heirs and successors, so help me God '.

Then you sign the Register of Members, and are led up to the Speaker, who shakes your hand. During this short walk Members cheer or make rude remarks.

Walking up that fifteen yards is a bit of an ordeal. There is a curious custom here. The cross benches in the front rows have strips of carpet before them. If you speak from these benches, you must not step off the carpet. If you stray, you suddenly hear cries of ' Order ', ' Order '. You wonder what is wrong, and a friend suddenly pulls you back on to the carpet.

The reason for this is again historical. In the old days, M.P.s wore swords. They also occasionally got excited—as we do now. But they might have got so angry that they drew their swords and went for the fellow opposite. That would never have done; it would have upset the proceedings—so the rule was made that anyone speaking from the cross benches must stick to his bit of carpet.

You may like to know the procedure by which the House can debate a subject in private. This happened several times during the war, and some of you may have seen the volume of Mr. Churchill's speeches ' in secret session '. In these cases, the Leader of the House, or Chief Whip, would get up and say, 'I spy strangers'. The Speaker (who had been warned before) would say 'Clear the Galleries', and then everyone not a Member, except the Sergeant-at-Arms and the Clerks of the House, was cleared out. Then the Motion would be put that the Proceedings of the House be taken in Secret Session, and when this was passed *nem. con.*, everything was private. No *Hansard* or Press reports, and no Member allowed to repeat what is heard. When the war was over, Mr. Churchill received special permission from the Cabinet to publish his speeches, which he had prepared before the Secret Sessions.

And last of all, you may like to know how proceedings can occasionally be stopped without waiting for the end of the day, or of business of the House. I took part in this once. A very dull subject was being discussed by a very dull man. Everyone wanted to go home. A Whip said to me ' you might count him out!' So I went into the Chamber and rising in my place said ' On a point of Order, Mr. Speaker, I beg to call your attention to the fact that less than forty Members are present.' The Speaker took note of the fact and ordered the Lobbies to be cleared. Bells rang all over the House, and Messengers shouted ' Count.' After two minutes, the Speaker began to count and, as there were still less than forty Members, the House automatically adjourned and we all went home.

BIGGLES in Arabia

by Captain W. E. Johns

ILLUSTRATED BY WILLIAM STOBBS

PART SIX

By this time Biggles thought he had the situation summed up pretty well. He had been watched in Aden. Ambrimos had been informed that the sabotaging of his aircraft had not produced the desired result, so he had followed him across the Red Sea, probably in the machine which had passed over aerodrome 137 just before the *haboob* broke. Biggles's aircraft had been in the hangar at the time and had escaped observation, but Ambrimos must have known that it was somewhere in the vicinity of El Moab, and was therefore more or less prepared for the situation that had arisen. Ginger's sickness had played right into his hands.

The Sultan was obviously content with the way things had panned out and seemed to be in no great hurry to force a final showdown. Anyhow, with studied fastidiousness he selected a cigarette from a massive gold case, put it in a gold and amber holder, and with a flourish lit it from a gold petrol-lighter. The aroma of Turkish tobacco drifted sluggishly across the room.

'You must understand, major, that I am a man of business,' he remarked airily.

'I seem to remember you telling me that before,' reminded Biggles coolly.

'With me, business comes first, first and last and all the time,' went on the Sultan. 'I work very hard, doing my best to please everybody, yet always the British Government puts obstacles in my way. You provide an example. You were sent here to upset my business—don't deny it. Being human I'm bound to resent that. It is true that, among other things, I deal in a commodity which is always in demand in the Middle East.'

'Say hashish, and have done with it,' suggested Biggles.

'Very well—hashish. What of it? I do not force my wares upon people. They demand them. I supply them, and by supplying them of course I make money.'

'And at the same time make havoc of their lives,' put in Biggles. 'You don't care how many lives you wreck, as long as you make money. All right. Now let's get down to brass tacks. What's the point of this conversation?'

'The point is this,' answered Ambrimos. 'I have no intention of allowing the British Government, or that inter-fering body which it supports, called the Central Narcotics Intelligence Bureau, to ruin the business which I have spent my life in building. Whatever they do, human nature being what it is, I shall always be able to buy a road. I imagine you know the meaning of our expression, buying a road?'

'No. That's a new one to me.'

'Buying a road is a nice way of saying that I am able to bribe officials along the routes by which my merchandise reaches its market. Everyone needs money, and this is money easily earned.'

Biggles raised a critical eyelid. 'Are you suggesting that I might earn my bread and margarine by this method?'

Ambrimos smiled sleekly. 'You would then have butter instead of margarine.'

'I'd rather have clean margarine than dirty butter.'

The Sultan sighed. 'Being a man of peace I always try peaceful methods first. I like you. There is a frankness, a directness, about the way you speak, that appeals to a certain softness in my own nature. I was hoping that you would consider it worth your while to accept an interest in my business.'

Biggles shook his head. 'Thank you,' he said shortly. 'But that happens to be a bit of a road that is not for sale.'

'Ah! a pity. Yes, a pity. . . . A great pity. I have for some time needed a good pilot. You know, of course, what happens to roads that refuse to be—er—repaired?'

'Just as a matter of interest, tell me this,' said Biggles curiously. 'Have you no fear that I might agree to your proposal, and then, having won your confidence, do a bit of selling myself—sell my information to the Narcotics Bureau, for instance?'

'No,' answered Ambrimos. 'That would probably be my way, because selling anything at a profit has always been a passion with me,' he confessed, with startling frankness. 'But you would not do that. The British are an obnoxious, meddlesome breed, but they have one characteristic which even we who hate them must admire. Having given their word they keep it. That, of course, although they do not seem to realise it, is their weakness. It is impossible to run a business on such lines and make it pay.'

'We haven't done so badly,' murmured Biggles.

'You would have done better had you been a little less

squeamish in your transactions.'

'Okay. Let's leave it at that,' suggested Biggles.

The Sultan regarded him from under half-closed eyelids. 'You realise that this refusal to co-operate forces upon me a painful alternative. Being a man of intelligence you will perceive that it would be folly on my part to allow you to cause me further trouble?'

'How are you going to prevent it?'

'That is a plain question, and one that calls for a plain answer,' returned the Sultan smoothly. 'I shall have you put to death.'

'That's plain enough,' admitted Biggles.

'I hoped you would see it like that,' said Ambrimos softly. 'With you disposed of, I shall produce more and more hashish—and other things.' The Sultan's pose of placid self-assurance began to break under mounting anger which revealed his real character. Gone was the silky quality of his voice. It took on a hard, vicious tone. 'I hate you British,' he went on. 'I will break you and your Empire. Do you hear me? In spite of all your soldiers, your sailors and your airmen, British rule shall wither like a leaf in the desert, and it will be I, Nicolo Ambrimos, who will do this. Do you know how? Perhaps you can guess, for I know why you are here, what you seek. Gurra, the weed of Paradise. Yes, I have it. More and more will go to your miserable country of fog and rain. It will flow into your factories to undermine the strength of your workers and turn them into useless human wreckage. Gurra shall do what guns and bayonets could not do. You will lose the will to fight. Then you will fall, fall to a great power that is waiting for that day. After that, Europe will fall, and Asia, mighty Asia, will rise again.'

Biggles was amazed. This political angle was something new. Clearly, it was not only money that Ambrimos wanted. He wanted power. He was planning to achieve his end, not with guns and bombs, but by drugs that would reduce whole nations to helplessness. Whether or not such a plan could succeed was open to question, yet obviously it could do an immense amount of harm. Ambrimos was more than a racketeer. He was a fanatic, and a dangerous one.

The Sultan was watching him. 'Fantastic, you think, eh?'

'Fantastic is the word,' agreed Biggles.

'But not so fantastic as you might think,' declared Ambrimos. 'Do you read history? Did you ever read of the conquest of Peru? Do you know why the Spaniard Pizarro, with a mere handful of men, was able to conquer a nation of ten millions? Because the Incas had rotted their brains and muscles with the drug cocaine, which they obtained by chewing the leaves of the coca plant, until they had no will of their own and only the strength of little children. That is what Pizarro himself said, and he knew. The Incas are no more. Thus will it be with Britain, and the rest of your vaunted Western Civilisation.'

Biggles smiled bleakly. 'I see. So you're aiming to be a modern Pizarro?'

Ambrimos smiled a superior smile. 'Pizarro conquered only one nation. I shall conquer many.'

'And then what?'

'The world shall be set free.'

Biggles shook his head wearily. 'Don't give me that line of hooey,' he said in a pained voice. 'There are enough people already singing that tune. The more talk there is of freedom the less freedom people get. What people like you *really* want is to put more shackles on everyone so that you can tickle your vanity playing Lord of Creation. If you really want to do people a bit of good, all you have to do is jump in the sea and drown yourself. In short, your real aim is to plunge the world into another war.'

'Certainly not! I am a man of peace,' declared Ambrimos.

Biggles drew at his cigarette and exhaled slowly. 'The old, old story. You want peace so you start a war to get it. If all you people who are so anxious for peace would pipe down, ordinary folk would forget that there is such a thing as war. They would then get on with things they really want to do instead of hurting themselves by throwing things at each other. What have you got to moan about, anyway? You've done yourself pretty well. But I know your sort. You tuck yourself in under the Union Jack because if you went anywhere else you'd get your throat cut. Then you turn round and bite the hand that protects you because it has something that you haven't got, and could never get. That something needs guts, not jelly, in its belly. Quit bleating, or else give me leave to go outside to be sick.'

The Sultan stared. His breath came faster. His face had taken on a curious pallor under its colour.

'Now I'll make a suggestion, a practical one,' went on Biggles. 'To-morrow let us pull up all the Gurra and burn it. Then I'll fly you back to Aden where you can live in comfort for the rest of your life as long as you drop the hashish racket, and stick to dates and frankincense. No man ever gave you sounder advice than that.'

My Favourite Flower

On the smooth chalky Chilterns where
The honeysuckle clings and climbs,
And her thin trailing arms entwines,
Spreading her fragrance on the air;

On every gorse bush, every thorn,
On every clump of brambles there,
The honeysuckle clambers fair,
And smiles to greet the summer morn.

Her buds are green and long and thin,
And slowly, surely, they unfurl,
To blossoms creamy as a pearl,
And wealth of honey lies within.

Then all the bees for miles do come,
To sip the nectar hidden there,
And oh the buzzing in the air,
That blows around my Chiltern home.

Janet Grattan (11)

'Only one word would have been necessary to cause murder there and then.'

Ambrimos continued to stare at Biggles. He moistened his lips. 'I do not need advice,' he said slowly.

'Have it your own way,' said Biggles. 'I have nothing more to say.'

Ambrimos clapped his hands for his manager, who had left the room. When the man came Ambrimos looked at Biggles and pointed to the door. 'Think over my offer,' he invited. 'Here we do nothing in a hurry. I'll give you a little while to change your mind.' He made a signal of dismissal.

Biggles and Ginger were escorted from the room.

The Sultan had not lied when he said that the men outside did not look upon Christians with favour. There was quite a crowd, every man armed, some with rifles of an obsolete pattern, some with spears. Biggles did not know enough about them to identify the types, but from what Zahar had told him he supposed some of them to be Danakils, and others, tribesmen from the Highlands of Abyssinia.

The appearance of the two white men was greeted with scowls, muttered vituperation, and a few shouts. There was some spitting. It was clear that only one word would have been necessary to cause murder to be done there and then. Ambrimos stood at his door, smiling, as the natives parted reluctantly to clear a path for the prisoners as they were taken to one of the several huts. At the entrance they were met by such a swarm of flies, and a stink so appalling that Ginger clapped a hand over his nose. Into the gloomy interior they were pushed, and two tall, scowling Danakils, took up positions at the entrance.

'Things may not look so bad to you, but they look pretty dim to me,' said Ginger, when he could speak.

'They might be worse,' replied Biggles evenly, as he lit another cigarette. 'After all, we're still alive.'

'How long is that pleasant state of affairs going to last?' enquired Ginger without enthusiasm.

'It's hard to say,' returned Biggles calmly, blowing smoke into the swarming flies.

'At any moment we may be shot, speared or strangled.'

'That's a possibility, I must admit,' agreed Biggles. 'But it's significant that the dirty work wasn't put in hand right away. It might have been. Ambrimos has been to some pains to point out our weaknesses, but he can't see his own. He hesitates.'

'That isn't because he's overcharged with the milk of human kindness.'

'True enough,' conceded Biggles. 'If he's overcharged with anything it's vanity. His real weakness is business—making easy money. It dominates his life. He wants a pilot, and he has the quaint idea that I'm the man. I think, Ambrimos is still hoping that I'll change my mind. I hope he goes on hoping. The longer he hopes the better chance we have of doing what we came to do. Now keep quiet for a bit. I want to do a spot of thinking.'

'Go ahead,' requested Ginger warmly. 'Think hard and fast, while the going's good.'

Bertie's errand to Aden occupied about four hours. It was entirely successful and he returned with the three items which he had been asked to fetch. These were, to be specific: a certain bright-eyed member of the R.A.F. officially known as L.A.C. Blakey, classified in the trade of acetylene welder; a parcel of dynamite with detonators and fuses; and a spare Moth wheel.

For the first item the accommodating Station Commander had been responsible. He had called for a volunteer and Blakey had stepped forward. As he told Bertie confidently when he stepped into the machine, he was willing to go anywhere and do anything to escape even for a short while from the blistering ash-bin named Aden. As Aden lies in the crater of an extinct volcano, this description of it was fully justified. The explosive had proved rather more difficult, as the purpose for which it was required did not, to the Engineer Officer, make sense. There was, he asserted, no water in the desert; alternatively, if there was, why spill it? However, Bertie pleaded urgency, and in the end the production of his police badge got him what he needed. L.A.C. Blakey's enthusiasm for the flight was somewhat damped when, asked to carry the parcel on his lap, he was told what it contained.

'Whatever you do laddie, don't drop it on the floor,' requested Bertie with unusual earnestness.

'If I drop it anywhere,' answered Blakey emphatically, 'it will be overboard.'

'Quite right—absolutely,' agreed Bertie. 'Let's tootle along.'

The flight back to aerodrome 137 was made without incident. Bertie, bearing in mind what he carried, made a careful landing, to find Zahar squatting alone on a mass of fabric which he had removed from the metal members of the old hangar.

'By Jove! You've certainly been busy with the jolly old bodkin,' observed Bertie. 'Where's the big white chief?'

Bertie's exuberance at the success of his mission suffered a set-back when Zahar explained what had happened. He scratched an ear. 'How deuced awkward,' he muttered. 'What do we do next?'

'The last message of Biggles Sahib was this,' answered the Arab without emotion. '"The wall that holds the water must be destroyed. If I return not, the task must be done." Biggles Sahib has not return. I fear his head has been struck off by the Kafirs.'

Bertie considered the matter. 'We shall have to do something about this,' he told Blakey at last. 'What I mean is I shall have to do something. What I want you to do is to stay here and clear the gubbins away from the aircraft so that we can get it airborne.'

'What about the Moth?' enquired Blakey.

'Yes, by Gad. I'd forgotten that. I'll give you a hand to get the new wheel on. As soon as we've got that on you can make a start on the hangar. When you've finished, if I'm not here, cover the machine with some of this old canvas in case those Wogs come back. Cover yourself up too, if they do, because if they catch you, you've had it.'

'What about your machine?' asked Blakey. 'Sitting out there in the sun won't do it no good.'

'Quite right. I'll trundle it into this other hangar before I go!'

'Go? Go where?'

'I shall have to try and find my chief.'

'You mean—you're going to start walking about the desert?' Blakey looked horrified.

'Walking? No fear. Not when I can ride. I might as well whisper round in the Moth. Let's get cracking on the undercart. Come on, Zahar, old coffee-berry, you can help.'

It did not take the three of them very long to get the damaged wheel off the Moth, and the new one on. After it had been tested, Bertie set Blakey on the real task for which he had been brought out, and then made preparations for departure.

'I don't know how long I shall be away,' he told Blakey. 'Expect me when you see me—that's the best thing. If you don't see me, don't expect me—if you get what I mean. If those beastly aboriginals happen to totter this way, get out of sight or they may snatch your scalp.'

'But half a mo',' requested Blakey. 'If you don't come back, how am I to get home?'

'Yes, by Jove, I never thought of that,' murmured Bertie. 'You'll have to pray that I'll come back. If I don't you'll have to hoof it. Keep travelling east and you're bound to come to the sea sooner or later.'

'And then what?'

'Get someone with a ship to give you a lift,' suggested Bertie. He turned to Zahar. 'What about you, old chocolate-drop? Are you going to stay here or are you coming with me?'

Zahar regarded Bertie dubiously. 'Where are we going?'

'We're going to pull the plug out of the Sultan's reservoir and then look for my friends.'

As he spoke, Bertie threw the sack of hashish out of the back seat of the Moth. 'No use humping that stuff around,' he observed.

'At El Moab we shall be deprived of our lives,' predicted Zahar, with fatalistic calm.

'And who will deprive us?' enquired Bertie.

'The men of Ambrimos. They are worse than the beasts of the desert. They sell their children. This is true, for my eyes have witnessed it—may God forgive them!'

Bertie polished his monocle. 'What nasty fellows. Well, we'll blow up their beastly dam and see how they like that. Which reminds me. I mustn't forget the jolly old squibs.'

He went over to collect the dynamite from where it had been put in a safe place. He picked it up and handed it to Zahar. 'Hold that, and hold it tight,' he warned. 'That is if you've decided to come with me.'

'I will come, seeking Abu bin Hamud, who left me to perish in the desert,' declared Zahar. 'The blood of Kuatim, who was my friend, calls for vengeance.'

'Absolutely,' agreed Bertie. 'Get aboard, then, and we'll waffle along while there's a drop or two of daylight.'

Actually, Bertie knew quite well what he was going to do. In his last message Biggles had ordered the destruction of the dam and it did not occur to him to do anything else.

With Zahar in the back seat, the dynamite on his lap, he took off and holding the machine low headed straight for his objective. He knew that the higher he flew the greater was the chance of his being seen; so he maintained a 'contour chasing' flight until he judged that he must be within a mile or two of El Moab. Then, choosing a level piece of ground, he cut his engine, flattened out and landed. It was a bumpy affair because the ground was littered with stones, some of them large ones; but the machine finished on even keel.

'God is great,' came the voice of Zahar fervently, from the rear seat.

Bertie stood up and looked around. The sun was now nearing the horizon, turning the sky turquoise, and the sandy wilderness to streaming gold. The only landmark was a wadi on his left, now a big pool of purple shadows.

'How far are we from the beastly place, old chestnut?' he asked Zahar.

'The distance is small,' was the reply. 'By walking on our feet, we could reach it by the setting of the sun.'

'Good enough,' returned Bertie. 'Sit still and hang on to your parcel.' He taxied the machine on a little way into a fold in the ground, where he thought there was less chance of it being seen. He then switched off, climbed down, and took the dynamite from Zahar while the Arab got out.

'Can you find your way to this wall that holds back the water?' he asked.

'Without difficulty,' was the comforting reply.

'Then lead on, Macduff, and let us get the business over,' said Bertie.

Zahar started off like a man who is at home in his surroundings.

A walk of some twenty minutes followed, and ended behind a ridge of rock and gravel beyond which Bertie could not see. Zahar turned and held a brown hand over his mouth. 'This is the place,' he whispered. He pointed half left. 'That way, in the wadi, is El Moab.' He pointed ahead. 'Before us is the wall that holds the water.'

'Jolly good work, Sambo,' complimented Bertie. 'You'd better sit here while I let the water out of the basin.'

'This will be a thing to remember,' swore Zahar.

Dropping on all fours Bertie crawled to the ridge and looked over. Zahar had been right. There, immediately below him, spanning the wadi, was the primitive reservoir, tapering to a point at the lower end where the dam had been built. He moved his position a trifle to the left so that he could get a clear view of what he intended to destroy, and was pleased to observe that it was not built on very substantial lines.

Beyond the dam the gorge continued, a gloomy cleft in the bed-rock through which the storm-water of untold ages had cut its way. The sides were not precipitous, but steep, and perhaps a hundred feet apart. This continued on below the dam for forty or fifty yards when the gorge made a sharp turn, cutting off the view of what lay beyond. Bertie imagined that from this point the gorge began to widen out to form the more shallow wadi, in which, was El Moab, with the plantations of narcotic plants. Rising to his knees he looked around. Not a soul was in sight.

Not for one moment did it occur to him that Biggles and Ginger might be in El Moab. There was nothing in Zahar's story to suggest such a thing. He imagined him to be in some native camp, doctoring Ginger, who was as yet unfit to travel. Had he known the truth, that both of them were at that moment within a hundred yards of him, his behaviour would doubtless have been very different from what it was. But he did not know. Having destroyed the dam he would get back to the aerodrome as soon as possible in order to let Biggles know that the job had been done. If it turned out that Biggles was not at the aerodrome, then he would take steps to find him.

He selected a spot almost in the centre of the dam, where two large, badly-fitting boulders left a cavity between them. Zahar, apparently unable to restrain his curiosity, had crept nearer, and lay watching; so signalling him to remain where he was Bertie made a precarious descent to the bottom of the gorge, and for the next few minutes busied himself with his task. He soon disposed of the dynamite as he had planned. The adjustment of the detonator occupied only a few moments. This done to his satisfaction, he backed away to the limit of the fuse, a matter of a few yards. Having prepared the end with his penknife he laid it on the rock, and humming softly to himself—for it had all been much easier than he had expected—produced a box of matches. All was now ready. He struck a match, but before applying it to the fuse, glanced up to make sure that Zahar was out of the danger area. He had not bothered to measure the fuse because, as the actual time of the explosion was unimportant, there seemed to be no point in it. As long as it was a 'time' fuse, and not instantaneous—and the Engineer Officer had assured him of this—that was all that mattered.

He expected to see Zahar watching him. Not seeing him, and wanting to know exactly where he was before

'There were now two figures, almost motionless. Zahar had taken a hand.'

he lit the fuse, he called: 'Hi! Sambo! Where are you?'

The words acted like a signal. From that moment the situation switched from one of passive inconsequence to one of brisk action. Things happened, and they happened fast.

A man, an Arab, suddenly burst into view, running along the brink of the gorge from the direction of the bend. Bertie supposed him to be Zahar, who had been scouting and was now hastening to warn him of danger. He only realised his mistake when the figure dropped on one knee and a rifle came into view. Obviously, it was not Zahar, for the Arab did not possess a rifle.

Bertie dropped the match he had lighted as the flame burnt his fingers, and jumped for the nearest cover. This was a large rock—the same boulder, in fact, on which he had placed the fuse. A split second later the rifle cracked, and the bullet ricocheted with a shrill whine from the same rock. He crouched lower, not daring to move; for he heard the bolt click in the breach and knew that the man above was only waiting for him to show his head to fire another shot.

Bertie did some quick thinking. Remain where he was he dared not, for the man above would only have to shift his position to bring him into view. All he could do was to watch the lip of the gorge for the man to appear. When the rifle went up, he decided, before the man could take aim he would jump to a better position in the black shadow of the dam.

Still motionless, watching, he became aware of a brisk

hissing noise, just over his head. Turning his eyes upward to ascertain the cause he saw a thin wisp of pale blue smoke rising into the calm air. He knew at once what had happened. The lighted match he had dropped in his startled haste had fallen on the fuse and set it alight. It must already have been burning for the best part of a minute; and the knowledge that the explosion might now occur at any time caused him to move with alacrity, bullets notwithstanding.

As he jumped from cover he looked up. The sharp shooter was still there, but he was no longer alone. There were now two figures, erect and almost motionless, though locked in close embrace. Zahar, apparently, had taken a hand.

Bertie went up the face of the gorge like a mountain goat, taking outrageous chances of breaking his bones as he leapt from ledge to ledge, sending loose stones rattling down behind him. As he neared the top, one of the figures, he knew not which, came hurtling down to miss him by inches and land with a thud in the bottom of the gorge.

Panting from his exertions he pulled up and flattened himself against the rock face. If it was Zahar who had gone down it would obviously be suicidal to continue the ascent, for the other man would be waiting to receive him, and with the butt of his rifle, knock him on the head before he was in a position to defend himself. Yet the explosion, should it occur now, would have an effect just as fatal.

He took the only course open to him. Everything depended on who was at the top, so he took immediate steps to find out. 'Hi! Sambo! Is that you up there?' he called.

The reply, to his unspeakable relief, came in Zahar's voice. 'O Sahib of the glass eye, it is me.'

Bertie scrambled over the top and found Zahar in the act of cleaning his dagger in the sand. 'What have you been doing with that thing?' he demanded.

Zahar sheathed the weapon. 'Good tidings,' he re-ported calmly. 'That Arab was Abu bin Hamud. He would have slain you, but Allah—may he be glorified—delivered him into my hands to be punished for his sins. It was written.'

Bertie had nothing more to say about it. He turned a puzzled face in the direction of the wadi as from it there came a great noise of shouting. 'I wonder what that's all about,' he murmured. 'Something seems to be going on. Let's go and have a dekko.'

He set off along the rim of the gorge towards a babble of voices which now came plainly to their ears.

(*Concluded on page* 282)

TUTTI FRUTTI TRUFFLES

3 oz. cooking or dessert dates. 2 oz. stoned raisins or sultanas. 2 oz. dried figs or prunes. 2 oz. glacé cherries. 2 oz. dried apricots or peaches. 3 oz. shelled walnuts, hazel nuts, almonds or peanuts. 1 oz. candied peel or preserved ginger.

Set up the mincing machine and see that it is firmly fixed to the table. Put a little of each ingredient into the mouth of the mincer and put a plate below the knife end. Press down the mixture in the mouth with the back of a wooden spoon. When the ingredients have all been minced, undo the knives and scrape out anything left on them or in the mincer with a teaspoon. Mix the mince well with a spoon then pinch off small pieces and roll into balls the size of marbles between the palms of your hands.

Leave the truffles on a rack in a cool place overnight. Next day, roll some in hundreds and thousands, some in chocolate rice, grated chocolate or cocoa powder and some in icing sugar. Store each batch separately in airtight tins or glass jars.

Y. C. TRETHEWY.

for LEOPARD

The leopard is a jungle cat,
and anyone will tell you that

though it may change the lives of those
more muscle bound, more adipose,

may teach the trusting heart to fear,
bereave the goat, deprive the deer,

and turn the living into dead.
When all is done and all is said

though change may all around it be
a tribute to its perfidy,

however much it plans and plots,
the leopard cannot change its spots.

V.G.

for **MONKEY**

Who's cross!
Who's at a loss
for words to convey
how much the day
displeases and appals!

Who has had a row
because somehow
breakfast was late,
and that addle-pate
the parrot, who calls

with the Jungle News
didn't. And whose
business, pray, is it,
if monkeys sit
till Niagara Falls

glowering out
at life's roundabout
like two old ladies
as cross as Hades
in home-knitted shawls!

V.G.

A Sticky Business—*continued from page* 208)

'Toffee-making?' said Mr. Dalton. Then to Miss Lacey:—'About that toffee. . . .' It was then that Nancy broke in, her voice unnatural, as if partly strangled. 'You needn't bother to find out about the toffee.' She gulped. 'Because . . . I did it myself. . . .'

She got no further. Miss Lacey gave a startled cry. Hubert, sitting next to her, had upset his cup of tea. There followed general consternation—the upset tea-cup concerning the grown-ups, the rest of us wholly occupied with Nancy's startling confession. My thoughts were now so confused that I cannot remember anything very clearly. I think Miss Lacey said something kind and forgiving to the apologetic Hubert. In the confusion Nancy's statement appeared to have passed unnoticed. Still more or less stupefied by it I waited for the next move.

It was Mr. Dalton who took us back to the toffee. He spoke to Miss Lacey.

'When all this happened I was just going to ask if you'd made that toffee you gave me to take back to my children?'

I felt rather than saw the sudden jerk of Nancy's head.

'It was only the bought kind, I'm afraid,' said Miss Lacey.

'Bought or not, they fell upon it. I was to thank you very, very much.' Mr. Dalton laughed. 'There was so nearly a tragedy over that toffee. I always leave my packing till I go to bed. And I was actually *in* bed before I remembered the jar still sitting on the table in the dining-room. So it only got into my suitcase by a narrow squeak —and at about midnight.'

'You—you. . . .' began Nancy—and stuck.

'Yes?' said Miss Lacey helpfully.

Nancy was scarlet in the face. 'Oh, Stephen. . . .' she began, then stopped again.

Miss Lacey got up. She turned to her nephew. 'Come along, Roger. The children seem to have secrets to talk about. We'll talk over ours in the other room. That letter. . . .' she felt in her pocket. 'I do so want your advice.'

Left on our own we sat silent for a moment or two— most of us remembering our suspicions of one another and not knowing how to begin patching things up. I was feeling awful—ashamed of my readiness to believe in Nancy's guilt, and now aware that her 'confession' had been made solely to shield me. Nancy, on her side, wanted to apologise.

'Stephen,' she said, 'I didn't know how to believe you'd pinched the beastly stuff, but things looked so awfully black against you—after Hubert found all those toffee papers in your pocket.'

So it was Hubert—not Nancy—who had been through our pockets.

'I wanted a knife,' he explained. 'And Tony said his was in one of his pockets. Your things were all mixed up, and I got hold of your trousers by mistake. Then I told Nancy what I'd found—those toffee papers.'

'And I couldn't help thinking . . . but I'm *awfully* sorry. I—I might have known. . . .' stammered Nancy.

'And I might have known you wouldn't go through my pockets,' said I, it being my turn to apologise. 'Or our room, either,' I added, remembering earlier fears and suspicions.

'But why—' began Nancy.

Under cover of the babble I gave her a warning kick. I knew what she was going to ask:—Why had I let her believe I was the culprit? To shield Tony, of course. I could not say so in front of him. Luckily—being Nancy —she was quick enough to realise I did not want to explain anything more just then. We were alone later, and only then was I able to find the right words for what I thought of her having tried to save me by taking the blame upon herself. By then it was my own shins I was wanting to kick, remembering how, only such a short while ago, I had been thinking we could never be friendly any more.

You can guess what good friends we are now. Sometimes we tease one another about that awful day of fears and doubts. But teasing doesn't count for anything. It never will again.

Scene from the Apocalypse, a Mural in the Church in Saint-Savin (France) painted about 1100–1125.

PAINTING for Those Who Cannot Paint

by Joseph Natanson

There are so many people painting and enjoying it, you should try too, if only to see what you can do.

These murals are reproduced from 'Romanesque Wall Paintings' (Thames & Hudson), published this month. The French edition was published by Editions Du Chene, Paris.

THERE IS VERY little difference now between a professional artist and an amateur. There are so many people who have chosen painting as a hobby and so many artists who have to make their living in another profession that the frontier between these two groups can be drawn only with great difficulty.

In former times it was quite different. The painter had to acquire a lot of technical knowledge. He would start his apprenticeship as a young boy (girls were very rare in the profession) and in the studio of his master he would learn how to prepare wood, canvas or a wall to receive the paint; how to grind pigments with an egg preparation, oil or any other medium used by the master; how to apply gold; how to transfer the drawing; how to underpaint in order to achieve greater intensity of colour; how to prepare varnishes; and so on.

To-day, instead of long years of learning, one walks into a shop, buys everything ready for use, and becomes a painter in five minutes in any technique one chooses. And not only that! A painter now has at his disposal a wider range of permanent and very brilliant colours than any old master had, because many pigments which we use now were invented only in the last century.

No wonder that outside the circle of professional artists there are thousands and thousands of people who are officially statesmen (like Mr. Churchill), dentists, lawyers, factory workers, salesmen, farmers, housewives, and taxi drivers, but at heart are artists and devote all their spare time to painting.

In a recent competition for amateur artists held in the U.S.A., more interesting paintings were discovered than in many a show organised by academic bodies of professional artists. A few of the winners had had some art training, but many of the most successful paintings were the work of artists who had no

artistic background and were self-taught.

Certainly you have seen and perhaps even taken part in an exhibition of children's paintings. There is a tendency nowadays to overrate children's art, but anyway everybody must agree that such exhibitions are more than amusing. There are always many well observed and very simply and originally expressed subjects from everyday life as well as many fascinating inventions drawn entirely from imagination. Even if certainly not all paintings are masterpieces, it is very difficult to find a dull or commonplace one.

What is the moral of all that?

If there are so many people painting and enjoying it, you should have a good try too—if only to find out what you can do.

If you have tried already and failed, it was perhaps because you were discouraged by your own or other people's criticism; and they might have been wrong. Remember that a person who is not especially interested in art judges a painting not by its likeness to life, its decorative or imaginative value, as one would expect, but by its likeness to what they think is good art. And this 'good art' is usually the second rate painting of a previous generation which survives until the next generation on Christmas cards, jigsaw puzzles, coloured advertisements and illustrations in cheap magazines. You should know better.

Or you may have failed because you have been using a technique foreign to your temperament. Out of all the techniques, media and colours available, you must try to find the one technique, medium and range of colours in which you will be able to express yourself best.

Now, having dealt with generalities, let's get straight down to practice.

1. COLOURS

Or should I have said 'pigments'? 'Colour' is, properly speaking, what appears on your paper, cardboard, canvas, or, if you are very ambitious, a wall. In painting, colours are produced by pigments.

Each time you start a painting you must be absolutely sure that the colours will not fade, darken or change. You must use permanent pigments. The manufacturers know all about that and they give you an indication on the label of 'artists' products'. But as some permanent pigments are rather expensive for children and students and commercial artists, they produce substitutes which they honestly label 'tint' or 'imitation'. As you will see, you can easily manage without these. There are quite enough cheap, permanent colours of great beauty and brilliance.

FIRST RULE: **Do not use too many colours.**

Titian, who was one of the greatest colourists, usually started a painting with only three colours: white, black, and yellow ochre. Only when the painting was well advanced did he add other colours on the surface.

A fresco is a painting on a wall that

Leslie A. Goss was awarded the gold medal for oils in ARTnews' National Amateur Painting Competition in U.S.A. He only started painting in 1945 when his sons and daughters gave him an easel and paints.

has just been plastered. Very few pigments can stand the quicklime and thus the range of colours is very limited. And yet nothing can be compared to the brilliant colouring of some frescoes by Tiepolo, or the paintings made by the Romans at Pompeii 2,000 years ago.

Many mediæval murals are painted only with yellow ochre, Venetian red (or a similar red earth), and a green earth (terre verte). They are very colourful to the eye.

Some contemporary masters purposely reduce their palette to three or four colours to achieve greater unity and stronger expression. Picasso painted many of his most striking pictures in only a few tones. Modern art, which tends to simplification, naturally emphasises the fact, known so well to the old masters, that a painting must be based on a harmony of contrast of a limited number of colours. All other colours are supplementary.

SECOND RULE: **The intensity of colour in a painting does not depend on the quantity of pigment used nor even on the brilliance of the pigments, but on the way the colours have been disposed and opposed to each other.**

Imitating the very old masters (in the choice of pigments, but not in their style —you are a very modern artist!) reduce your palette to:—

Ivory black.
Yellow Ochre.
Red (Venetian red). Green (terre verte).
White (flake or titanium or any other permanent white).

1. *Pablo PICASSO.*   *Night fishing at Antibes.*   *Painted in 1939.*

An artist of such power of imagination as Picasso invents entirely new forms to tell his story.   Do you see the fishes terrified by a sudden light, the boys in the boat stabbing them with tridents, the two girls watching from the pier, and especially the one who has stopped with her bicycle and devours her ice cream without taking her eyes from the fascinating scene for one moment?

Mixing them together you will find tones of great subtlety and depth.

'But,' I hear you saying, 'how can I paint a blue sky when there is no blue, or a lemon when there is no "lemon" yellow?'

Try! And I assure you that you will find great pleasure in painting a perfectly blue sky and a very yellow lemon.

There is no need, of course, to confine yourself for ever to those colours. And one has to remember that the intensity of a colour is decreased in proportion to the number of different pigments mixed together in making it.

You will find that sometimes you need a different harmony or a bold touch of colour, and then what an opportunity you have to explore the possibilities of other pigments. Try some of these:—

Naples yellow, a light yellow with a mysterious luminosity.

Golden ochre or Roman ochre.

Alizarin crimson.

Viridian, expensive but the best of our greens.

Ultramarine blue. Prussian blue.

If you add to these colours (sparingly, because they are expensive)

Cadmium yellow pale,

Cadmium yellow,

Cadmium red,

you will have enough pigments to explore for the rest of your life the infinite range of colours they can produce.

Marion Churchill, aged 6, called this ' A clown with all lights round '. It was in the National Exhibition of Children's Art, organised by the ' Sunday Pictorial ' last year.

THE SEEKERS

A Play by Roland Pertwee
ILLUSTRATIONS BY G. F. BYRNE

List of characters in order of appearance :

ALBERT
PETER TREFUSIS—*Red Pete*
MICHAEL FANE—*Black Michael*

SIMON LAKE—*Simon the Scourge*
DELIA FANE—*Meg the Terror*
WILLIE

SCENE : A room in a ruined cottage

TIME : A summer morning in 1950

The Scene is an empty room in a ruined cottage among sand dunes by the sea. Right of back wall is a door leading to a small entrance hall. Centre of left wall is a window with a broken frame and centre of right wall a fireplace. There may be a built-in cupboard, but it is not important. There is no furniture other than a couple of old sugar boxes and perhaps a barrel or two thrown up by the sea and brought in by tramps or picnickers. The wind has blown a lot of sand into the room and over the boxes.

If providing a scene offers too many difficulties, the Shakespearian method of exhibiting a notice bearing the words : A RUINED COTTAGE BY THE SEA *will serve nearly as well.*

When the curtain rises we hear the plaintive cry of sea-gulls. Albert, rather a horrid small boy, wearing a cotton sun hat and paddlers over his knickers, is tiptoeing from the fireplace towards the door. From some way off a woman's voice cries shrilly :

VOICE. [*off*]. Elbert! ELBERT!

(Albert stops and grinds his teeth with rage.)

VOICE. [*cont. louder*]. ELBERT !

(Albert goes to the window and makes an angry 'keep quiet' gesture.)

ALBERT. Give over, Auntie Mor-erd! Lettin' everybody know what I'm doin' of.

VOICE [*off*]. All right, miss yer bathe, we're not waiting.

ALBERT. [*in a panic*]. You got to. It isn't fair. Wait for me—wait!

(He dashes for the door, trips over one of the boxes, rises, rubbing a knee and limps off howling with misery. As his moans die away, a boy's head looks cautiously through the window. It belongs to Peter Trefusis, at the moment known as Red Pete, and is adorned with a brightly coloured handkerchief knotted at the back. Over one eye he wears a black patch and, with the aid of a burnt cork he has given his chin an unshaven appearance and drawn a fierce, piratical moustache on his upper lip. He glances over his shoulder and beckons.)

PETE. Coast clear, me hearties. If the rogue had tarried longer I would have slit his weasen with me cutlass.

(While he is saying this, two other boys' heads appear similarly adorned, but without eye patches. One belongs to Michael Fane, at present known as Black Michael, who wears brass curtain rings in his ears; the other to Simon Lake, at present known as Simon the Scourge. He looks less piratical than his companions, partly because he wears spectacles and partly because he is self-conscious at being dressed up.)

MIKE. Aye, or nailed him by the ears to the mainmast.

SIMON. I wonder what the little blighter wanted.

PETE. [*in disgust*]. Little blighter! Look, there's no sense in you being called Simon the Scourge if you don't talk like one.

MIKE. I know. Couldn't you have said varlet or something?

SIMON. [*blinking*]. But is a varlet a blighter?

PETE. Oh, I dunno, but I know what *you* are.

MIKE. If the treasure is to be found let's not waste time in parley, Red Pete. We must rejoin the schooner ere the tide turns.

PETE. Well said, Black Michael, but keep your eyes peeled for a trap.

(Pete and Mike disappear from the window leaving Simon standing there blinking uncomfortably.)

SIMON. [*to their retreating backs*]. Shall we have any time for prawning when you're fed up with the treasure hunt?

(There is no reply. Pete and Mike enter furtively by the door. They wear open-necked shirts, coloured sashes with pistols, knives and cutlasses stuck into them.)

MIKE. *So good so far.*

SIMON. Oughtn't it to be so far so good?

MIKE. You shut up.

PETE. Aye, the cribs is empty—as empty as this thrice-accursed rumbling tum of mine.

SIMON. Were you born with it?

PETE. With what?

SIMON. A thrice-accursed rumbling tum.

PETE. No, I wasn't.

MIKE. He got it out of a book called 'Pirates All.' Any fool would know that.

SIMON. Oh, a book! I thought there was something the matter with it.

PETE. Honestly, Simon, you are the rottenest actor I ever knew.

MIKE. [*shaking his head*]. Thoroughly scurvy.

SIMON. [*hopefully*]. Well, if you'd rather do without me, I could always go prawning.

MIKE. You'll do nothing of the kind.

PETE. You'll jolly well play up like the rest of us.

SIMON. [*sadly*]. Oh, very well.

(He climbs into the room, bringing with him a basket-work carrier which he rests against one of the boxes.)

I only hope I don't look as big a fool as I feel.

PETE. You look a jolly sight bigger one if you want to know.

MIKE. Nay, nay, no fisticuffs till the treasure be found. 'Tis always then that rogues fall out.

SIMON. I don't believe there is a treasure.

MIKE. You wouldn't.

PETE. How many more times must I tell you that my great-great-grandfather, Bernard Trefusis, left a chart showing where the beastly stuff is hidden.

SIMON. Then why hasn't it been found?

PETE. Because everybody was too big a fool to understand the chart, you fool.

MIKE. (*shaking his head*.) I should have thought any fool would have seen that.

SIMON. But that makes it all the funnier your father suddenly solving it at the end of breakfast.

PETE. No, it doesn't.

MIKE. Anyway he did, or he wouldn't have tipped us off where to look.

SIMON. He can't have thought it was worth much or he'd have looked for it himself.

PETE. He couldn't, he's too busy. He has to write a short story for a magazine.

MIKE. So snubs!

SIMON. I only thought if there wasn't a treasure that I might as well . . .

PETE. If you mention prawning again I'll scrag you.

SIMON. Oh, all right!

MIKE. [*brightly*]. Why, if coming here did nothing else, it gave us the chance to give my sister the slip.

PETE. That's a jolly good show in itself, [*then to Mike*] not but what she's a decent enough sort.

MIKE. She's all right, but one doesn't want a girl tagging on all the time.

SIMON. Why not? I like Delia.

MIKE. You would.

SIMON. Don't you, then?

MIKE. Course I do.

PETE. So do I.

SIMON. Then you would, too.

MIKE. PETER. [*together*]. Now, look here . . .

(Delia, who is a year older than Mike, pops her head through the window.)

DELIA. Cuckoo!

(They turn and stare, Mike and Pete with frowns, Simon with a welcoming smile.)

MIKE. Oh, Lor!

SIMON. Hallo, Delia!

PETE. How on earth did you know we were here?

DELIA. I tracked your footsteps through the sand dunes like Good King Wenceslas.

MIKE. You would.

DELIA. Anyway I'm jolly glad I did.

MIKE. We're not.

DELIA. Not for that reason, but because I found two rabbits in wire snares and set them free.

SIMON. Good!

MIKE. Sort of idiotic thing a girl would do.

DELIA. They thought it was awfully sensible.

PETE. Did they say so?

DELIA. Yes, and the last one promised never to make such a silly mistake again. Then I found a lot more wire nooses and buried them. May I come in?

MIKE. No.

SIMON. Yes.

DELIA. Thanks.

(She climbs over the sill, then reaches outside for a prawning net.)

SIMON. Oh goody, you brought a net!

PETE. I don't know whether you know it, but you're butting in on a treasure hunt.

MIKE. And people who do that take their lives in their hands.

DELIA. Are you supposed to be the pirates who hid it or the ones who are going to find it?

PETE. Both. I'm Red Pete, Mike's Black Michael, and that's Simon the Scourge, though you wouldn't believe it.

SIMON. [*apologetically*]. It wasn't my idea.

DELIA. No, you look like somebody else's idea.

SIMON. [*sadly*]. I know just what I look like.

MIKE. So do we.

DELIA. I think I'll be Meg the Terror.

PETE. Who was she?

DELIA. Nobody, I've just made her up.

MIKE. Then if you don't mind my saying so, it's a jolly rotten make up.

DELIA. I don't mind a bit. Brothers always say that sort of thing. But wait a minute, if it's the Trefusis treasure we're looking for, it won't be here.

MIKE. Why not?

DELIA. Because it was buried at least a hundred years before this cottage was built.

SIMON. Then let's go prawning.

PETE. That's all rot.

MIKE. Uncle Reggie wouldn't have told us this place if there was nothing in it.

PETE. 'Course he wouldn't.

DELIA. He may have said here to get you out of the way while he finishes his short story.

PETE. Dad would never play such a dirty trick.

SIMON. Can't see why not. Must be a fearful curse trying to write with a shindy going on outside the window.

PETE. Anyway until I've washed this muck off my face, I'm going on believing the treasure's here.

MIKE. And so i'faith am I, s'blood.

SIMON. [*to Delia*]. What did he say?

DELIA. S'blood.

PETE. Well spoken, Black Michael. You are a sorry knave after my own heart. How say you, shall we splice the mainbrace with a noggin' ere putting spade to earth?

MIKE. Aye, and pledge each other in good Jamaica rum.

(Pete sweeps sand off one of the boxes into the open basket leaning against it, then sits.)

PETE. [*to Delia and Simon*]. If you two want to join in, you'll have to jolly well keep in the spirit of the thing like we are.

SIMON. I only know 'Fifteen men on a dead man's chest' and I can't keep saying that.

PETE. Then say nothing and shove over the grub basket.

SIMON. It's beside you.

PETE. [*pushing the basket to Simon with a foot*]. You're supposed to be in charge of the prog and the grog.

(They plant themselves on tubs and boxes for a little refreshment.)

DELIA. We'd better make the most of these elevenses because they don't want us back before two at the earliest.

(Simon is getting ginger beer bottles out of the carrier.)

MIKE. [*in horror*]. Two! I shall never hold out till then.

PETE. Dad can't expect us to starve just so he can write a short story.

SIMON. You'd starve if he didn't.

MIKE. Oh, shut up, and pass the ginger beer, I mean rum.

(Simon throws him a bottle.)

PETE. Ignore him, Black Michael. Such scum are only fit to be keel-hauled. Don't keep all the cake to yourself, Simon my good Scourge.

(Simon produces some slices of cake and gives one to Delia.)

SIMON. It's lucky there's an extra piece or one of us would have to have gone without.

(Delia thanks him with a smile.)

MIKE. We jolly well wouldn't. Pirates never pander to wenches. It would be different if we were highwaymen.

PETE. Cut the cackle, and hand me me prog. This thrice-accursed tum of mine is rumbling like a train in a tunnel.

DELIA. There were no trains when people talked that way.

MIKE. [*darkly*]. No, but there were plenty of ducking stools for girls who shot their mouths off too much.

(Pete gives a gruff laugh, takes a big mouthful of cake, splutters and dives for the window to get rid of it.)

PETE. Ow! Some frightful fool has smothered the cake with sand.

DELIA. It must have been you when you brushed it off that box. [*nibbles cake*]. Wow, mine's just as bad!

MIKE. [*eating a crumb*]. Mine's worse.

PETE. It's Simon's fault for putting the basket where sand could get into it. He's to blame.

(He throws away his cake through the window, the others following suit.)

SIMON. That thrice-accursed tum of yours will have something to rumble about now.

(Delia laughs delightedly.)

PETE. I suppose you think that's funny?

DELIA. I do—awfully funny.

MIKE. You would.

DELIA. But I think Simon *is* funny.

MIKE. So he is—to look at.

PETE. Ha, ha, you had him there, Black Michael! Colossal snubs! But it's a bit thick mucking up our elevenses.

MIKE. So 'tis, for never was a man more sharply set.

PETE. How about going home and raising some more?

DELIA. We can't upset Uncle Reggie by doing that.

SIMON. Not possibly.

DELIA. Specially after all the trouble he took to get rid of us.

PETE. That's all very well, but it's no fun treasure hunting on an empty stomach.

SIMON. [*brightly*]. Then why don't Delia and I go prawning and bring back what we catch and boil them up in an old tin or something?

MIKE. While we sit and twiddle our thumbs, I suppose?

DELIA. I can't help feeling we owe it to Uncle Reggie to go on looking for the treasure.

PETE. What's the use? You said yourself this place was built *after* the stuff was buried.

DELIA. Ah, but that was Delia Fane speaking. I'm Meg the Terror now.

MIKE. What difference does that make?

DELIA. [*darkly*]. Only that Meg the Terror has reason to believe the treasure is lying in this very spot.

(Mike and Pete look at her with interest.)

MIKE. And Uncle Reggie got wind of it, you mean?

PETE. That's an idea.

(Delia nods and glances cautiously over her shoulder.)

DELIA. Walls have ears, but I have heard it mooted that one, Everard Trefusis, known in these parts as Everard the Nitwit, chanced upon the treasure while digging out a ferret that was lying up, and, with rare cunning, caused the cottage to be built to mark the spot where it lies hidden.

SIMON. [*greatly impressed*]. Have you just made that up?

DELIA. Nay, nay, good Simon the Purge....

PETE. *Scourge.*

DELIA. ....but I dare not breathe the source from which it came.

PETE. If you ask me it's just a lot of bunk.

MIKE. Or me, but I must say the damsel got it off jolly well.

SIMON. Why's it bunk?

PETE. Because no one but an idiot who'd found treasure would be such an ass as to leave it in the ground.

SIMON. I don't know so much—he can't have been called Everard the Nitwit for nothing.

DELIA. [*clapping her hands*]. Good old Simon! They hadn't the sense to see that.

PETE. [*thoughtfully rubbing his chin*]. Hm! Well, I've never known Dad to send me on an absolutely wild goose chase. There may not have been a treasure in all of them, but there was always something. My gosh, wouldn't it be marvellous if we did tumble on the merry old hoard!

MIKE. Wizard!

SIMON. I wonder what sort of treasure it is?

DELIA. [*quoting*]. 'Apes, and ivory, and peacocks,'....

PETE. The apes and peacocks will pong a bit by now.

DELIA. [*quoting*]. ....'Topazes, and cinnamon, and gold moidores,'....

MIKE. What are moidores?

SIMON. Pieces of nine, of course.

PETE. Eight, you idiot.

SIMON. No, nine. They're bigger than pieces of eight.

DELIA. Where did Uncle Reggie tell you to look?

MIKE. Nowhere exactly, but he must have meant this cottage.

DELIA. [excitedly]. Of course, he did! I've just remembered him saying he passed it this morning on his crack-of-dawn-idea-hunting walk.

SIMON. So he did!

PETE. What's that go to show?

DELIA. Don't you see? He must have a sudden feeling that this was where the treasure was hidden.

PETE. Feeling?

MIKE. She means he's physic.

DELIA. Psychic.

PETE. What's psychic?

DELIA. What Mike calls physic.

SIMON. It means knowing what you can't possibly know but do.

PETE. Then that explains what he was driving at in the piece of poetry he made up for us.

MIKE. Yes, yes!

DELIA. How did it go?

PETE. Search me.

SIMON. Wait a minute! I remember.

PETE. Bet you don't.

SIMON. Bet I do.

MIKE. You would.

(Simon shuts his eyes, screws up his face and repeats in a sing-song.)

SIMON. ' Hidden in the sand dunes,
　　　Between the hills and the sea,
　　　The ruins of a cottage
　　　Are beckoning to me.'

DELIA. Yes, yes, go on!

SIMON. ' And when I tightly shut my eyes
　　　I see as plain as plain
　　　Cut-throats from a pirate crew
　　　Who sailed the Spanish Main.'
Wait a minute—wait a minute ... yes, I've got it ....
' They slink along with bars of gold
　　　Or gems in either hand
　　　And plunge them deeply out of sight
　　　Beneath the shifting sand.'

DELIA. How simply glorious! Was that all?

SIMON. Yes.

MIKE. He said he hadn't time to make up any more, but he was certain it would pay us to give this place a rummage.

DELIA. If he said that, I'll bet it will. Let's start.

(They all get up.)

SIMON. Yes, come on, Delia, we'll search upstairs and they can do the outhouse and down here.

PETE. I thought I was running this show.

MIKE. You are—and anyway there isn't an upstairs.

DELIA. If it's buried under our feet, the best way to find it is to chuck down a lot of water and dig up where it runs into.

PETE. That's a wizard idea.

MIKE. Aye, the wench is not such a numb-skull as her looks disclaim, but where's the water coming from?

SIMON. Perhaps the sea would spare us a drop.

PETE. One more crack out of you ....

MIKE. No good, wash it out. We haven't a bucket.

DELIA. Then we must think of another way.

(They screw up their faces and ponder.)

PETE. I've got it! A mine detector. They're absolutely smashing. Just after the war they used them all over these sand dunes.

SIMON. But it wasn't a mine the pirates were supposed to have buried, was it?

PETE. No, you great boot, but gold's a metal, isn't it? And they detect one sort as easily as another.

SIMON. Oh, all right, then, let's have one.

DELIA. Where do we get it?

PETE. Borrow it from some soldiers, of course.

MIKE. I should have thought any fool would have known that.

DELIA. There aren't any nearer than Plymouth.

MIKE. But that's forty miles away!

PETE. Yes.

SIMON. It looks to me as if the mine detector is out.

MIKE. [scathingly]. It would.

PETE. Never mind, we'll easily think of something else.

SIMON. It isn't any good.

PETE. Why not?

SIMON. Because if they used mine detectors round here, it's ten to one they found the treasure and stuck to it.

MIKE. Gosh.

SIMON. So we may as well go prawning after all.

(Delia moves to the window.)

PETE. Now look here ....

DELIA. [ducking]. Look out! Somebody's coming.

(Pete takes a furtive glance through the window, nods, and beckons to the others, who line up along the back wall so that, when the door opens, they will be hidden from anyone who comes in. After a breathless silence, the door creaks open, revealing Albert on all-fours. He has started to creep into the room when Willie, another and even more dreadful small boy, appears. Willie, who carries a wooden spade and a bucket and who is licking a lollipop, suffers from a terrible lisp.)

WILLIE. I thee you.

ALBERT. [jumping]. Silly great fool! Startling anyone like that.

WILLIE. Only babyth play bearth.

ALBERT. I wasn't playing bears, I didn't want to be seen that's all.

WILLIE. [taking a lick at his lollipop]. Oh.

ALBERT. I fort you'd gone rabbiting with Uncle Sydney.

WILLIE. I did, but it wathn't any uth. Thumbody had taken away the wire noothes.

(Delia nudges Simon and nods significantly.)

ALBERT. Well, he didn't 'ave no right to catch rabbits anyway.

WILLIE. He ithn't 'alf wild and tho am I. 'e promithed I should break their neckth if he caught any.

(Delia looks revengeful. Willie drops his lollipop on the floor.)

WILLIE. Aou!

ALBERT. Shut up, letting everybody know where we are.

WILLIE. I dropped my lollipop and ith all thandy.

(He doesn't even bother to pick it up.)

ALBERT. Serve you right for letting go of it.

(He crawls into the room, followed by Willie, then, to their dismay, the door is slammed behind them and they see the pirate band.)

WILLIE. Good heaventh! Thweepth! [sweeps].

(He makes a dash for the door, but Pete puts his back against it and stands there with folded arms. Albert darts towards the window, but Mike gets there first and holds him off with a pointed cutlass.)

ALBERT. Aunti Mor—erd, 'elp! Uncle Sydney!

MIKE. Silence, dog, or I'll spit you as I would a capon.

PETE. Mount guard over the knaves, good Simon, while we put them to the question.

DELIA. [producing a wire noose from her pocket]. Let's tie them together with a rabbit noose. I kept one to show Uncle Reggie.

(Continued on page 268)

A COTTAGE BY THE SEA

How to make set and costumes for 'The Seekers'

Fix clothes lines from wall to wall of your room leaving some space for 'backstage' passage on three sides, forming an oblong stage in half of room. Side and back ropes will hold brown paper walls weighted with bricks as shown in picture. The fourth clothes line is to hold the two sheets which will make ceiling of hut. If you have a screen available which you could cover with paper painted blue with a yellow edge of sand on bottom to form background to hut, it will make it look very real, but it is not absolutely necessary. In the left wall an irregular square is cut for a window. The broken frame is either painted brown or covered with veneer paper and fastened to the top corner of the window with a nail driven into a broomstick. Behind the paper wall the top of which is fastened to the clothes line, the back wall has another unevenly-shaped opening for a door but here the frame has to be reinforced with cardboard. Frame and door can be painted or covered with veneer paper. The door works on four wire loops for hinges. Behind this door you need another bit of wall large enough to cover backstage view from all points of the audience and set up about one yard from the door. This represents the 'outhouse'. This wall can be held straight by two chairs behind it. You cut another opening into right-hand wall but not the way you did window and door. Mark the size of the fireplace then cut along centre and top in T shape, fold back flaps to form sides of fireplace, put cardboard mantelpiece on them. The grate must be built separately of strong cardboard and be glued to back of wall. It has to be higher than the fireplace-opening to look like a chimney. Black grate-polish completes the illusion. The walls need shading in grey paint along corners and where they have peeled, and along the bottom to show damp patches. The bricks are painted in red with a large flat brush. Any greengrocer will let you have orange and veg. boxes or even a herring barrel. This increases the authenticity of a sea shore scene by its smell,

but there may be objections. Clean sand for the bottom of the back door may be obtained from dealers in building materials or from a kind-hearted foreman on any building site in your neighbourhood.

If you have a gramophone, or can borrow one, play a selection of sea shanties, or something from 'The Pirates of Penzance' by Gilbert and Sullivan while your audience assembles. This will cover the bumps and whispers which happen behind the scenes at the last minute, and keep the audience distracted if you should be a bit late in starting.

G.F.B.

Costumes:

RED PETE, gumboots turned inside out on top, with red crêpe paper or painted cardboard flap covering it, fastened to leg with elastic. Red crêpe paper sash round his waist; sword cut out of stiff board pasted with silver metal paper. Red scarf on his head; eye patch made of black felt and fastened with black elastic. A red shirt if possible.

BLACK MIKE, cut useless old pair of socks at ankles to make leggings, paint yellow stripes on them. Get one of your father's old shirts and tuck it half-way under the royal blue crêpe paper waistband. If sleeves are too long, make a seam on upper arm, leave cuffs open. A yellow scarf on his head, brass curtain rings hung on his ears and a silver-papered knife complete the costume.

SIMON THE SCOURGE, an orange scarf on his head, a green sash round his waist and a gold-covered dagger are his outfit to go with a neat white shirt and grey trousers; glasses.

MEG THE TERROR, any old summer clothes.

ALBERT, the more worn and clumsy the garb the better.

WILLIE, bloomers and T shirt, wooden spade, bucket and lollipop.

(continued from page 266)

WILLIE. Aou! Thath my Uncle Thyney'th and you thtole it!

DELIA. Bloodthirsty little beast you, wanting to break their necks!

SIMON. [pointing towards the fireplace]. Stand over there, you chaps.

(They move to the fireplace and stand side by side.)

PETE. They aren't chaps they're knaves.

MIKE. Arrant knaves who would swing from a yard-arm if they had their deserts.

PETE. They will yet if they fail to speak the truth.

WILLIE. Barmy, thath what they are, all of them.

PETE. Silence! [to Albert]. Now rascal, what business brought you hither?

ALBERT. We come on a charrybong with our uncle and auntie.

MIKE. To do what, villain?

WILLIE. Have a picnic by the thea.

MIKE. Then what are you doing with that spade?

WILLIE. I been digging carthleth with it.

PETE. Castles foresooth!

ALBERT. That's right, but the sea washed them away.

WILLIE. And my thtarfith with them.

SIMON. His what?

DELIA. Starfish.

WILLIE. I wath going to dry it out in the thun.

DELIA. I'd like to dry you out in the sun.

PETE. What think you, Black Michael? Are they as simple as they would have us believe? Or shall we test their inveracity with a turn of the thumbscrew?

MIKE. [slapping his pocket]. A plague on it, I left my thumbscrew on the bedroom mantelpiece.

SIMON. Look here, they're horrible specimens, let's tell them to buzz off.

MIKE. To raise the alarm and have the King's men and every coastguard in the neighbourhood at our heels?

DELIA. But we can't get on with anything while they're about.

MIKE. True, but if we set them free they will be the first ever to escape from Red Pete and Black Michael with whole skins.

WILLIE. Don't arf talk thilly, don't they?

PETE. Put a sock in it. [to Mike]. Then how say you messmate, shall we turn them loose?

MIKE. Aye, for I would not blunt my cutlass on such a pair of simps.

ALBERT. Simps yourselves.

PETE. One more back answer and you'll be for it. Now scram.

ALBERT. We don't want to.

DELIA. Want to or not, you jolly well will.

ALBERT. We can't—not yet.

WILLIE. Not till we got what we come for we can't.

DELIA. [excitedly]. Do you hear that?

MIKE. We heard.

PETE. So the rascals were lying to us after all.

SIMON. [amiably]. What did you come for, chaps?

ALBERT. [nudging Willie]. Nuthin'.

WILLIE. Nuffin'.

PETE. They heard of the treasure and sought to steal a march on us. This needs heavy ponderment. [He beckons to Mike and Delia and the three go into a whispering huddle.] I agree. I agree. Take them to the outhouse, good Simon, and mount close guard over them while we ransack the joint.

WILLIE. [wails]. Nooooooo!

ALBERT. I don't want to go into no out'ouse.

SIMON. Cut the squawking, chaps, the sooner you're in, the sooner you'll be out, and I can go prawning.

(While speaking, he breaks a bit of chocolate in half. Both Albert and Willie open their mouths wide to yell:)

ALBERT. Autie Mor-erd!

WILLIE. Hel-up!

(Simon thrusts a bit of chocolate into each of their open mouths and seizes them.)

SIMON. Bite on that and shut up. Come on.

(He runs the pair of them out, hooking the door shut with one of his feet.)

DELIA. Ready, steady, go!

(She, Mike and Pete start a wild search, rolling over the barrels and one of the two boxes, peeping into the cupboard and hammering on walls and floor.)

MIKE. Swift, but leave no stone unturned. [to Pete]. Look out with that sand, you idiot, I don't want an eyeful.

DELIA. Rip up the floorboards, Black Michael. Belike it lies beneath.

PETE. Tear down the walls.

MIKE. Let's to the schooner for a barrel of gunpowder and split the place wide open.

DELIA. I know the treasure's nigh by the pricking in my thumbs.

PETE. Ow! I've got a splinter in one of mine.

MIKE. It'll have to be gunpowder, me hearties, naught else will serve.

DELIA. [quoting]. 'Sink me the ship, master gunner,
Sink her, split her in twain,
Better to fall into the hands of . . . .'

(Enter Simon looking sheepish.)

SIMON. I say, you know those two varlets—well, they gave me the slip.

MIKE. You absolute rotter!

PETE. You did it on purpose.

SIMON. I didn't honestly. I shut 'em in the outhouse, but didn't notice a hole at the other end of it which they got out by. Have you found it yet?

MIKE. Would we still be looking for it if we had?

SIMON. Have you looked under these boxes?

(As he asks he moves the box which has not yet been moved.)

(Continued on page 280)

'DOES MOTHER KNOW?'

by Klaxon

Asked by his Aunt Rose to call on her budgerigars when he next visits the Zoo, Lousy does so. The result is surprising, but highly satisfactory, even to Mr. Manders.

IT WAS NOT USUAL to see all the members of Form IVb on a Paddington platform except at the beginning and end of term, but it happened that several of the School Governors were Fellows of the Zoo, and had presented tickets to the Headmaster.

As a cricket match had been scratched because the opposing eleven were in quarantine and as Mr. Manders, too, had a free Saturday and as it was nearly the end of the summer term, the Head had, for once, relaxed his rule about expeditions in term time.

For once, too, Lousy was more popular than Lailey, who was sulking over being taken for what he described as a ' kid's outing' instead of being allowed to practise at the nets.

Lousy's father was a Fellow too, the boy knew the Zoo well and was friendly with many of the keepers. He had a spare wad of pale green tickets in his pocket, and he carried a string-bag full of locust beans (for giraffe feeding), raisins and nuts (for birds), and a tin of dog meat. All these things had been sent from home. His sponge-bag (also in the string-bag, and Mr. Manders did not know this), was stuffed with herring-heads—the result of scrounging in the school refuse bins after Friday's fish supper.

All the way up in the carriage, which (by accident) he and they shared with Mr. Manders, his co-mates had been pestering him with requests.

' I say, Lousy—I mean Knightshead, if there is a chance of going behind and seeing those tiger cubs, bags I to come with you.'

And—

' Lou—I mean Knightshead, let me come with you to see the tarsiers. . . . No, *I* asked first. . . . I say, Sir, d'you know Lou—I mean Knightshead says tarsiers can jump nine foot from a sit-still, and we're descended from them, and they've got a special sort of grooming-claw on their front paws so that they can comb their own hair, Sir. It shows how we've sort of gone back, doesn't it? I mean we've to have proper combs, Sir.'

Of course, Mr. Manders had not been able to resist the temptation of explaining that since Knightshead's hair was in such need of combing, he must be in direct descent from some much lower form of animal life than tarsiers.

Only Lailey had laughed: the others were all seeking Lousy's company, and Bravington Minor took up the tale—

' D'you know, Sir, one of Lou—I mean Knightshead's ancestors or uncles or something had a tame leopard somewhere out East in a planter's hut or somewhere, and it wasn't allowed on his bed. And one evening he came

in and he found the leopard or panther or whatever it was on his bed, and he took it by the scruff of the neck and slapped it hard three times, and it gave him a frightful sort of look, Sir, and sloped off into the jungle, and then, and THEN, Sir, the bloke, I mean Lousy's ancestor saw his own panther lying good as gold in its own corner. Then he turned bright pea-green, the chap, I mean, Sir, not the panther—Lousy's uncle—and was frightfully sick all over everything to think what could have happened to him. That's right, isn't it Knightshead? Sick all over everything! '

Lousy had replied monosyllabically—' Leopard.'

Mr. Manders had commented, ' A most unpleasing story.'

' Yes, Sir, but it might show that Knightshead's got a way with leopards, I mean hereditaments and that sort of thing, so bags I, if he has.'

It was then that Lousy, knowing he would be in need of future peace, had muttered, ' S'matter of fact I'm more interested in budgerigars now. My aunt's got some—at the Zoo, I mean. One says, " Does Mother know? ".'

Lailey had laughed loudly, and Mr. Manders more nastily. The latter had added, ' I congratulate you, Knightshead, on a neat escape. It is a pity to boast. Budgerigars are safer than leopards. I believe their inflicted bites are not particularly savage—at least in comparison with those of leopards.'

' Yes, Sir. My aunt's ones ate wallpaper. I mean they stripped it off when she let them loose. I expect it was the paste, Sir, like Friday's pudding only we don't—like it I mean, Sir.'

So here they all were—Form IVb, complete with Mr. Manders on a Paddington platform. Half an hour later, they passed through the turnstile of the Zoo's main entrance, and their way took them by the pelicans' enclosure.

Lousy was brooding in his usual melancholy-seeming fashion. There were several things he wanted to do, to visit the tiger cubs, last time he had seen these they had been kittenish: now, at six months old, they would be the size of bull-terriers—pads and claws would need watching. He might not, unless he were alone, be allowed into their wire enclosure behind the Big Cat Houses. He would not, anyway, be allowed unless his keeper friend, who knew his father, was there. He wanted to see Peggy, the pigmy hippo, who might be persuaded to lumber out of the water and open her vast jaws for locust beans. Peggy *looked* as though she were made of soft, cold indiarubber, but the black, shiny rolls about her shoulders were warm to the touch and as hard as truncheons. Lousy wanted to fondle (if one may use such a word about such an unpettable creature) her again. The feeling of those dark, rubbery folds made a kind of secret between him and Peggy. She was temperamental, too, disliking the sound of passing aeroplanes.

Then there were the zebras, sleek, well coupled, fond of sugar, and sharing with horses that mysterious love of warm, human breath being blown into their nostrils. There were the deer, some tit tupping on light and delicate hoofs, with their soft, wild eyes, and their shyness. But, how happy they were, when human fingers found the scratching place between and behind the horns and before and behind the ears.

Yes, he wanted to see all these creatures, but he wanted to see them alone because the shrill voices and violent movements of his co-mates would not be likely to give even a captive animal confidence. Besides, the others had no patience; they would run, yelping, from enclosure to enclosure in an attempt to see as much as possible of everything which meant they would see nothing of anything. But before he could begin to enjoy himself in his own way he must visit the budgerigars that had been presented to the Zoo by his Aunt Rose, who had gone to live in Scotland.

Lousy happened to be fond of his aunt. She had written only a few days ago, begging him to visit the birds next time he went to the Zoo, and to send her news of them.

By now they had reached the bears, who were sitting behind their bars, and extending pleading paws for the pieces of stale bread that had been stowed away in pockets after breakfast.

Lailey, the school's best bowler, was showing off a bit. Every scrap of bread he hurled went into a waiting jaw or paw. Mr. Manders was being reproached by other bears as his bread hit the bars and bounced backwards.

'Bad luck, Sir!' yelled Lailey, when he had emptied his own pockets. 'Oh bad luck!' and 'You nearly got it that time, Sir: it was awfully *near*. If you'll lend me your stick, I think I could scoop that bit back.'

This commentary did not improve Mr. Manders's temper, and in answer to cries of—'Can we see the lions, now Sir? . . . Oh, no, the wolves. . . . We ought to see the rhinos, Sir. . . . But what about the sea lions?' He said, 'Knightshead has expressed a wish to look at budgerigars. Let us make his day a happy one. Lead us to the Parrot House, please, Knightshead.'

Lousy led the way gloomily.

Now, as Zoo visitors know, a long line of perches runs down the middle of one of the Parrot Houses. Chained to these perches are the macaws. Some are as harmless as butterflies, but a notice warns visitors that if they handle them they must do so at their own risk.

A small, mild-looking, elderly woman was playing with a splendid blue-and-yellow macaw. She gripped his perch and the bird came sidling along her arm, appeared to whisper in her ear and then rubbed his savage beak against her cheek.

'Gosh!' whispered Bravington Minor, 'Gosh! And it looks as fierce as an eagle!'

It happened that only a few days before Bravington Minor had made what Mr. Manders called 'an exhibition of himself' over a large spider that had mounted guard over his ink-well. He could not help being afraid of spiders: a hornet would not have worried him half so much. Mr. Manders had not been very merciful and the form (with the exception of Lousy, who had reminded everybody that Lord Roberts was 'scared of cats, but that didn't stop him from winning wars, did it, Sir? And a

cat's only got *four* legs. I think it's the legs that count, Sir, over spiders') had jeered.

So now, Bravington Minor was anxious to prove himself and, looking a little green about the gills and pinched about the nose, strode down to the far end of the Parrot House where there was another blue-and-yellow macaw that was simply begging for trouble.

Lousy did not notice all this for he had found, in a cage by the door, his Aunt Rose's golden budgerigar, Jimmy. Sharing a perch was Jimmy's wife, Jane. As a rule, only the lone budgerigar talks, but Jimmy had been brought up alone (Jane had come later) and Lousy soon found that the bird had not forgotten its repertoire though it needed a certain amount of reminding. At the end of five minutes of this reminding, it enquired huskily, 'Does Mother know?' and added, 'Don't tell Ma.'

Lousy decided he had done all that he need do for his Aunt Rose. He glanced round the Parrot House, and saw that the whole of Form IVb was clustered together at the far end of the building. This was his chance—he could nip out through the swing doors and visit—the tiger cubs?—the deer?—Peggy? Which should it be? While he stood wondering, and swinging his string-bag, the smell of yesterday's herrings revived other memories. Yes, his sponge-bag was leaking through the meshes of the outer bag. He went down on his knees and began to repack.

He was trying to decide between the tiger cubs and Peggy when the voices of Form IVb were raised in tumult. There was nothing very new about that, and the noise did not disturb Lousy. Although his reports mentioned, and very often too, that he 'lacked concentration' the reports erred. When he did not concentrate on Latin or French, he was concentrating hard on his own private affairs. Nobody can concentrate thoroughly on more than one thing at a time.

So Lousy did not notice the rushing of feet or the clearance of his end of the Parrot House. Nor did he know that Bravington Minor, having done the bravest deed of his life, was now proving the fact that though you may lead a horse to the water you cannot make him drink. In other words, Bravington Minor was finding out that though it is easy enough to lure a macaw on to an outstretched arm it is not so easy to get him off again. The macaw was heavy. He may not have cared for his new perch's hair or the set of his ears, or he may have taken a great fancy to him. Bravington Minor was trying to find out, and he was not enjoying himself.

Lousy, having coaxed the herring's head back into its retreat, and having decided to visit Peggy first, was just going to get up, when suddenly he noticed legs in grubby grey flannel trousers, and heard the satisfactory sound of good wire-cutters at work. The owner of the legs and the flannels was snipping the wires of the cage that held Aunt Rose's yellow budgerigars. He did not look quite like a keeper, though he wore a dark-blue peaked cap that might once have belonged to a Zoo official or a railway porter.

It was odd that he should be using wire-cutters, but perhaps something had gone wrong with the padlock.

A macaw, from a nearby perch, screamed, 'Kiss me, Charlie!'

Bravington Minor, from the far end of the Parrot House, gave a despairing yell.

Then, just as Mr. Manders, shouting, 'Keeper! Keeper!' came hurrying past the macaws, the strange man dropped the wire-cutters, and went charging out of the building by way of the swing door.

Lousy, who had been knocked to his knees again just

as he was rising from them, picked up the cutters, righted himself, and handed the implements to Mr. Manders, who took them automatically.

'Bravington Minor's been bitten,' he said, 'Don't stand gaping there, boy. Find a keeper. Can't think where the fellows have got to.'

Just then, a keeper came in through the opposite entrance, and Lousy went out.

A backward glance through the plate-glass window of the door showed him that the man was talking to Mr. Manders. There could be no need of two keepers. It would be better to see what was happening to his Aunt Rose's budgerigars.

He caught up with the stranger just outside the brown bears' enclosure at the foot of the steps leading to the Mappin Terraces. The man's hands were in his jacket pocket and Lousy guessed that he was holding the birds there.

It was all very peculiar. The peaked cap gave the man an air of rather random authority. It was possible that he was moving the birds to an aviary in another part of the grounds. Or perhaps he was continuing their education. Or could Aunt Rose have decided that she wanted her pets back?

Lousy decided to ask. He pushed his way between a go-cart and two children, and caught up with the man.

'I say,' he began, 'do you happen to know my Aunt Rose, I mean Mrs.—'

'Haven't the pleasure,' replied the man, 'Aunt Polly's the one I cottons on to.'

'I haven't got an Aunt Polly!' Lousy found he was addressing a surprised-looking old gentleman, and he pushed his way towards the crowd now surging down from the Mappin Terraces.

'You see,' he said, having found the man again, 'Aunt Rose asked me to find out about Jimmy and Jane. It's all right, she sort of put me in charge of them, so if you're moving them or—'

The man scowled down at him: 'You go and chase yourself—you and your Aunt Rose!'

It was not a polite answer, but Lousy was slow to anger. He remembered a maxim of his father's—'If you have any authority show it at once—*always*, and don't waste time in arguing.'

Lousy had no authority he could *show*, but—

'I know I may seem a sort of stranger,' he said politely, 'but I can prove I know Jimmy and Jane if you'll just sort of free their heads so that they can listen. Jimmy might answer back.'

He laid a hand on the man's arm, and spoke in loud imitation of budgerigar voices—'Does Mother know? Don't tell Ma! Don't tell Ma!'

Now it is difficult with hands in pockets, especially when each hand is grasping a bird, to shake off another hand.

The man could only shake himself, and scowl down at Lousy. An interested crowd was collecting, but the boy was less self-conscious than the man.

'Don't tell Ma! Don't tell Ma! Don't tell Ma!' screeched Lousy.

'Shame!' shrilled a woman in the crowd, 'big hulking brute and a poor little chap like that. Ought to be ashamed of himself.'

'Don't tell Ma! Don't tell Ma!' begged Lousy of the budgerigar in the man's right-hand-pocket.

'Now then, what's the trouble, Sonny?' A tall man edged through the crowd, patted Lousy's head, and added, 'You needn't be afraid to tell me.'

The crowd, now many layers thick, closed in round the three of them.

'Shame!' repeated the woman, and several keepers drew near.

But more helpful to Lousy than many keepers was the sight of his father's old friend, Mr. Lithgoe, an ex-Curator who was one of the very big noises of the Zoo.

'It's Lou' Knightshead, isn't it? What's up?'

'It's a great big bully of a man tormentin' a little boy, and the kid's scared!' announced the woman.

'It's only Aunt Rose's budgerigars, Sir,' explained Lousy, 'I was sort of put in charge of them, and this man didn't seem to believe that I knew them. So I was sort of trying to show him. He was moving them from the parrot house. . . . Oh!' Lousy turned apologetically to the man at his side, 'You dropped your wire-cutters. They'll be all right. Mr. Manders has them.'

Whistles blew, a couple of keepers stepped forward, and the crowd grew thicker.

Then the man with the budgerigars made his error.

'I know it's against regulations to bring pets into the Zoo, Sir,' he whined, 'but these two as I brought seemed pinin' for a sight o' their own kind, and bird-lover as I am, Sir, I couldn't resist yoomerin' 'em. Had 'em from the egg, Sir. 'Atched out in Pimlico they was, Sir. I've always been a bird-lover same as you, Sir.'

'We'll discuss bird-loving in the Parrot House, shall we?' suggested Mr. Lithgoe. 'Yes, bring him along, Jones.'

*   *   *

There were keepers in the Parrot House as well, and there was a Plain Clothes Policeman too, AND there was Mr. Manders.

When a man, even a Preparatory Schoolmaster, is found beside an empty and damaged cage, and when he has wire-cutters in his hand, and when he appears distraught, suspicions are likely to be formed. They *had* been formed, and now Mr. Manders was even more distraught.

Lousy was kind about him to Mr. Lithgoe.

'He needed a keeper, Sir, and I'd have got one for him, but then he had one so I sort of went away to look after Aunt Rose's budgerigars, Sir.'

After that nearly everybody was made happy, except the man who had stolen the budgerigars. It turned out that he was one of many who, since birds and tortoises and small rodents had become more valuable, turned dishonest moneys by adding to the stocks of pet-shops.

Mr. Manders, though ruffled, was soothed by being taken to lunch in the Fellows' restaurant by Mr. Lithgoe. Lousy went too, and the presence of his form master did not affect his appetite, for the iced melon and roast chicken was followed by meringues WITH ice cream.

Bravington Minor, returned from the First Aid Room, felt that a Macaw's bite was nothing in comparison with the glory of the tale he had to tell, over and over again, while lunching with the other members of Form IVb.

In a new cage, Jimmy asked Jane, 'Does Mother know?' and then, nestling against her golden feathers, pleaded, 'Don't tell Ma!'

By this time, Lousy, now provided with several chits of introduction from Mr. Lithgoe to keepers, was behind the scenes with the tiger cubs. Their hard bodies rubbed against his legs, their soft muzzles nosed him, and their undomestic scent made the boy happy. He rubbed the coats that were harsher than those of dogs, and dense as ferrets' fur, but without that sticky quality, and then sniffed his palms contentedly. With any luck, he might be able to dodge washing for a couple of days. He wondered if the school cat would scent tiger.

ABOUT LIKING POETRY

by

Bernard Fergusson

WHO DOESN'T LIKE poetry, and why not? I was taught to like poetry as a small boy, and I was very surprised when I went to school to find how few other boys of my own age cared for it. However, I went on reading it and liking it and learning a lot of it by heart; till now if I am driving a car or going for a long walk I can repeat poetry to myself for hours and hours.

But a lot of people don't care for it, and I often wonder why not: because a few centuries ago, when there were no cinemas and few books, everybody enjoyed long tales in verse, or lyrical poems. When did it go out of fashion? Only a few years ago somebody said to me that So-and-So was an odd chap; and when I asked why, I was told that he read poetry. I had the great satisfaction of saying in reply: 'Does he? Well, I write it.' So I did, though to my great grief I seem to be losing the knack.

The first poem that I distinctly remember enjoying was Tennyson's *Ballad of the Revenge*. I used to get people to read it aloud to me, or I would read it aloud to myself. Even now, when I know so very much more poetry, I still know very little that conjures up for me a more wonderful and vivid picture of a great sea-battle, with the palm-trees and the snowy line of breakers upon the beaches in the background, and the puffs of smoke billowing out from the cannon of the tall Spanish ships. I think that, to exercise its full spell, all poetry should be read aloud, or at least mouthed, unless one is very practised at it; just as only a really good musician can get a really good impression of a piece of music by merely looking at the score. I defy anybody to read the 'Revenge' aloud (booming a little bit, perhaps, and really trying to get the best out of it) without being moved at all. If it doesn't move you at all, then you are one of those very unlucky people who will have to go through life missing one of the pleasantest things that it has to offer.

It is often comforting to have poetry as your companion. Lord Wavell has said that once, during a crisis of battle, he was flying up to the front in a Wellington bomber; he had a lot to be anxious about, for things were going badly wrong; and he happened to find in a newspaper a poem which he didn't know. He was able to take his mind off his worries by committing it to memory. I can think of several experiences like that which have happened to me.

Once I had a very difficult decision to make. With over a hundred men, I was surrounded by the enemy, who were closing in on us. One half of my mind was advising me to sit still, hoping for the best; the other half was telling me to be bold and break out. While I was turning the problem over and over between the two halves of my mind, I suddenly remembered some verses by a great Scottish soldier, the Marquis of Montrose, who fought for King Charles against the Parliament in the Civil War; my great-great-great-great-great-great-great-grandfather commanded a troop of horses under him: —

He either fears his fate too much
Or his deserts are small,
Who dares not put it to the touch
To win or lose it all.

So then I thought that Montrose would have done the bold thing, and that what was good enough for Montrose was good enough for me; so we put it to the touch, and most of us got through.

Another time, when a great friend of mine had just been killed, and we were all very tired and hungry, and rather frightened and dispirited, I remembered some lines taught me by a master at school: —

Though much is taken, much abides;
and though
We are not now that strength which
in old time
Moved Earth and Heaven, that which
we are, we are :
One equal temper of heroic hearts,
Made weak by time and fate, but
strong in will
To strive, to seek, to find, and not to
yield.

We didn't feel in the least heroic, but remembering these lines cheered me up anyway. I repeated them to one of my companions, but all he said was: 'I never did like poetry!' I felt rather snubbed, but even more sorry for him, because he couldn't share the encouragement which had come my way.

I didn't know then, but I discovered later, that I am not the only man who has suddenly remembered those lines many miles out in the blue at a moment when he needed comfort. When the bodies of Captain Scott and his companions were discovered by some of his friends, somebody thought of that last line; and on the wooden cross erected over their grave far out into the Antarctic snows, were inscribed the words: 'To strive, to seek, to find and not to yield.' No doubt Lord Tennyson wrote them in a warm study, lined with books, with a fire in the fireplace and a hot bath waiting for him upstairs; but two groups of worried, weary men have been grateful to him for them.

Never let anybody persuade you that there is anything unmanly about liking poetry. Sir Philip Sidney and Sir Walter Raleigh both wrote good poetry, and Sir Philip Sidney's friends were all drawn from the poets of his day. Spenser, indeed, a far greater poet than Sidney, owed much to Sidney's advice and encouragement. A young cavalry officer called Julian Grenfell, who was killed more than 300 years after Sidney, but who has often been described as an Elizabethan in character, wrote the greatest poem called forth by the war of 1914, which will never be forgotten.

For some reason poetry is read today much more in Scotland than in England. The English are apt to laugh at what seems to them the quaint, even comic, language in which Robert Burns wrote all his good verses; but the fact remains that the English have no poet who is read, as Burns is in Scotland, by people from all walks of life and of all standards of education. From time to time I have heard many soldiers, farm-hands and others recite the whole of *Tam O'Shanter* (216 lines long) without the book; and many others of their companions hanging eagerly upon every word.

One of the great arguments among poetry-lovers is whether or not the words which make up a poem need mean anything. I have often argued that they must; yet I am not sure. I have often heard poems recited in Latin (with which I have not for many years been familiar) and poems in ancient Greek (with which I have never been familiar). Yet when such poems are recited with feeling in an attractive voice, I often find them moving. And once I heard a Turkish general reciting some Persian poetry about the spring. We were sitting with some other people not far from the foot of a high mountain on which the winter snows were melting. I could speak not more than twenty words of Turkish, he not twenty words of English; one of his officers and I could speak to each other in French. Near us a swollen river was running full to the brim with snow-water; the sun was out; buds were bursting on the trees around us; the sky above us and the sea to the south of us were a gorgeous blue; and the General suddenly said something to his staff officer, and watched me with a smile while the officer translated. 'General Fakhri Bey,' he said, 'is going to recite to you some Persian poetry about the spring.'

And he did. I don't know what it meant, though I can remember the rhythm of it now; but I do know that it was beautiful.

Much modern English poetry, on the other hand, seems to me to be beautiful neither in thought nor in sound. I have to remind myself that there are plenty of people who like it, and that I am obviously missing something in not liking it: so I am careful not to say that it is silly, but that I am sad that I am shut off from enjoying it. Yet although I am missing something, there is so much poetry, old and new, in which I can delight that I mustn't grumble.

Many of you, I am sure, enjoy poetry already. Some of you may have made up your minds that you will never like it. A good number of you may never have given it a try, so here is a word for them. I have said already that you want to try saying it aloud. Don't be afraid to give it a chance. Don't read out Tennyson's 'Revenge', for instance, as if you were reading the London Telephone Directory or the catalogue of the Army and Navy Stores—both of them excellent and useful works, but not such as to make your hair stand on end, or your flesh tingle. It is hard for me to make suggestions to you, because I don't know how to start you off, beyond the advice I have already given. Would you like James Elroy Flecker, I wonder? I like him, because he wrote about countries which I know and love—Turkey and Syria and Cyprus and Greece, and because he has managed to put into words the colour of them—the blues and whites of their seas, skies, houses and roads. Here are some instances of his sense of colour, the first a description of the Mediterranean:—

The dragon-green, the luminous, the dark, the serpent-haunted sea,
The snow-besprinkled wine of earth, the white-and-blue-flower foaming sea

or:—

I have seen old ships sail like swans asleep
Beyond the city that men still call Tyre
With leaden-aged o'er-cargoed, dipping deep,
For Famagusta, and the hidden sun
That rings black Cyprus in a lake of fire . . .

Is it necessary to know those waters to appreciate that? I used to sail in them in a little yacht, and I have seen many an old cargo-vessel with patched sails making for the sunset from Tyre and Sidon, knowing that they will get there some time tomorrow afternoon, when the hills of Cyprus will be showing black against the red of the setting sun.

Julian Grenfell, who I have already spoken of, wrote that:—

Life is colour, and warmth, and light,
And a striving evermore for these . . .

and poetry has the power of grasping life, colour, warmth, light, and setting them down for us on the printed page.

A great poet, in fact, can catch for us the central idea of an experience or a sensation, just as you, if you are skilful enough, can catch a butterfly in a butterfly net. When you have caught the butterfly, you may say of it: 'It is as lovely or lovelier than it was on the wing.' When your poet has caught the idea for you, you may say: 'I never thought of it that way, but he is plumb right. It's exactly as he says.' Good poetry must appeal to some nerve, some sympathy, which you have inside yourself; and given a chance it nearly always will.

Now, what about writing poetry? I am quite sure that some of you will have tried that; perhaps some of you are trying it now. Perhaps you might be interested in what luck I have had in writing poetry. I published my first poem nineteen years ago, and I wish now that I hadn't. Luckily I did it under another name. Since then I must have written 200, and of those I must have burnt 120 as being hopelessly bad. Of the remaining eighty, I probably kept forty for a year or two, burnt some and still have others which I hope I might one day make something of. I have, I suppose, published twenty-five or thirty (not counting frivolous verses), and of these I am only proud of three. Of those three, one took me over a year to write, what with polishing and scrapping and trying and starting again; one took a week, one half an hour. Another, which

I was fairly satisfied with, I wrote in a three-hour flight in an aeroplane in India.

The point is, with anybody who is trying to write, that you mustn't be too easily satisfied. Anybody can string rhymes together, but nobody can write a poem unless he or she is deeply moved by or about something; and even then, unless he or she is highly exceptional, it is twenty to one that the poem which results will be no good. If you are genuinely given to poetry, and think that you have a poem coming, then you will be able neither to eat nor sleep nor live normally until the poem is out of you, just as if you have a swelling in your hand due to a thorn in it, you won't be happy until the thorn has worked itself out. And even when the poem has worked itself out of your system, there is no certainty that it will be any good. But if you think that it is no good, persevere nevertheless: prod, polish, pull, pick at your poem, and it will be good practice. Finish it, put it away, bring it out months later, and consider, with a fresh approach, whether or not it might be any good if you worked on it afresh. The only judge, finally, whose judgment is worth having is somebody who doesn't know you, and who will say honestly what he thinks about it, without any regard to your feelings. Don't whatever you do take it to a friend, and ask him or her what he or she thinks of it. It isn't fair on the friend. And that applies to prose writing too.

It says in the Psalms: 'Let everything that hath breath praise the Lord.' Let everybody that has a taste for writing have a shot at it. A very few years will show whether it is fact or fancy. More people think that they have the gift than actually have it; but for all it is fun to try.

THE LOST STAR

Twilight came
calm and cool.
and a star
lay in a pool,
a beautiful
point of flame,
fallen so far
it had lost its name,
lost, lost
its heavenly name.

It trembled. O,
was it weeping
among the waving weeds,
and sleeping
shadows, and creeping
tadpoles? *Sso . . .*
sighed the reeds
to and fro,
sso . . . sso
softly, *sso . . .*

A wind crossed
that place,
it muffled and ruffled
like grey lace
the pool's face,
the grasses tossed,
the star was shuffled
away, and lost,
for ever and ever
lost, lost.

ELEANOR FARJEON

273

Fantasia

by J. A. Glossop (13.7)

Illustrated by Ann Harvey (13)

LORD JUSTICE Seron shuddered as the cold steel of a sharp oriental knife stuck in his back. His head swam and he put up his hands to balance himself, but he choked violently, his legs gave way beneath him and he collapsed to the floor.

Then, all of a sudden pain ended and everything lapsed into blackness; he seemed to be rushing at great speed through nothing but blackness.

It was an eerie sensation which lasted for about five minutes and then Lord Seron felt himself gliding on a sort of chute down which he rapidly slid to land on a nice soft cushion.

Very much dazed he began to look round him, the chute had brought him into a small room with two doors, one marked 'WAITING ROOM' and the other, 'STAGNANT ROOM'. Inside the room was a desk and several easy chairs. At the desk sat a ghostly apparition.

At first, what Lord Seron noticed did not register, but when he had woken up a little and saw the dreadful apparition at the desk he let out a bloodcurdling scream.

The apparition didn't seem surprised or angry at Lord Seron's behaviour. Apparently, he was used to people screaming at him. As soon as the first stage of utter horror had passed over, the apparition remarked coolly in a foreign tongue, that Lord Seron couldn't name but could understand perfectly, that he ought to take a look at himself.

Lord Seron followed this advice and received a nasty shock as he did so, for on seeing his legs, arms, feet and hands, found that they were of the same ghostly looking substance that the apparition's limbs were made of. He hopefully looked down his nose to see if his lovely (lovely in his eyes alone) mutton chop whiskers were still in existence. Alas! they were not.

'Now to business,' announced the apparition, interrupting Lord Seron's train of horrified thought. 'Sit down,' he added, indicating a chair.

Lord Seron rose from the cushion on which he had been deposited at the beginning and sat down in the chair indicated.

'My name's Crippen—Dr. Crippen,' the apparition continued, 'and I suppose yours is Green.' Dr. Crippen opened a large book that reposed on the desk and said after a short space of time, 'See,

you went in for poaching and petty larceny didn't you?'

'Petty larceny and poaching! ME!' Lord Seron nearly choked with anger, but he just couldn't get another word out.

'I used to be a murderer myself,' went on Dr. Crippen. 'My wife, you know. Well, I shall soon have served my penalty and be a free ghost.'

At this statement, Lord Seron decided that he was dealing with a madman and proceeded to say so with very little tact. 'Are you mad, sir? First you call me Green, and then accuse me of poaching and petty larceny!'

Crippen seemed amazed, 'Aren't you called Green?' he asked.

'Of course I'm not Mr. Green,' snapped Lord Seron, 'I am Lord Seron —Lord Justice Seron.'

'Lord Justice Seron,' repeated Crippen. 'I thought it was a bit early for Green to arrive, he's due in about five minutes. Oh well! I remember your name. Ah yes! I've got it. We started a growth in your right lung the other day, but you can't have died from that yet.'

'You mean that I'm dead!' shrieked the unhappy judge.

'I should imagine so,' remarked Crippen carelessly, 'It's not often that you arrive here when you've got a chance in a hundred of returning back to the world, but you never know with these doctors. By the way, how did you die, did you commit suicide, were you run over, or were you murdered?'

'I really don't know,' was the unhappy reply, 'I don't remember dying at all.'

'No,' said Crippen, 'they . . . .' Here he was interrupted as the telephone bell began to ring. He lifted off the receiver and said, 'Crippen speaking, Deposit No. 517.' Lord Seron could hear every word that was said. The conversation was as follows:

'Bracer speaking, intelligence department, a man called Lord Justice Seron has just been stabbed in the back by a chap called Brian Dickey. He should arrive at your deposit in about ten minutes.'

'He's already arrived,' Crippen put in drily, as he jotted down what Bracer had just told him on a piece of paper.

'Oh,' said Bracer, 'Well you'd better put him in the Stagnant room. He's most likely to die, but you never know with these accursed doctors.'

'Righto!' said Crippen. 'Where's his body at the moment?'

'In St. Mary's Hospital, Chatham.' Bye.'

'Thanks,' said Crippen, 'Goodbye.'

'Now,' said Crippen, 'you know what to do, go through that door marked

Stagnant and wait. If you hear a bell ring, come back in here and go into the waiting room; if you don't hear a bell you'll wake up to find yourself in St. Mary's Hospital, Chatham.'

As Lord Seron left the room, Goodbyes were exchanged and he found himself in a large room that was full of easy chairs, and he selected the nearest and sat down and tried to think things out. He remained in the same position for nearly half an hour and then suddenly came out of his reveries with a start— everything was disappearing in the room including his own ghostly body. Then all went black, he was conscious of a nasty throbbing pain in his back. Once again he was rushing through blackness. Suddenly, the rushing sensation ceased, he felt he was in a comfortable bed and he opened his eyes and heard a doctor say, 'He'll be all right now nurse.'

A few months later Lord Seron sat talking to his physician, and told him all about his fantastic adventure, and Dr. Hendren after a thorough examination, found the small growth mentioned in the right lung, with which he was able to deal.

Lord Seron often wonders if Deposit No. 517 is tired of waiting for him.

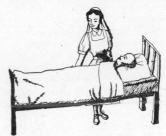

Maiden Voyage

by John C. Hart (16)

Illustrated by David Barnes (16)

THE SUMMER HOLIDAY was two weeks old. It had been a busy time for three young children. Harry, aged 16, Jack and Shirley, both aged 15, had been building a raft, and now it was complete and ready for launching.

Their father, Mr. Blair, was the senior partner in the shipbuilding firm of Blair and Pocock Ltd. They had always lived at the small town of Doulton (on the coast of England), which boasted a small harbour.

Their raft, which was to be christened *Quicksilver*, had been built mainly from spare bits of wood from their father's shipbuilding yard. That morning she was to be officially launched. They had asked their father to perform the ceremony. He had agreed, and now, using a bottle of diluted lime juice cordial in lieu of champagne, was on the point of launching her.

'I name this craft *Quicksilver*, and give her my best wishes for pleasant trips.' With that, he banged the bottle on the end which they called the bow, and she slid into the sea on the wooden rollers. Harry, the captain, then paddled her into the Doulton harbour, where,

amid much friendly jeering, he moored her.

'She's ready for this afternoon's voyage,' said Jack, 'it'll take us about an hour to get to Sinkin's Isle.'

'She's all right,' replied Harry, 'we'd better go and stock up now. Come on.'

They went off.

In the afternoon, they planned to take *Quicksilver* on her maiden voyage to Sinkin's Isle—a small uninhabited islet a mile off shore. They would land, explore, have their meal and then return. It was a perfectly calm, cloudless day. What could be more harmless or enjoyable?

Two o'clock came, and *Quicksilver* left her berth amid much cheering from the crew of an incoming cargo boat. Harry solemnly lifted a hand in salute as they passed her. They left the harbour, and *Quicksilver* was going well in a calm sea.

'How long will it take us, Harry?' asked Shirley.

''Bout an hour,' was the reply, 'we should be there at about three, and we must start back by five. That leaves us two hours to eat and explore.'

'The sea's getting choppy, Harry, and I don't like the look of those clouds over there,' observed Jack.

Harry nodded. He had been watching those clouds for quite a while. He told Jack to paddle faster. The sea was getting choppier and the sky darker. The wind was springing up.

'Do you think we ought to go back?' asked Shirley.

'Dunno! We are more than half way across now.'

'I think we'd better, you know, Harry,' said Jack.

'O.K! Here goes.' Then down came the rain. In a few moments, they were drenched to the skin. The wind got stronger and the sea rougher and Harry and Jack's progress became less and less rapid.

Suddenly a big wave lifted them right up and down. Harry, surprised, let go of his paddle. He groaned. 'That's torn it,' he said.

The driving rain had cut down visibility to a few yards. *Quicksilver* was bobbing about like a cork and her drenched crew clung miserably to her.

'When do you think it will stop?' asked Shirley.

'Soon, I hope,' responded Harry.

'Listen!' said Jack. They listened, and heard what Jack had heard. Breakers on a shore.

'Will it be the mainland or Sinkin's?' asked Harry.

'May be neither. There are other islands,' replied Jack. 'We may . . . . Hey! HOLD TIGHT!' he yelled. They did—none too soon, for a big wave tossed them on to some rocks. Another took them further up.

'Quick!' yelled Harry, 'Dash on to the beach!' Just in time, they managed it, as another terrific wave crashed on to *Quicksilver,* and she got stove in by a jagged rock.

'Look! There's a hut up there,' shouted Shirley. They followed her pointing finger and saw it. They raced pell-mell towards it. When they reached it, Harry tried the door and, to his surprise, found it unlocked. They went in and shut out the storm. The hut was about fifteen feet square and had one window. There was a table against one wall and two old chairs against another.

'Well, the first thing,' said Shirley, 'is to get dry. I'm going to light that fire.' She found a box with two matches in it. The fire was laid with wood. She was just going to light it when suddenly Harry said. 'Listen!'

Above the roar of the surf, could be heard the throbbing of a motor-boat. Then Jack, looking out of the window saw it. It was making straight for a sandy cove in the lee of the island. She beached and five burly individuals got out, moored their craft and came towards the hut.

'I don't like the looks of that crowd,' said Shirley.

'No, but where can we hide?' asked Harry. 'There's just nowhere here.'

'Oh no? What about this?' called Jack. They looked at his find—a trap-door in the floor, under the table. It was about four feet square.

'Down it, quick!' commanded Harry. They piled in and Harry closed the trap-door. None too soon, for the hut-door opened and the toughs came in. They were heard stamping and then voices came. 'Wot a noight,' said one.

'Ay,' said another, 'it be goin' ter rine orl noight as well. Forecast says . . . '

'Ee bah gum, lad, can't tha' be quiet?' asked a third, definitely hailing from the north. 'We've got business to discuss. Listen now. At two this morning, we . . . . '

'Gee, buddy,' said a nasal voice, obviously American, 'how about a glass of something while you're talking?'

'Eh, lad, ye're brainy. Go down into the passage and get a couple o' bottles of ale.'

'O.K. boss. Say, Alf, did yer leave the trap-door unbolted last week?'

'Nay lad, I'm sure I didn't.'

'Well, it is now. Here goes. Hey you! Come here!'

'Eh, Hiram, lad. What's to do?'

At the first signs of danger, Harry had crouched behind a case of beer, having sent the other two to explore the passage. His hiding-place had proved inadequate and the man Hiram had seen him. Harry decided to give up. If he ran away, the others would get caught as well, but if he let himself be taken, they might get away. So, pretending to be overcome with fear, he let Hiram take him.

'Gee, boss, it's a kid! What are yuh doin' here?'

'Bring 'im up, Hiram. Ee, lad, tha' shouldn't come 'ere. We'll have to keep you quiet for a while . . . . '

Meanwhile, Shirley and Jack had gone off down the passage. Together with Harry, they had found the toughs' cellar and something else—half a dozen packing cases. They were not able to open them, so Harry had sent them to explore. It was dark, but they felt their way along. They rounded a bend.

'Look!' said Shirley. 'Daylight—at least, twilight.'

'Yes,' said Jack, 'I . . . . listen!'

'Gee, boss it's a kid! What are yuh doin' here?'

A north country voice answered.

'Come on,' Jack commanded, 'let's get out of here.' They hurried as fast as possible from the passage, to find themselves about fifty yards from the toughs' launch.

'Listen, let's pinch their boat, and go and fetch the police. I know how to work those boats.' So Jack and Shirley sped for the boat and pushed off. Jack started up the engine with a roar and they saw the hut door open and five men piled out, and bore down to the water's edge. Jack, however, had got up speed by now and they were fast leaving the island. CRACK! A bullet whistled past in the dusk. CRACK! Jack stepped on the gas and they roared through the night towards Doulton. As they neared the lights of the town, they saw the light of another launch bearing down upon them. Jack slowed down and the new launch came alongside. A voice hailed them.

'Who are you?'

Jack explained, realising that this was the police launch.

'Oh, your parents are wondering what's happened to you. We're supposed to be looking for you—amongst other things.'

'Would one of the other things be looking for a gang of toughs?' queried Jack.

'Yes. Do you . . . . ?'

'This is their boat. This way, please!' Jack turned round and went back to the island, the police in the rear. When they neared the island, they turned off their engines and glided into the shore. There was a light in the hut. The inspector gave instructions and they advanced.

They had gone fifty yards, when there was a roar of a boat starting up.

'To the boat,' shouted Inspector Clifton. It was their own launch the crooks had used, and so the police piled into their launch with the two children. They had seen the toughs had a bundle with them and had seen it struggling. The police launch gave chase and began to overhaul the other.

CRACK! CRACK! The crooks were using their weapons, but their aim in the dark at the speed the boats were shifting was wide. The two launches were now bearing along at an alarming rate. The moon offered scant assistance to either helmsman.

'LOOK OUT!' roared Clifton to the crooks. 'Too late!' The crooks' launch hurtled straight on to Shipsea Rock. There were splintering and grounding sounds. The craft was sinking. The police launch was alongside. Detective-Sergeant Hancock leaned over and hauled Harry, bound hand and foot, on to the launch, while the others yanked three swimming crooks aboard. The other two were nowhere to be seen.

'Ee, it's a fair cop, lad,' said the Lancastrian. 'Where's Bill and Hiram? They can't swim.'

Although the launch cruised round for an hour or more, the American and Bill were not found. The crooks' boat had sunk—' Not the first wreck there, by any means,' said Clifton. The three survivors were all exhausted and offered no resistance when bracelets were produced. The launch returned to Doulton, arriving at three in the morning. The three children and the crooks went to bed, though in different kinds of bedrooms.

Next morning, Inspector Clifton paid a call at the Blair abode, and over a cup of coffee explained the previous night's happenings.

It appeared that the Lancashire lad—Rimmer—was head of a gang of thieves, whose headquarters had been discovered by the Blairs. The packing cases were filled with the results of their robberies. The police had an idea who these malefactors were, but hadn't the proof. The Inspector ended up by congratulating the children on their part of the affair. There would be a reward for the previous day's work, and he stated that he would tell their father to build them a boat for themselves with this money.

'And now,' wound up Clifton, 'I must be off. By the way, what are you going to call your new ship?'

There was a rapid, whispered conversation.

'We'll call her *Quicksilver II*,' announced Jack.

Trough Gardening

by Judith M. Deason (16)

I EXPECT many of you wish you could have a garden of your own, but probably owing to lack of space you are unable to have one. If this is your case you may be interested to know something about trough gardening, so in this article I am going to do my best to explain the way in which you should set about this hobby.

First, I think I had better tell you that the main idea of trough gardening is to grow rock gardens in troughs. Do not be alarmed and think that you have got to produce a stone trough from somewhere. If you do happen to possess one so much the better. Otherwise a wooden box will do just as well. You will probably be able to obtain one from the grocer. You should try and get a box about as deep as your kitchen sink. If you get your box from the grocer it probably won't be painted, so I think it would be an improvement if you gave it a coat of paint. If you have absolutely no outdoor space at all and you have a window box you could try and grow a rockery in that. A metal or shiny surfaced trough is no good at all, because the soil will be unable to drain. A wooden box is porous (that means it will absorb moisture) and most rough stone is porous, but I think a stone trough should have a hole in the bottom just to be on the safe side.

The next thing you will require is soil. After various attempts at growing rock plants I have discovered that they thrive best in well drained sandy soil. If you live in the town and have no garden at all, you will have to collect some soil when you go for a day's outing in the country. If the soil you get is heavy and sticky it might be worth while to experiment and mix it with some sand. Keep the soil manured then you will not have to change it for two years at least.

Now you will need some rocks. If you live in the town, these again will have to be collected when you go for a day in the country or on your holiday. You will naturally get different sorts of rock according to what part of the country you collect them from. It might be rather interesting to see how many different kinds of rock you can collect for your trough garden.

Now comes the question of collecting rock plants. They have an advantage over other plants, they can be planted at almost any time of the year, but I advise you to get them planted well before the winter sets in, if you want them to flower the following spring, as you must give them plenty of time to get accustomed to their new position. Collecting rock plants is rather similar to collecting stamps. When one collects stamps one

does not suddenly get them all at once, but one collects them a few at a time and one's collection is never complete. That is the way one collects rock plants. You might see a rock plant that you care for in Woolworths or any other shop, or a friend may give you some cuttings, and so your collection grows. Later on when your trough garden is well established you will be able to swop cuttings with a friend. Here is just one hint about planting your rock plants. When you are arranging the rocks, arrange them so they slope down towards the plant they are near. If they slope away from the plant, they will drain the water away from it, and then it will have insufficient water. Here are the names of some rock plants: Aubrietia, Alyssum and Campanula. These names might be a help to you when buying plants.

I once saw a unique miniature Chinese garden made in a trough. The plants represented trees and shrubs and little crazy paving paths made out of very small pebbles wound in and out of the rocks and plants. There was also a very small Chinese summer house and someone with clever fingers had made a miniature rustic bridge, and little Chinese figures stood in the garden. The whole thing was simply delightful. You also could have lots of fun making miniature gardens in your trough. Of course they need not be Chinese ones, for you could make all sorts of novelty gardens.

ALICE

Alice had a swing beneath the dappled
    cherry-tree,
And there, when Nurse was scolding,
    she was always sure to flee;
For the blossom was so white, and Oh!
    the blackbird sang so sweet,
And if she swung up hard she touched
    the branches with her feet.

TONI WILLIS (16).

*   *   *   *

There was a young lady named Lindsay,
Whose clothes were remarkably flimsy,
    They said, if you dress
    In a little bit less,
You will certainly die of a quinsey.

LINDSAY MACMILLAN (Age 14)

THESE ARE USEFUL KNOTS

by Richard Graves
(Author of 'A School for Adventure')

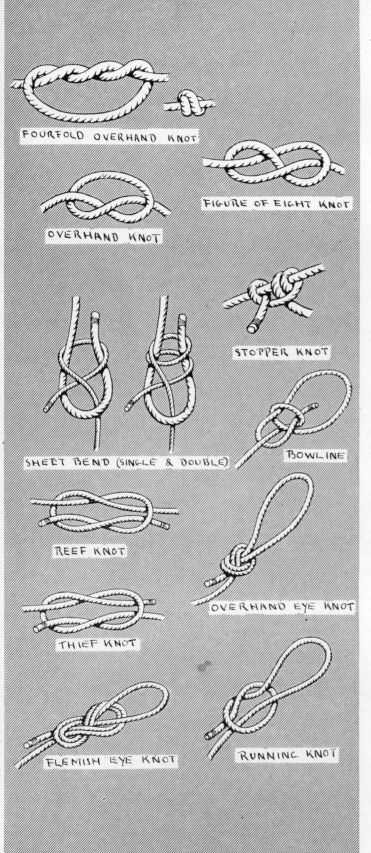

FOURFOLD OVERHAND KNOT

FIGURE OF EIGHT KNOT

OVERHAND KNOT

STOPPER KNOT

SHEET BEND (SINGLE & DOUBLE)

BOWLINE

REEF KNOT

OVERHAND EYE KNOT

THIEF KNOT

FLEMISH EYE KNOT

RUNNING KNOT

Long before man learnt to make fire he learnt to tie knots. Knots are the most ancient of all skills, and their usefulness persists to this very day. The cave man tied strips of sinew or plant fibre together to give greater length, and today you do the same with pieces of string. Cordage, whether string or rope is used daily by everyone, and because we never learn how to tie knots properly, we break our nails, and gnaw our teeth in a hopeless effort to undo that which should be so easily undone.

In the first group of knots are those which may be required to give either a better grip on a rope, or serve as a stopper at a rope's end.

Overhand knot. This will give a hand or foot grip to a thin rope for climbing, and by coiling the rope in a series of half hitches and then passing the last half hitch through all the others before a rope is thrown it will cast with these knots spaced out at regular intervals.

Fourfold overhand knot. This makes a larger knot, and gives a better grip than the simple overhand.

Figure of eight knot. This also provides a good grip on a thin rope, and has the advantage of being easy to untie.

Next are the knots which can be used for joining ropes together.

Reef knot. This knot should only be used if the two ropes are of equal thickness. Note carefully that in a reef knot the free ends are both on the same side of the knot, and that the loop encloses, and does not divide the two ropes of the ends.

The thief knot, similar to the reef knot is a trick knot. It may be used if you wish to know if someone has been tampering with your cordage. They will glance at the knot, assume it is a reef knot, and retie a reef. (Sailors used to tie up their sea chests with a thief knot, hence the name.)

Sheet bend. This knot may be used to tie together two ropes of unequal thickness. The thicker of the two ropes is 'bent' into the bight (loop) and the thinner of the two passed through, and fastened with either a single or double turn. Both are shown.

Stopper knot. This is one of the most useful of all knots. because it can be slid along the rope at will in either direction, but will not slip by itself. It is particularly useful if there is a strain on a rope, and you wish to tie another rope to the one which is taut, and so divide the weight.

Then there are knots which may be needed to make loops in your rope . . . loops that will slip, or loops that won't . . . they need different knots.

Running knot. This is the easiest of all looped knots to tie, and perfectly secure. It is easy to untie, and the loop will slip to any enlargement required. Sometimes sailors call it a 'slip' knot.

Overhand eye knot. This is simply the rope bent double, and a common overhand knot tied on the bight to form a loop.

Flemish eye knot. This is made by looping the rope, and then tying a figure eight, so that the loop is below the knot.

The Bowline. This is probably the most useful of all looped knots and certainly the easiest to untie. The loop will never slip.

Bowling on a bight. This makes a double loop, which will never slip.

You can roughly divide the Hawk moths into two groups; the rare ones, which are mostly migrant visitors to this country, and the common or indigenous ones. Here are the rare ones: the Striped Hawk, the Silver Striped, the Bedstraw, **Spurge** (shown here), and the Oleander, and the Convolvulus and Death's Head.

The rarer Hawk moths seen in Britain come under their own wing-power; and what power there is in those compact furry bodies and strong 'strutted' wings, built on similar lines to our modern fighter planes. The fore- and hind-wings of these moths are joined by a hook-and-eye arrangement, presenting a single surface of wind resistance. These foreign vagrants are, on the whole, more gaudy than our home bred Hawk moths.

The Death's Head Hawk moth is the largest of all our insects. The skull mark on the back of its head, the orange-yellow body with lines like the ribs and spine of a human skeleton, and its 'cry' when touched, created a belief that the moth was a bringer of evil tidings. But in Egypt, where they breed commonly, they are known as 'The Father of the Family' and are welcomed indoors. The moths come here singly, under cover of darkness, and soon after the females have laid their eggs on young sprouting potato plants they die and are seldom seen. Later in the season, the huge yellowish-green caterpillars, striped with violet and sprinkled with black dots, will strip all the foliage off the plants and ruin the crop.

The Eyed Hawk is the only one that can be called a 'garden' Hawk moth. Apple leaves being a favourite food-plant, the caterpillars may quite often be found in small orchards. Unless you know exactly what to look for, a branch will be almost defoliated before you notice the caterpillars, so well is their shape and size 'broken-up' by the slanting white stripes on each side of their rough greenish-white bodies. The brown and rosy tinted moth hides the striking eye-spots on its hind-wings during the day unless disturbed. It will then agitate the fore-wings up and down, alternatively covering and exposing the two realistic dark-ringed 'eyes', making it appear that they are blinking at you. The effect that this would have on a nervous bird or animal is obvious!

The Humming Bird Hawk loves to fly in the sunshine. Like a tiny exotic bird, it darts from flower to flower, hanging perfectly poised for a few seconds before a spray of honeysuckle, or a purple petunia, probing the nectaries with its exceptionally long tongue. Then quicker than the eye can discern it flashes away. They aren't really British moths at all, but come to us every spring from the warm Mediterranean. On arrival the females lay eggs on bedstraw plants and within a couple of months the caterpillars have fed up, pupated, and the next generation, born in Britain, is on the wing here. But they cannot survive our cold and damp winters, and unless there were regular migrations every spring, we shouldn't see this pretty little Hawk moth at all.

The Pine Hawk is undoubtedly rarest British Hawk moth. It has come much commoner within li memory and is now firmly establishe separate colony breeds in the area c the South-Eastern counties, while prising Dorset and Hampshire. Ther no mistaking the sombre grey n once you have found one at rest c tree-trunk, especially of a Scot's but they take some finding as they so excellently camouflaged in t surroundings.

HAWK

by L. H

PHOTOGRA

Small Elephant caterpillars may found on heathland and commons wl yellow bedstraw grows. The caterpi may be mistaken for Great Elepha but they have no 'horns' at all, c two ugly 'warts'. When the caterpi are full grown, they are blackish-br in colour, like the hide of an eleph and when they are questing for fc moving the extended front segments their bodies to and fro in the air, do not look unlike elephants' trunks.

Privet Hawk is the largest truly
sh Hawk moth. It appears on the
late in June, and haunts the
ering privet bushes for nectar and
ing enormous as it hovers with
lly vibrating wings. The females lay
eggs on privet bushes, ash, lilac or
sionally on holly bushes. The fully
caterpillar is a noble fellow; bright
e green striped with purple and
e, and the horn at the tail end is
rb—black, polished like ebony, on
upper surface and yellow beneath.

IOTHS

man, F.R.E.S.

URRAY

Convolvulus Hawk is the second
est Hawk moth, and this great grey
ant is most usually seen, or rather
d, at dusk when it comes to visit
cco flowers for nectar. It will be
ost too dark to see anything, but then
suddenly become conscious of a faint
as the moth circles round, and you
even feel a breath of wind as it
es close by to your face.
the tobacco plants are nodding in
, you been watching this Hawk
h feeding, without realising it.

The Large Elephant caterpillars feed
principally on willow-herb, and are most
likely to be found where this 'fire-weed'
grows plentifully. Clearings in woods,
and waste ground are likely places, or by
the water's edge. When small, the caterpillars are pale green with long thin
'horns' on their tails, and tiny eye-spots
close above the head. Fully grown, they
are fearsome creatures and are often
looked upon with awe by superstitious
people, especially in remote parts of
Ireland. When in repose, with the head
drawn in, the false 'eyes' on its head
become distended, and a fully grown
caterpillar seems to regard one with a
hostile stare. It is easy to understand
how ignorant people could be frightened
by this caterpillar that behaves in such a
curious way.

There are two species of **Bee Hawks**
in Britain, one has a broader border
round the outer margin of its wings than
the other, and they are named respec-
tively the Broad- and the Narrow-
bordered Bee Hawks. Both have furry
bodies not unlike a large bumble-bee and
when on the wing 'buzz' their wings
like these other large clumsy insects. The
Broad-bordered frequents woodland
glades from mid-May for a brief period
of about three weeks, when it can be
seen feeding on nectar from wild flowers,
and it is particularly fond of visiting
flowering azaleas and rhododendrons. The
females lay their eggs on honeysuckle, and
the caterpillars can be found later in the
summer on these plants that twine
amongst bushes and round tree-trunks.

If you have poplar trees in your garden
there is always a chance that you may
find a colony of **Poplar Hawk** moths
breeding during the summer months. At
rest during the daytime, on the trunk of
a tree, the Poplar Hawk can easily be
recognised by its grey colouring and
sharply 'cut away' wings, but the
beautiful rust-red patch on its hind-wings
will be hidden from view, as the fore-
wings fold over the hind pair. All these
Hawk moths have the Latin family name
of *Sphingidae*. The caterpillars assume
a characteristic attitude when not feeding,
with the front part of the body raised.
The Latin name was evolved because
there is a very definite resemblance between the caterpillar and the crouching
Sphinx in the Egyptian desert.

The Striped Hawk is the one you are
most likely to come across. Anywhere
in Southern England one may come upon
a few of these huge blackish caterpillars
with conspicuous lemon yellow stripes
down their sides, feeding on outdoor vine
fuchsia, or on common dock in un-
cultivated fields. A very good rule to
make, if you find a large Hawk moth
caterpillar with a 'horn' on its tail, and
it isn't one you are familiar with, is to
note the food-plant it is eating, and then
take it home with you and feed it in
captivity until it burrows underground to
pupate. Then keep it really warm, in
a box half filled with earth, and in a
few weeks' time a Hawk moth will
emerge and the chances are it will be a
rare one.

279

The Seekers—*continued from page 268)*

PETE. Of course we have!

SIMON. [*stooping and picking something up*]. You can't have. Here's a tanner.

MIKE. [*staring*]. It *is* a tanner.

DELIA. [*pointing*]. And look! Somebody's scraped an arrow on the floor pointing at the fireplace.

PETE. So they have.

DELIA. Try the chimney, Simon.

SIMON. Which end shall I try first?

PETE. This one, you idiot.

SIMON. All right. [*He goes down on his knees, rummages among the rubbish in the grate and finds a shilling*]. Here's a bob!

PETE. Calloo, calloo! Wealth untold! I bet there's bags more up the chimney. Put your head up, Simon.

(*Simon screws his head round and looks up the chimney.*)

SIMON. Can't see anything.

MIKE. Have a feel round inside.

SIMON. Won't it be rather dirty? [*Rather unwillingly, he puts an arm up the chimney. There is an immediate fall of soot which covers his face, followed by a good-sized parcel which bounces off it*]. Oh, pooh!

PETE. [*seeing parcel*]. Gosh, what's that?

MIKE. Lummy!

(*Pete grabs the parcel and blows the soot off it in Delia's face.*)

DELIA. Oh, you pig!

PETE. [*fingering parcel*]. It feels soft.

SIMON. [*rubbing his head*]. I don't think so.

MIKE. Open it up—go on!

(*The parcel is opened and a pile of sandwiches and slices of cake are revealed.*)

PETE. Well, of all luck!

MIKE. Grub!

PETE. And smashing fine grub, too! Fall to, my hearties, fall to.

(*They seize upon the sandwiches ravenously.*)

DELIA. Three cheers for Uncle Reggie!

MIKE. Why you don't think he put them there?

SIMON. One thing's certain—great-great-grandfather Trefusis didn't.

DELIA. He wanted us out of the way, but didn't want our treasure hunt to be for nothing.

SIMON. So he baited the trap with eighteen pence and a jolly fine lunch.

(*As they talk they are munching enthusiastically.*)

PETE. I must say we've got to hand it to Dad over this.

MIKE. Every time. [*takes a bite from another sandwich*]. Egg and sardine—numm!

PETE. Mine's ham and absolutely whizzo.

DELIA. [*tucking in*]. Lush! Don't know about the rest of you, but I'd rather have this any day than a piece of eight.

SIMON. Or nine. [*Everybody laughs. There is a distant peal of thunder*]. Hallo, there goes Pete's thrice-accursed rumbling tum.

PETE. It was thunder, you blink.

MIKE. Must be a storm brewing.

DELIA. Who cares? We've a roof over our heads. . . .

MIKE. A sumptious banquet. . . .

PETE. And as merry a party of rogues to eat it as ever slit a throat. Pipe up, messmates, and let the rafters ring. [*He beats time with a sandwich and starts to sing*]. 'Fifteen men on a dead man's chest . . . .'

THE OTHERS. [*joining in lustily*]. 'Yo-ho-ho and a bottle of rum. Drink and the devil may take the rest. Yo-ho-ho and a bottle of rum.'

(*While they are singing, Albert and Willie peep in through the window.*)

ALBERT. Aoh! They've found out where I 'id it!

WILLIE. Aou! They're eating it!

ALBERT. Oh, you filfy things! (*All heads turn towards them.*) Auntie Mor-erd! They're eatin' our dinners up.

WILLIE. Fetch Uncle Thydney!

(*They vanish.*)

PETE. Gosh!

MIKE. We've eaten their picnic!

PETE. What are we going to do?

SIMON. Go prawning.

PETE—MIKE. [*together*]. Shut up, can't you?

ALBERT. [*heard off*]. There's Uncle Sydney! Uncle Sydney!

WILLIE. [*heard off*]. Uncle Thydney, come here quick!

SIMON. On second thoughts, let's get back to the schooner ere the tide turns.

(*Led by Delia, there is a general rush for the door as lightning flashes and thunder roars.*)

THE CURTAIN FALLS

WHO? **HOW MANY?** **WHICH?** **WHY?** **WHEN?** **WHERE?**

Anybody's Guess

1. How many of the Shetland Isles are inhabited: (a) less than 5? (b) more than 5 but less than 10? (c) more than 10?

2. Are these statements true or false? (a) a serpent bites, it does not sting. (b) Florence Nightingale was a Boer war heroine. (c) Sir James Whittle was a pioneer of jet propulsion. (d) A common snail has over 200 teeth.

3. In each group lurks an 'intruder,' one who stands apart from the rest: find the intruders:—(a) Copernicus, Galileo, Herschel, Pasteur, Newton. (b) Michelangelo, Tintoretto, Inigo Jones, Christopher Wren. (c) Hazelnut, Catkin, Tomato, Poppyhead.

4. You are in the Northern Hemisphere, the position of the sun is approximately due South, your shadow points approximately due North. What is the time? (Make no allowance for 'Summer time.')

5. If you had the following four things to dispose of in one way only, would you: (a) give them to a museum? (b) eat them? (c) use insect-destroyer on them?—(a) Lobscouse, (b) Pomelo, (c) Skilly, (d) Bergamot.

6. The three EDMUNDS:— (a) Edmund —— was a great Shakespearean actor.
(b) Edmund —— wrote an allegory, and Una was one of the characters.
(c) Edmund —— had a naturalist son and a naturalist father and was a distinguished man of letters who died in 1928.

7. Whom did the winged horse Pegasus throw to his death?

8. Is it true that some snakes can swallow and digest several times daily a mammal larger than themselves?

9. Which qualities or conditions do you associate with:— (a) Croesus? (b) A church mouse? (c) A cricket? (d) A fiddle? (e) A raven? (f) Punch? (g) Uriah Heep? (h) Mrs. Gummidge? (i) a new pin?

10. Are these things animal, vegetable, or mineral? (a) a 'miller's thumb' (not a real live miller's, of course)? (b) a siskin? (c) nainsook? (d) moss-agate? (e) roseola?

11. Who wrote in a poem about:—(a) A chameleon's hump, (b) a turkey who performed a marriage ceremony, (c) buttercups and melon-flowers.

Threesomes

An example will perhaps best explain this puzzle, which is to find one word to complete three others. For instance, the word 'TEN' will make ROT into ROTTEN, HEAR into HEARTEN, and BIT into BITTEN. Now for the nine words (none of them plurals) to complete the threesomes below:

1. LONG RAIN CROSS	2. OVER IN SIDE	3. PIG WAG BOB
4. SPA HER COVE	5. CHAR PAD HEM	6. SEA NOTE PRAISE
7. FORE BLOCK HOT	8. UNDER WITH OUT	9. BACK HOME FOR

A Square with a Secret

THE SECRET contained in the following crossword puzzle, is a hidden proverb. To find the 5-word proverb, read (in this order) 2 across, 7 down, 6 down, 12 down, 10 across.

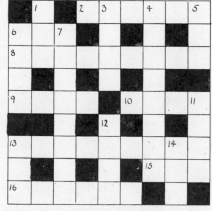

Crossword Clues

Across 2. First word of proverb. 6. Smitten with thigh, also a hedge fruit. 8. These tests do not necessarily take place in a laboratory (two words 4, 5.) 9. Every one. 10. Fifth word of proverb. 13. Kind of chant. 15. Many pairs went into this. 16. Something may be done not by accident but by . . . . . .

Down 1. Nervous affliction. 3. Preposition. 4. This place, ending in madness, contains a satin M.A. 5. Printers' measures. 6. Third word of proverb. 7. Large earthenware vessel. 11. Indispensable in kitchen. 12. Fourth word of proverb. 13. Deity. 14. Verb that is almost area.

Can You Say How Many . . .

1. Legs a spider has?

2. Hours a 25-watt lamp will take to burn one unit of electricity?

3. Holes there are in a telephone dial?

4. Wives had Henry VIII?

5. Pennies weigh an ounce?

6. Eggs you have if you take two eggs from three eggs?

7. Stamps may be added to a Postal Order?

8. Different golf clubs may be used in a match?

9. Times Dick Whittington was Lord Mayor of London?

10. Grooves there are on one side of a 10-inch gramophone record?

11. Bones there are in a giraffe's neck?

12. Bones there are in the human little toe?

13. Books there are in the Old Testament?

14. Stripes there are on an American flag?

15. Ounces of pure gold in 24 ozs of 14-carat gold?

16. Pounds in a ton?

Bookworms Will Know

1. Which Shakespearean character said: 'Deeper than did ever plummet sound, I'll drown my book.' And in which play?

2. What was the name of James Boswell's friend who published a dictionary?

3. Give the pen names of three famous Victorian sisters who were all novelists.

4. Who is famous for writing a book of nonsense?

5. In which famous books do the following characters appear: (A) Mr. Rochester; (B) The Fat Boy; (C) The White Knight; (D) Mr. Collins?

6. Who said (a) 'Many's the long night I've dreamed of cheese—toasted, mostly.' (b) 'There's nothing like eating hay when you're faint.' (c) who was made to: 'drink Lavender water tinged with pink'?

7. Which Shakespearean character spoke of finding: '. . . . books in the running brooks, sermons in stones, and good in everything'?

Double-Me-Ree

The clues furnish two words, built up from line to line.

Firsts in crayon, one in chalk,
Seconds in both march and walk,
Thirds in crown as well as chin,
Fourths in home but not in inn,
Fifths in sister and in daughter,
Both are craft upon the water.

(Answers on page 291)

BIGGLES in Arabia

ILLUSTRATED BY WILLIAM STOBBS · by Captain W. E. Johns

PART SEVEN

FOR BIGGLES AND GINGER the day passed slowly. For Ginger, still feeling the effects of the drug, it was a nightmare of heat, noise, flies, and the overpowering stench of filth. What Biggles thought about it all was a secret he kept to himself. He rarely spoke, but sat for the most part deep in thought, smoking cigarette after cigarette with the object, as he said, of keeping the flies at a distance and off-setting to a certain extent the disgusting stink.

One thing was to Ginger quite evident. Whatever Biggles was planning it was not escape. That was out of the question, for apart from the sentries, every native in the camp had foregathered at the spot. The mob surrounded the hut, talking, shouting and gesticulating, in a state of high excitement. To get through such a barrier would have been impossible. There was, as Biggles once remarked, just nothing they could do about it.

Towards evening, a caravan comprising men, women and children—presumably the slave party—formed up, and with its beasts of burden filed away towards the east, in the direction of the Red Sea. This was one of the occasions on which Biggles had something to say. 'So Ambrimos is in the racket, too. What a skunk the fellow must be. Anything for money.'

'They have at least taken some of the flies with them,' observed Ginger morosely. 'I didn't know there were so many flies in the world.'

'Where there's dirt, you'll always find flies,' answered Biggles tritely. 'The dirtiest fly of the lot is Ambrimos. He's halfway to becoming a maggot. Someone should have put a heel on him long ago.'

Silence fell.

Some time later Ginger said: 'I wonder what Bertie's up to?'

Biggles flicked the ash off his cigarette. 'Probably waiting for us at the aerodrome.'

'He may decide to look for us and drift along.'

'Why should he come here? He doesn't know we're here. Zahar didn't know where I was bound for so he couldn't tell him. If he did come, he'd only get his block knocked off. He could do nothing against this crowd.'

'Do you mean you're just going to sit here and wait for Ambrimos to bump us off when it suits him?'

'Can you think of any way of preventing it? I can't. If we went outside those savages would simply make pincushions of us. They'd ask for nothing more.'

Another silence.

'I landed you in this mess,' remarked Ginger miserably.

'Don't talk nonsense,' answered Biggles shortly. 'We came here together. We knew the risks. Things happened to go wrong, that's all. When things go wrong, to start talking about whose fault it was gets you nowhere. We'll just have to take what's coming. If I can grab a spear from one of these toughs and stick it into Ambrimos I shall be satisfied that we've done a good job, whatever happens afterwards. We can rely on Bertie to knock a hole in the dam.'

The day wore on. The sun sank below the rim of the wadi, which at once began to fill with shadows. The babble outside increased rather than diminished.

Suddenly a hush fell.

'Now what?' muttered Ginger expectantly.

'I'd say it's Ambrimos, coming to gloat,' returned Biggles.

He was right. The crowd of wild-eyed, mop-haired natives parted, and the Sultan appeared at the door of the hut. He called to Biggles and Ginger to come out.

They obeyed. 'You were wise to stay outside,' Biggles told him. 'The smell inside was quite bad enough.'

'I'm sorry, but it was the only shady place I had to offer,' purred Ambrimos, missing the sting in Biggles's remark. 'Have you thought about my proposition?'

'There was nothing to think about,' Biggles told him.

Ambrimos sighed. 'You know the alternative?'

'You told us.'

'Very well, upon your own heads be it,' came back Ambrimos, his voice hardening. 'You have meddled in my affairs and this is what happens to people who do that.'

'One day you'll learn what happens to people who do what you're thinking of doing,' answered Biggles.

Ambrimos smiled. 'Not here,' he said softly. 'The arms of you British may be long, but it does not reach as far as this.'

'Don't fool yourself,' Biggles told him grimly. 'It can reach as far as you're ever likely to get.'

The Sultan frowned. 'So even now you dare to threaten me? Very well. Stiff-necks, they call you British. I can at least find a way to loosen yours.' He made a signal to the waiting crowd and stepped back.

Some of the natives, silent now, at once closed in. Biggles and Ginger were each held firmly by half-a-dozen hands. A lane was made through the throng.

Ginger soon saw what Ambrimos intended. The man had spoken literally. In the middle of the wadi stood an ancient fig tree with many branches that spread out at right-angles from the trunk. From one of these, two ropes, each with a noose at the end, hung side by side. Below these a rough plank had been placed across two packing cases. He drew a deep breath. 'Looks as if we've had it this time,' he said softly.

Biggles did not answer.

In a curious sort of anticipatory silence the prisoners were led to the tree.

'You will excuse me if my methods seem a little old-fashioned,' mocked Ambrimos in a silky voice. But it is not often that my men get a treat of this sort. They are anxious to make the most of it and I feel that I must oblige them. Were I not here to keep order the manner of your departure from this world would, I fear, be more prolonged and more painful. Bearing that in mind, will you be so obliging as to mount the plank?'

Ginger was thinking desperately. Of all the perilous positions they had ever been in, this was the most hopeless. All along he had hoped that Biggles would do something, but now, looking around at the brutish faces that surrounded them, he realised that there was nothing that he could do. There was no hope of escape, or of rescue. Even if by some remote chance Bertie and Zahar had managed to track them, and arrived on the scene, what

'Of all the perilous positions they had been in, this was the most hopeless.'

could they do against such a mob? For the first time in his life Ginger abandoned hope. In the crimson glow of the setting sun he mounted the plank on which Biggles had already climbed, and from this elevated position gazed down at a sea of hostile faces. He looked at Biggles, sure that it was for the last time.

Biggles smiled a curious apologetic smile. 'So long, laddie,' he said. 'Sorry I brought you into this. We've had a long run and I suppose it had to happen sometime.'

A hush fell over the scene as a giant Sudanese climbed on to the plank with the apparent object of adjusting the ropes. He was reaching for the nearest when, from no great distance away, there came the crack of a rifle shot.

All heads turned in the direction of the sound. There was some muttering. Ambrimos spoke swiftly to his manager, who got up and began walking along the wadi towards the place where it narrowed into a gorge. The Sudanese was staring up the gorge, too, his attention, like the rest, distracted for the moment. Ginger saw Biggles edging slowly towards the heavy knife that the man carried in his belt; but before the movement was completed, through the sultry air there came a hail.

'Hi!' shouted a voice. 'What's going on down there?'

Ginger's eyes switched to the top of the wadi, and he was seized by an insane desire to laugh when he saw Bertie standing there, clear against the sky, in the act of adjusting his eye-glass. Zahar was with him.

'Mad as a hatter,' he heard Biggles mutter.

'What are you chaps doing?' called Bertie.

'They're hanging us,' yelled Ginger, who thought it was time that Bertie knew the truth.

'Are they, by Jove,' came back from Bertie. He pointed a threatening finger. 'Ambrimos! Stop that, you infernal scamp!' He started scrambling down the sandy bank of the wadi.

'Crazy,' murmured Biggles simply.

Every head had turned. A swelling mutter of astonished voices arose from the crowd, and those who were nearest started to run towards the intruder, with the clear object of seizing him. And in this they must have succeeded, in spite of the fact that Bertie drew his pistol and opened a brisk fire, had there not come at this juncture a further interruption, one more startling than the first.

Biggles had just snatched the knife from the Sudanese, and kicked him off the plank, when from somewhere close, though out of sight, came a tremendous explosion that soon marked its position by sending into the air a cloud of smoke, sand and rocks. Following closely upon it, before the reverberation had died away, came a low roar as if of distant thunder. An instant later there swept into sight a wall of water, a wave nearly twenty feet high that curled over at the top in a swirl of yellow foam.

For perhaps two seconds no one moved. Then a wild yell went up as every man in the wadi perceived his danger and fled for safety. It was obvious that none could reach it, for the water was travelling at the speed of a train, sinking a little as it filled the wadi from side to side.

Ginger stood still, his brain reeling from shock. In a detached sort of way he saw Biggles fling the knife at Ambrimos, who was running with the rest. Then, turning, Biggles shouted: 'The rope! Quick! Up the rope!'

Ginger recovered his senses with a rush. He realised what Biggles meant. Grabbing the rope which was to have taken his life, but was now the only means of saving it, he went up it hand over hand. He was only just in time. As it was he had to lift his legs as the crest of the wave clutched at them, and whirled away the support on which a moment before he had stood. Gasping, he managed to get a hand over the branch to which the rope had been tied. Another second and he sat astride it, staring in a dazed sort of way at a swirling yellow flood that raced below. He gazed around. The only persons in sight that he could see were Bertie and Zahar, who, being safely above the flood, had sat down to watch. Every man, and everything else in the wadi except the tree, had been swept away by the raging waters which still filled the wadi although most of its early force had been spent.

'There was more water in that reservoir than I thought,' came from Biggles, who had adopted the same posture as Ginger a couple of yards away.

Ginger looked at him somewhat blankly. He was still suffering from shock, and a curious sense of unreality at this almost miraculous escape when all seemed lost.

Biggles lit a cigarette. 'Nice work!' he called to Bertie. Bertie raised his hat in acknowledgment.

'He certainly made a beautiful mess,' remarked Ginger, finding his voice and gazing at the devastation around him.

'He'll never make a better one, or one better timed,' replied Biggles with conviction.

'What's the drill now?' asked Ginger. 'If any of these Wogs are left alive they'll be really angry.'

'I'd say most of them, if they're still alive, have something else to think about than what we're doing,' answered Biggles. 'I don't suppose any of them could swim—not that swimming would help. We shall have to stay where we are until the water subsides, anyway.'

This took about ten minutes, by which time it was nearly dark. Bertie ascertained that it was safe for them to descend by wading out through a few inches of mud and puddles.

'All right, you lads, you can stop playing monkeys,' he informed them. 'I say, what a beastly mess! Look at my feet—my only decent pair of shoes, too. Disgusting!' Biggles dropped into the mire.

'I suggest we get out of this while the going's good,' said Ginger, as he dropped with a splash beside him.

'I don't think we've much to worry about now,' returned Biggles. 'I'm not going until I've seen how much damage

has been done to the gurra plantation. Bertie, how did you get here so quickly? Did you know we were here?'

'I hadn't an idea of it,' stated Bertie. 'You told Zahar to tell me to blow up the dam. So I pushed it over. I was going to look for you afterwards. By Jove! Did my eyes pop out when I saw you standing on that beastly plank. Shook me to the wick, I can tell you.'

'Did you walk here?'

'No bally fear. I aviated hither in the Moth, at a maximum altitude of about six inches.'

'Where is it now?'

'A mile or so back. Zahar will remember the place—I hope.'

They walked together out of the mud and silt left by the flood to the dry bank of the wadi, up which they climbed without meeting anyone or hearing a sound to suggest that anybody was left in El Moab. From the top there was just enough light left to enable them to survey the scene.

The deluge had done even more damage than Ginger had supposed. In its first tremendous rush it must have carried everything before it, for the floor of the wadi had been practically swept clean. Not a building was left standing. All that remained of the huts was a quantity of planks and splintered wood scattered along the course of the flood.

The plantation could not have escaped; but Biggles was determined to make sure. He went down to examine the area where the gurra had been under cultivation. He was soon back. 'Either the plants have been washed clean out of the ground, or else they are buried under tons of silt,' he reported. 'I couldn't find any sign of them.'

What had become of Ambrimos and his mob was in some doubt. There was no time to find out. Darkness had now closed in, so anything like a real search was out of the question. As there was nothing more they could do, Biggles decided to get back to the aerodrome as quickly as possible. They were all in need of food and rest.

'I say, old boy, that poor old Moth won't carry the four of us,' Bertie pointed out.

'It will, if we don't try to get it off the floor,' argued Biggles.

'You mean, you're going to taxi all the way home?'

'Why not? The chap who owned the machine won't be needing it for a long time, I imagine. Riding is better than walking, isn't it?'

'Absolutely, old boy, absolutely,' agreed Bertie warmly.

And so, an hour later, the wild creatures of the desert saw the strange spectacle of an aircraft bumping across the moonlit wilderness with two figures sitting side by side on the centre-section, one of them an Arab whose *gumbez* fluttered like a victory flag in the slip-stream of the airscrew.

From the back seat came the sound of Bertie's voice, uplifted in a song about a bicycle made for two.

The party arrived back at aerodrome 137 at about midnight, to find L.A.C. Blakey sitting very bored, and more than a trifle peeved, on the sack of hashish near the ruins of the hangar on which he had been working.

'What's the idea?' he demanded. 'It's been no joke sitting here half the night with wild beasts howling about the place.'

Biggles laughed. 'It was only a jackal or a hyena, I imagine,' he said consolingly. 'It wouldn't hurt you.'

'Whatever they were I don't like 'em,' declared the airman. 'What have you all been up to? Left me stuck 'ere with no grub and no water while you joy-ride about this perishing no-man's land, four up in a Moth. You won't 'ave done that machine no good.'

'*Gasping, he managed to get a hand over the branch to which the rope had been tied. Another second and he
sat astride it, staring at a swirling yellow flood below.*'

'Doesn't matter—it isn't ours,' answered Biggles lightly.
'How did the job go?'

'Oh that—nothing to it. I had it all buttoned up in a
couple of hours.'

'We can get the machine out?'

'Start her up and she'll fly away.'

'That's fine! Sorry we had to leave you alone for a
bit, but we had work to do. I'll recommend you for a spot
of leave when I get back. Meanwhile we could all do
with a bite of something to eat.' Biggles went to the locker
of the now free aircraft and came back with some tins
of bully and sardines, biscuits and a bottle of water. 'We
shall have to make the best of this for the time being,' he
announced. 'Help yourselves.'

The airman produced his jack-knife and removed the
lids of the tins with a dexterity born of experience. 'How
long are we staying here?' he wanted to know.

'Only till it gets light,' Biggles told him. 'Anybody
who wants to sleep can go ahead. I'm not tired, so I'll
mount guard.'

The night passed without alarm, and at the first streak
of dawn Biggles had everyone on the move.

'What are you going to do with the Moth?' asked
Ginger.

'Leave it where it is,' answered Biggles. 'We'll take
the hashish with us, though. We'll dump it at Aden and
let the Narcotics Bureau know about it. If they want
the Moth, they can fetch it. It may have been the property
of Ambrimos, or it may not. No doubt the authorities

will be able to trace ownership, and find out the name of
the fellow who was flying it.

Biggles's machine was taxied out of the hangar in which
it had been imprisoned, and after it had been examined
for possible damage Biggles divided the party between the
two aircraft now available. He took Ginger and Zahar
with him. Bertie took Blakey. The bag of hashish was
put into Biggles's machine and after the Moth had been
wheeled into the one more or less serviceable hangar, the
two aircraft left the ground together.

Biggles did not fly straight back to Aden. Keeping low
he made a detour that took him over El Moab—or what
remained of it. The area that had been under cultivation
appeared to be washed clean to the bedrock. It seemed
that there were some survivors after all. At any rate, a
number of natives were seen in the vicinity, some rounding
up stray animals and others delving amongst the ruins.
Zahar said they were searching for loot before returning
to their homes, which was probably true. Anyway, the
fight had gone out of them, for on the arrival of the aircraft
most of them sought cover or tried to hide.

'I don't think they'll trouble anyone for some time,'
observed Biggles, as he turned away and took up a course
for Aden. 'I'd like to know what happened to Ambrimos.
He was the real villain of the piece. That man was
dangerous. He was a fool. He'd made his pile. Had he had
the wit to go straight, as I suggested to him, he could have
slept on velvet for the rest of his days. Instead of which
it rather looks as if he's going to sleep for a long time in

(*Continued on page* 291)

285

The Lions That Ran Away

by Penelope Bourn (aged 12), Horsham, Sussex.

Illustrated by Geoffrey James (12), Exeter, Devon.

'I DON'T LIKE this cage,' said Mr. Lion. 'It's too small and too cold and utterly unbearable, don't you think so, my dear?'

'Yes, I agree with you,' answered his wife, 'sometimes when those two-legged creatures come and stare at us, I feel I could eat the whole lot. Grr-rr-rr. What right have they to shut us up in these pokey, little cages, what right? What do you think about it my friends?'

'We think it is shameful,' cried the rest of the Lions, 'if only we could escape.'

Suddenly, Lenard Lion piped up with his little voice. He was the youngest of the Lions, and a month old.

'I've got an idea,' he said, 'my friend Maurice Monkey, said that last week he found a bar of his cage loose and he has been working at it ever since, and he says he thinks that tonight or soon, it might come right out, and then he could get through the bars, then he'd be able to draw back our bolt and we would be free.'

By this time, he was so excited that he was tearing round and round his cage. Mrs. Lion embraced him and called him 'My dear little piece of cheese,' and such names, while the other Lions set about making plans.

They had planned to escape at midnight, but Maurice Monkey's bar was not quite loose enough to come out that night nor the next, but the third night he worked at it again, and at six-thirty the bar came out and Maurice climbed

through and pulled back the bolt of the Lion's cage and the Lions were free.

The first thing they did, was Lenard's idea. They went and found the butcher's shop (which took half an hour), and each Lion took a piece of meat while the butcher was next door. Lenard took two of the biggest pieces he could find, and was scolded for being greedy by Mrs. Lion. Then feeling rather tired, they looked for somewhere to sleep. At last, Uncle Lion found an old barn with one or two sacks on the floor, and the Lions lay down to sleep. But Lenard could not sleep. He tossed and turned until Auntie Lion was quite tired of telling him, 'Little Lions mustn't bump their Aunties, but must lie down and go by-by.'

At last Mrs. Lion took him in hand and said that if he did not lie down and be good she would tan his behind, which she eventually did and sent him howling off to his brothers and sisters.

Although Lenard lay still after his tanning, he was not asleep and, when the other Lions were safely asleep, he crept out of the barn and set about to do a bit of exploring. It was half past seven by then, and several people were about, so Lenard walked up to talk to them, but when they saw him they screamed and ran away. Then he saw a brown and white thing with horns (Lenard knew it was a cow because one had escaped into the Zoo, and it had taken half an hour to drive it out). So he walked over to talk to it but it also ran away. Then feeling rather peckish, he looked for some more food. After a bit he found the butcher was not there, he started to eat his fill. He had just eaten all he could when the butcher came back and, seeing something stealing his meat, he picked up his broom and hit Lenard hard on the back.

If he had noticed that a LION was stealing his meat, doubtless he would have run away too, but this time it was Lenard who ran away with a tingling back. He lay down by his brothers and sisters and went to sleep.

In a few hours the other Lions woke up, and they also went to find some food, but all the houses and

shops were barricaded, and there was not a living creature (nor a dead one in fact) in sight.

At last, tired and hungry, they all returned to the Zoo, where the keepers were in such a fluster about their having escaped, that they had left the cage doors open, so they crept in and lay waiting for their breakfast.

THE POOR OLD CARTHORSE

A poor old carthorse,
Patient and strong,
Work work, work.
The whole day long.
Here comes the harvest,
Work once again,
With the jingle of harness
And the shouts of the men.

CAROLYN FLEMING (11)

The Osprey

by Jane Darlington (14.9) Sheffield, Yorks.

'WHEN IS THE NEXT train for Lancaster please?' A porter turned round. The speaker was a boy of about thirteen. He had red hair, and his cap was that of the Liverpool Grammar School.

'Six twenty, lad. Platform two.'

'Thanks,' replied the boy. 'Come on Jack.'

Tom and Jack Douglas were on their way to camp in the grounds of an old house owned by their friend Dick Johnson, the ornithologist.

They turned towards platform two, and just at that moment the train came in. They found an empty Third Class carriage, and settled down in the window seats.

Half an hour later the train pulled up at a small station. Dick was waiting for them on the platform. 'Hullo,' called Jack.

'Hullo,' answered Dick, 'so here you are. I couldn't see you. My car is outside. You can camp on the moor at the bottom of my garden. It is an open moor covered with rocks and heather. There's a stream there, too. The heather is very good for making into mattresses, and the rocks would make quite good pillows.'

Tom laughed. 'Yes,' he said. It sounds grand. Are there many birds about?'

'Quite a few,' answered Dick. 'Why? Are you interested?'

'Yes, only we don't know much about them.'

'Well, I'll soon teach you if you like.'

'Thanks.'

The car turned into a drive, and the boys saw an old house in front of them. The garden was bounded by a stone wall, and outside the moor was covered with heather and rocks, just as Dick had said. The stream was clear, and widened out into quite deep pools.

'Here we are,' said Dick. 'You might as well start pitching your tent. Come and have supper with me this evening, as you won't have time to cook any for yourselves. It will be in half an hour.'

'Thanks,' said the boys. 'We'd love to.'

'Right. See you at eight o'clock then,' and Dick strode away.

Left to themselves the boys started unpacking their tent. Then off they went to supper. At ten o'clock they came back. When they got to bed they found it difficult to get to sleep. The night was airless, and their tent hot and stuffy. 'I'm going out for a walk to get cool, Tom,' said Jack. 'Coming?'

'Yes, I will,' replied Tom.

Jack crawled to the door of the tent and looked out. Tom came and peered over his shoulder. 'Jack!' he cried. 'Look down there by the trees. There's a glow coming out of the ground. You don't think it could be a ghost, do you?'

'Don't be so stupid,' said Jack. 'It's someone with a torch. I'll go and see if you like.'

'Yes, perhaps we'd bett . . . OH! what's that?' He clutched Jack as a shriek sounded from the direction of the light.

'I-i-i-t's g-g-ghosts!' stuttered Tom. 'Don't go, Jack.'

'Don't be silly. There aren't such things. I'm going to see what it is. Someone may be hurt. That torch's battery is running out. Are you coming?'

'No.'

'All right, then. I'll go by myself.'

'No, don't do that. I'll come.'

'Good, man. Come on then.'

They crept out into the darkness towards the light. It was in a ditch at the top of the rise behind their camp. As the boys reached it the light suddenly went out, and again something shrieked overhead. 'Look,' said Tom. 'There's a castle at the bottom of the valley over there. It must be haunted. Let's go back to our beds for heaven's sake! I'm getting jittery.' And back they went to bed.

The next day Tom was early. He shook Jack. 'Wake up,' he said. 'Let's cook breakfast now, and then we can look for that castle we saw last night.'

After breakfast they set out, armed with Jack's camera, for as Jack had said: 'If there are any ghosts we might as well get a photo of them!'

When they reached the ditch they searched about for any sign of footprints, but they found nothing but a funny little grub-like beetle. 'I say,' said Tom. 'Look at this beetle. I wonder if it was that that was screaming and glowing last night!'

Jack laughed. 'Don't be silly,' he said. 'How could a beetle hold a torch? Let's go and look at the castle.'

The castle was half ruined. The keep was nearly intact, and there was one tower. 'Let's go up the tower,' suggested Tom.

'You're sure you're not frightened of ghosts?' asked Jack laughingly.

Tom was serious. 'No, I don't think so,' he replied. 'Though I must admit that I wouldn't like it at night.'

'No, I wouldn't either, really,' replied Jack. 'A bit too much of a good thing!' The tower was very dark inside, and it took the boys' eyes a short time to get used to it. The winding staircase inside smelt of bats and spiders. At the top was a door, and opening it they found themselves in a large, bare room. 'Look,' said Jack, 'on top of that beam. There's a white owl up there.'

'Gosh, so there is,' cried Tom. 'And in that corner over there. There's a sort of nest. Let's have a look at it.' The 'nest' consisted of a few straws and the bones of mice and other small animals. In it were a couple of baby owls. At the boys' approach they turned over on to their backs, stuck their claws out, and hissed. 'My hat,' gasped Tom. 'Do owls hiss?'

'I never knew it before,' replied Jack.

At the end of the room was a door. Tom opened it. It led on to a stone parapet high above the ground. As he opened it there was a flurry and scuffle, and a weird shriek, as a white shape brushed across his face. Jack snatched out his camera with great presence of mind, and got a snap of the fast-retreating object.

'Quick, Jack,' gasped Tom. 'Let's get out of here. It's too spooky for me.' And they took to their heels and ran.

Outside in the sun once more they stopped and looked at each other. 'Let's go back and develop this photo,' said Jack.

'Right-ho,' said Tom. 'No more castles for me.'

They made a darkroom in the attic of Dick's house. When the photograph was developed the 'ghost' turned out to be a large, white bird. 'Let's take this and show it to Dick,' said Jack. They took it down and told him all about it.

'Well,' he said, 'you are lucky. This bird is an osprey, a very rare kind of eagle.'

'Did it make the shrieks?' asked Tom.

'No,' answered Dick. 'Those would have been the shrieks of a barn owl. That was the white owl you saw in the tower.'

'And the light?' questioned Jack. 'Surely an owl did not make that?'

'No,' replied Dick, 'that would be a glow-worm. You were very lucky to see the osprey. In fact, I'll give you a pound each for the photo and story, as I'm sure the "Lancashire News" would like to have them. And now, I hope you've had enough adventure for one holiday!'

Baseball

Elaine Douglas,
Georgetown, Canada.

Baseball is a game very much like cricket, only there are two kinds, softball and hardball, which are played with either a soft or a hard ball as their names imply. Children mostly play softball, being the easier game. The main object of the game is to hit the ball, thrown by the 'pitcher' to the person standing on home who is ready to hit the ball, and (supposed to) send it flying into the field. Then the 'upper', having hit the ball, runs to first base, but if the ball reaches there before him he is out, otherwise if there is enough time after touching first base he runs to second and then on to third. When on third, he must run home, only when the person 'up' has hit. All the way around if he is hit with the ball at any time except when he is on a base he is out! If he strikes at the ball three times and misses, he is out then too.

Hardball has the bases about 90 ft. apart because the ball being hard and the bat having a metal filling, the ball can be hit harder and travel further. In the game there are nine men, as you can see in the diagram. Professionals and big-time amateur teams have uniforms—a short-sleeved baggy shirt of

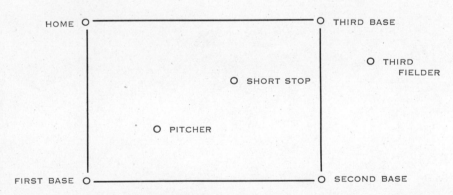

cotton over a tight woollen jersey with long sleeves. The uniforms—sometimes striped—are baggy so that there is plenty of room to move about. But girls and boys just wear play clothes.

Most Canadians and Americans start to play very young, as baseball is the king of sports. I first hit a home-run (when the ball is hit far enough so you are able to run all the way around back to home) when I was six, and I started to play at five. But I am not the only one that has done that, there are so many hundreds of people who, from that, have built themselves everlasting records.

To most Yanks and Canadians, this will not be a perfect story by any means. The names that I call these are mostly what 'Our Gang' has nick-named them. But the game is no nickname. It is one of the world's greatest sports, and to us it is the very best in the great world.

A Summer Holiday for Winter Evenings

By JOSEPH NATANSON

A general map of the route taken. This can be made very attractive by the use of colour. The numbers refer to the relevant pages in the book.

EVERY YEAR my summer holiday is an adventure. I take to the road. I have a small tent and I see all the stars above my head before falling asleep. As I do not carry a bathroom with me, I am very careful to camp near a river in order to have a good swim morning, noon or night. Some rivers have the bad taste to breed mosquitoes, but I have a net in the windows of my tent and at night carefully close the side which opens, once I am in. My dining room changes for almost every meal. At noon especially I look for large trees to protect me from the hot midday sun. I have a small petrol stove for cooking my meals and some aluminium pots and pans, battered by so much travelling but well polished by the sand of the many rivers in which they have been washed. For a long time I used to drink cocoa of a special make because it is sold in very practical rectangular tins, which take up less space than the cylindrical ones. When they were empty, I painted on them 'sugar,' 'tea,' 'coffee,' etc., and secured the lids with sticky tape.

I have a small car, now getting rather old, but still very reliable. Sometimes I believe she is like a crab. Not in her looks or her speed (she is lovely in my eyes and for her 10 h.p. she manages quite well when she is in a hurry). But, you know, when a crab loses a leg or a claw in a fight, it grows again in no time. My car has similar possibilities. When something goes wrong and there are some hundred miles to go before things can be attended to, she never stops and usually things get all right again. All through winter, except for rare occasions, she hibernates like a bear. Probably she dreams about the mountains we have climbed, the towns we visited, the rivers we slept by last summer, and new mountains, towns and rivers yet unknown to us that we are going to see this summer.

Making a Book

My summer holiday does not stop when I get home. It carries me through many winter evenings. There are photographs to be developed and printed, sketches sorted, maps drawn, postcards and other souvenirs arranged, and many details found from books and maps. When all this is done a book is made bearing the date on its back, and then almost without interval, planning for next year's holiday starts.

My holiday book consists of a map I draw for myself, and the collection which I have just described, spread over as many pages as I can make from these. Having decided its size I start with loose leaves made from paper folded in two. Each of these makes two pages which are easier to bind into a volume. Usually I use grey or brown paper, because snapshots, sketches, notes and other souvenirs stand out better against a coloured background.

The title page should be inside the first folded sheet, leaving the first page entirely bare. In the same way, the contents should finish on the first page of

*At first you see the huge figure of
the Pope*

*As the houses grow bigger, the Pope
comes down on top of them*

*Suddenly the enormous figure appears to
disappear down the chimney*

the last sheet. On the title page I write in my best lettering my name, and—France and Spain, Summer 1950. On the back of this page I write all the general data of the journey; the day of departure and of arrival back, the total mileage of the car, the highest spot I reached in passing through mountains, and any other striking facts about the journey. Facing that on the next page there is a general map of the route taken. Here I use a lot of colour, but I have made a special copy for you in black and white. The numbers on the

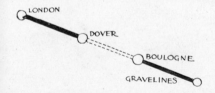

map refer to the relevant pages of my book and were added when the book was finished. All the proportions on the map are not exactly accurate as I had to emphasise some details and did not care much for the others.

As you know by now, I am very interested in painting, sculpture, architecture, and all works of art, but as I like painting landscapes, beautiful scenery attracts me as well. Geographical maps are so unimaginative. The same dot represents a magnificent ancient town with walls and towers, buildings of exquisite style and lofty cathedrals of carved stone, as well as some dreary, modern industrial town where there is not one single monument worth seeing. The empty space on both sides of a straight line representing a road on the map can be a lavish succession of hills and mountains, colourful vegetation with scattered romantic villages in its midst, as well as flat country for miles, with unattractive factories on the horizon.

When the page is turned, the description of the journey starts. Across the

two pages there is a diagram of the first episode. A diagonal line links circles indicating towns. The road is in red and the sea crossing in blue (of course).

There is just one photograph. Everyone takes it, and I am sure that some of you who have been abroad in your family car have done it already. The poor car looking so small and so hopeless, hanging in mid-air on its way to the boat.

Near the photograph there is a note torn from my notebook: 'Waiting for embarkation, made friends with children in next car. Small car—father and mother, four children, enormous amount of luggage, coming from Scotland. Very excited, going to see all the castles on the Loire, intend camping on their way. On the boat, conversation with unpleasant lady, who told me it was hopeless to go to Spain in old car, will break down certainly on bad roads'. She was so convinced that I would not make the

journey as I planned it that she gave me her address as she was curious to know what would happen to me in the end. Unless she reads *Collins* she will never know!

Turning the page again, I am already in France going to see my friends in Châtillon sur Marne, near Rheims. Châtillon sur Marne is now a very small village without any importance, although beautifully situated at the top of a hill looking round the wide valley where the river Marne flows and where some of the best wine in the world is made. In the Middle Ages, Châtillon sur Marne was a very important place indeed with a magnificent castle. Here was born the future Pope Urban II, famous because he started the first Crusade. Some fifty years ago a huge monument was built to him on the top of the hill where the castle used to stand, and now miles away you can see a colossal figure, his right

*The poor car, looking so small and so hopeless, hanging in mid-air on its
way to the boat*

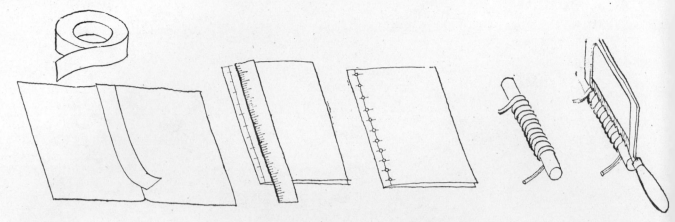

BINDING THE BOOK.   After pasting the pages together, they should be left to dry under some heavy books.   Copper wire should then be wound tightly round a piece of wood or a metal rod.   Then saw across as shown and you will have the rings ready

hand raised to bless the countryside. But when you motor up the steep road leading to the village, a strange thing will happen if you keep well in the middle of the road. And I assure you it is the great joy of all the children. At first you see the huge figure of the Pope high above the houses, yet as you drive nearer, by a strange trick of perspective, as the houses grow bigger and bigger the Pope comes down on the top of them just above the chimney of a small house. And suddenly the enormous figure starts to disappear as though going down the chimney, as easily as if he were now no more than a foot or two high.

I pasted my sketches on the Châtillon sur Marne page along with photographs of my friends which I took there. Of course, you will not find something as amusing as that in every village you visit, but in many places which are not described in any guidebook you can often find something worth mentioning in your own book, beautiful or interesting, and sometimes more precious to you than the obvious monument you find in a famous place, simply because it is your own discovery.

Binding the Book

When the material is ready and you have finished drawing, painting, writing, and sticking things all over the pages, then the assembling begins. I hope you have not forgotten to put each page, as soon as it was ready, to dry flat under some heavy books. Now you should take each set of pages, flatten it, and all along and across the hinges paste bands of paper at least an inch wide. This will make the book stronger and also will allow for the additional bulk of pasted photographs. Carefully fold the pages as they were before so that they are all even and straight, and leave them to dry again under some heavy books.

Here is an opportunity to do some fine bookbinding. Some time ago I went into a detailed description of how to bind a set of *Collins Magazines*. In the same way, the holiday book can be made. But as it is more of an album than a book, a much simpler method can be used. All you need is some copper or brass wire, thick enough not to bend easily. Make it into rings, each ring taking two or three inches of wire according to the thickness of the book.

Choose a piece of pipe or a wooden or metal rod, and coil the wire tightly around it. If you can clamp the whole thing strongly and have a metal-cutting saw you need only saw across the coils and in no time you will have all the rings ready. If not, slide away the coiled wire from the rod and cut each ring separately with pincers. But then you will have to file the sharp ends.

On every set of pages, accurately, at the same distance from the hinge, stamp two holes either with a special punching tool, or with the familiar hole-maker from any office.

Now you must find a piece of paper for the cover. It should be much larger than the usual sheet that makes two pages of your book. Paint a bold pattern in waterproof ink, let it dry, fold it in two, turn it over and paste on a band of strong paper to reinforce the hinge (this band should be as wide as your book is thick, plus one inch on each side). Let it dry beneath a weight. I leave it to your own initiative to find out how to mark the places for the holes in the cover—anyway, you can look at the drawing. For making holes, the little office machine is useless here, but as the cover has no tendency to move (because it is wrapped around the first and last pages of the book—that is why they have to be left bare), the holes can be made square shaped with a razor blade. Don't forget to put a piece of cardboard underneath whilst you are cutting.

The assembling is very simple. The rings have to be unbent slightly. First they go through the cover. Next slide in the sheets, one after another. At the end fold the cover carefully over the first and last page, tighten the rings, and the book is ready.

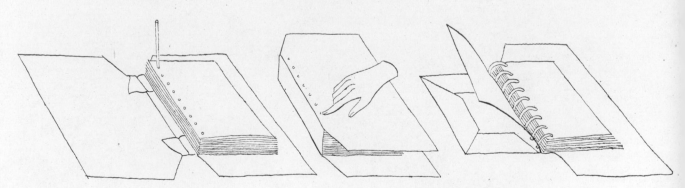

Holes should be stamped with great accuracy to correspond with the copper-wire rings.   Now find a strong piece of paper or cardboard for the cover.   You can paint on this a decoration to suit your own taste but be sure it is done with waterproof ink

Anybody's Guess

1. (c) is correct. Twenty-seven are inhabited.
2. (a) is true. (b) is not true: For 'Boer' read 'Crimean.' (c) is not true: For 'James' read 'Frank.' (d) is true: It has 135 rows of 105 each.
3. (a) Pasteur (the rest astronomers). (b) Tintoretto (the rest architects). (c) Catkin (the rest are fruits).
4. Noon.
5. (b) as all are edible: (A) is a sailor's dish; (B) is a grapefruit; (C) is a thin gruel, and (D) is a pear.
6. (a) Edmund Kean. (b) Edmund Spenser. (c) Sir Edmund Gosse.
7. Bellerophon.
8. No. The snakes can swallow the large mammal, but it may be months before the digestion is completed.
9. (a) being rich; (b) being poor; (c) being lively; (d) being fit; (e) being black; (f) being pleased; (g) being abject; (h) being miserable; (i) being neat.
10. (a) animal: a fish. (b) animal: a bird. (c) vegetable: muslin. (d) mineral. (e) as it means the rosy rash of measles, there are certainly strong animal connections!
11. (a) Rudyard Kipling ('Just So Stories'). (b) Edward Lear ('The Owl and the Pussy Cat'). (c) Robert Browning ('Home Thoughts from Abroad').

? **ANSWERS** ?

TO

PUZZLES ON PAGE 281

Threesomes

1. BOW; 2. STEP; 3. TAIL; 4. RING; 5. LOCK; 6. WORTHY; 7. HEAD; 8. STANDING; 9. WARD.

A Square with a Secret

Across 2. Little. 6. Hip. 8. Acid tests. 9. Each. 10. Ears. 13. Gregorian. 15. Ark. 16. Design.

Down 1. Tic. 3. Into. 4. Tasmania. 5. Ems. 6. Have. 7. Pitchers. 11. Sink 12. Long. 13. God. 14. Are.

Secret proverb: Little pitchers have long ears.

Double-Me-Ree

Yacht, Canoe.

Can You Say How Many?

1. Eight. 2. Forty. 3. Ten. 4. Six. 5. Three. 6. Two. 7. Two. 8. Fourteen. 9. Four. (1397, 1398, 1406, 1419). 10. One continuous one. 11. Seven. 12. Three. 13. Thirty-nine. 14. Thirteen. 15. Fourteen. 16. 2,240.

Bookworms Will Know

1. Prospero, in 'The Tempest.' 2. Dr. Samuel Johnson. 3. Currer Bell, Ellis Bell, Acton Bell; pen names of Charlotte, Emily and Anne Brontë. 4. Edward Lear. 5. Jane Eyre. The Pickwick Papers. Through the Looking-Glass. Pride and Prejudice. 6. Ben Gunn, in 'Treasure Island'. The White King, in 'Through the Looking-Glass'. The Pobble who has no toes, in Edward Lear's 'Nonsense Songs'. 7. The Duke Senior, in 'As You Like It'.

EVENING

The others have gone in now,
To the comfort of the room
But I'm still in the garden,
Tired garden—
And I'm looking at the moon.

The dew is gathering slowly
And on the grass my feet
Leave a trail of ghostly footprints
Small footprints—
In the summer evening's heat.

SHIRLEY RUDDIMAN (13)

Biggles in Arabia (continued from page 285)

the sand. If he is still alive I don't think he'll dare to show his face in Aden again, or anywhere else in the Middle East, knowing that I shall have a few things to say about him in my report. That means he's lost his business and everything else, even if he hasn't lost his life. It was sheer greed that tripped him up. He wasn't content simply to sell gurra. He wanted a monopoly of it and committed murder to get it.'

'There is no God, but God,' put in Zahar, who was listening.

'We'll see about getting back home right away to set the Air Commodore's mind at rest,' concluded Biggles.

The return flight to Aden was merely a matter of routine, and as Biggles was anxious to make a verbal report of the affair to Air Commodore Raymond, he stayed only as long as was necessary to fulfil certain obligations. Immediately on landing, Zahar was rewarded for his services with a sum of money that brought a smile to his taciturn face.

'*Wallah!* God is great,' he cried. 'May he be glorified, and long may you live, Sahib! With this money I shall buy a she-camel and her offspring will make me rich.'

'As long as she makes you happy, it doesn't matter about the riches,' Biggles told him, smiling. 'Play fair and fight fair from now on, remembering that for your part in avenging the death of Kuatim your name will be spoken with honour in every *menzil* from Mosul to Muscat.'

As a matter of detail, later on, in view of the recommendation contained in Biggles's report, he was taken into Government service and with a caravan of camels now supplies the needs of outlying airstrips in Southern Arabia.

After a bath, a square meal and a rest, Biggles went down to see Norman, to thank him for his assistance and to tell him in confidence what had happened in the desert.

Then, having thanked the Station Commander for his helpful co-operation, fulfilled his promise to recommend L.A.C. Blakey for leave, he started on the first leg of the journey back to London.

In due course the two Proctors touched down on their own airfield. Within an hour Air Commodore Raymond was listening with no small astonishment to the tale that Biggles had to tell.

Some weeks later, when the affair was half-forgotten, Biggles was reminded of it when he received a letter from Captain Norman.

Rumours of what had happened, said Norman, were now trickling through from the other side of the Red Sea, but no one seemed to be quite sure of the facts, as Ambrimos and his native assistants had disappeared. One thing seemed certain, however, Nicolo Ambrimos, known up and down the Red Sea as the Sultan, dealer in frankincense, dates, and other less commendable commodities, had ended his career at El Moab, either by drowning or by suffocation under the collapsing walls of the wadi. He had not returned to Aden, nor had he been seen at any of the other ports from which he conducted his questionable enterprises. Of his native helpers who had survived, none seemed to know what had caused the explosion.

At this point, Bertie, polishing his monocle, remarked: 'As the worthy Zahar would say, it must have been the will of God.'

Biggles nodded. 'Only a fool would dispute that,' he said softly.

THE END.

The full-length version of this story has been published under the title 'Another Job for Biggles', by Messrs. Hodder & Stoughton.

WHEN THE CAT'S AWAY–!

By J. Jefferson Farjeon.

ILLUSTRATED BY URSULA McCANNEL

In this adventure, Bob Sugg, newsboy and amateur detective, is involved in the strange case of the Thursday - Paper - Buyer and Squinty - Dark - Eyebrows

'**P**AIPER ! PAIPER ! '
Some people might think it dull to stand at a street corner and sell papers. Just standing there, and seeing people come up to you, and handing them papers in exchange for pennies. Yes, some people might get fed up. You might get fed up yourself !

But Bob Sugg never got fed up. 'Everything's interestin' if yer watchin' aht fer it,' was his motto. 'Little things as well as big things—yus, and every nah and then the big things 'appen ! I can count five of 'em on me fingers ! '

At this moment, however, Bob was only watching for the little things. (He did not know that a big thing was very shortly coming.) For instance, here was a bloke who was always snuffling.

' 'E's 'ad a cold as long as I've knowd 'im, and that's more'n nine months. Paiper, sir ? Thank yer, sir. Why don't 'e git a doctor to cure 'im ? '

And then here was the funny old lady who never knew which paper she wanted, and when you shoved a *Star* at her, wanted an *Evening News*, and when you gave her an *Evening News* changed to a *Standard*. Not a bad old thing, she'd given him a sweet once, but it must be funny having meals with her—if she asked for the salt you could bet she meant mustard !

' Paiper ! Paiper ! Orl the winners ! Paiper ! '

Ah, here came the constable. Of course, policemen never bought papers. They just got you to show 'em the headlines and then winked at you and passed on.

' When are you goin' to buy one ? ' asked Bob.

' One day next year, sonny,' grinned the constable.

' Nex' year I may be in me corfin' ! ' Bob grinned back. ' I expeck that's why yer called coppers—yer knows 'ow ter save 'em ! '

The constable sauntered on, and Bob gazed after him enviously. That's what he wanted to be when he grew a bit taller. Not that he'd stay a constable ! No fear ! Detective-Inspector Robert Sugg, that's how he'd end up. . . .

' Come, come, my boy ! Attend to your business ! '

Bob stopped day-dreaming, and handed a paper to the disagreeable customer who had sharply brought him back to earth. And a mighty disagreeable customer he looked. ' I've seen you afore,' thought Bob. ' 'Angin' around all the week, lookin' fer trouble ! Why don't yer find somewhere else to go and 'aunt ? '

But the next moment he cheered up as a more welcome customer approached.

' 'Ere comes Old Thursday,' he chuckled.

He called him Thursday because it was only on Thursdays that Bob Sugg ever saw him, and he was a man after Bob's own heart because, besides being a decent old josser, he was also a bit of a mystery.

It was about three months since Bob had first seen him—on a Thursday, of course. A car had deposited him outside a building a few doors away from Bob's pitch. He was a rather professorial-looking old chap with untidy grey hair, but his chauffeur was almost grimly neat, and had made some protest, Bob recalled, when Old Thursday had made a dive at Bob to buy a paper.

' Nonsense, nonsense, Smith, don't be so fussy ! ' Old Thursday had exclaimed. ' May I not even buy a paper by myself ? '

Then he had gone into the building, watched frowningly by the grim and protesting Smith.

The next Thursday, when the car again appeared and stopped, there was another altercation, and this time it was Smith who won, and who left his seat and bought the paper. For four Thursdays after that, the same thing happened. Then matters seemed to come to a head, and Old Thursday bought the paper, smiling triumphantly as he did so.

' Did you ever know such nonsense, my boy ? ' exclaimed Old Thursday. ' My chauffeur seems to imagine you'll eat me ! '

' I wouldn't do that, sir,' replied Bob. ' I've 'ad me lunch.'

' Bless my soul ! ' cried Old Thursday. ' I wish my chauffeur had as much humour as you ! I shall buy a paper from you every week—buy it myself—if only to get a laugh ! '

And then, still chuckling, he had turned and run into the building. And every Thursday since, he had trotted across to Bob for his paper and his laugh, and he always got his laugh because Bob spent the whole week thinking up something funny to say to him.

A queer little pavement friendship had grown up between the old man and the boy, and Bob often wondered who the old chap was, and what he did, and why the grim Smith was always so watchful with him. He was a funny sort of fellow, Old Thursday was, you couldn't get away from it, with his white hair and high forehead and dreamy eyes. He looked both brainy and dippy. But whatever he was and whatever he did, Bob would have missed him if he had not seen his car arrive each Thursday, and watched him jump out and dive in his direction. . . .

And now here he was again, with his customary beam, coming towards Bob for his paper.

'Good afternoon, good afternoon!' he exclaimed. 'And what's my laugh going to be to-day?'

'A dream I 'ad last night, sir,' answered Bob.

'Indeed? And what did you dream?'

'That Mr. Attlee and Mr. Churchill met and kissed each other.'

'Bless my soul!' chuckled the old man, delightedly. 'I believe that would make even my chauffeur Smith laugh! I'll try it on him, and if it does you shall have half-a-crown.' Then, suddenly, he bent forward and whispered in Bob's ear, 'Terribly stern and solemn is Mr. Smith—I'd much rather have you to look after me!'

Bob watched the old fellow trot away and disappear. So that was what the chauffeur did, was it? Looked after him? Poor Old Thursday! Bob hoped this did not mean that he was really dippy.

'Well, I don't care if 'e is,' he decided, 'I like 'im any'ow! Paiper! Paiper! Another dockyard explosion! Paiper!'

*   *   *

Now that was a day of little happenings—little happenings, at least, as far as Bob Sugg was concerned. The explosion in the dockyard was not his affair, aside from the fact that it sold him a few extra copies of his papers. It was a week later that the big happenings occurred.

He was standing at his street corner as usual, looking forward already to his little weekly meeting with Old Thursday although it would not occur for another hour—Old Thursday's car always turned up punctually at exactly the same time—when he noticed the disagreeable customer who had reprimanded him the week before. The sight of this unpleasant individual—he was even more unpleasant than Mr. Smith, with his thick dark eyebrows and a bit of a squint—took some of the sunshine out of the afternoon.

'Why does 'e keep on 'angin' around?' thought Bob, complainingly, 'and why is 'e always 'ere on Thursdays?'

Yes, that was a funny thing! Bob had not thought of that before. Squinty-Dark-Eyebrows always turned up on the same days as Old Thursday. Probably that was just the way it had happened to happen, but it was a bit funny like, wasn't it?

The customer with the permanent snuffle diverted Bob's attention for a moment ('fair snufflin' like a grampus terday, 'e is!' reflected Bob), and then he began watching Squinty-Dark-Eyebrows again. When you didn't know people's

'Bob feigned faintness, and tottered against Squinty-Dark-Eyebrow's chest.'

names, you had to make 'em up, didn't you? Hallo, was that somebody making a sign to him across the road? Thin, fair-haired chap. Seen *him* before once or twice, too. Still, p'r'aps Bob was mistaken about the sign.

Ah, p'r'aps they were bookies? How about that? Not that bookies generally did their stuff across a London street! And anyhow, the fair-haired one had sloped off now, and Squinty-Dark-Eyebrows was beginning to move, too. Beginning to move in Bob's direction.

' Do yer know wot I think? Something's goin' to 'appen!' Bob told himself. ' Don't ask me wot—but *something*!'

He felt it in his bones. And when Bob felt anything in his bones, you could wager ten to one that his bones were right. Just as some hazel-twigs can detect water, so some bones can detect trouble.

Now Bob Sugg had long ago worked out that there were two ways of meeting trouble. The first was to try to avoid it, the second was to try to make something out of it, and he always chose the second. He chose it now.

Drawing up to him, Squinty-Dark-Eyebrows stopped and spoke. His voice was more friendly this time, but Bob did not believe its friendliness one little bit.

' I see you're attending to your business to-day,' he said.

'Corse I am,' retorted Bob. ' That's the on'y way to get on, ain't it?'

' Ah! And, naturally, you want to get on?'

' 'Oo doesn't?'

Squinty-Dark-Eyebrows nodded. ' I like you, young man,' he said, ' and I'm sorry I was cross with you last week. Do you remember?'

' Yus,' replied Bob. ' It upset me proper—I've been cryin' all the week!'

' Really? Well, I'd like to do something to make up for it.'

' Go on!'

' It's a fact, my lad. Would you like—— ?'

' 'Arf a mo', guvnor. Paiper, lady? *News*? No, *Star*? Oh, *Standard*. There y'are, lady. All abart the explosion in the dockyard!'

As the lady moved off with her paper, Bob turned back to his alleged benefactor.

' Wot was you sayin', sir?'

' Would you like to walk a little way with me to see a man who could put you on to a good thing?' answered Squinty-Dark-Eyebrows.

Bob thought for a moment, then shook his head. One reason he did so was that, all at once, he had seen the thin fair-haired man again standing a little way up a narrow by-street.

' Why not?'

' Well, yer see, sir, larst week yer told me to attend to me business,' answered Bob, ' and I mustn't leave my pitch.'

It was a good thrust, and S.D.E. did not appreciate it. He suddenly shrugged his shoulders, put a hand in his pocket, and held it out. Bob gathered there was a coin in the half-closed fist.

' Very well, my boy,' said S.D.E., ' you've had your chance, so don't blame me if you've lost it. Give me a paper. Any-one'll do. Make it nippy!'

His tone had changed. Bob handed him a paper. In exchange, the man thrust something into Bob's fingers, covering his action with the newspaper he had taken with his other hand. Conscious of the beginning of a sharp prick, Bob acted with the amazing swiftness on which he had been more than once complimented by a police-inspector. For Bob Sugg was both wise and experienced for his years.

' There's some game on!' his mind raced. ' Lummy, don't ask me what, but they want to put me to sleep! This is dope, this is! Orl right, I'll pretend I've 'ad it!'

And drawing his hand away sharply under cover of the newspaper, he feigned faintness, and tottered forward against S.D.E.'s chest.

Now it was unfortunate for Bob Sugg that his faintness was not entirely feigned. A little of the dope had already entered him before he drew his hand away, and he only had a dim recollection of the events that immediately followed. Vaguely he gathered that S.D.E. was sympathising with him—and that, of course, *was* entirely feigned! He heard the word, ' Doctor,' and then, ' the little chap's had a blackout—I'm looking after him.' And then—this was the last memory before the blackout truly occurred—he found himself in the narrow by-street and had a vision through a mist of the thin fair-haired man.

After that—nothing, for quite a while.

* * *

How long Bob Sugg remained unconscious he had no more notion when he opened his eyes, than he had of why he had been made unconscious at all; but, as he learned later, it was only for a very short while, thanks to the incompleteness of the dose he had received. Had he received the full dose, he would have continued his oblivion for two or three hours. He found himself now in a small room rendered dim by the fact that the blind was down. Vaguely surprised that he was not bound and gagged, and rightly gathering from this that the Enemy had believed it unnecessary in their ignorance that he would regain consciousness so soon, he lay still for two or three minutes to get rid of his dizziness, and then very carefully sat up to take his bearings.

He was on a small bed. The room was so small that there was only room for a chair in it besides the bed. It was dirty and shabby, and the paper was peeling off the walls.

' Wot beats me,' thought Bob, as his head began to clear, ' is wot they've done it *for*? Wot good am I to 'em? I'm proper foxed!'

He hoped that when his head was quite clear he would see the reason, but he was disappointed. No reason dawned.

He moved gingerly off the bed, and tested his feet. Good! A little wonky, but not too bad. He could get to the door. . . . But a lot of good that was! The door was locked. After all, what could you expect?

The next move, obviously, was the window. The room was so tiny that it took only a couple of steps to reach the window. He pulled the blind up, and looked down on a collection of roofs and back yards. The back yards were an unpleasantly long way down. There were no people about to shout to. Only a black cat, and cats are no good, really, when you want a bit of help.

But anyhow, Bob decided, he did not want to shout just yet. For one reason, it might bring the wrong people along, and for another, he was not worried about himself. He didn't suppose he was going to be murdered, and he wanted to get to the bottom of the mystery. He wanted to do a little more thinking and poking around.

Turning from the window he gave a quick glance round the room, and his eye spotted something in a corner of the floor, near the door. It was a newspaper, either thrown there, or more likely dropped, by someone entering or leaving the room. He went to it, stooped, and picked it up.

' Funny if this was the paiper I sold the blighter!' thought Bob.

It was the right paper, and the right edition. But, hallo! What was this? The heading, " Another Dockyard Explosion," had been underlined. What did that mean? Special interest?

The next thing Bob saw, however, interested *him* even more. In the Stop Press space something had been written in pencil. Bob's eye popped. Lummy! Crikey! Seizing a pencil stump from his pocket, Bob added three words fiercely, pocketed the paper, and sped back to the window. He was going to get out of that window somehow, if he broke his neck doing it!

Yes, there was a water-pipe. (What, thought Bob, would life be without them?) Unfortunately it only went a part of the way down the wall, and it began at the next ledge, which meant a bit of a jump, but you couldn't worry about things like that, not after reading what Bob had just read in the Stop Press column. He opened the window wide, and as he did so he heard steps approaching the door of the room.

That settled it!

Clambering out on to his own ledge, Bob jumped to the next as the door opened. If anybody was in the next room outside the window of which Bob's body now suddenly appeared, well, that was another of those things he couldn't stop to worry about. He wasn't stopping for anything, and he had slid down the full length of the water-pipe almost before he had started.

The water-pipe ended at another window two floors lower. The window was closed and fastened, but who cared? You didn't have to open a window if you were in a hurry and had a boot. Bob's boot was through the glass in a trice; also his fist. A couple more kicks, and Bob was through himself. He heard a woman scream, but he hardly saw the woman as he shot by her. Then something shot by him. It was an iron the woman had been using. Fortunately it missed, and once more he escaped defeat. He heard the iron crash against a wall as he flew out of the door.

The luck was with him so far, but would it last? If there had been time Bob would have gone down on his knees to beg for it, but this was not the moment for prayers. He had to get back to his pitch! He had to get back there in the next three minutes! A clock in the hall through which he was now dashing told him that!...

*　　*　　*

Old Thursday leaned back in his seat, and said to the grim driver beside him: 'You know, Smith, I don't think we shall be making many more of these little trips.'

'I hope not, Professor,' answered Smith.

'You've had enough of them, too, then, eh?'

'I certainly have! If you want the truth, this is one of the most wearing jobs I've ever had. May I ask, sir, what makes you think we're near the end of it?'

'You may ask,' replied Old Thursday, 'but I doubt whether you would understand my information if I gave it to you in detail. But that, of course, is what I must not do. I must only give it to our friend X. From my head direct into his head. I must not even write it down, in case some naughty person or other should see it. But in safe, general terms, Smith,' he went on, 'my work this last week has been completely successful. My latest experiment has finally proved my theory, and—h'm—shall I go on?'

'I should be interested, sir.'

'So would plenty of other people. Particularly on the other side of the Iron Curtain, eh? But, after all, I was merely going to say that the information I shall pass on to our friend X to-day should satisfy him that I have really and truly discovered the answer to the atomic bomb. Three months ago he merely smiled at me. He thought I was mad. *You* still think so, do you not, Smith?'

For once, Smith smiled, though faintly.

'Unusual, sir, shall we put it?' he answered.

'Excellent! I am unusual!' chuckled Old Thursday. 'Well, perhaps I am content with that! I have certainly escaped being kidnapped an unusual number of times.'

'But for me, sir, you'd have been kidnapped the first time!'

'I believe that, sergeant, and I am duly grateful. You have looked after me wonderfully since the authorities sent you to guard me, and I have no doubt that after the result of to-day's interview is known to our Back Room Boys, you will receive a medal—while *I* shall be able to return to a little peace! But there is one thing I shall regret, Smith, when these little trips are over.'

'*He was going to get out of that window somehow, if he broke his neck doing it.*'

'What is that, sir?'

'My little paper boy. He's such a nice little fellow. And bright, too. You could do with a little of his humour, Smith. Did I tell you what he said to me last week?'

'You mean about that dream he had?'

'Yes, so I did. And you thought it silly, while I thought it funny. That's because you've stopped being a boy yourself—you've forgotten all its fun. Ah, here we are—arrived at last.' The car drew up. 'Now you must excuse me for a few seconds, while I buy my paper.'

He got out of the car. As he did so, a thin man with light hair approached Smith excitedly.

'There's someone calling for help over there!' he exclaimed. 'A woman! Come along, quick, and give her a hand—just round that corner!'

Smith turned his head, to follow the man's direction. It was the direction opposite to that of the paper boy's pitch, to which Old Thursday was trotting.

Then Old Thursday got a surprise, too. His little paper boy was not there. Standing in his place was an unpleasant looking fellow with dark eyebrows and a slight squint.

'Hallo! Where's my young friend?' enquired Old Thursday, disappointedly.

'Took ill, sir, an hour ago,' replied the man, 'so I'm carrying on for him. Which paper do you have, sir? *Star*? *News*? Or *Standard*?'

The man spoke quickly, and a taxi drew alongside as he spoke, stopping at the curb immediately beside them. The taximan groped backwards with his hand and swung the door open casually.

'Dear me, I'm sorry,' murmured Old Thursday. 'Poor little chap! I hope—well, well, give me a *Star*.'

The paper man held out the paper, holding the copy in such a way that it covered his other hand, preparing to receive the professor's penny. The professor fumbled for his coin. He procured it and held it out . . .

'*Oi! Look aht. Don't touch 'im! Oi!*'

The next few seconds were perhaps the most astonishing seconds that had ever happened at that street corner. The man with the dark eyebrows and the squint dropped his bundle of papers and leapt into the taxicab. He was joined in a flash by the man with light hair. Sergeant Smith twisted his head back from the direction in which he was trying unsuccessfully to find a woman who had called for help, and as the taxicab drove off at top speed, Bob Sugg came tottering to the corner, grubby, dishevelled, with fingers bleeding, and breathless, yelling : 'Git its number ! Git its number ! The Taxi ! Git its number !'

It was Old Thursday who caught the tottering boy in his arms and held on to him fast.

*   *   *

Later that day, when things had cooled down, and breath had been regained, and matters sorted out, Bob Sugg sat in the office of his good friend, the inspector.

'Bob,' said the inspector, 'I'm not allowed to tell you all you've done because it involves official secrets, but you can take it from me it's a pretty big thing, and it includes rounding up another little spies' nest. One day, even if you don't grow any more, we'll have you in the force yet. Meantime, I am to give you this, with Professor Wroughton's love, and besides getting a little present from us, your name will figure very honourably on our official records of this case. Well done !'

He patted the boy's shoulder, as he handed him an envelope. Bob opened it, and found himself blinking at ten one-pound notes, with a scribbled message : 'From a grateful old boy to a mighty smart young one. You've got everything that counts in life, my lad—courage and a smile.'

But—it was funny—at that moment Bob felt a little tearful. Emotion gets you, doesn't it ?

'I didn't do it for no reward, sir,' he muttered.

'We know that, Bob,' answered the inspector. 'That's why you deserve one. But, tell me—how the dickens did you get on to it ?'

With a faint smile, Bob Sugg drew a newspaper from his pocket, and held it out to the inspector, with a finger at the Stop Press column.

'You'll find two things writ there, sir,' he said. 'The fust was writ a bit too soon !'

The inspector read. The first, in a hurried pencilled scrawl, said : " Mysterious Disappearance of Professor Wroughton." The second was Bob's own addition : "*I don't fink !*"

SUGARING FOR MOTHS

by John and Marigold Keeble

Perhaps the photographs on page 278 have fired you with the ambition to start a collection.   This article will help you to set about this in the right way.

IF YOU ARE thinking of collecting Moths, it is a good plan first to study a reliable book with coloured illustrations. You will then learn what to look for, and be able to recognise anything you may find.

Because Moths usually fly about at night, it is not possible to rush after them with a net, as you can butterflies, by day. So you must try some way of attracting the Moths to a spot where it is easy for you to catch them. This is how we went 'sugaring'.

It was a hot day, with the promise of a warm night. We chose our trees. There were several trees, standing fairly near each other in a meadow. They happened to be cherry trees, but that is not necessary.

We collected nets and torches, and prepared our killing bottle. We shredded laurel leaves very finely into a jam jar with a screw top, mixed camphor balls with them, and then put the lid on firmly. This is supposed to be a painless way of killing moths, but if you do not want to make a collection, an empty glass jam jar will do, for observation, letting the Moths out afterwards.

Then we found an old unwashed treacle tin we had been saving for this very purpose, and poured in a little hot water. To this we added the dregs from empty beer bottles which had also been carefully saved, and mixed everything together. We also added the washings of an empty honey jar, stirred well, and our sugaring mixture was ready.

After tea, we set out while it was still light, and smeared the mixture on the lee side of the trunks of the trees. Then we had to wait until it grew dark. This was the hardest part of all. The evening seemed never ending!

At last it was time to go, so we gathered up nets, torches, and killing bottle, and took with us also a white cloth. This was to put on the ground, under the trees, in case the Moths fell off, and became invisible in the dark grass beneath. We crept along. If a Moth was startled, it would soon fly away, even if it was by now, a trifle drunk!

We stood round the first tree feeling terribly excited. What would there be? A Hawk Moth at least, perhaps even a Death's Head! The sheet was carefully spread on the ground. Nets were at the ready. Then the torch was flashed on the tree. Not a Moth to be seen, only the trunk, still sticky with the mixture!

Feeling rather disheartened, we moved to the next tree, but even in the darkness we could see a quivering white shape. Quickly we spread the sheet and then flashed the torch. Yes, it was a white Ghost Moth, and a beautiful specimen too. But we had one already, so we did not need it for our collection. Lower down the trunk was a Yellow Underwing, but that again we already had.

The third tree had no Moths on it, and we walked to the fourth and last, forgetting to be quiet. As the sheet was put on the ground, not so carefully as before, a big brown Moth fluttered from the trunk and fell. Quickly the torch was turned on to it, but the net was not ready, and away flew a large Oak Eggar! These Moths are rare in our part of the country, so we considered ourselves lucky to have seen it, though had we been more careful, it would have been added to our collection.

Another night we found far more Moths in number, but nothing so rare as the lost Oak Eggar. However, perhaps you will have better luck.

Families are evacuated before a blasting operation, and take their possessions with them until the 'all clear' sounds.

Electric drill prepares holes for the special powder which does not splinter the marble.

WHERE DID THE MARBLE ARCH?

PHOTOGRAPHS BY 'CAMERA TALKS'

CARRARA marble is the most famous in the world and has been quarried for two thousand years. So it is that a great number of the world's best known statues and buildings have been made from its exquisite white marble, with the fine grain. Michelangelo used it a great deal. In 1508 blocks were sent to him in Rome, out of which he carved his statue of Moses, and the two figures of Slaves, which are often claimed to be his greatest work. In 1518 he went to Carrara so that he himself could supervise the blocks he wanted to use being extracted from the quarry.

It is quite possible that to-day there may be descendants of the workmen he watched, still on the same job. Nowadays a certain amount of machinery is used but

The blasting is controlled by intricate instruments.

Sounding the 'all clear' on a primitive trumpet.

Loading smaller blocks on to trucks by crane.

(Left) A modern statue towers in shining white at an entrance.

(Right) Clouds of white smoke enfold the mountainside as tons of valuable marble are blasted out of the quarry.

a good deal of the work needs the craftsman's eye and skill, exactly as it used to centuries ago. There are four hundred quarries and the claim is made that in spite of the huge amount of marble which is blasted out and carried away each year, the outline of the mountains from a distance has not been spoiled.

The Emperor Augustus of Rome said that he had found the city brick and left it marble. That was centuries ago—about 50 B.C. If you want to see what Carrara marble looks like, without travelling so far afield—jump on a bus and visit Marble Arch, that familiar London landmark!

GAY

Written and illustrated by
ALICE MOLONY

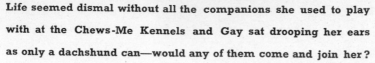

Life seemed dismal without all the companions she used to play
with at the Chews-Me Kennels and Gay sat drooping her ears
as only a dachshund can—would any of them come and join her?

SOMEWHERE in the garden the Allans were playing tennis; somewhere in the garden their cook, Mrs. Fritter, was picking raspberries; somewhere in the shrubbery lurked a dark and burly man, while on the doorstep of the house sat Gay, a miniature longhaired dachshund puppy, chilled and disheartened.

At the Chews-Me Kennels, which Gay had left only that morning for this bleak new home of hers, if men were to lurk behind bushes, the Chews-Me dachshunds would soon have put an end to that lurking—would have driven them into the open like rabbits. . . .

Here, when Gay had done her utmost to tell the Allans that she'd found, not tennis balls, but a dark stranger behind the syringas, they hadn't believed her. They'd told her to stop barking and scolded her for trampling the geraniums flat, and then sent her back to the house—the great gloomy house of Merrylees—alone.

Gay wondered that so dull a place had been called Merrylees, for as far as she could see, it was not merry anything. She wondered which she disliked most—Mr. and Mrs. Allan, or Mrs. Fritter, or Mrs. Fritter's cold-eyed cat Winsome, for all—except Winsome—kept on saying 'don't' in a very discouraging way. Most of all, perhaps, she disliked this house; this large quiet house that stood above her, listening, waiting for her to do the wrong thing.

Gay knew what she wanted to do. She wanted to cry, but it would be a shocking thing to make a sound, to break this spell of silence; the house would disapprove.

So Gay sat where she was, and drooped as only a dachshund can, and wished that she were back at the Chews-Me Kennels, dashing up and down the paddock in the wake of all the other little dachshunds, led, of course, by Gloria.

That morning when the Allans had arrived at the Kennels to buy a dachshund, Gay's sister Gloria was the one they had chosen — Gloria, the beauty of the family and the leader; Gloria with her vivid autumn chestnut colouring and quicksilver clever ways. But Gay was the one they had bought, for Gloria cost a lot of money, and Gay with her darker coat, puzzled face, elephant ears and awkward paws cost a great deal less. Still, Mr. and Mrs. Allan said they were sure that she would make a splendid companion for Rachel and Betty when they came home for the summer holidays. The children, they said, were looking forward already to meeting so lively, bright and intelligent a little playmate.

And—

'Oh, Gloria!' Gay whispered in despair, for she knew that she was none of these things; that without Gloria she was a failure, stupid, bewildered, lost. Gloria walked close beside her to the car. Gay sat on the back seat beside a plush rug that looked rather like a leopard. She stared out of the window, and suddenly everything was moving, Gloria was a speck in the distance and here was goodbye to her. . . .

Gay curled up quietly and chewed the rug and was scolded and cried all the way to Merrylees, her new home.

And now it was evening, and Gay sat alone on the doorstep of this strange and unfriendly house, growing hungrier and hungrier. At this hour, at the Chews-Me Kennels, every nose would be deep in its supper dish. Perhaps here they expected you to hunt about for your own supper . . . perhaps?

Still anxious not to break the solemn silence, she went quietly across the hall to the kitchen. Winsome lounged in the arm chair, and her pale-eyed stare froze Gay. She went out again quickly, and now stood facing the pantry; the door was open; through the little window high in the wall came the last of the daylight, the last song of the blackbirds. The pantry was full of shadows, its shelves were full of food. On the lowest shelf of all stood a beautiful pink blancmange. It glowed in the light of the setting sun. Gay wanted it more than she had ever wanted anything. She was sure that with all that bright pinkness inside her, she herself would be more cheerful.

She ate a mouthful or two and it slid down well, and the pink flavour was wonderful. For a moment longer though, she hesitated. Was this, after all, the correct thing to do—would Gloria help herself to a blancmange that might possibly belong to someone else?

Gay looked about her doubtfully, and then it was that she first noticed the mirror. That mirror in its heavy frame seemed to Gay like a window through which you looked in at another house, at another puppy with a sadly puzzled face. And that puppy, too, had before her a dish of blancmange; she too had a broad rim of pink around her nose. Of course, that made everything perfectly all right. If the other puppy in that other pantry could lap up blancmange, then so could Gay.

She lapped and lapped till almost all was gone, and a heavy step resounded in the hall, and Mrs. Fritter, back from her raspberry picking, came sailing in like a storm cloud, and very upset indeed to find that though Gay's legs were short, the rest of her was as long as a ladder.

Mrs. Fritter slapped Gay, and as she slapped, she spoke:

'There now,' she said, 'that's for helping yourself to my blancmange; no one is allowed to set foot in my pantry—let you remember that!'

By the time the slapping was over, Gay knew that she would indeed. Then Mrs. Fritter put Gay on a lead, and fastened the lead to a chair and flounced away into the kitchen to make another blancmange. Gay knew, for later she saw Mrs. Fritter carry it into the pantry.

And now house and hall were gloomier than ever, darkened not only by the anger of Mrs. Fritter but by night-time shadows as well. Gay looked in the glass to see how that other puppy had fared. Had she, too, been slapped? Yes; she peered back at Gay out of the dimness, a poor bewildered little thing, with the tell-tale rim of pinkness still around her nose. Gay pressed her nose to the glass and so too did that other puppy, and somehow, in spite of the coldness between, the result was comforting. Gay curled up on the floor and they both fell asleep at the same moment.

Later, when Gay awoke, the house was very still and dark. Only the mirror shone dimly, like a great misty pool. There was a bitter coldness in the air. Gay shivered, not just because she was cold, but because she could see that the other puppy had her ears pinned back, as though she were listening for something she didn't want to hear . . . something rather frightening. . . .

And now in the depths of the glass Gay saw a shadow move, a door swing slowly open and a streak of moonlight shimmer down on the burly figure of a man standing in the doorway.

Well, that was a queer affair if you like; Gay was very glad indeed that such things didn't happen here in her own house. She was glad now that Mrs. Fritter was so particular about not allowing anyone in *her* pantry.

A blast of icy night-time air blew in on Gay.

She turned. . . .

There, in her own house, in the doorway of Mrs. Fritter's own pantry, stood a man. The great wild hulking man of the syringas, too; the very same.

In silence they stared at each other.

He can't know about Mrs. Fritter, Gay thought, or he wouldn't stand there staring. He wouldn't dare. What was it Mrs. Fritter said—'no one is allowed to set foot in my pantry, let you remember that.'

He was up to no good, that man: he was after the pink blancmange. It would be a dreadful thing if Mrs. Fritter were to lose two blancmanges in one evening.

'Mrs. Fritter—Mrs. Fritter—he's after your blancmange!' Gay shouted, barking in a shrill clear voice.

And then everything seemed to happen in one wild flash.

As Gay's bark shattered the silence, the man sprang forward, Gay sprang back. The man tripped over Gay's lead and fell sprawling. Gay rushed round, winding her lead still more tightly about his legs. Mr. Allan came pounding down the stairs; Mrs. Fritter too, her hair in a pigtail, herself in a green dressing-gown.

The man was struggling to his feet now, and Mr. Allan was knocking him flat again. And—

'Look out, Sir—he's got a pistol!' screamed Mrs. Fritter while Gay went on barking like mad.

'Ah, you would, would you?' shouted Mr. Allan, hitting the man's arm, and the pistol went off with a frightful roar; the bullet struck the mirror, glanced aside, and hit Gay in the shoulder.

And then Mr. Allan, Mrs. Fritter, Gay's burglar—all Merrylees in fact, seemed to go whirling about her in the most confusing way, so that afterwards she could scarcely remember the end of the fight when the police arrived and led her burglar away captive.

Still, she did remember hearing them all speak in queer far-away voices of a brave little dog who had done her best to defend her home. But, of course, they couldn't have meant her, Gay, for she had only tried to defend Mrs. Fritter's pink blancmange. . . . Perhaps they were speaking of that other puppy, her dear dismal little friend beyond the glass.

It was a grand and glorious thing to have been shot by

a burglar; Gay discovered this at the Dog's Hospital where she was taken on that wild night; driven in the Allan's car, its headlights blazing a path past hedgerows and sleeping houses, while Gay lay still and quiet, wrapped in the leopard-skin rug she had so thoughtlessly chewed that morning.

The dogs at the hospital spoke all the time of their homes. There really wasn't anything else to think about, except how poorly you felt and how much you disliked the too-clean smell of carbolic.

Home was the place where all good things were to be found, the best food, the kindest people. Therefore, it was indeed a fine thing to have been shot while defending it—the sort of thing that as a rule happened only to film star dogs. Gay didn't explain that she had only lived there for one day, that there was nothing homelike about Merrylees, that it was a dull and dreary place and that she hadn't been defending it, but only a blancmange. She didn't explain, because it was nice to discover that for once she had done absolutely the right thing. So when the dogs asked her to tell them about her home, the burglar and the shooting, she just said that it was a long story, and that possibly sometime she might write a book about it.

Day after day while she was getting better, she sat listening to those other dogs talking of food and fires and

friends and walks in the woods, and the hospital was so cold and cheerless that in the end she, too, began to picture Merrylees as a sort of fairyland where Mrs. Fritter handed you a supper of your choosing and Mr. and Mrs. Allan played tennis with you all day long; and she, too, began to look forward to the day when she should return to this splendid home.

At last that day arrived, and Gay was driven away past rows of houses and then down miles of twisting country lane.

And at the end of her journey, there were the high privet hedges, the neat geranium beds, the clipped lawns of Merrylees, and the solemn grey house itself, all as gloomy as doom, while on the doorstep stood Mrs. Fritter, looking fussed and cross as usual, with Winsome circling her ankles like a slinky lynx.

She took Gay into the kitchen and gave her a scanty pat and told her to wait there till she called Rachel and Betty.

Wait—wait alone in the kitchen with Winsome?

Gay's heart sank. This was not the welcome she had hoped for. As soon as Mrs. Fritter disappeared, she ran out into the hall to find that other puppy again, to tell her the real story of her adventure, and to complain a little, too, about the stiffness of her shoulder, the bleakness of her return and welcome.

In the dim half light of the hall, Gay turned eagerly to the mirror, but now no other puppy stared back at her from its shattered depths. The glass was starred, splintered and smashed. There was nothing beyond; no friend, no comfort anywhere in all the world. . . .

At that moment the garden door opened and Rachel and Betty Allan came rushing in. Rachel picked up Gay and told her that she was brave and good, that everyone was proud of her, and that now she was going to live happily ever after, the way princesses did in books.

'There now Gay—is that a proper welcome?' she asked.

It was indeed. These were nice well-meaning girls; Gay licked Rachel's nose.

'Let me have her now, Rachel,' Betty said, 'it's my turn, I want to welcome her, too.'

But Rachel said, 'No, I'm oldest, I've chosen Gay. She's mine. You can have Gloria.'

GLORIA?

Through the open doorway Gay could see across the garden. She could see Mrs. Fritter sailing along in the distance; she could see a little dog go dashing past her, across lawns and flowerbeds, a little red dog, bright as the scattered geraniums—Gloria, her own dear sister!

And now the old house no longer seemed gloomy as doom; it positively glowed with the warmth and cheerfulness of all those welcomes as Gay and Gloria met again.

In place of the broken mirror there hangs now a large photograph of Rachel, Betty, Gay and Gloria. Everyone on seeing this picture exclaims about the children—who look very nice indeed—and about Gloria, too, for she has arranged herself beautifully in the foreground.

Gay, in the background, still looks small and homely, and no one exclaims about her. Perhaps they scarcely notice her. But we who have known her in times of doubt and disaster can tell now by her eager glance and by the more dashing way she carries those elephant ears of hers, that, for Gay, life is fun again, and Merrylees the grandest, happiest old home in the world.

HANDS

Now rest in abeyance
  From market and mill
Millions of hands
  Unaware of their skill;
Hands pale as faience,
  Hands brown as hazel,
How can I praise all
  Those that are gifted?
Hands like the rose
  To the wild rose grafted,
How from such good
  Can I choose?
Some lovely food
  Have spicily garnished
(Sauces and stews);
  Others, nail-varnished,
Have tapped like the yaffle
  A texture of news.

Now sleep-arrested
  They lie on the pillow,
Or clasped in a fellow,
  Or open, uncurled;
And some are as shell-pink
  As the silk petals
  Of roses unfurled,
The soft hands of children,
  The hope of the world.

GEOFFREY DEARMER

BLACKSMITH

Written and illustrated by

MARION RIVERS-MOORE

CLANKETY-CLANG, clankety-clang—the blacksmith plays a tune on his anvil. He does not lay down his hammer quietly and still between his strokes. It bounces unnecessarily with a little lilting tune upon the iron surface to give a rhythm to his necessary strokes. Big strokes, little strokes, he shapes the red hot iron to his will, until, too cool to shape further he takes his big long pincers and thrusts it into the heat of his furnace again. The bellows wheeze into action and up fly the sparks in the dark and dusty interior of the shop. There are piles of iron and odds and ends in the corners now weirdly glowing in the light of the flame and the draught sways hundreds of cobwebs. Along the beams hang many sets of shoes of all shapes and sizes, a size to suit every regular four-footed customer who comes to the forge. Sometimes they are labelled—Prince, Duke, Duchess, etc., but usually the smith keeps these matters in his head.

Although not always under the traditional spreading chestnut tree, the smithy is usually in the centre of the village and it is always a centre of attraction. All day passers-by stop and chat from the doorway of the forge, peering into the darkness within. Unlike the gardener, who stops his work and leans upon his spade to gossip, the blacksmith keeps on steadily with his job and answers between his hammer's blows. The iron must be shaped while

it is the right temperature. He will not leave it to talk to you and risk its growing cold. If the smith down-tooled to talk to all, he would never get through his work. Besides, his customers get restive if they have to wait too long for their shoes.

Making a Horse-shoe

The shoes are made from long, straight strips of iron. The required length is cut from the end and heated in the forge. It is shaped on the anvil by hammering it round the varying curves of the anvil's tapering nose. At the centre of the front shoes a portion of the iron is hammered up into a point to form a clip which will come in the middle of the front of the horse's foot when the shoe is in place. On the hind shoes, two clips are made, one on each side, as a clip in the front of a hind foot would be liable to catch on the shoes of the front feet when the horse is moving at fast paces.

The forge fire burns a special type of coal called 'smith's breeze', which is very fine, so that it lies close. But it burns easily and gives a very strong red heat when the bellows drive the air through it. Many smiths nowadays have their bellows operated by electricity which saves them a great deal of work. The fire is kept up together and re-fuelled with a sort of long-handled light shovel called a 'forge slice'. Beside the fire is a long shaped tank filled with murky-looking water, in which float countless flakes of iron which have been burnt off and have fallen away when the red hot shoes, gate hinges and such, were plunged into it to cool.

The blacksmith has to make quite a number of different types of shoes. He may have to make special shoes for a horse that is lame or has a diseased foot, and he makes several different standard kinds for the various kinds of work

that horses have to do. The shoes for farm horses are broad and flat and fairly heavy. They usually have seven nail holes, four one side and three the other, but sometimes they have eight. Shoes for horses working on hard roads are strengthened by the addition of a heel at each end. These are called 'calkins', and are made by knocking back the ends of the piece of iron so that it has a double thickness for the last inch each side. It is here that the wear is hardest and the extra depth of iron makes the shoes last a great deal longer. There is not much to be gained in making shoes to last more than a month as they should be taken off within that time in any case so that the foot can be cut back. Otherwise, the toes grow too long and make the horse apt to stumble and the growing of the horn pulls the clinches out.

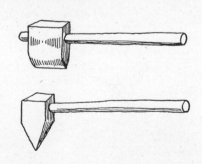

A hunter's shoes differ in several ways from those of a heavy horse or roadster. In order to make them light to save the horse from fatigue in the gruelling days he sometimes has, the smith makes a deep groove along the middle of the iron with a tool called a 'fuller'. He does it when the iron is still in straight rods, before he begins to shape it for the shoes. For this job you need a keen eye and a steady hand as well as a good deal of strength. Two men have to work together. One holds the fuller in position on the iron rod and the other wields the heavy sledge hammer with good and straight blows aimed on to the flat top of the tool. The fuller's shaped under side cuts the groove inch by inch into the hot iron, as the smith moves it along to receive the blows. The fullered iron is shaped into shoes in the usual way. Then the ends are filed smooth, and bevelled off round the inside edge. This rounded edge helps to prevent the horse from picking up mud and flinging it in the faces of the riders behind him. Unfortunately for the comfort and appearance of people out hunting, the result is not entirely successful but it certainly helps. The nail holes in the shoes are made with a pointed tool called a 'pritchell', which is held on to the red hot iron and driven through with a sledge hammer in the same way as a fuller is used. The nail holes are made along the fullered groove so that when they are driven in, the heads of the nails lie below the general surface of the shoes where they escape the wearing impact of the roads.

Preparing the Hooves

When a horse comes to the forge, the smith's first job is to take the old shoes off. The tool he uses to do this is yet another one which is knocked on its back with a hammer. He uses it to bend down the ends of the nails which hold the shoes in place. Then he takes a large pair of pincers and pulls the shoes off. If he tried to do this before knocking the nails down properly the hoof would be damaged. Horses' hooves grow just like our nails do, so the blacksmith has to cut back what has grown since the last set of shoes were put on. This is no more painful to the horse than cutting our nails is to us. To

get a smooth finish, the smith uses an outsize nail file, called a rasp. When all four feet have been trimmed and shaped, he hooks down a suitable set of shoes from his selection, and begins to fit them. He sticks a little spiked tool through one of the nail holes and holds a shoe against one of the horse's feet. He sees whether it is too wide or too narrow and whether the ends reach round too far. Then he plunges the shoe into the fire and blows his bellows until the shoe is hot enough to work. He then shapes it on the anvil with his hammer until he thinks it is right. While it is still hot he holds it against the horse's foot again and up go clouds of the wonderful smelly smoke, which is typical of the blacksmith's shop. When he takes the shoe away, the blacksmith can tell by the pattern burnt on to the horse's foot just where the shoe needs adjusting. Where the shoe presses too hard the burn will be dark and black, and where it does not lie close enough there will be hardly any burning

at all. He goes to the anvil again and makes his final alterations accordingly. Then back he comes with his tools and his nails and puts the shoes on, driving the nails upwards and outwards and clipping off the ends of the nails a little above the surface of the foot. He has to leave enough of the nail protruding to bend over to 'clinch'. When all four shoes are on, the clinched ends of the nails are filed off level with the feet. If the horse is quiet and well behaved, he is made to rest each foot in turn on an iron tripod while this is being done. The hooves are finally brushed over with an oily brush to hide the marks of the file, and to make the whole job look neat and workmanlike.

It takes about an hour to take off a set of old shoes and put a new set on—if the horse behaves himself. If he does not, it takes any number of hours. There is now an extra charge for unruly horses, so it pays to teach your horse to be sensible by picking up his feet and tapping them with a hammer when he is young, long before he ever goes into a blacksmith's shop. You should also get him used to going into strange places and hearing unusual noises. If he has done all this, and he is confident in you because he knows you will not hurt or frighten him, you should not have any trouble to speak of even the very first time your pony is shod.

The Disappearing Blacksmith

Nowadays, there are far fewer blacksmiths than there used to be. In the days before motor cars, if your horse cast a shoe you would not have far to walk him before you could have it put on again. Now you would probably find only a petrol station where the smithy used to be. The lack of smiths makes it difficult to make long journeys on horse back, as also do tarred roads and garages instead of stables at the inns. For the same reason, it is difficult to visit your friends on horse back, for there is no stable for him when you get there, and certainly no tea for him while you have yours. So as the blacksmith has disappeared, so has the horse, and most smiths nowadays do many other jobs besides shoeing. They repair farm implements, sharpen harrows, put new handles into tools, grind the blades of mowing machines and even do repairs to your bicycle. Many of them also do welding. A few still make things like ornamental garden gates, fire screens and fire baskets in the most beautiful and intricate designs.

The smith's work is varied and interesting, and he is his own master. It is a hard life but it is also a healthy and very satisfying one, and it seems odd that more boys who like working with their hands and using tools and making things, do not apprentice themselves to it. They could hardly fail to earn a living.

Picture Post

A scene that is fast disappearing from England's countryside—the village blacksmith at his anvil.

Making a Coracle

by Richard Graves

Earlier in this volume is an article about the Australian 'School for Adventure'. This is yet another of their activities.

Sydney Morning Herald
The finished coracle afloat

I**F YOU ARE** camping by a canal or lake, and have no boat you can always make a coracle in about an hour, using the waste material of the neighbourhood, such as bracken fern or weeds, for your coracle walls, and your japara hike tent, a car cover or a piece of canvas for your coracle cover, and presto! you have a perfectly safe and waterworthy boat, capable of seating three or four people. You can even put your packs aboard and make quite a voyage down a river in your coracle. It will be almost uncapsizable.

First measure the length and width of your coracle cover or tent, and make your coracle frame three feet smaller for each dimension. Say your tent, opened out, is seven feet by nine, your coracle frame will be four feet by six.

On a clean piece of ground, close to the water, scratch an oval of this size, and nine inches to a foot inside this scratch another oval. Now cut about thirty dead straight stakes no more than an inch or so thick, and drive these around the outer and inner ovals so that they are about nine inches apart. A heavy stone held in one hand will make a good driver. The stakes must be upright.

Between these two rows of stakes pack green fern, or weeds or small bushes until you have a wall at least eighteen inches high. This wall is then bound with either ground vines, long strips of bark, or grass rope. It is not necessary to pack the wall down too tightly, but it must not be flimsy, and of course you must not use gorse or blackberry or other thorny plants for the filling.

When the wall is bound, cut three or four straight sticks at least an inch thick, and nearly as long as the coracle and four or five nearly as wide. Tie these sticks across the top, the long sticks lengthways and about six inches apart and the shorter sticks crossways. If these sticks are green, it will be better if you weave them together.

Spread your tent or cover evenly on the ground, and lay a three-inch layer of grass or fern over the centre. This layer should be a foot wider and longer than your coracle frame. Now lift the oval of green material straight up from between the stakes, turn it over so that the sticks once at the top are underneath, and so lay it right in the centre of the cover.

Lift the sides of the cover, and without straining the cloth too much take the cover right up and over the sides and ends and tie down to the sticks which are on the floor.

When this is complete your coracle is ready for launching. Lift it clear off the ground. Do not under any conditions drag it, or you may tear the cloth of the covering, and lay it gently in the water. It will float freely in an inch or two of water.

If the water is shallow, as in the Broads, you simply pole it along, but if the water is deep you must make a couple of paddles, and these can be made from any old boards or flat pieces of bark or split wood and held in the hands. You must paddle evenly on both sides at the same time.

It is important to sit, squat, or kneel inside the wall. Do not ever sit on it, or your weight will break the wall down and water will pour in. By squatting or kneeling on the sticks on the floor you have more power for either paddling or poling.

If you are camping and want to use your tent as a coracle cover by day and as a tent by night, lift the coracle ashore after your day on the water, undo the ties to the floor, and lift the coracle frame cleanly off the bed of fern or grass. Remove this layer, and pitch your tent. Next day you can launch your coracle within five minutes of striking your tent.

If by any chance the material for your cover is not quite waterproof, and leaks through the weave, you can, if the cloth is not too loosely woven, make it waterproof with a candle. Lay the cloth on the ground in the sun, and when the cloth is quite dry rub it with a candle, holding the candle sideways. Let the cloth lie in the sun for half an hour, so that the grease can be absorbed by the cloth, and then it should be quite waterproof. Of course, if you are going camping and know that there is good water, it is better to take a piece of heavy waterproof canvas about eight feet by ten along with you, and use this for a permanent coracle cover.

A coracle is very stable, perfectly safe, and excellent for fishing. You can stand upright for casting, without any feeling of being off balance.

For long journeys down rivers it is not advisable to use a light weight hike tent for your coracle cover. The cloth is not strong enough to withstand a snag, and you should, if planning such a trip, use heavy canvas.

If you do get a tear in the coracle cover, a piece of adhesive tape from your first-aid kit will quickly repair the damage, or a piece of 'scotch' tape will serve as well.

It's fun making your tent into a coracle.

LIGHT WEIGHT TENT

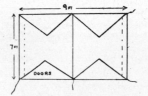

TENT FOLDED FOR CORACLE

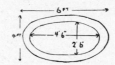

OVAL MARKED ON GROUND

STAKES DRIVEN INTO GROUND FOR INNER AND OUTER OVALS

BOUND FRAME STILL IN THE STAKES

CORACLE FRAME NOW RIGHT SIDE UP ON COVER

READY FOR THE WATER

Whither Do You Wander?

BY L. HUGH NEWMAN, F.R.E.S.

L. Hugh Newman, a butterfly farmer and a trout fisherman, here describes some of the fascinating work of the Severn Wild Fowl Trust, where geese are followed in their flight across whole continents

ON 16th December, 1945, Peter Scott stood on the grassy salt marshes of the Severn Estuary and watched 2,000 geese on what had been their main winter feeding ground for centuries. A year later the Severn Wildfowl Trust was founded, with Peter Scott as Director, and Field Marshal the Right Honourable the Viscount Alanbrooke as President. By the end of the first summer of 1946, a nucleus of the tame collection of waterfowl had been established, some of which had been in Peter Scott's private collection at his lighthouse before the war. Work on a decoy was in progress and six thatched observation huts had been built between pillboxes which overlooked the salt-marsh.

On September 21st the first flock of wild geese arrived, and the studies of their habits and behaviour began. Day by day the numbers grew, and by the middle of October, nearly three hundred White-fronted geese could be counted. Many more Pinkfeet had arrived since the first gaggle were seen a month before, and altogether ten of the thirteen British species and subspecies were recorded that first autumn.

The peak period for the White-fronted geese is from the middle of December until the end of January. At that time they number anything from 3,000 to 4,000. They remain until March 10th every year, when they leave for their breeding grounds in the far north of Siberia. The Pinkfeet leave early in December. Where they go is still a mystery. It is these mysteries concerning the migratory movements of ducks and geese that are one of the primary concerns of the Trust. Wild ducks are caught in the decoy, and ringed and released. From reports that come in many months later from various parts of the world, a picture of their movements is slowly built up.

Rocket propelled net

Ringing wild geese presents greater difficulties. These wary creatures feed by day only, in wild, lonely spots, and roost at night far out on the sand banks, and will fly on sight of their chief enemy, man. With the invention of the Rocket Propelled Net, immense possibilities opened up.

A site was chosen for setting out the apparatus within a hundred yards of an old disused sea-wall which would give cover. Next morning, stumbling over awkward ditches in the darkness it took the party over an hour to reach the 100-acre field, but by 5.15 a.m. everyone was assembled with their share of the gear by the old sea-wall ' and like a party of smugglers or body-snatchers all seven of us,' Peter Scott wrote, ' went out together across the flash at its lowest crossable point and down to the edge of the wheat to the corner of the fence.'

From then on it is a race against time and the coming of dawn. The net had to be laid out with extreme care, the rockets set out and the firing led back to a hastily erected hide. ' Already the eastern sky was bright and we knew that we had a bare twenty minutes before the arrival of the geese.' But the rocket expert insisted that he must fire a couple of cartridges in order to test the circuit. The circuit was correct, for two little sparks of light flashed at each end of the net. And then there was the final rush across the field to slip the rockets into the pistols, while someone made some sort of attempt at camouflage by strewing handfuls of grass over the rocket heads.

Hardly had positions been taken up when about 300 geese came straight in and landed in the middle of the 100-acre field, down-wind of the net; the 'actors' had arrived and the stage was set. From then onwards, more geese came slipping in over a belt of trees, skein after skein in an almost unbroken stream. By the time the sun rose there must have been more than a thousand geese feeding in the field. And then there was a startling development. A family party of geese rose in the air and flew low towards the corner of the field where the net was laid out. Others followed and settled about 40 yards away. The next hour was one of pent up excitement as this company of feeding geese moved slowly forward into the ' catching area ' —all unsuspecting—ten yards, five yards, two yards, and then over the line, a milling crowd of hungry geese ready to be trapped.

A critical hitch

At this point there was a shocking anti-climax; the leads to the wireless battery were missing. A quick look through an observation slit in the front of the hide showed the black, shiny insulating wire turned off at right angles just outside—and on the same side as the geese were feeding. Someone must have kicked it aside in the last minute rush. With infinite care Peter lifted up one corner of the hide and felt amongst the brambles and grass for the missing flex, and after agonising seconds his fingers closed over it. The geese had moved another five yards closer to the net.

Now the critical moment had arrived. The crowd in the ' catching area ' had about reached saturation point, and with a glance towards Mr. Schermuly, who held the ends of the flex in his hands, Peter gave the word ' All right, let her go!' The rockets exploded and simultaneously the whole flock of some 1,300 geese rose

The Greater Snow Goose, an Upland or Magellan Goose, and a common domesticated Chinese Goose feeding peaceably at the water's edge.

in the air with a roar of wings and mighty chorus of voices. Everyone sprang up from his hiding place to watch the geese rise, and at once it could be seen that a small number of flapping geese had been trapped. A quick count showed thirty-two geese under the net; it was a satisfying sight. The first great catch of live geese for ringing had been made; the experiment was a success!

Duck decoy

Catching ducks in a decoy may not present so many difficulties but nevertheless requires considerable skill and patience.

The construction and working of a decoy is not perhaps generally known. The pool must be not less than half-an-acre in size and must be well sheltered by trees and undergrowth. From it, two or more curved ditches lead off into the surrounding trees. Large metal hoops, covered with wire netting, are fixed at regular intervals along the length of each 'pipe', getting smaller and smaller as they reach the end, until they are narrowed down to within a foot or so of the water.

Each pipe is flanked with overlapping screens thatched with reed or straw, and they are so arranged that the decoy man is invisible to the birds on the pond but can, at the critical moment, appear *behind* the ducks in the pipe, between them and the pond, and barring their retreat. The ducks then have no alternative but to fly yet further up the pipe, round its bend, and on into the cul-de-sac at its end. There are various methods employed to entice wild duck from the pool into one of the four pipes; food may be used, or tame decoy ducks may be trained to give them confidence. It takes time to build up a proper 'lead' of wild ducks which can only be achieved with a nucleus of tame call-ducks.

But by far the most usual, and at the same time the most extraordinary method is by using a specially trained small dog. The ducks' natural instinct is to mob the dog, for they know it cannot catch them so long as they remain in the water, and, if the dog appears always to be running away, their bravado increases! In this way they can be lured into the pipe, whereupon the decoy man runs back to the 'show-place' and drives the birds forward into the detachable net at the end of the tunnel. Here the birds are extricated without any difficulty, and they are then ringed and released.

Through the iron curtain

The catch for the season 1948-49 was double that of the previous year—total of 269 birds, including Mallard, Teal, Widgeon, Shoveler, Pintail and Garganey. Recoveries are coming in slowly. Among the most interesting are two Widgeon which flew straight through the Iron Curtain and were shot in Russia, in the Eastern Ural mountains, and another Widgeon shot on the lagoons near Venice.

The rings are issued to the Trust by the British Trust for Ornithology and

A party of Mallards in the newly constructed House Pipe of the Severn Wildfowl Trust's decoy. Here the ducks are caught, ringed and afterwards released for migration.

The closed end of the duck decoy pipe. Peter Scott and a friend have come to inspect the 'catch'.

bear the address of the British Museum of Natural History, London.

The Waterfowl Collection of the Trust now consists of some 600 ducks, geese and swans of 105 different species and sub-species and is undoubtedly the finest in the world. Some of the birds have been loaned to the Trust, others presented and many exchanges have been made with Zoological Societies and private collectors all over the world. A list of names would convey little, but mention must be made of the Greater Snow Goose, made famous by Paul Gallico's book which is illustrated by Peter Scott. Seven of these

Snow Geese are at liberty to fly if they wish, and one of the most beautiful sights at the New Grounds is these lovely white birds circling overhead and then landing at one's feet to feed from the hand.

The Trust, which has a membership of about 2,500, is open to the public and thousands of visitors manage to find their way to the New Grounds every year. More members are still urgently needed and anyone interested should apply to the Secretary, The New Grounds, Slimbridge, Gloucester, for further details.

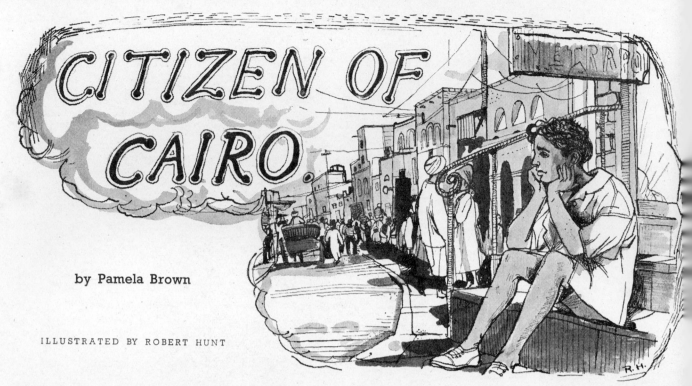

CITIZEN OF CAIRO

by Pamela Brown

ILLUSTRATED BY ROBERT HUNT

FAROUK SAT on the steps of the Hotel Metropole, and the life of Cairo seethed round him. The continual frenzied hooting of taxi horns, the cries of the street salesmen, the chatter of the passers-by, he heard only as from a distance, for Farouk was busy thinking. He was a small boy for his age, with coffee-coloured skin and liquid brown eyes, and he wore a pair of very old and patched khaki shorts and a shirt to match that had once belonged to an American soldier. Both these garments were spotlessly clean, for he washed them out himself each night in the little mud and straw hovel where he lived, in the Muski quarter of the city, with his mother and father and seven little brothers and sisters. These garments were never ironed but still he managed to look neater and cleaner than any of the other little urchins who hung round the entrances to the large hotels ready to open car doors or shine shoes, or quite openly to beg for a few piastres. In this way Farouk tried to keep himself a cut above the others in their grubby galabiyehs—the long white shirts that reached nearly to their bare feet. Farouk had a pair of old white plimsolls that he wore for work, but removed as soon as his tired feet turned into the Arab quarter on his way home. He scorned shoe-shining and car-door-opening, and openly jeered at the boy beggars, for *he* was a guide. Each day he attached himself to a prosperous looking group of tourists as they came out of the Hotel Metropole, and clinging to them like a limpet he insisted on showing them the sights of the city—the Citadel, the fortress built high above the city, the Muski with its beautiful Blue Mosque, the Zoo, and the Museum.

It was the Museum for which he had the most pride and affection, and he would never let a tourist leave Cairo without visiting it if he could help it. But at the Museum there was a serious drawback—the official guides attached to it would very often refuse to let him in. They liked to escort the tourists themselves and receive the tip for doing so. It was only on busy days when the other guides were all engaged that Farouk was able to slip in. And then he felt that he was in heaven—the heaven that Mohammed the prophet had promised to all good Mohammedans. Open-mouthed and starry-eyed he would gaze at the treasures of

bygone days—the jewels and gold and silver that had been discovered in the Pyramids. But most of all he loved the room that was given over to the treasures found in the tomb of Tutankhamen the royal prince of Ancient Egypt who had lived so long ago that Farouk could not imagine such a length of time. These jewels were better than anything in the modern jewellers' shops in the Avenue Suliman Pasha—there were enormous gold bracelets set with emeralds and rubies and jewels so bright and rare that Farouk could not put a name to them. There were necklets and earrings that looked so heavy he could not imagine anyone being able to walk about carrying such a weight.

It was of these that Farouk was thinking that morning as he sat on the hot stone steps of the Metropole expecting every minute to be chased away by the hotel porter.

'I want to be rich—' he thought. 'I want jewels like those of Tutankhamen to give to my mother and my little sisters—I want a car like the King's—a red one—I want to sit in the cabarets at night surrounded by my henchmen and watch the dancing and eat grand meals—'

Farouk was an ardent admirer of the King of Egypt, after whom he had been named, and when the King was driven through the streets in the royal car—the only one in Egypt that was allowed to be painted red—his cheer was the loudest and his waving more frantic than anyone else's.

'But this is not the way to make myself a rich man,' he reflected, sighing as he rose. The sun was well up in the piercingly blue sky and it was time to start his morning's work. He watched the swing doors of the Hotel. What would it be to-day? Genial Americans with money to throw away and a thirst to see as many of the sights in as little time as possible? Or would it be cautious English people, anxious not to be rooked of a piastre, and intent on seeing everything thoroughly and having it all explained to them? Whoever it might be, he hoped they would want to go to the Museum, but his heart sank when he saw the three men who were now descending the steps. They were dressed in the American style but did not look a bit genial. In front was a large stout man in a white linen suit and a Panama hat, with a pale face that was marked with little pits like the skin of an orange. He had a large cigar in his mouth and wore a fierce scowl. Behind him came a little shabby man wearing a sun-helmet that was too big for him, accompanied by a dark-skinned man with side whiskers. Farouk looked at them doubtfully. Business men, he was afraid. They would make for the nearest bar and stay there until it was lunch time. But perhaps they would want to be directed to a nice cool bar—he advanced rather less eagerly than usual. Then the miracle happened. The large man turned to Farouk and demanded loudly, 'Say, kid, which way do we go to this Museum?' Farouk's heart leapt and his usual broad glistening grin swept across his face.

'O.K., Mister. I take you. I show you Museum. I am very good buddy. See, a Yankee soldier he give me this shirt. He was my friend. Come with me. The Museum is very beautiful place.' And he was off down the street beside them, talking at top speed, smiling his broad professional smile, flattering them, cajoling them, entertaining them, but in his mind's eye counting up the number of piastres he might get from them at the end of the sight-seeing. If only he could get into the Museum to-day—

'Yes, Mister, I go to the English school. I am a Boy Scout,' he told them, and saluted vigorously, 'But best I like the Yankees—some day I go to America, when I am very rich man—'

As he led the way down Kasr el Nil he wondered about these three men. They were not of the type who usually demanded to see the Museum, before anything else. This only happened with elderly studious Englishmen who wore funny spectacles that clipped on to their noses. These three were more the sort who would drive out to the Pyramids in a 'ghari', take one look at them, and head for the Mena House Hotel—it was really most strange—but he offered up a prayer to Allah that their tips might be as sumptuous as their coloured silk ties.

'Gee—' cried the stout man. 'This side-walk sure is hot—how much further are you dragging us, Abdul?' Farouk was used to being called by every name but his own. Abdul—George—Mohammed—it was all the same to him.

'Shufti, Mister. There is the Museum.'

'And, begorrah, it's about time,' whined the little weedy man. The dark man wiped his face expressively. The large imposing Museum buildings drew nearer, and Farouk increased his pace, longing for the cool and quiet of the lofty halls, lined with glass cases. He hurried on ahead up the steps and peered into the foyer. There was not a guide in sight. They must all be engaged at the moment. He signalled the three men to hurry. 'Come this way, Misters. I will show you everything. I am very good guide. I come here all the time.' He led them to the entrance where they must pay a few piastres admission. The official who was handing out the tickets looked at Farouk suspiciously.

'I am with these gentlemen,' Farouk explained to him in Arabic, 'You let me in—I share the baksheesh. Plenty baksheesh. They are rich American gentlemen.' The official gave an understanding nod, and charged the men for Farouk's admission as well.

Once inside, he could hardly refrain from dancing with delight. Allah was being good to him to-day! He showed them everything, talking all the time, boasting of the glories of his country, past and present. The room that contained the treasure of Tutankhamen he saved until the last. The three men followed him round almost in complete silence, looking at everything with an awed uneasy interest. Occasionally the large man would say, 'Gee—' the little man, 'Begorrah—' and the dark man 'Sapristi'. Apart from the exclamations and the creaking of the brown and

white shoes of the fat man, they passed in silence down the corridors of Ancient Egypt's glories. But when Farouk mentioned Tutankhamen their faces altered. He was glad to see that the fame of the young prince was so widespread.

'This Tutan-what-have-you character'—said the large man, 'where are all his remains?'

'Follow me. I show you,' said Farouk, delighted, and he led them to the Tutankhamen room, which was heavily guarded by Egyptian police because of the value of the ancient jewels. On the threshold Farouk hesitated.

'No cameras, misters. They do not allow pictures taken.' The fat man had a small expensive-looking Leica slung round his neck.

'Aw, gee—' he grumbled, 'I'm not leaving this with any Wog—' Quite unoffended, Farouk winked.

'I fix, mister. Leave it to Farouk.' Deftly he slipped it off the man's neck, suspended it from the belt of his own shorts and pulled his shirt out so that it flapped loosely round him and covered it completely. Blandly he led his patrons past the guards, and then they were among the wealth of Tutankhamen.

Farouk showed them the coffin made of gold in which the body of the young prince had been discovered, and they glued their noses to the glass case and looked at it for a long time. Farouk could have sworn that the mouth of the little man was watering. Then the fat man ground the stub of his cigar under his heel, and said in a low voice, 'Too heavy.'

'It's a cryin' shame, that's what it is,' breathed the weedy one. They went on to the jewel case and stared as though hypnotised.

'Gee, Mike—they're mighty pretty,' murmured the large one. Farouk thought that they would never come away from the case of small jewels covered with thick plate glass. They would look intently at it, then step away and survey the whole room, then the case from a distance, then come up close to it again and start staring again. Suddenly the large man looked at his watch.

'O.K., boys. We knock off. Seen everything you need to?'

'Sure, chief,' they replied and they walked briskly out into the bright sunshine.

'Now, mister, I take you to see the Blue Mosque—began Farouk, 'Oh, no, you don't, buddy, we need to get us a drink, then eat, then get a bit of a siesta. Hey, now, hand over that Leica of mine—' Farouk had had a faint hope that he might have forgotten it, but he unfastened it and handed it over, then he showed them the way back to the hotel. They all seemed deep in thought, and even Farouk was quieter than usual.

'Too heavy—' 'A crying shame—' 'Seen everything you need?' These were strange tourists indeed—

Outside the hotel Farouk began wondering about baksheesh.

'I have shown you well, mister?' he began. 'You like Farouk for your guide? I come again to-morrow?' The large man reached inside his jacket and pulled out a wallet that bulged with Egyptian pound notes. He looked at Farouk for a long time with his tiny shrewd eyes, then, pressing a note into his hand, said thoughtfully, 'Yeah, kid—You come back to-morrow.'

Farouk ran off down the busy street clutching the note. He was hurrying back to the Muski with his riches. Now his mother could go to the market and buy them food—Their evening meal would be a feast—And to-night he and his father would sit in front of Abdul Karim's coffee shop drinking cup after tiny cup of the thick sweet brew, and his father would smoke from the enormous communal

He punched one of the policemen full on the jaw and Mike flung himself on the other.

pipe, and be proud of his eldest son, whom Allah had obviously destined to be a rich man—

Next day, promptly at ten, Farouk was outside the Metropole. He was neat and tidy and his stomach still felt pleasantly full from last night's festive meal. A lot of the pound was still remaining, and he jingled the coins in his pocket appreciatively. There was still the man at the Museum to be squared, of course—To-day it was impossible that he would be so fortunate again.

And now here were his three gentlemen hurrying out of the hotel in a business-like manner, looking determined, somehow, and as uneasy as ever.

'Saida, misters,' began Farouk, 'to-day I take you to the Citadel, the beautiful fortress built by—' But he was cut short.

'No, no, sonny,' said the fat man in an unnaturally sugary tone. 'We want to go to the Museum again. Isn't that so, Giuseppe?' he turned to the dark man.

'Sure, chief—Sure.' Farouk did not know what to think. Another morning at the Museum suited him very well, but somehow it did not seem natural.

'Yes, sir. We go there.' He turned down the Kasr el Nil. The fat man put an arm about his shoulder in a friendly fashion.

'We kinda liked what we saw yesterday. Didn't we boys?'

'We sure did, boss,' echoed the other two.

'So we want your help again to-day, Abdul. Now, my friend here, Mike, is a camera fiend, isn't that so, Mike?'

'I am an' all, chief—'

'And he wants to take some photos of those jewels and whatnot we was looking at yesterday. So will you do something for us, buddy? Just stand by the door of the room and if there is any trouble—any fighting or anything —you shout, loud as can be, 'That way—that way—he went thataway—'

'That way—that way—he went thataway' echoed Farouk, as though repeating a lesson. Then after a pause he asked, 'Who went what way, mister?'

'Never you worry your little head, sonny. That's our business. Just a gag, see? To fool those police of yours, so Mike can get his pictures to take home to his little boy. He's got a little boy—just like you. Isn't that so, Mike?' Mike looked rather doubtfully at Farouk.

'The spittin' image' he agreed.

'And you'll get the camera inside again for us like yesterday?'

'Yes, mister,' replied Farouk, still a bit baffled.

At the Museum all went well. At first the other guides did not want to let Farouk in, but Farouk paid up his debt to the ticket man and was passed through. Soon they were standing in the Tutankhamen room, Farouk with the little camera tucked under his shirt. The three men stood round him, pretending to look in one of the show cases. 'Give the camera to Mike,' ordered the fat man, under his breath, 'But careful-like—don't let those guys in the uniforms see.' Slick as a conjurer, Farouk extracted the Leica and handed it to Mike, who sauntered away to the other end of the room nearest the policeman.

'Attaboy,' said the chief to Farouk. 'Remember what you gotta say. Go over and stand by the door. Giuseppe, you back up Mike. Keep 'em busy, mind, and leave the rest to me.' Farouk strolled over to the door, his mind working very quickly. Something was about to happen, he felt sure, but he did not understand exactly what. It seemed a lot of fuss about a photo or two. Of course he would get caught. One of the policemen, imposing in his red fez, strode over to Mike, pointed to the camera and gesticulated, telling him that photos were not allowed to be taken. Mike snarled at him, 'Er—yer dirty Wog— kindly keep yer hands off me, will ye?' The policeman took him by the arm—and then Giuseppe stepped in. He punched one of the policemen full on the jaw and Mike flung himself on the other. Instantly there was a mêlée of arms and legs—of shouts in Arabic, Irish and Italian-American. From all the other galleries of the Museum people ran in to see what was wrong. A small crowd had gathered round them in a matter of seconds.

'If there's any fighting—' the fat man had said. This then, was Farouk's cue. He glanced towards the fat man who was in the far corner of the room, and was in time to see him swing over his shoulder a leather glove, weighed with something heavy, and bring it down on to the case that held some of the small but priceless pieces of jewellery. The dull thud and the splinter of glass was lost in the noise of the disturbance near the door. Deftly the man extracted a few objects from the case and slipped them into his pocket. Then he strolled down the room and joined the fringe of the fighting, shouting crowd. He gave Farouk a meaning scowl and a jerk of the head that meant 'Get on with it—'

Farouk hesitated, and thought more quickly than he had ever thought before in his short life. This man had committed a brilliantly clever robbery. Farouk had been brought up in surroundings where theft was not a crime, but often a necessary part of earning the daily bread. He could not feel any pangs of conscience on that score. But still he hesitated. If he chose, he could help to complete the robbery by setting the police to follow a mythical thief who was supposed to have escaped already. Then he could insist on sharing the proceeds. His imagination boggled at the probable worth of the jewels that had been stolen. He would be a rich man indeed if he got his fair share—

But suddenly he was filled with a burning rage. What right had these foreigners to come into *his* country—to *his* Museum—to steal the jewels of *his* Prince Tutankhamen, to take them and sell them in other countries, and expect him to help—probably for a few meagre piastres. No—the glories of his country's past must stay in Egypt, in this Museum, for people to come and marvel at, and for Farouk to boast of. Besides, if all the treasures of Egypt were to be carried away, what would happen to his own livelihood? All these thoughts, half-formed and jumbled-up rushed through his head as he stood in the doorway, with the leader of the gang scowling menacingly at him. Then his mind was made up. Flinging himself into the midst of the crowd he caught the nearest policeman by the arm, and shouting in Arabic, he dragged him out of the scrum.

'The foreigner—' he cried, 'He steals the jewels of Tutankhamen—see the case is broken. They are in his pocket—'

Still bewildered by the fight, the policeman merely stood and gasped for breath. Farouk flung himself at the fat man, who was now trying to make furtively for the door. Like a little wild cat Farouk clung on to him despite his efforts to kick him loose.

'In his pockets—Look in his pockets, master—' he called. The policeman did so, rather gingerly, and his eyes nearly popped out of his head when he drew out a marvellous jade ring that he recognised as being one of the exhibits.

'Comrades—' he called to his fellow-policemen, 'A thief—a thief—'

In the pandemonium that followed, Giuseppe and Mike disappeared into thin air, but Farouk had the satisfaction of seeing their chief marched off between two armed guards, and he watched the jewels being replaced in their case. Then he went across to the statue of Tutankhamen, and made a low obeisance. 'Sire—' he breathed, 'Your treasures are restored. Praise be to Allah.'

To-day Farouk does not hang about outside the Hotel Metropole waiting for the tourists. He is one of the official guides of the Museum, and conducts parties round it with a fine flow of his colourful English. And it is with an especial gleam in his brown eyes that he reaches the part of his narrative that begins, 'And now, ladies and gentlemen, I show you the relics of Tutankhamen—'

He had the satisfaction of seeing the chief marched off between two armed guards.

Certain Observations on Catapultry

by ROLAND PERTWEE

THERE ARE MANY differences of opinion as to how a catapult, or, to give it the earlier and more suggestive name, a strod should be made. The old school favoured a fork of yew or ash with a spread of two and three-quarter inches between the tines and a grip seven inches long. To this were attached ten-inch 'pulls' of quarter-inch square elastic. The pouch was of leather and about four inches long. The result was a sturdy, stubborn weapon well suited to slinging quite large pebbles of the kind found on beaches or in gravel pits. These were commonly known as chuckers or chaquers, the latter word being derived from *The Saga of Ugwoni, the First Strodite,* a mythical hunter of the period of two-toed horses and sabre-toothed tigers.

To stretch this heavy elastic needed considerable strength and much of the power put into the shot came from a slinging, overthrow action with the left hand. The right hand was couched on the right breast, below the right or master eye. The chaquer was released as the left hand completed its outward stretch and was whipping downward. The chaquer described a fairly high arc before striking the mark, which it did with smashing force.

In the First World War, four strodites, armed with this heavy type of strod, reduced a German steel helmet to a shapeless mass inside five minutes. They were using steel strods forged in a mobile workshop, the Germans having cut down and burnt all the wood in the neighbourhood. The ammunition was shrapnel bullets taken from a defused Hun shell which had failed to explode, I am thankful to say. If I remember rightly, each shell contained 365 bullets, one for every day of the year, if you were lucky enough to live so long. One of the

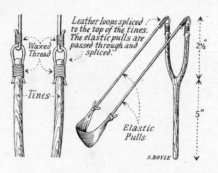

Leather Pouch showing how a loop is formed at the narrow ends for attaching the elastic pulls
Elastic Pull
Elastic Pulls
Leather Pouch
Leather Bootlaces for attaching to tines
S.BOYLE

team was our interpreter from whom I learnt that the French for catapult is *lance-pierre.*

The common method of attaching elastic 'pulls' was to cut grooves half an inch below the tops of the tines, loop the 'pulls' round them, short ends outermost, stretch and get someone else to bind and knot them before allowing

them to relax. I always disliked this kind of fastening because the elastic very soon broke at the bind. I found the use of leather thongs or strips of leather bootlaces far more effective. Just short of each end a slit was cut, through which the thong was thrust to form slip loops, one to attach to the tine and the other to the end of the 'pull'. The pouch was attached to the 'pulls' in the same way, its ends, in which were the slits, being narrowed to avoid a bulky union. In my belief this is far and away the best attachment and I can see nothing but disadvantage in introducing other

Leather loops spliced to the top of the tines. The elastic pulls are passed through and spliced.
Waxed Thread
Tines
Elastic Pulls
2½"
5"
S.BOYLE

material such as waxed twine. It is like two men doing one man's job.

A pretty variation on the groove is to splice neat leather loops, large enough for the elastic to pass through, to the tops of the tines. This again involves binding the pulls, but they do not break so readily with a flexible attachment.

The school which believes in lightweight strods favours the use of well-seasoned privet forks with a spread of little more than an inch and elastic 'pulls' an eighth of an inch in diameter or even less. The result is a delicate, sensitive weapon with a sweet and silent action. For ammunition they demand either B.B., buck or swan-shot.

The light strod is fired from a nearly fully extended left hand, the 'pulls' being stretched by the right. But although considerable accuracy is displayed by exponents of the method, I have never adopted it as I hold the view that in catapultry, as in golf, the perfect shot demands a smooth and generous follow-through.

It is said that the use of a narrow fork is a valuable agent in sighting a target, but this I believe to be rubbish as some of the best shots I have ever known (among them Hugh Moore and H. E. S. Huth) could hit a mark just as surely when firing from the hip line.

Success with a strod is not dependent upon sighting, but upon co-ordination between hand and eye, plus an instinctive confidence that you will not miss. Your super-strodite develops this as a sixth sense and, within reasonable range, is

just as certain of hitting what he sees as he is of seeing what he is looking at. The strod is one of the most primitive and natural of weapons and readily becomes as much part of the user as the fingers of his hand.

About forty-five years ago a revolutionary design was introduced which was taken up and exploited by a firm of London gun-makers. In this the fork was superseded by a piece of hard wood, about five-eighths of an inch thick and the length of a man's hand. The top, in which a half circle the width of a halfpenny was cut, was two inches wide and tapered to an inch and a half at the base. Alongside the half circle, two holes were drilled through which loops of soft cord were threaded. The ends of the 'pulls' were put into the loops and, while stretched, were drawn through the holes until enough elastic emerged on the far side to form nice little cushions when the strain was relaxed and the cords removed. Unfortunately, this admirable fixing, which never shifted, was not practicable for use in the older types of strod as it tended to split the tines. The gun-makers who adopted the new design used aluminium instead of wood and produced a handy catapult of considerable merit. Lack of personality was its de-merit, for your true strodite has nothing but repugnance for a standardised weapon.

The most imaginative strod was conceived by Hugh Moore, who melted a lot of candle-wax and, gripping it in his

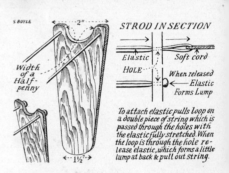

S.BOYLE
Width of a Halfpenny
2"
HOLE
1½"
STROD IN SECTION
Elastic
Soft cord
Hole
When released Elastic Forms Lump
To attach elastic pulls loop on a double piece of string which is passed through the holes with the elastic fully stretched. When the loop is through the hole release elastic, which forms a little lump at back & pull out string.

left hand, obtained a precise impression of and depression for every finger. The top was modelled to his own design and the whole thing set aside to cool. But it went no further on account of difficulties in getting it cast in a suitable light metal.

The Strodmaker's Union, of which I had the honour to be president, was formed in 1906 and flourished exceedingly on the Western Front in the First World War. It has now been disbanded for lack of membership. It possessed interesting records of early strodites, including the original manuscript of *The Saga of Ugwoni* and some priceless examples of primitive strods, including a genuine William Kemp. These were placed in a sealed tin and buried for safety in a Devon cliff. But a floating mine, exploding in the neighbourhood, brought about a landslide in which the records vanished for ever.